NUCLEAR and RADIOCHEMISTRY

NUCLEAR and RADIOCHEMISTRY

Revised Version of Introduction to Radiochemistry

GERHART FRIEDLANDER
Senior Chemist, Brookhaven National Laboratory

JOSEPH W. KENNEDY
Late Professor of Chemistry, Washington University, St. Louis

JOHN WILEY & SONS, INC., NEW YORK · LONDON

FOURTH PRINTING, FEBRUARY, 1960

Library of Congress Catalog Card Number: 55-9363

PRINTED IN THE UNITED STATES OF AMERICA

PREFACE

In 1949 we prepared *Introduction to Radiochemistry* as "a textbook for an introductory course in the broad field of radiochemistry, at the graduate or senior undergraduate level, taking into account the degree of previous preparation in physics ordinarily possessed by chemistry students at that level."

The title of this new book reflects some changes in our thinking about terminology. In 1949 we wrote: ". . . to our minds nuclear chemistry emphasizes the reactions of nuclei and the properties of resulting nuclear species, just as organic chemistry is concerned with reactions and properties of organic compounds. We think of tracer chemistry as the field of chemical studies made with the use of isotopic tracers, including studies of the essentially pure tracers at extremely low concentrations. In the title of this book we have meant the term radiochemistry to include all the fields just described. . . ." Discussions with a number of chemists working in these fields have led us to adopt a somewhat narrower meaning for "radiochemistry," a meaning not including nuclear chemistry but including chemical manipulations of radioactive sources and much of tracer chemistry. In this connection it may be noted that isotopic tracer techniques have become standard parts of well-established and diverse fields such as inorganic chemistry and archeology; radiochemistry will continue to include new applications of nuclear science to chemistry and to introduce advances in borderline fields. Nuclear chemistry and radiochemistry interact strongly with each other, and indeed are so interdependent that their discussion together is almost necessary in an introductory textbook.

From this evolution both in subject matter and in terminology comes the present, slightly ungrammatical, title for our book, *Nuclear and Radiochemistry*. We will be pleased if this revised version meets the current need even partly as well as *Introduction to Radiochemistry* did six years ago. We have written in the same spirit, and to the same purpose, and have had the very valuable advice of half a hundred colleagues. (This advice has been followed to the fullest extent consistent with the fact that it was often contradictory.) The new book includes considerably more factual information, mostly in the form of tables and graphs. Although the new chapter outline is not much different from the earlier one through chapter 10, there have been many additions, much rewriting, and several important rearrangements. We have tried to present more of the essentially chemical discussions somewhat earlier because many teachers, including one of the authors, are unable to get through all the chapters within the limits of their courses. We have concluded with two new chapters, 12 and 13, which may tempt some students into unassigned reading.

Again it is a pleasure to acknowledge the assistance of many friends who have contributed to the task of seeking errors large and small, particularly Professors J. M. Miller and A. C. Wahl, who read the entire manuscript and made many valuable suggestions. Professor Eugene Feenberg and Dr. Irving Kaplan have trustingly permitted us to examine before publication manuscripts of their books *The Shell Theory of the Nucleus* and *Nuclear Physics*. Professor R. W. Dodson remains the authority for the treatment of statistical phenomena in chapter 9. Dr. A. O. Allen's criticism and advice were most helpful in the preparation of the section on radiation chemistry in chapter 7. And again the Brookhaven National Laboratory and Washington University, not to mention our families, have borne our neglect of other duties during the weeks of rewriting. We thank Adrienne Kennedy and Gertrude Friedlander for their aid in preparing the manuscript and in proofreading. Dorothy Pollock's meticulous typing of the appendices is gratefully acknowledged.

A last quotation from the preface of our 1949 book remains timely. "Throughout the book we have drawn upon the work and ideas of other investigators, but in keeping with its character as a textbook have not attempted to include more than a very few specific references. The references listed at the end of each chapter were selected to call attention to a large number of standard works and to introduce the student to some of the recent literature on specific topics. The exercises given at the end of each chapter are intended as an integral part of the course, and only with them does the text contain the variety of specific examples which we consider necessary for an effective presentation."

GERHART FRIEDLANDER
JOSEPH W. KENNEDY

Blue Point, N. Y.
St. Louis, Mo.
May 1955

CONTENTS

CHAPTER 1

RADIOACTIVITY

A. DISCOVERY OF RADIOACTIVITY

Becquerel's Discovery. The more or less accidental series of events which led to the discovery of radioactivity depended on two especially significant factors: (1) the mysterious X rays discovered about one year earlier by W. C. Roentgen produced fluorescence (the term phosphorescence was preferred at that time) in the glass walls of X-ray tubes and in some other materials; and (2) Henri Becquerel had inherited an interest in phosphorescence from both his father and grandfather. The father, Edmund Becquerel (1820–1891), had actually studied phosphorescence of uranium salts, and about 1880 Henri Becquerel prepared potassium uranyl sulfate, $K_2UO_2(SO_4)_2 \cdot 2H_2O$, and noted its pronounced phosphorescence excited by ultraviolet light. Thus, in 1895 and 1896 when several scientists were seeking the connection between X rays and phosphorescence and were looking for penetrating radiation from phosphorescent substances, it was natural for Becquerel to experiment along this line with the potassium uranyl sulfate.

It was on February 24, 1896, that Henri Becquerel reported his first results: after exposure to bright sunlight crystals of the uranyl double sulfate emitted a radiation which blackened a photographic plate after penetrating black paper, glass, and other substances. During the next few months he continued the experiments, obtaining more and more puzzling results. The effect was as strong with weak light as with bright sunlight; it was found in complete darkness and even for crystals prepared and always kept in the dark. The penetrating radiation was emitted by other uranyl and also uranous salts, by solutions of uranium salts, and even by what was believed to be metallic uranium, and in each case with an intensity proportional to the uranium content. Proceeding by analogy with a known property of X rays, Becquerel observed that the penetrating rays from uranium would discharge an electroscope. All these results were obtained in the early part of 1896. Although Becquerel and others continued investigations for several years, the knowledge gained in this phase of the new science was summarized in 1898, when Pierre and Marie Sklodowska Curie concluded that the uranium rays were an atomic phenomenon characteristic of the element and not related to its chemical or physical state, and they introduced the name "radioactivity" for the phenomenon.

TABLE 1-1

SOME URANIUM AND THORIUM MINERALS

Name	Composition	Uranium Content	Thorium Content	Color and Form
Uraninite (pitchblende)	Uranium oxide, UO_2 to U_3O_8, with rare-earth and other oxides	60–80%	0–10%	Grayish, greenish or brownish black; cubic, amorphous
Thorianite	Thorium and uranium oxides, $(Th, U)O_2$, with UO_3 and rare-earth oxides	4–40%	30–82%	Gray, brownish or greenish gray, black; cubic
Carnotite	Potassium uranyl vanadate, $K(UO_2)VO_4 \cdot nH_2O$	~45%		Yellow; hexagonal, rhombic
Monazite	Phosphates of the cerium earths and thorium, $CePO_4 + Th_3(PO_4)_4$		Up to 16%	Red, brown, yellowish brown; monoclinic
Pilbarite	Thorium lead uranate and silicate	~25%	~25%	Yellow
Autunite	Calcium uranyl phosphate, $Ca(UO_2)_2(PO_4)_2 \cdot 8H_2O$	~50%		Greenish yellow; rhombic
Thorite or orangite	Thorium orthosilicate, $ThSiO_4$		Up to 70%	Brown or black (thorite), orange-yellow (orangite); tetragonal

The Curies. Much new information appeared during the year 1898, mostly through the work of the Curies. Examination of other elements led to the discovery, independently by Mme. Curie and G. C. Schmidt, that compounds of thorium emitted rays similar to the uranium rays. A very important observation was that some natural uranium ores were even more radioactive than pure uranium, and more active than a chemically similar "ore" prepared synthetically. The chemical decomposition and fractionation of such ores were the first exercise in radiochemistry and led immediately to the discovery of polonium—as a new substance observed only through its intense radioactivity—and of radium, a highly radioactive substance recognized as a new element and soon identified spectroscopically. The Curies and their coworkers had found radium in the barium fraction separated chemically from pitchblende (a dark almost black ore containing about 75 per cent U_3O_8), and they learned that it could be concentrated from the barium by repeated fractional crystallization of the chlorides, the radium salt remaining preferentially in the mother liquor. By 1902 Mme. Curie reported the isolation of 100 mg of radium chloride spectroscopically free from barium and gave 225 as the approximate atomic weight of the element. (The work had started with about two tons of pitchblende, and the radium isolated represented about a 25 per cent yield.) Still later Mme. Curie redetermined the atomic weight to be 226.5 (the 1952 value is 226.05) and also prepared radium metal by electrolysis of the fused salt.

Becquerel in his experiments had shown that uranium, in the dark and not supplied with energy in any known way, continued for years to emit rays in undiminished intensity. E. Rutherford had made some rough estimates of the energy associated with the radioactive rays; the source of this energy was quite unknown. With concentrated radium samples the Curies made measurements of the resulting heating effect, which they found to be about 100 cal per hr per g of radium. The evidence for so large a store of energy not only caused a controversy among the scientists of that time but also helped to create a great popular interest in radium and radioactivity. (An interesting article in the *St. Louis Post-Dispatch* of October 4, 1903, speculated on this inconceivable new power, its use in war and as an instrument for destruction of the world.)

Early Characterization of the Rays. The effect of radioactive radiations in discharging an electroscope was soon understood in terms of the ionization of the air molecules, as J. J. Thomson and others were developing a knowledge of this subject in their studies of X rays. The use of the amount of ionization in air as a measure of the intensity of radiations was developed into a more precise technique than the photographic blackening, and this technique was employed in the Curie laboratory, where ionization currents were measured with an electrometer. In 1899 Rutherford began a study of the properties of the rays themselves, using a similar instrument. Measurements of the absorption of the rays in metal foils showed that there were two components. One component was absorbed in the first few thousandths of a centimeter of aluminum and was named α radiation; the other was absorbed considerably in roughly 100 times this thickness of aluminum and was named β radiation. For the β rays Rutherford found that the ionization effect was reduced to the fraction $e^{-\mu d}$ of its original value when d centimeters of absorber were interposed; the absorption coefficient μ was about 15 cm^{-1} for aluminum and increased with atomic weight for other metal foils.

Rutherford at that time believed that the absorption of the α radiation also followed an exponential law and gave for it $\mu = 1600$ cm^{-1} in aluminum. About a year later Mme. Curie found that μ was not constant for α rays but increased as the rays proceeded through the absorber. This was a very surprising fact, since one would have expected that any inhomogeneity of the radiation would result in early absorption of the less penetrating components with a corresponding decrease in absorption coefficient with distance. In 1904 the concept of a definite range for the α particles (they were recognized as particles by that time) was proposed and demonstrated by W. H. Bragg. He found that several radioactive substances emitted α rays with different characteristic ranges.

The recognition of the character of the α and β rays as streams of high-speed particles came largely as a result of magnetic and electrostatic deflection experiments. In this way the β rays were seen to be electrons moving with almost the velocity of light. At first the α rays were thought to be undeviated by these fields. More refined experiments did show deflections; from these the ratio of charge to mass was calculated to be about half that of the hydrogen ion, with the charge positive, and the velocity was calculated to be about one-tenth that of light. The suggestion that the α particle was a helium ion was immediately made, and it was confirmed after much more study. The presence of helium in uranium and thorium ores had already been noticed and was seen to be significant in this connection. A striking demonstration was later made, in which α rays were allowed to pass through a very thin glass wall into an evacuated glass vessel; within a few days sufficient helium gas appeared in the vessel to be detected spectroscopically.

Before the completion of these studies of the α and β rays, an even more penetrating radiation, not deviated by a magnetic field, was found in the rays from radioactive preparations. The recognition of this γ radiation as electromagnetic waves, like X rays in character if not in energy, came rather soon. For a long time no distinction was made between the nuclear γ rays and some extranuclear X rays which often accompany radioactive transformations.[1]

Rutherford and Soddy Transformation Hypothesis. In the course of measurements of thorium salt activities Rutherford observed that the electrometer readings were sometimes quite erratic. During 1899 it was determined that the cause of this effect was the diffusion through the ionization chamber of a radioactive substance emanating from the thorium compound. Similar effects were obtained with radium compounds. Subsequent studies, principally by Rutherford and F. Soddy, showed that these emanations were inert gases of high molecular weight, subject to condensation at about $-150°C$. Another radioactive substance, actinium, had been separated from pitchblende in 1899, and it too was found to give off an active emanation.

The presence of the radioactive emanations from thorium, radium, and actinium preparations was a very fortunate circumstance for advancement of knowledge of the real nature of radioactivity. Essentially the inert gaseous character of these substances made radiochemical separations not only an easy process, but also one which forced itself on the attentions of these early investigators. Two very significant consequences of the early study of the emanations were: (1) the realization that the activity of radioactive substances did not continue forever but diminished in intensity with a time scale characteristic of the substance; and (2) the knowledge that the radioactive processes were accompanied by a change in chemical properties of the active atoms. The application of chemical separation procedures, especially by W. Crookes and by Rutherford and Soddy, in 1900 and the succeeding years revealed the existence of other activities with characteristic decay rates and radiations, notably uranium X, which is separated from uranium by precipitation with excess ammonium carbonate (the uranyl carbonate redissolves in excess carbonate through formation of a complex ion), and thorium X, which remains in solution when thorium is precipitated as the hydroxide with ammonium hydroxide. In each case it was found that the activity of the X body decayed appreciably in a matter of days, and

[1] In the nomenclature of this book concerning radioactive decay processes the term γ rays will include only nuclear electromagnetic radiation; accompanying X rays will be designated as such, even though this is not an entirely uniform practice in the literature.

that a new supply of the X body appeared in the parent substance in a similar time. It was also shown that both uranium and thorium, when effectively purified of the X bodies and other products, emitted only α rays, and that uranium X and thorium X emitted β rays.

By the spring of 1903 Rutherford and Soddy had reached an excellent understanding of the nature of radioactivity and published their conclusions that the radioactive elements were undergoing spontaneous transformation from one chemical atom into another, that the radioactive radiations were an accompaniment of these changes, and that the radioactive process was a subatomic change within the atom. However, it should be remembered here that the idea of the atomic nucleus did not emerge until eight years later and that in 1904 Bragg was attempting to understand the α particle as a flying cluster of thousands of more or less independent electrons.

Statistical Aspect of Radioactivity. In 1905 E. v. Schweidler used the foregoing conclusions as to the nature of radioactivity and formulated a new description of the process in terms of disintegration probabilities. His fundamental assumption was that the probability p for a particular atom of a radioactive element to disintegrate in a time interval Δt is independent of the past history and the present circumstances of the atom; it depends only on the length of the time interval Δt and for sufficiently short intervals is just proportional to Δt; thus $p = \lambda\,\Delta t$, where λ is the proportionality constant characteristic of that species of radioactive atoms. The probability of the given atom not disintegrating during the short interval Δt is $1 - p = 1 - \lambda\,\Delta t$. If the atom has survived this interval, then its probability of not disintegrating in the next like interval is again $1 - \lambda\,\Delta t$. By the law for compounding such probabilities the probability for the given atom to survive the first interval and also the second is given by $(1 - \lambda\,\Delta t)^2$; for n such intervals this survival probability is $(1 - \lambda\,\Delta t)^n$. Setting $n\,\Delta t = t$, the total time, we have $\left(1 - \lambda \frac{t}{n}\right)^n$. Now the probability that the atom will remain unchanged after time t is just the value of this quantity when Δt is made indefinitely small; that is, it is the limit of $\left(1 - \lambda \frac{t}{n}\right)^n$ as n approaches infinity. Recalling that $e^x = \lim_{n\to\infty} \left(1 + \frac{x}{n}\right)^n$, we have $e^{-\lambda t}$ for the limiting value. If we consider not one atom, but a large initial number N_0 of the radioactive atoms, then the fraction remaining unchanged after time t we may take to be $N/N_0 = e^{-\lambda t}$, where N is the number of unchanged atoms at time t. This exponential law of decay is just that which

Rutherford had already found experimentally for the simple isolated radioactivities.

Chapter 9 will present a more detailed discussion of the statistical nature of radioactivity.

B. RADIOACTIVE DECAY AND GROWTH

In the preceding section we mentioned that the decay of a radioactive substance followed the exponential law $N = N_0 e^{-\lambda t}$, where N is the (large) number of unchanged atoms at time t, N_0 is the number present when $t = 0$, and λ is a constant characteristic of the particular radioactive species. This will be recognized as the rate law for any monomolecular reaction, and, of course, this should be expected in view of the nature of the radioactive process. It may be derived if the decay rate, $-\frac{dN}{dt}$, is set proportional to the number of atoms present: $-\frac{dN}{dt} = \lambda N$. (This is to say that we expect twice as many disintegrations per unit time in a sample containing twice as many atoms, etc.) On integration the result is $\ln N = -\lambda t + a$, and the constant of integration a is evaluated from the limit $N = N_0$ when $t = 0$: $a = \ln N_0$. Combining these terms, we have: $\ln (N/N_0) = -\lambda t$, or $N/N_0 = e^{-\lambda t}$.

The constant λ is known as the decay constant for the radioactive species. As may be seen from the differential equation, it is the fraction of the number of atoms transformed per unit time, provided the time unit is chosen short enough so that only a small fraction of the atoms transform in that interval. In any case λ has the dimensions of a reciprocal time and is most often expressed in reciprocal seconds. It is to be noticed that for most radioactive substances no attempt to alter λ through variation of ordinary experimental conditions, such as temperature, chemical change, pressure, and gravitational, magnetic, or electric fields, has ever given a detectable effect.[2]

The characteristic rate of a radioactive decay may very conveniently be given in terms of the half-life $t_{1/2}$, which is the time required for an initial (large) number of atoms to be reduced to half that number by transformations. Thus, at the time $t = t_{1/2}$, $N = N_0/2$ and

$$\ln \tfrac{1}{2} = -\lambda t_{1/2}, \quad \text{or} \quad t_{1/2} = \frac{\ln 2}{\lambda} = \frac{0.69315}{\lambda}.$$

[2] The exceptional cases in which slight changes of λ have been achieved are considered in chapter 6, p. 166.

In practical work with radioactive materials the number of atoms N is not directly evaluated, and even the rate of change $\frac{dN}{dt}$ is usually not measured absolutely. The usual procedure is to determine, through its electric, photographic, or other effect, a quantity proportional to λN; we may term this quantity the activity $\mathbf{A}$, with $\mathbf{A} = c\lambda N = c\left(-\frac{dN}{dt}\right)$. The coefficient c, which we may term the detection coefficient, will depend on the nature of the detection instrument, the efficiency for the recording of the particular radiation in that particular instrument, and the geometrical arrangement of sample and detector; a usual feature of the experimentation is careful precaution to keep all these factors under control. We may now write the decay law as it is commonly observed, $\mathbf{A} = \mathbf{A}_0 e^{-\lambda t}$.

The usual procedure for the treatment of data measuring $\mathbf{A}$ at successive times is to plot log $\mathbf{A}$ versus t; for this purpose semilog paper (with a suitable number of decades) is most convenient. Now λ could be found from the slope of the resulting straight line corresponding to the simple decay law; however, in this procedure there is a possibility for the confusion of units or of different logarithm bases. It is more convenient to read from the plot on semilog paper the time required for the activity to fall from any value to half that value; this is the half-life $t_{1/2}$.

In this discussion we have considered only the radioactivity corresponding to the transformation of a single atomic species; however, the daughter substance resulting from the transformation may itself be radioactive, with its own characteristic radiation and half-life, as well as its own chemical identity. Indeed among the naturally occurring radioactive substances this is the more common situation, and in chapter 5 we shall treat quite complicated interrelated radioactive growths and decays. For the moment consider the decay of the substance uranium I, or U_I. This species of uranium is an α-particle emitter, with $t_{1/2} = 4.50 \times 10^9$ years. The immediate product of its transformation is the radioactive substance uranium X_1, or UX_1, a β emitter with half-life 24.1 days. For this pair of substances, the parent uranium may be separated from the daughter atoms by precipitation of the daughter with excess ammonium carbonate, as already mentioned. The daughter precipitate will show a characteristic activity, which will decay with the rate indicated; that is, it will be half gone in 24.1 days, three-fourths gone in 48.2 days, seven-eighths gone in 72.3 days, etc. The parent fraction will, of course, continue its α activity as before, but will for the moment be free of the β radiations associated with the daughter. However, in time new daughter atoms will be formed, and the daughter activity in the parent fraction will return to its initial value, with a time scale corresponding to the rate of decay of the isolated daughter fraction.

In an undisturbed sample containing N_1 atoms of U_I, a steady state is established in which the rate of formation of the daughter UX_1 atoms (number N_2) is just equal to their rate of decay. This means that $-\frac{dN_1}{dt} = \lambda_2 N_2$ in this situation, because the rate of formation of the daughter atoms is just the rate of decay of the parent atoms. Using the earlier relation, we have then $\lambda_1 N_1 = \lambda_2 N_2$, with λ_1 and λ_2 the respective disintegration constants. This is sometimes more convenient in terms of the two half-lives: $N_1/(t_{1/2})_1 = N_2/(t_{1/2})_2$. This state of affairs is known as secular equilibrium. No account is taken of the decrease of N_1 with time, since the fraction of U_I atoms transformed even throughout the life of the experimenter is completely negligible. In general, wherever a short-lived daughter results from the decay of a very long-lived parent, this situation exists. The same relation, $\lambda_1 N_1 = \lambda_2 N_2 = \lambda_3 N_3$, etc., may be applied when several short-lived products arise from successive decays beginning with a long-lived parent, provided again that the material has been undisturbed (that is, no daughter substances removed or allowed to escape) for a long enough time for secular equilibrium to be established.

The concept of secular equilibrium suggests a convenient way to handle experimental data concerned with the rate of growth of a short-lived daughter substance in a freshly separated long-lived parent fraction. Because all the rates of decay are entirely independent of the chemical manipulations in the separation (say of UX_1 from U_I), the sum of the amounts of daughter UX_1 in the two fractions always continues at the constant value given by $\lambda_1 N_1 = \lambda_2 N_2$. Thus by the time the isolated daughter preparation is practically inactive the growth in the parent will have practically re-established the secular equilibrium condition. If measurements of the amount of daughter activity in the parent fraction are obtained as a function of the time t, then these activity values may be subtracted from the final value approached as t becomes long compared to $(t_{1/2})_2$, and the differences plotted on semilog paper versus t to give a straight line like a decay curve. In fact this curve describes the decay of the isolated daughter fraction. In this way the daughter half-life may be obtained from its rate of growth in a very-long-lived parent. (It may be useful here to emphasize that a plot directly of the growing daughter activity in the parent fraction, on either a linear or semilog basis, cannot give a straight line and in either case gives a curve approaching the secular equilibrium value as an asymptote. See figure 5-3, page 133.

C. NATURALLY OCCURRING RADIOACTIVE SUBSTANCES

Uranium, Thorium, and Actinium Series. All elements found in natural sources with atomic number greater than 83 (bismuth) are radioactive. They belong to chains of successive decays, and all the species in one such chain constitute a radioactive family or series. Three of these families include all the natural activities in this region of the periodic chart. One has U_I (mass 238 on the atomic weight scale) as the parent substance, and after 14 transformations (8 of them by α-particle emission and 6 by β-particle emission) reaches a stable end product, radium G (lead with mass 206); this is known as the uranium series. (This series includes radium and its decay products; these are sometimes called the radium series.) Since the atomic mass is changed by four units in α decay and by only a small fraction of one unit in β decay, the various masses found in members of the family differ by multiples of 4, and a general formula for the approximate masses is $4n + 2$, where n is an integer. Therefore, the uranium series is known also as the $4n + 2$ series. Figure 1-1 shows the members and transformations of the uranium series.

Thorium (mass 232) is the parent substance of the $4n$ series, or thorium series, with lead of weight 208 as the stable end product. This series is shown in figure 1-2. The $4n + 3$, or actinium, series has actino-uranium, AcU (uranium of mass 235), as the parent and lead of mass 207 as the stable end product. This series is shown in figure 1-3.

The fairly close similarity of the three series to each other and in their relations to the periodic chart is interesting and helpful in remembering the decay modes and nomenclature for the active bodies. Actually, these historical names may some day become obsolete, and the designations of chemical element and atomic mass become standard; already we are more familiar with U^{238}, U^{235}, and U^{234} than with U_I, AcU, and U_{II}. (This trend is favored by the fact that names like UX_1 and RaD do not immediately suggest that these substances are chemically like thorium and lead, respectively; also, in some of the early literature the nomenclature is different from current usage, which leads to some confusion. On the other hand, many of the historical names like RaA, RaB indicate immediately positions in the decay chain; and, furthermore, the name Pa^{234} would not distinguish between UX_2 and UZ.)

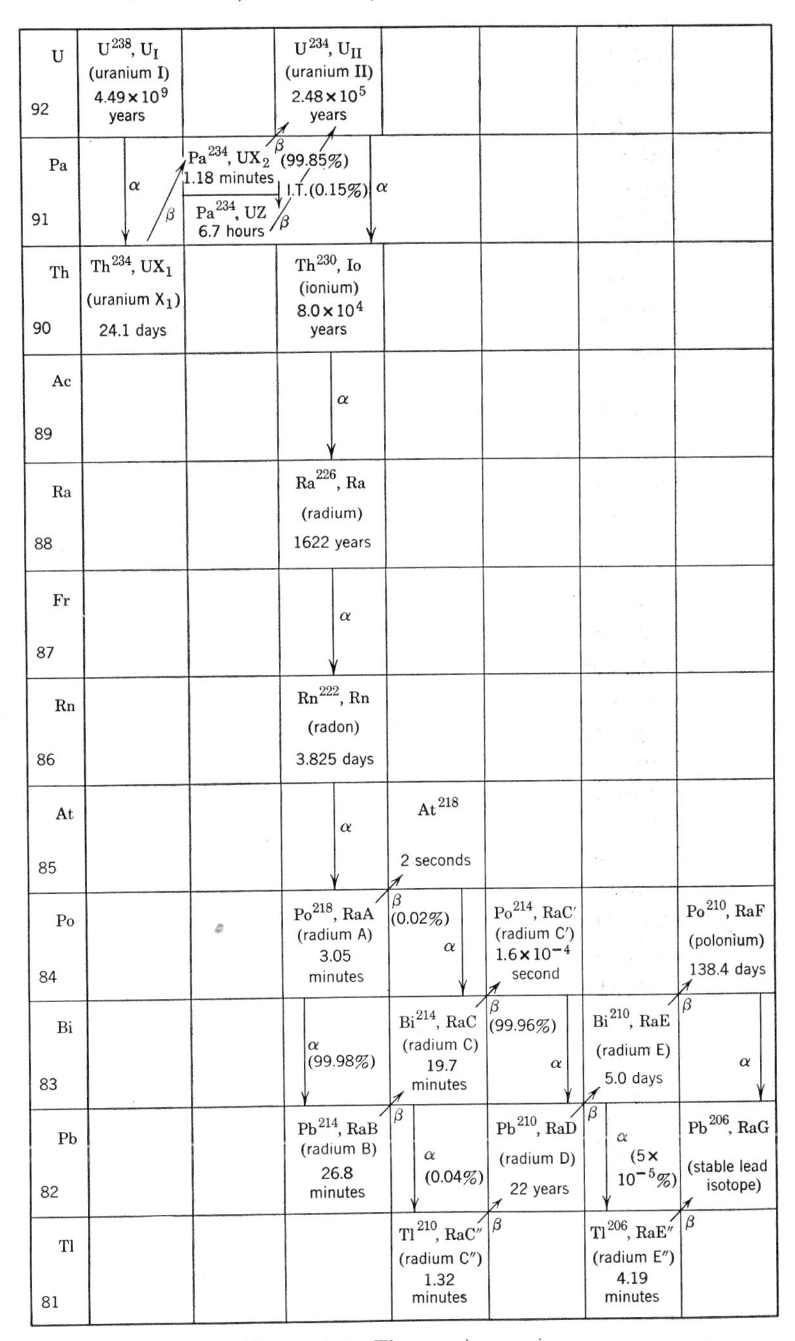

FIGURE 1-1. The uranium series.

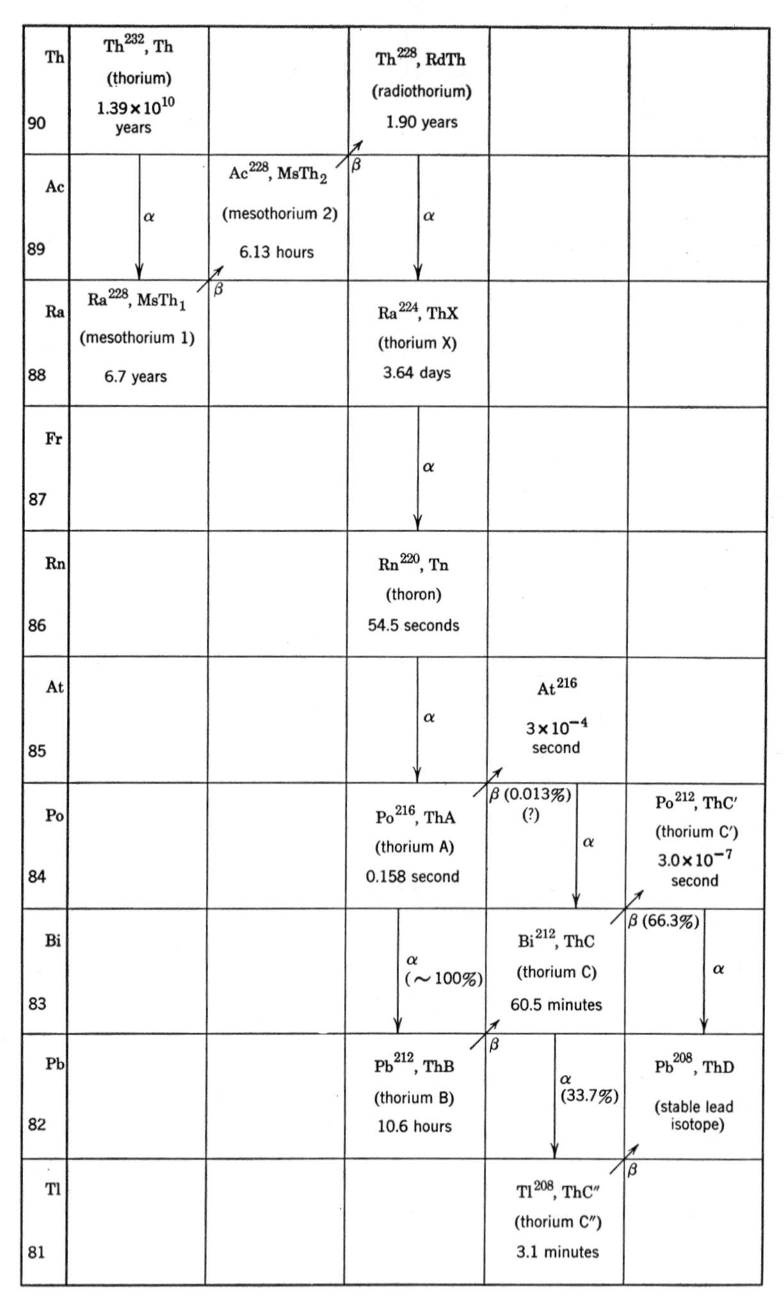

Figure 1-2. The thorium series.

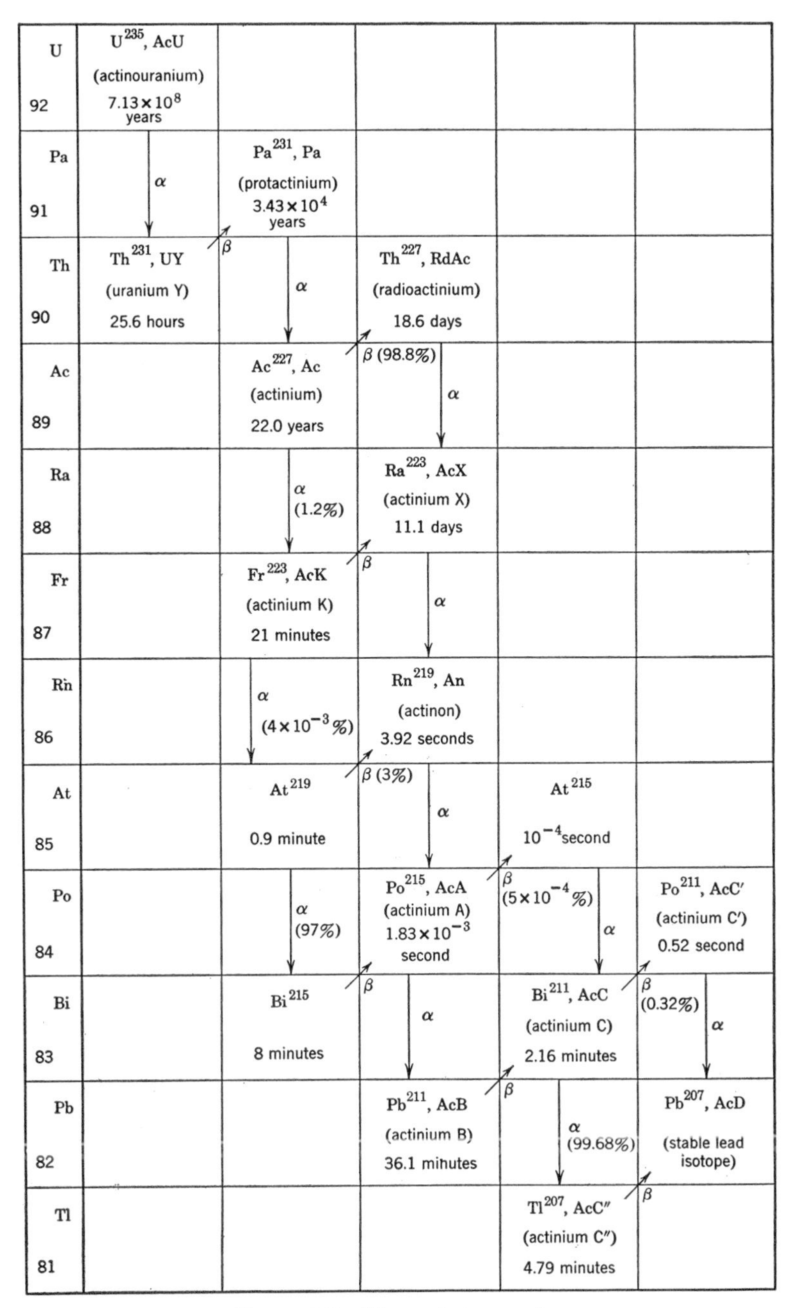

FIGURE 1-3. The actinium series.

The existence of branching decays in each of the three series should be noticed. As more sensitive means for the detection of low-intensity branches have become available, more branching decays have been discovered. For example, the occurrence of astatine of mass 219 in a 5×10^{-5} per cent branch of the actinium series was recognized only in 1953. With further refinements in technique, additional branchings will undoubtedly be found.

One important result of the unraveling of the radioactive decay series was the conclusion reached as early as 1910, notably by Soddy, that different radioactive species of different atomic weights could nevertheless have identical chemical properties. This is the origin of the concept of isotopes which we have already used implicitly in writing such symbols as U^{235} and U^{238} for uranium of atomic weights 235 and 238. Further discussion of isotopes will be deferred until chapter 2, p. 29.

In each of the three families occurs an isotope of element number 86, radon (sometimes called emanation). These rare gas radioactivities, radon, thoron, and actinon, are the emanations which we mentioned earlier and which were so important for the early understanding of radioactivity. It is due to the gaseous character of these substances that their descendants, the A, B, C products, etc., of the three families, can be so readily isolated from their longer-lived precursors. These descendants of the emanations are referred to as *active deposits*. The active deposit from any of the three radioactive series may be collected by exposure of any object, or more efficiently of a negatively charged electrode, to the emanation.

Other Natural Radioactivities. Since the discovery of radioactivity practically every known element has at one time or another been examined for evidences of naturally occurring radioactivity. In 1906, N. R. Campbell and A. Wood discovered weak β radioactivity in both potassium and rubidium, and for about 25 years these remained the only known radioactive elements outside the three decay series. In 1932, G. Hevesy and M. Pahl reported a radioactivity in samarium, and more recently several other naturally occurring radioactivities have been found. The presently known natural radioactivities other than those of the uranium, thorium, and actinium series are listed in table 1-2, together with some of their properties. In some of these elements the particular isotope responsible for the radioactivity occurs in very small abundance, and in other cases the half-lives are extremely long. Either of these two factors makes such activities very difficult to detect. Without question, additional natural radioactivities will be discovered.

TABLE 1-2

ADDITIONAL NATURALLY OCCURRING RADIOACTIVE SUBSTANCES

Active Substance	Type of Disintegration	Half-life in Years	Relative Isotopic Abundance in %	Stable Disintegration Products
K^{40}	β, EC *	1.2×10^9	0.012	Ca^{40}, A^{40}
Rb^{87}	β	6.2×10^{10}	27.8	Sr^{87}
In^{115}	β	6×10^{14}	95.8	Sn^{115}
La^{138}	EC,* β	$\sim 2 \times 10^{11}$	0.089	Ba^{138}, Ce^{138}
Nd^{144}	α	$\sim 5 \times 10^{15}$	23.9	Ce^{140}
Sm^{147}	α	1.3×10^{11}	15.1	Nd^{143}
Lu^{176}	β	4.6×10^{10}	2.60	Hf^{176}
Re^{187}	β	$\sim 5 \times 10^{10}$	62.9	Os^{187}
Pt^{190}	α	$\sim 10^{12}$	0.012	Os^{186}

* The symbol EC stands for electron capture. This type of decay is briefly described in the following section and more fully treated in chapter 6, page 165.

In attempts to extend the search for new radioactivities to very low intensity levels difficulty arises from the general background of detectable radiations present in every laboratory. In part this general background is due to the presence of traces of uranium, thorium, potassium, etc., and in large part to the cosmic radiation of unknown origin, which will be discussed in chapter 13. The cosmic rays reach every portion of the earth's surface; their intensity is greater at high altitudes but persists measurably even in deep caves and mines. The magnitude of the background effect is indicated in the discussion of radiation-detection instruments in chapter 8, page 236. In recent years there have been occasional temporary increases in background radiation due to scattered residues from large-scale atomic and thermonuclear explosions.

D. ARTIFICIAL RADIOACTIVITY

Historical Development. The naturally occurring radioactive substances were the only ones available for study until 1934. In January of that year I. Curie (daughter of Mme. Curie) and F. Joliot announced that boron, aluminum, and magnesium could be made radioactive by bombardment with the α rays from polonium. This very important discovery of artificial radioactivity came in the course of their experiments on the production of positrons by bombardment of these elements with α particles. The positron had been discovered only two years earlier by C. D. Anderson as a component of the cosmic radiation; it is a particle very much like the electron but positively charged. A number of laboratories quickly found that positrons could be produced in light elements, especially in beryllium, by α-ray bombardment. The Curie-Joliot discovery was that the boron and aluminum targets continued to emit positrons after removal of the α source, and that the induced radioactivity in each case decayed with a characteristic half-life (14 min for B, 3.25 min for Al).

Much earlier, in 1919, Rutherford had produced nuclear transmutations by α-particle bombardment, and the new phenomenon of induced radioactivity was therefore quickly understood in terms of the production of new, unstable nuclei. From boron the unstable nucleus N^{13} is produced (the stable nitrogen nuclei are N^{14} and N^{15}); from aluminum the product is P^{30} (the only stable phosphorus is P^{31}). These are examples of but one of the many types of nuclear reactions now known to produce radioactive products and discussed in chapter 3.

At the time that artificial radioactivity was discovered several laboratories had developed and put into operation devices for the acceleration of hydrogen ions and helium ions to energies at which nuclear transmutations were produced. In addition, the discovery of the neutron by J. Chadwick in 1932 and the chemical concentration of deuterium by G. N. Lewis and R. T. Macdonald in 1933 made available two additional bombarding particles which turned out to be especially useful for the production of induced activities. In the twenty years following Curie's and Joliot's discovery there occurred an almost unbelievably rapid growth of the new field. The number of known artificially produced radioactive species reached 200 in 1937, about 450 in 1944, about 650 in 1949, and is almost 1000 in 1954. At least one radioactive isotope is now known for every element in the periodic table, and some elements have as many as 20 or more. The measured half-lives range from a small fraction of a microsecond to many millions of years. Very many artificially produced radioactivities have found important applications in such diverse fields as chemistry, physics, biology, medicine, and engineering. A table of the presently known radioactive species may be found in appendix G.

Types of Radioactive Decay. Although the first artificial radioactive substances decayed by positron emission, this is not the only or even the most common type of decay. Alpha-particle emitters are found also, but only among the heavier elements. Ordinary β decay, as in the natural radioactive series, is commonly found throughout the range of the periodic table. In this type of decay negative electrons are emitted and the atomic number is increased by one unit

Positron emission results in a decrease by one unit in atomic number. There is also another type of decay in which the atomic number is

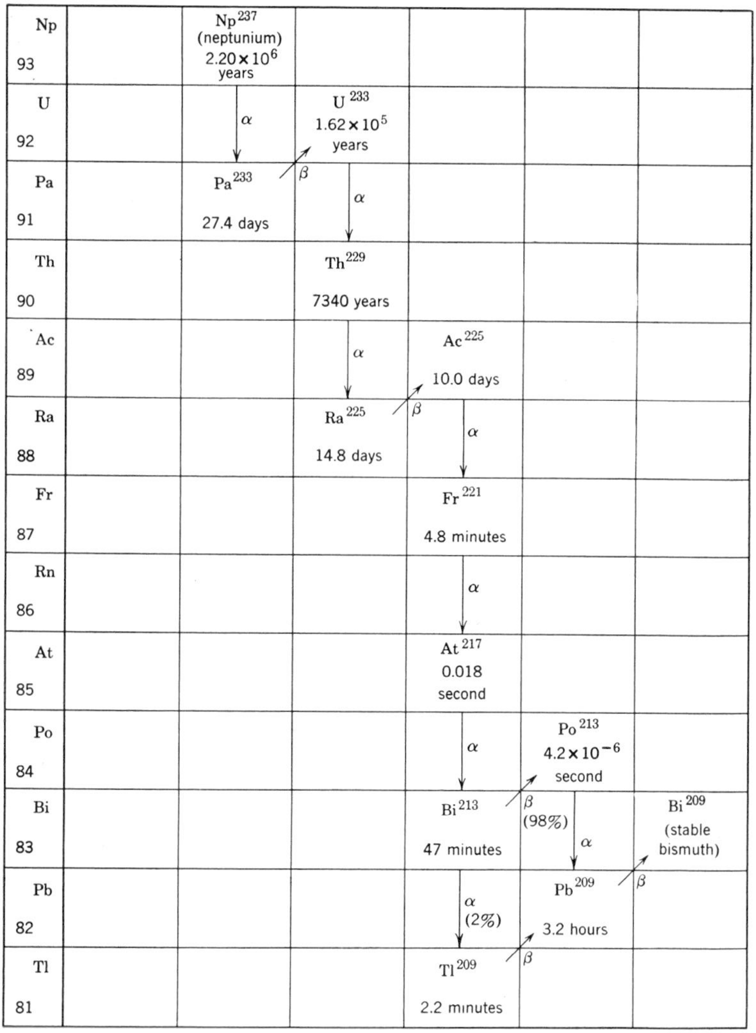

Np 93		Np^{237} (neptunium) 2.20×10^6 years				
U 92		α ↓	U^{233} 1.62×10^5 years			
Pa 91		Pa^{233} 27.4 days ↗ β	α ↓			
Th 90			Th^{229} 7340 years			
Ac 89			α ↓	Ac^{225} 10.0 days		
Ra 88			Ra^{225} 14.8 days ↗ β	α ↓		
Fr 87				Fr^{221} 4.8 minutes		
Rn 86				α ↓		
At 85				At^{217} 0.018 second		
Po 84				α ↓	Po^{213} 4.2×10^{-6} second	
Bi 83				Bi^{213} 47 minutes ↗ β (98%)	α ↓	Bi^{209} (stable bismuth)
Pb 82				α (2%) ↓	Pb^{209} 3.2 hours ↗ β	
Tl 81				Tl^{209} 2.2 minutes ↗ β		

FIGURE 1-4. The $4n + 1$ series.

decreased by one unit, in this case by spontaneous incorporation into the nucleus of one of the atomic electrons (most often one from the K shell of the atom). In these three processes the atomic mass remains essentially constant while the atomic number changes; all three are generally classed as β-decay processes and may be distinguished by the names negatron emission, positron emission, and electron capture (or sometimes K capture).

Synthetic Elements and the $4n + 1$ Series. Not only has it been possible by transmutation techniques to produce radioactive isotopes of every known element, but also a number of elements not found in nature have been synthesized. In each case the new element has first been recognized in unweighably small amounts detectable only by its radioactivity; but often macroquantities have been prepared later. The best-known of the synthetic elements is probably plutonium, an element that within less than five years of its discovery was available in sufficient quantities to serve as an ingredient in atomic bombs. Up to the year 1954 eight new elements beyond uranium in the periodic table had been produced by artificial transmutations, and also the elements technetium (atomic number 43) and promethium (number 61) which are not known to occur naturally on the earth. The subject of the new elements will be treated more fully in chapter 11.

In past years there has been speculation as to why elements beyond uranium are not found in nature. The most plausible explanation is that there is no transuranium species of sufficiently long half-life to have survived since the original formation of the elements. Similarly there has been much comment about the nonexistence of a $4n + 1$ radioactive series in nature. Among the artificially produced radioactivities in the heavy-element region a well-developed $4n + 1$ series has been prepared and investigated. The part of this series which begins with its longest-lived member, neptunium of mass 237, is displayed in figure 1-4. This decay sequence has a general resemblance to the three natural radioactive families and has as its stable end product bismuth of mass 209.

EXERCISES

1. One hundred milligrams of Ra would represent what percentage yield from exactly 2 tons of a pitchblende ore containing 75 per cent U_3O_8?
Answer: 26 per cent.

2. Calculate the rate of energy liberation (in calories per hour) for 1.00 g of pure radium free of its decay products. What can you say about the actual heating effect of an old radium preparation?
Answer to first part: 25 cal/hr.

3. A certain active substance (which has no radioactive parent) has a half-life of 8.0 days. What fraction of the initial amount will be left after (*a*) 16 days, (*b*) 32 days, (*c*) 4 days, (*d*) 83 days? *Answer:* (*a*) 0.25.

4. How long would a sample of radium have to be observed before the decay amounted to 1 per cent? (Neglect effects of radium A, B, C, etc., on the detector.)

5. Find the number of disintegrations of uranium I atoms occurring per minute in 1 mg of ordinary uranium, from the half-life of U_I, $t_{1/2} = 4.49 \times 10^9$ years.

6. How many β disintegrations occur per second in 1.00 g of pitchblende containing 70 per cent uranium? You may assume that there has been no loss of radon from the ore. *Answer:* 53,000 per sec.

7. If 1 g of radium is separated from its decay products and then placed in a sealed vessel, how much helium will accumulate in the vessel in 60 days? Express the answer in cubic centimeters at STP. *Answer:* 0.028 cm^3.

8. The artificially produced radioactive species in the region of the natural radioactive families may be classified into the four families according to mass and are known as collateral members of the families. Find these in appendix G and place them in figures 1-1, 1-2, 1-3, and 1-4 so as to indicate their decay relationships to other members of the series.

9. What is the natural radioactivity of neodymium in disintegrations per minute per gram of ordinary neodymium? *Answer:* $\sim$0.26 d min^{-1} g^{-1}.

REFERENCES

G. E. M. Jauncey, "The Early Years of Radioactivity," *Am. J. Phys.* **14,** 226 (1946).

E. Rutherford, J. Chadwick, and C. D. Ellis, *Radiations from Radioactive Substances,* Cambridge University Press, 1930.

G. Hevesy and F. A. Paneth, *A Manual of Radioactivity,* Oxford University Press, 1938.

M. S. Curie, *Traité de radioactivité,* Paris, Gauthier-Villars, 1935.

S. Meyer and E. Schweidler, *Radioaktivitaet,* Berlin, B. G. Teubner, 1927.

H. Becquerel, *Recherches sur une propriété nouvelle de la matière,* Paris, Firmin-Didot & Co., 1903.

E. Rutherford, "Collision of α Particles with Light Atoms, IV. An Anomalous Effect in Nitrogen," *Phil. Mag.* **37,** 581 (1919).

F. Joliot and I. Curie, "Artificial Production of a New Kind of Radio-Element," *Nature* **133,** 201 (1934).

G. T. Seaborg, "Artificial Radioactivity," *Chem. Revs.* **27,** 199 (1940).

G. T. Seaborg, "The Neptunium ($4n + 1$) Radioactive Family," *Chem. and Eng. News* **26,** 1902 (1948).

W. W. Meinke, A. Ghiorso, and G. T. Seaborg, "Artificial Chains Collateral to the Heavy Radioactive Families," *Phys. Rev.* **81,** 782 (1951).

I. Perlman, "The Transuranium Elements and Nuclear Chemistry," *J. Chem. Educ.* **25,** 273 (1948).

CHAPTER 2

ATOMIC NUCLEI

A. ATOMIC STRUCTURE

Early Views. At the time the phenomenon of radioactivity was discovered the chemical elements were regarded as unalterable; they were thought to retain their identities throughout all chemical and physical processes. This view became untenable when it was recognized that radioactive disintegration involved the transformation of one element into another. As a result of Thomson's discovery of the electron in 1897 it had already become clear that atoms, until then regarded as the indivisible building blocks of matter, must have some structure. From experiments on the scattering of X rays and electrons by matter, Thomson and others concluded that the number of electrons per atom was numerically about equal to the atomic weight (actually more nearly equal to half the atomic weight as was later established by C. G. Barkla in 1911). This conclusion, together with Thomson's determination of the electron mass as approximately one two-thousandth of the mass of a hydrogen atom, led to the assumption that most of the mass of an atom must reside in its positively charged parts.

The problem that remained then to be solved was: how are the positive and negative charges distributed inside the atom? Thomson in 1910 proposed a model of atomic structure in which positive electricity is uniformly distributed throughout the volume of the atom (atomic dimensions were known to be of the order of 10^{-8} cm) and the electrons occupy certain stable positions in this heavier, positively charged jelly.

The Nuclear Model of the Atom. Thomson's model was soon found quite inadequate to account for experiments carried out by Rutherford and his coworkers on the scattering of α particles by thin metal foils. If a collimated beam of α particles is allowed to strike a thin film of matter, some of the α particles are deflected from their original direction in passing through the film. This scattering is clearly caused by the electrostatic forces between the positively charged α particle and the positive and negative charges in the atoms of the scattering material. It is readily seen that the passage of α particles through Thomson atoms would result in rather small deflections because the charges in the scattering atoms are so diffuse. Experiments by H. Geiger on scattering in extremely thin foils did show that single encounters between α particles and atoms indeed resulted predominantly in very small scattering angles (of the order of 1°). On the basis of this information the probability of multiple scattering processes in foils could be calculated statistically, and this probability falls off very rapidly with increasing angle. When experiments of Geiger and E. Marsden showed that large scattering angles were orders of magnitude more frequent than could be accounted for by the Thomson model and multiple-scattering theory, Rutherford realized that a different model of the atom was required.

In his classic paper of 1911, Rutherford proposed that the observed large-angle scattering was due to single scattering processes. To account for this he postulated an atomic model in which the positive charge and most of the mass of the atom resides in a very small region, less than 10^{-12} cm in diameter, and a number of electrons sufficient to balance the positive charge are distributed over a sphere of atomic dimensions. The positive center later became known as the nucleus. The large deflection of an α particle from its path was then supposed to result from Coulomb repulsion between the α particle and the positive nucleus of an atom, both considered as point charges. With this simple assumption and the additional restriction that the nucleus is so heavy as to be considered at rest during the impact Rutherford set up the conditions for conservation of momentum and energy and derived from these his famous scattering formula,

$$n(\theta) = n_0 \cdot \frac{Nd}{r^2}\left(\frac{Ze^2}{M_\alpha v_\alpha{}^2}\right)^2 \cdot \frac{1}{\sin^4(\theta/2)},$$

where $n(\theta)$ is the number of scattered α particles falling on a unit area at a distance r from the scattering point when the angle between the directions of the initial and scattered α particles is θ; n_0 is the incident number of particles, d the thickness of the scatterer, N the number of nuclei per unit volume of scatterer, and Ze the charge per nucleus. M_α and v_α are the mass and initial velocity of the α particle.

Rutherford's hypothesis thus predicted that the number of scattered particles per unit area was proportional to the thickness of the scatterer and to the square of the nuclear charge, and inversely proportional to the square of the α-particle energy and to the fourth power of the sine of half the scattering angle. The number of scattered particles has been carefully measured as a function of scattering angle, α-particle energy, and thickness of scatterer, and the results have been found to be in excellent agreement with the Rutherford formula, provided that heavy elements were used as scatterers. For light scatterers, that is, for the case where the nuclei of the scatterer cannot be considered at rest during the impact, a more complicated expression must be substituted for the Rutherford formula. If this is done, the agreement between theory and experiment is again satisfactory, provided that the α-particle energy is not too great.

This experimental verification of the scattering formula, principally by Geiger and Marsden, led to a general acceptance of Rutherford's picture of the atom as consisting of a small positively charged nucleus, containing practically the entire mass of the atom, and surrounded by a distribution of negatively charged electrons. In addition, the scattering law made it possible to study the magnitude of the nuclear charge in the atoms of a given element, because the scattering intensity depends on the square of the nuclear charge. It was by the method of α-particle scattering that nuclear charges were first determined, and this work led to the suggestion that the atomic number Z of an element, until then merely a number indicating its position in the periodic table, was identical with the nuclear charge (expressed in units of the electronic charge e). This suggestion was subsequently confirmed by H. G. Moseley's work on the X-ray spectra of the elements.

The Bohr Atom. Rutherford's hypothesis of the nuclear atom introduced a new dilemma, concerning the stability of a system which consists of a positive nucleus of very small volume and a number of electrons surrounding it. Clearly, such a system cannot be stable if the electrons are at rest. If an electron of mass m and charge e is considered to move with velocity v in a circular orbit of radius a around a nucleus of charge Ze, we can set up the condition for mechanical stability by equating the Coulombic attractive force to the centrifugal force on the electron:

$$\frac{Ze \cdot e}{a^2} = \frac{mv^2}{a}. \tag{2-1}$$

However, according to classical electromagnetic theory such an atom is not stable and should lose energy continuously because the electrons, being accelerated in the Coulomb field of the nucleus, would emit electromagnetic radiation. Furthermore, as the radius of the of magnetic fields (Zeeman effect) and could not be extended satisfactorily to more complex atoms.

Wave Properties of Matter. During the 1920's Bohr's theory of atomic structure was superseded by another approach to the problem which may be harder to visualize, but which is of much wider applicability and which gives results in better quantitative accord with experimental observations. This is the wave-mechanical approach developed by E. Schroedinger.

In 1923 L. de Broglie had pointed out that Bohr's quantum condition (equation 2-2) followed directly from the assumptions that an electron of mass m and velocity v had associated with it a phase wave of wavelength $\lambda = h/mv$ and that the orbit circumference must be an integral multiple of λ. The idea that material particles have wave properties associated with them has had far-reaching consequences in the development of modern physics, and we shall need to make reference to it on a number of occasions. The relation between the momentum p of any particle and its *de Broglie wavelength* λ is, as indicated above, $\lambda = h/p$. It may be noted that this relation holds for photons also, since the momentum of a photon is $h\nu/c$ or h/λ. The first experimental demonstration of the wave properties of matter came when the passage of electron beams through crystals was found to result in diffraction patterns similar to those obtained with X rays. Electron diffraction and more recently neutron diffraction have actually become powerful tools in crystal structure investigations. Diffraction of electrons by ruled gratings and even diffraction of beams of molecules by slits have been demonstrated.

Quantum Numbers. In pursuing further the idea of wave properties associated with material particles, Schroedinger suggested that each quantum state of a particle, such as an electron in an atom, represents a normal mode of oscillation in space, analogous to a standing wave on a string supported at both ends. Just as all the possible normal modes of a violin string may be obtained as the solutions of a differential equation, Schroedinger showed that the allowed quantum states of an atom may be identified with the solutions of a certain differential equation, called the Schroedinger wave equation. We know that the various harmonics on a vibrating string represent integral multiples of the fundamental frequency, and the integer characterizing a certain harmonic may be considered as a quantum number describing that particular mode of vibration. Similarly, each wave function or eigen function which represents a solution of the (three-dimensional) Schroedinger equation for a particular system is characterized by three integers or quantum numbers.

electron orbit decreased, the frequency of the emitted radiation w
increase continuously, a consequence of the theory quite incompa
with the observed emission of line spectra.

In 1913 N. Bohr found a way of dealing with these difficulties applying the principles of M. Planck's quantum theory to atom structure. He postulated that an atom could exist only in certai discrete energy states corresponding to particular circular orbits o the electrons around the nucleus, and that it could lose or gain energy only in transitions from one of these quantum states to another. The monochromatic radiation absorbed or emitted in such a transition should then be related to the energy difference ΔE between the two energy states by the quantum relation $\Delta E = h\nu$, where ν is the frequency of the radiation and h is Planck's constant. In considering the simplest atom, that of hydrogen, Bohr found he could obtain good agreement with observed frequencies in the hydrogen spectrum if he made the assumption that the electron was restricted to those orbits whose angular momenta were whole multiples of $h/2\pi$.

The angular momentum of an electron of mass m and velocity v traveling in a circular orbit of radius a is mva, and Bohr's quantum condition is

$$mva = \frac{nh}{2\pi}, \tag{2-2}$$

where n is an integer. By combining equations 2-1 and 2-2 to eliminate v, we obtain

$$a = \frac{n^2h^2}{4\pi^2mZe^2}. \tag{2-3}$$

Thus the radius of each Bohr orbit of the electron in the hydrogen atom is characterized by the so-called principal quantum number n. In the lowest or normal energy state of the hydrogen atom, $n = 1$, and the radius of the electron orbit is $h^2/4\pi^2mZe^2 = 5.3 \times 10^{-9}$ cm.

In the years following 1913 Bohr's theory underwent a series of refinements. The motion of the nucleus was taken into account through replacement, in Bohr's equations, of the electron mass m by the reduced mass of the system $Mm/(M + m)$, where M is the mass of the nucleus. A. Sommerfeld generalized the theory by introducing elliptical as well as circular orbits, with the nucleus at one focus. In spite of these refinements the theory, although very successful in accounting for the main features in the spectra of hydrogen and other one-electron systems such as He^+, Li^{++}, Be^{+++}, failed to account for some details, such as the fine-structure splittings under the influence

The three quantum numbers which appear in the wave functions are usually designated by the symbols n, l, and m. Of these, n is identified with the principal quantum number of Bohr's theory, and it may have any positive integral value, 1, 2, 3, etc. For each value of n the wave equation has proper solutions only for a certain range of values for the other quantum numbers: for any n, l can have any integral value from 0 to $n - 1$; for any l, m can have any integral value from $-l$ to $+l$, including 0. Thus we see that the number of solutions of the wave equation for any particular value of n is

$$\sum_{l=0}^{l=n-1} (2l + 1) = n^2.$$

In the application of these results to atomic structure, the principal quantum number n for an electron is related to its average distance from the nucleus, according to equation 2-3. The azimuthal quantum number l is a measure of the orbital angular momentum of the electron [1] in the unit $h/2\pi$; the possible projections of the momentum on any axis are $l, l - 1, l - 2, \ldots l - 2l$. In the usual notation, states with $l = 0, 1, 2, 3, 4, 5 \ldots$ are referred to as $s, p, d, f, g, h \ldots$ states, respectively, and the numerical value of n is written before the letter. The number of electrons with particular values of n and l is often written as a superscript. Thus the symbol $3d^5$ means five electrons with $n = 3$ and $l = 2$. We shall employ the same notation in our discussions of nuclear energy states. Another terminology, taken over from X-ray spectroscopy, refers to the electron states characterized by $n = 1, 2, 3, 4, 5, 6 \ldots$ as the $K, L, M, N, O, P \ldots$ shells.

The magnetic quantum number m is related to the orientation of the angular momentum vector with respect to magnetic fields. In the absence of such fields quantum states differing only in m have the same energy, but in the presence of a field such states are split; this is the Zeeman effect. A fourth quantum number, unfortunately also denoted by the letter s, was introduced when G. Uhlenbeck and S. Goudsmit showed that certain features in atomic spectra could be accounted for if the electron were assumed to have spin, that is, to rotate about its own axis. The quantum condition for the electron spin is that any projection of its intrinsic angular momentum is ½, in the unit $h/2\pi$, and may be either parallel or antiparallel to the pro-

[1] Actually the angular momentum is $\sqrt{l(l+1)}\, h/2\pi$, but its projection on any axis does not exceed $lh/2\pi$.

jection of its orbital angular momentum. Thus the spin quantum number s can have the values $+\frac{1}{2}$ and $-\frac{1}{2}$.

Taking into account the two possible spin states of each electron, we can now see that there are $2n^2$ possible quantum states for each principal quantum number n. For $n = 1, 2, 3, 4$ the numbers of quantum states are then 2, 8, 18, 32, and this sequence of numbers is quite familiar to chemists in connection with the lengths of the various periods in the periodic table. The structure of the periodic table can best be understood in terms of quantum mechanics; for this purpose account must be taken of the important exclusion principle formulated by W. Pauli in 1925. A consequence of this principle is that in an atom no two electrons can occupy a quantum state characterized by the same values of the four quantum numbers n, l, m, and s. Thus any s state is filled when occupied by two electrons, any p state by 6, any d state by 10, etc. In atoms, the order in which electron levels are filled, that is, the order of increasing energy, is $1s$, $2s$, $2p$, $3s$, $3p$, $4s$, $3d$, $4p$, $5s$, $4d$, $5p$, $6s$, $4f$, $5d$, $6p$, $7s$, $5f$. For each value of n, the levels fill in order of increasing l. In fact the preference for low angular momenta is so great that $4s$ states have lower energy than $3d$; $5s$, $5p$, and $6s$ states are lower than $4f$; etc. We shall see that for nuclear quantum levels the order is very different.

Uncertainty Principle. A physical interpretation has been given by M. Born to the wave function ψ which is the solution of Schroedinger's equation for a given system such as an electron in an atom. He assumes that ψ is the amplitude of the wave associated with the electron and that the square of this amplitude at any point in space represents the fraction of the total time that the electron spends there. Thus in wave mechanics the notion of well-defined orbits for the electrons has to be abandoned, because only the time average of the positions of the electrons can be derived from the equations. This is also in accord with the Heisenberg uncertainty principle, which states that the inherent uncertainty Δx in the position of a particle whose momentum is known within an accuracy Δp is such that the product $\Delta p \cdot \Delta x$ is of the order of magnitude of $h/2\pi$.

More generally, the uncertainty principle is applicable not only to position and momentum, but to any two associated quantities whose product has the dimensions of h, erg-seconds. One of the forms of the uncertainty principle which we shall have occasion to apply is the relation between the lifetime Δt of a quantum state and the uncertainty ΔE in its energy (often called its level width): $\Delta t \cdot \Delta E \approx h/2\pi$. This relation may be used to estimate level widths from observed lifetimes, or to estimate lifetimes (especially those that are too short to be measured) from level widths determined by other means.

B. NUCLEAR STRUCTURE

Proton-Neutron Model. We shall now return to a consideration of the atomic nuclei whose existence was revealed by the α-particle-scattering experiments. We have seen that a nucleus is a small positively charged particle whose mass accounts for almost the entire atomic mass and whose charge is equal in magnitude but opposite in sign to the sum of the charges of all the electrons in the neutral atom. The dimensions of nuclei are of the order of 10^{-12} to 10^{-13} cm whereas atomic dimensions, as determined, for example, from gas kinetics, are about 10^{-8} cm. Nuclei, therefore, are very much more dense than ordinary matter; the density of nuclear matter is in the neighborhood of 10^{14} g per cm^3 or 10^8 tons per cm^3.

According to present ideas nuclei consist of protons and neutrons. The simplest nucleus is that of the common hydrogen atom; a single proton constitutes this nucleus. A proton, therefore, carries a positive charge equal in magnitude to the charge on an electron, 4.8025×10^{-10} electrostatic unit (esu). The mass of a proton is approximately equal to that of a hydrogen atom and, therefore, nearly equal to 1 on the atomic weight scale. The neutron is an uncharged particle whose mass is very nearly equal to but slightly greater than the proton mass.

Nuclear Forces and Mesons. The nature of the forces which hold neutrons and protons together in nuclei is still not well understood. It is clear that the force cannot be simple electric (Coulombic) attraction, because the neutron carries no charge. Gravitational forces are too weak by very many orders of magnitude to account for nuclear binding. Many experimental facts indicate that nuclear forces have a very short range, in fact, a range somewhat smaller than nuclear dimensions. The type of force which is now rather generally believed to act between nucleons (a collective term for protons and neutrons) is a so-called exchange force, that is, a force which holds the nucleons together through a continuous exchange of some constituent particles between them.

What are the particles that are being exchanged between nucleons to produce nuclear binding? Electrons have been considered in this connection, but the calculations show that they give much too weak a bond. In 1935, H. Yukawa concluded that an exchange particle about 150 times as heavy as the electron would lead to about the right magnitude and range for nuclear forces. A few years later S. H.

Neddermeyer and C. D. Anderson first observed particles of approximately this mass in cosmic rays. These new particles were subsequently found to have masses equal to about 210 electron masses. They are called mesons, from the Greek word *meso,* middle, because they are intermediate in mass between electrons and protons.

More recently other kinds of mesons have been discovered in cosmic rays, and several types have also been produced with high-energy accelerators. The original cosmic-ray meson with a mass of 210 electron masses, now called the μ meson, was for a long time thought to be the particle responsible for nuclear binding. But in 1946 when experiments showed that the interaction between these μ mesons and nuclei was much weaker than required by the meson theory of nuclear forces, this idea had to be abandoned. The subsequently discovered π meson (mass = 275 electron masses) appears to have many of the properties required by meson theories of nuclear forces and is currently the favorite candidate for the particle that is supposed to account for nuclear binding. Positive, negative, and neutral π mesons have been found and their properties extensively studied. Meson theories of nuclear forces taking into account only neutral, only charged, or both charged and neutral mesons have been developed. None of the theories is completely satisfactory; yet sufficient success has been attained to justify the hope that a really adequate meson theory of nuclear forces will eventually emerge.

Atomic Number and Mass Number. The number of protons in a nucleus is called the atomic number Z and determines the chemical properties of the element. The atomic numbers of the known elements range from 1 for hydrogen to 100 for the most recently discovered transuranium element. The number of neutrons in the nucleus is sometimes called the neutron number N. Nuclei are known with values of N from 0 to 155.

The total number of nucleons (neutrons plus protons) in the nucleus of a given atomic species is called its mass number A; this is the whole number nearest the atomic weight of that particular atom. Mass numbers are known in the range 1 to 255. The difference $N - Z$ (or $A - 2Z$) between the number of neutrons and protons in a nucleus is referred to as the neutron excess or isotopic number.

The symbol used to denote a nuclear species is the chemical symbol of the element with the atomic number as a left subscript and the mass number as a superscript, usually to the right, for example, ${}_2He^4$, ${}_{27}Co^{59}$, ${}_{92}U^{235}$. The atomic number is often omitted because it is uniquely determined by the chemical symbol.

Isotopes, Isobars, Isotones, and Isomers. Atomic species of the same atomic number, that is, belonging to the same element, but having different mass numbers are called *isotopes*. In the nuclei of the different isotopes of a given element the same number of protons is combined with different numbers of neutrons. For example, a $_{17}Cl^{35}$ nucleus contains 17 protons and 18 neutrons, whereas a $_{17}Cl^{37}$ nucleus contains 17 protons and 20 neutrons. Deuterium, a rare isotope of hydrogen, has a nucleus containing one proton and one neutron.

The word isotope has been used also in a broader sense to signify any particular nuclear species characterized by its A and Z values. In this meaning it should probably be replaced by the word *nuclide* suggested by T. P. Kohman and defined as "a species of atom characterized by the constitution of its nucleus, in particular by the number of protons and neutrons in its nucleus."

Atomic species having the same mass number but different atomic numbers are called *isobars*. A few examples of isobars are $_{32}Ge^{76}$ and $_{34}Se^{76}$; $_{52}Te^{130}$, $_{54}Xe^{130}$, and $_{56}Ba^{130}$; $_{80}Hg^{204}$ and $_{82}Pb^{204}$.

Atomic species having the same number of neutrons but different mass numbers are sometimes referred to as *isotones*. For example, $_{14}Si^{30}$, $_{15}P^{31}$, and $_{16}S^{32}$ are isotones because they all contain 16 neutrons per nucleus.

Among the natural radioactive bodies discussed in chapter 1 there are two, UX_2 and UZ, which have the same mass number as well as the same atomic number, but differ in their radioactive properties. This is an example of nuclear *isomerism*. Although UX_2 and UZ had been known for several years, the phenomenon of nuclear isomerism did not receive much attention until another pair of isomers, Br^{80}, was discovered among artificially produced radioactive species in 1937. Well over 100 cases of isomerism are now known. Nuclear isomers are different energy states of the same nucleus, each having a different, measurable lifetime (except that the ground state may be stable). In a number of cases, more than two isomeric states have been found for a given A and Z. For example, three radioactive species, of half-lives 60 days, 1.3 min, and 21 min, have been assigned to Sb^{124}. The notation which has become fairly standard for representing isomeric states other than the ground state is a superscript m (for metastable) following the mass number; if there are two or more excited isomeric states, they are labeled m_1, m_2, etc., in order of increasing excitation energy. Thus, the isomers of Sb^{124} will be denoted as Sb^{124} (60 day), Sb^{124m_1} (1.3 min) and Sb^{124m_2} (21 min). We shall consider each isomeric state as an individual nuclide. (In this connection see the discussion of isomerism on pages 156–158.)

Comparison of the Proton-Neutron with the Older Proton-Electron Hypothesis. Before the discovery of the neutron there existed the idea that nuclei were composed of protons and electrons. In this model the nucleus contained enough protons to account for its approximate mass (one proton for each unit of atomic weight) and enough electrons to reduce the net positive charge to the proper value; thus the neutral atom was to contain as many total electrons as protons, with some in the known atomic orbits or energy levels and the remainder within the nucleus. This model now not only is unfashionable but also presents difficulties which are not easy to resolve, when compared with the proton-neutron nuclear model. One difficulty is that the electron is "too large to be in the small space of the nucleus"; we shall consider two aspects of the question of the size of the electron.

With the assumption of unlimited validity for Coulomb's law (perhaps an improper assumption) it is clear that the electron cannot have zero radius since its potential energy would then be infinite. We may use the known mass of the electron to set an upper limit to this potential energy through the mass-energy relation $E = mc^2$, with the rest mass of the electron $m = 9.11 \times 10^{-28}$ g and the velocity of light $c = 3.00 \times 10^{10}$ cm sec^{-1}. Imagine the assembly of the electronic charge e ($= 4.80 \times 10^{-10}$ esu) from infinitesimal units dq of charge; take q for the charge already collected within the radius R. The (repulsive) force on dq at a distance r from the center of the electron under construction is given by Coulomb's law as $f = -q\,dq/r^2$. The energy required for assembly of the electron of radius R is then

$$E = -\int_{q=0}^{q=e}\int_{r=\infty}^{r=R} \frac{q\,dq}{r^2}\,dr = \frac{e^2}{2R}.$$

From this,

$$R = \frac{e^2}{2E} = \frac{(4.80 \times 10^{-10})^2}{2 \times 9.11 \times 10^{-28} \times (3.00 \times 10^{10})^2} = 1.4 \times 10^{-13} \text{ cm}.$$

This figure is not to be believed as a literal radius of the electron; often the quantity e^2/E (that is, twice the preceding value) is considered merely as a convenient unit of length and termed the "classical radius of the electron."

The length just obtained is of the order of nuclear dimensions. However, if the electron is to be thought of as being within the nucleus its de Broglie wavelength $\lambda = h/mv$ must be of the order of nuclear dimensions; this requires a very high momentum and consequently high kinetic energy. For example, to make $\lambda = 10^{-12}$ cm, the required total energy is readily calculated to be far in excess of the energies known to be associated with nuclear changes involving one nucleon. On the other hand, a similar calculation shows that a neutron or proton (mass $M = \sim 1.66 \times 10^{-24}$ g) of de Broglie wavelength 10^{-12} cm has a kinetic energy of about 10^{-5} erg, which is just in the range of experimental energy changes for the addition or removal of one nucleon. On the basis of this argument the proton-neutron model of nuclear structure is more acceptable than the proton-electron model.

Additional difficulties of the proton-electron model which stemmed from considerations of angular-momentum conservation and statistics were also removed with the introduction of the proton-neutron model. Some mention of this will be made in the following section.

C. NUCLEAR PROPERTIES

Mass and Energy. Masses of atomic nuclei are so small when expressed in ordinary units (less than 10^{-21} g) that they are generally expressed on a different scale. The scale used is the *physical atomic-weight scale* in which the mass of an atom of O^{16} is taken as the standard and assigned a mass of exactly 16.00000 units. It should be noted that this scale is not identical with the *chemical atomic-weight scale* (which is used for expressing atomic weights in chemical calculations); in the chemical scale the atomic weight of the natural isotopic mixture of oxygen (containing small amounts of O^{17} and O^{18}) is assigned the value of exactly 16.00000. The unit used is, therefore, larger in the chemical than in the physical scale, and the numerical value of any atomic weight is smaller when expressed on the chemical scale. The conversion factor between the two is 1.000272 ± 0.000005, the uncertainty being due to the uncertainty in the isotopic composition of normal oxygen.

The values of isotopic masses given in this book and in most of the literature on nuclear physics and chemistry are on the physical scale and are not nuclear but atomic masses; that is, they include the masses of the extranuclear electrons in the neutral atoms. This convention turns out to have some advantages in the treatment of nuclear reactions and energy relations.

The experimental determination of exact atomic masses involves the use of a mass spectrograph or mass spectrometer. In most of these instruments the charge-to-mass ratio of positive ions is determined from the amount of deflection in a combination of magnetic and electric fields; different arrangements are used for bringing about either velocity focusing or directional focusing or both, for ions of a given e/M. Instruments which use photographic plates for recording the mass spectra are called mass spectrographs; those which make use of collection and measurement of ion currents are referred to as mass spectrometers. More recently the fact that ions of the same kinetic energy and different masses require different times to traverse a given path length has been utilized in the design of several types of so-called time-of-flight mass spectrometers. These devices have already proved particularly useful for the determination of accurate mass values.

Mass determinations throughout the mass range from hydrogen to bismuth have been made with precisions varying between about 1 and 10 parts per million. For precision mass determinations the method generally used is the so-called doublet method. This substitutes the measurement of the difference between two almost identical masses for the direct measurement of absolute masses. All measurements must, of course, eventually be related to the standard O^{16}. But for convenience the masses of H^1, H^2, and C^{12} have been adopted as substandards and for this purpose have been carefully measured by determinations of the fundamental doublets:

$(C^{12}H^1{}_4)^+$ and $(O^{16})^+$ at mass-to-charge ratio 16,
$(H^2{}_3)^+$ and $(C^{12})^{++}$ at mass-to-charge ratio 6,
$(H^2)^+$ and $(H^1{}_2)^+$ at mass-to-charge ratio 2.

On the physical scale the mass of a hydrogen atom (sometimes loosely called the proton mass) is 1.008142, the mass of a neutron 1.008982, and that of an electron 0.0005486 mass units. One mass unit equals 1.661×10^{-24} g.

One of the important consequences of Einstein's special theory of relativity [2] is the equivalence of mass and energy. The total energy content E of a system of mass M is given by the relation

$$E = Mc^2,$$

where c is the velocity of light (2.99776×10^{10} cm per sec). Therefore, the mass of a nucleus is a direct measure of its energy content. The measured mass of a nucleus is always smaller than the combined masses of its constituent nucleons, and the difference between the two is called the binding energy of the nucleus.

To find the energy equivalent to 1 mass unit we put $M = 1.661 \times 10^{-24}$ g and $c = 2.998 \times 10^{10}$ cm sec^{-1} and find $E = Mc^2 = 1.493$

[2] A summary of the most frequently used relativistic equations may be found in appendix B.

$\times 10^{-3}$ erg. However, energy units much more useful in nuclear work than the erg are the electron volt (ev), the kiloelectron volt (kev; 1 kev = 1000 ev), and the million electron volt (Mev; 1 Mev = 10^6 ev). The electron volt is defined as the energy necessary to raise one electron through a potential difference of 1 volt.

$$1 \text{ ev} = 1.602 \times 10^{-12} \text{ erg}; \qquad 1 \text{ Mev} = 1.602 \times 10^{-6} \text{ erg}.$$

Using these new units, we find

$$1 \text{ mass unit} = 931 \text{ Mev},$$

and

$$1 \text{ electron mass} = 0.5107 \text{ Mev}.$$

As an example we shall calculate the binding energy of He^4. The mass of He^4 is 4.00387; the combined mass of two hydrogen atoms [3] and two neutrons is $2 \times 1.00814 + 2 \times 1.00898 = 4.03424$. Thus the binding energy of He^4 is $4.03424 - 4.00387 = 0.03037$ mass unit or $0.03037 \times 931 = 28.27$ Mev. The binding energy per nucleon in He^4 is, therefore, approximately 7.1 Mev.

The binding energy of the deuteron calculated by the same method is found to be 2.23 Mev. Actually this value was determined experimentally from the threshold for the photodisintegration of the deuteron and combined with the mass-spectrographically measured masses of proton and deuteron to calculate the neutron mass. No accurate method for a direct measurement of the neutron mass is known.

The average binding energy per nucleon is about 6 to 9 Mev throughout the table of elements except in a few of the lightest nuclei. The binding energy per nucleon is found to have a maximum (near 8.8 Mev) for nuclei in the neighborhood of iron (mass ~ 55). Toward the heavy elements the dropping off is very gradual, and the average binding energy per nucleon reaches values near 7.5 Mev for the heaviest nuclei. On the light side of iron the values drop much faster, and among the lightest nuclei a number of irregularities occur; in particular the binding energies of $_2He^4$, $_6C^{12}$, and $_8O^{16}$ are very high. These trends have some important consequences. The sun's radiant energy is believed to result from a series of nuclear transformations whose net effect is the building up of helium atoms from hydrogen atoms, which is a very exoergic process. The energy released in the fission of the heaviest nuclei is large because nuclei near the middle of the periodic table have higher binding energies per

[3] Since the mass of He^4 includes the mass of two electrons it is clear that it is the *atomic* mass of H^1 which must be used.

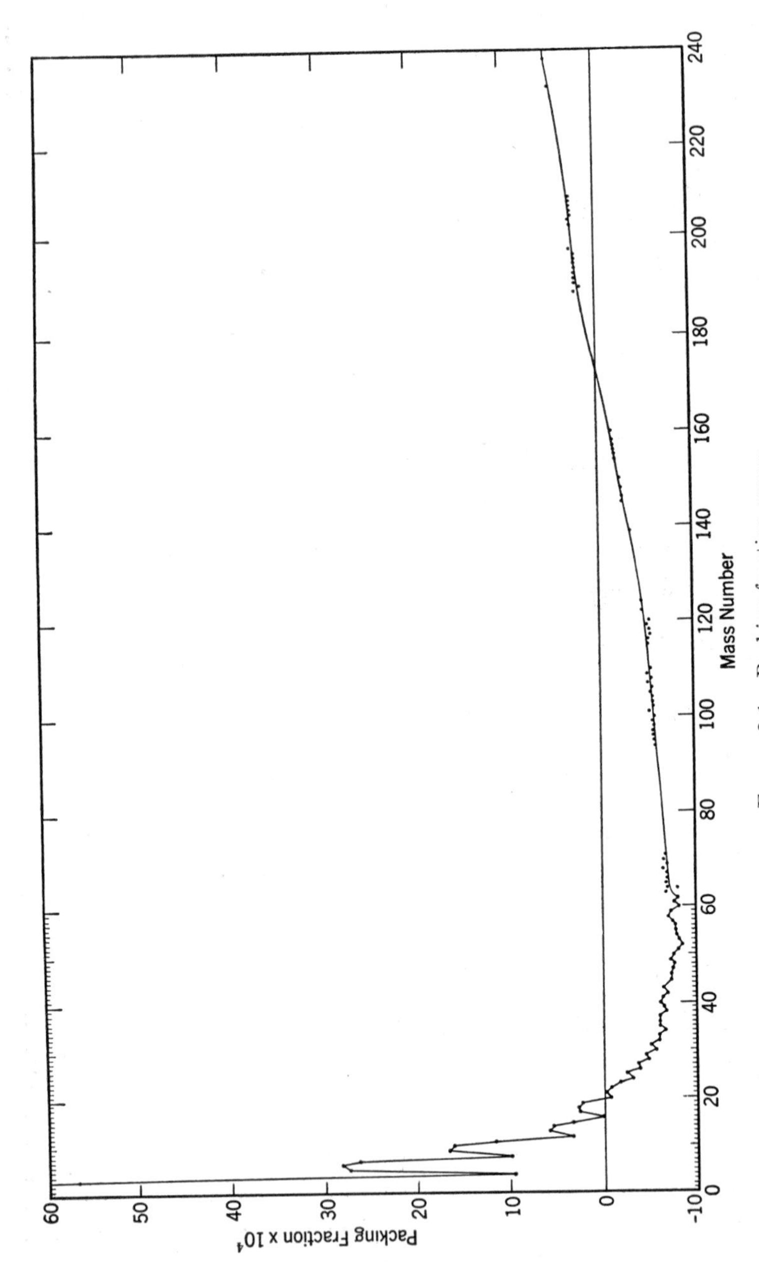

Figure 2-1. Packing-fraction curve.

nucleon. There is evidence that the earth's core consists largely of iron and nickel, and this may well be connected with the maximum in the nuclear stability curve in the region of these elements.

Quantities related to the binding energy are the mass defect and the packing fraction. These are, in fact, more frequently tabulated than the binding energies. The mass defect Δ is the difference between the atomic mass M and the mass number A: $\Delta = M - A$. (Some authors call this the mass excess.) The packing fraction f is the mass defect divided by the mass number: $f = \Delta/A$. (Sometimes f is defined as Δ/M; the difference is negligible.) The packing fraction goes through a minimum in the region of iron. Since the atomic masses fall below the corresponding mass numbers between $A \approx 20$ and $A \approx 180$ the packing fractions are negative in that region. For convenience in tabulation packing fractions are often multiplied by 10^4. A packing-fraction curve is reproduced in figure 2-1.

Except among the lightest nuclei the packing fraction, or the average binding energy per nucleon, is a rather slowly varying function. On the other hand, the contribution to the binding energy from the addition of one more proton or neutron shows large fluctuations from one nucleus to the next. (Chemists may enjoy thinking of the binding energy of one additional nucleon as a sort of partial molal binding energy.) The quantity may be defined here as the mass of the nucleus plus the mass of the additional nucleon minus the mass of the resulting nucleus, expressed in energy units. We tabulate some illustrative values of the binding energies for an additional neutron (table 2-1) and for an additional proton (table 2-2).

The masses of some radioactive nuclei can be determined from an accurate knowledge of the energy balance in nuclear reactions involving these nuclei and from their disintegration energies. This subject is discussed in chapter 3.

Charge and Radius. Nuclear charges were first determined in the α-particle-scattering experiments mentioned in section A. The most reliable way to determine nuclear charge is by Moseley's relation between Z and the energy characteristic of the K X rays emitted when the element is used as a target in an X-ray tube:

$$\text{energy} = 10.25(Z - 1)^2 \text{ ev.}$$

A number of different methods have been employed to measure nuclear radii. The results are not all in agreement, and to understand the discrepancies we must consider the shape of the field of force around a nucleus. At distances outside the range of nuclear forces only Coulomb forces act, but closer in towards the center of the nu-

TABLE 2-1

BINDING ENERGY FOR AN ADDITIONAL NEUTRON (IN MEV)

H^1	2.23	Mg^{24}	7.32	Cr^{49}	13.4
H^2	6.26	Mg^{25}	11.11	Mn^{54}	10.2
He^3	20.58	Mg^{26}	6.43	Mn^{55}	7.3
He^4	−0.66	Al^{27}	7.72	Fe^{53}	13.8
Li^6	7.24	Si^{27}	17.12	Fe^{54}	8.8
Li^7	2.04	Si^{28}	8.47	Fe^{55}	11.3
Be^7	18.90	Si^{29}	10.60	Fe^{56}	7.6
Be^8	1.67	Si^{30}	6.60	Co^{55}	10.2
Be^9	6.81	P^{29}	9.72	Co^{59}	7.7
B^9	8.44	P^{30}	12.60	Ni^{57}	11.7
B^{10}	11.47	P^{31}	7.92	Ni^{58}	9.0
B^{11}	3.36	S^{31}	4.96	Ni^{59}	11.5
C^{11}	18.71	S^{32}	8.65	Cu^{63}	7.9
C^{12}	4.95	S^{33}	11.33	Cu^{64}	9.9
C^{13}	8.17	S^{34}	6.89	Sr^{85}	9.5
N^{13}	10.54	Cl^{35}	8.55	Sr^{87}	11.1
N^{14}	10.84	Cl^{36}	10.54	Y^{88}	11.6
O^{15}	15.60	Cl^{37}	6.11	Zr^{89}	12.5
O^{16}	4.15	A^{36}	8.8	Nb^{92}	8.7
O^{17}	8.05	A^{37}	11.7	Mo^{91}	13.3
F^{17}	9.12	A^{40}	6.1	Mo^{96}	7.1
F^{18}	10.41	K^{39}	7.8	Ce^{139}	9.1
F^{19}	6.60	K^{40}	10.0	Ce^{141}	7.2
Ne^{19}	16.80	K^{41}	7.4	Pr^{140}	9.4
Ne^{20}	6.75	Ca^{40}	8.6	Pb^{205}	8.1
Ne^{21}	10.52	Ca^{41}	11.4	Pb^{206}	6.7
Ne^{22}	5.19	Ca^{42}	8.1	Pb^{207}	7.4
Na^{22}	12.25	Ca^{43}	11.3	Pb^{208}	3.9
Na^{23}	6.95	Sc^{48}	11.7		
Na^{24}	9.2	V^{51}	7.3		

TABLE 2-2

BINDING ENERGY FOR AN ADDITIONAL PROTON (IN MEV)

H^2	5.49	O^{16}	0.61	Ni^{60}	5.5
H^3	19.90	O^{17}	5.59	Ni^{64}	7.4
Li^6	5.60	O^{18}	7.97	Sr^{88}	6.2
Li^7	17.25	A^{37}	5.14	Cd^{113}	6.4
Li^8	15.32	A^{38}	7.48	Cd^{114}	5.8
Be^9	6.58	A^{40}	7.8	In^{114}	9.2
Be^{10}	11.23	K^{39}	8.1	In^{115}	11.3
C^{12}	1.95	K^{40}	8.8	Tl^{205}	7.0
C^{13}	7.54	K^{41}	10.2	Tl^{206}	7.5
C^{14}	10.20	Ca^{44}	6.8	Pb^{207}	3.7
N^{14}	7.35	Fe^{55}	5.9	Pb^{208}	3.8
N^{15}	12.11	Co^{59}	9.8	Bi^{209}	5.0

cleus the nuclear attractive forces play the dominant role. This gives rise to a potential-energy curve for a nucleus and a positive particle separated by a distance r (measured between centers) somewhat as sketched in figure 2-2.

The first experiments that gave an indication of nuclear dimensions were those on α-particle scattering. Since Rutherford's scattering formula was based on the assumption of purely Coulombic forces, deviations from it are expected if the α particle approaches closely enough to the scattering nucleus to be within the range of its nuclear forces. In scattering experiments with elements heavier than copper no deviations from the Rutherford scattering formula were observed, because the available α-particle energies did not permit approach to the surface of these nuclei. The minimum separation distances achieved in the early experiments, 1.2×10^{-12} cm for copper and 3.2×10^{-12} cm for gold (as calculated from the α-particle velocities and scattering angles), merely set upper limits to these nuclear radii. In lighter elements definite deviations from the Coulomb law were observed. Scattering experiments in aluminum, for example, show marked deviations from inverse-square forces at a distance of about 8×10^{-13} cm. This value presumably corresponds roughly to R in figure 2-2. Beams of high-energy protons and α particles from accelerators have been used for the determination, by scattering experiments, of nuclear radii for heavier elements.

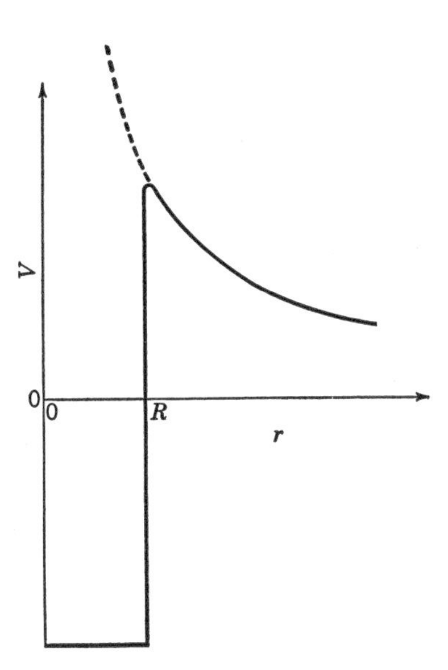

FIGURE 2-2. Potential energy in the neighborhood of a nucleus. R is the radius of the potential well.

The radius R of the potential well inside which the short-range nuclear forces are of importance can be determined in several other ways. The cross-sectional "area" which a nucleus presents to a beam of fast neutrons can be determined from experiments on fast-neutron absorption and scattering. This method yields values of R from about 6×10^{-13} for $A \approx 50$ to about 1×10^{-12} for $A \approx 200$. A quantum-mechanical treatment of α-particle decay yields a formula connecting half-life and nuclear radius (see chapter 6); from the known half-lives of the naturally occurring α emitters nuclear radii between 8.4 and 9.8×10^{-13} cm are obtained for these heavy elements. This method involves a calculation of the probability of penetration of the potential barrier around the nucleus by the α particle. By computation of the barrier-penetration probabilities for charged particles from the yields of nuclear reactions between charged particles and nuclei, radii of lighter nonradioactive nuclei can be determined.

The nuclear radii determined by the methods described can be represented approximately by the empirical formula

$$R = 1.5 \times 10^{-13} A^{1/3} \text{ cm.} \tag{2-4}$$

We see from this that the nuclear volume is roughly proportional to the nuclear mass and that the volume per nucleon is about constant. Various values have been recommended for the constant of proportionality. The one given, 1.5×10^{-13}, is in good agreement with α-decay and other barrier penetration data. Some recent measurements, for example of electron scattering by nuclei, indicate that for some purposes a smaller value, perhaps as low as 1.2×10^{-13}, might be more appropriate. Since nuclear radius is not a very well-defined quantity, it does not seem unreasonable that different types of experiments should give somewhat different indications.

Spin and Nuclear Moments. The intrinsic angular momentum of a nucleus is always expressed as an integral or half-integral multiple I of $h/2\pi$. This spin I is zero or integral for nuclei of even A and half-integral for nuclei of odd A. Apparently all nuclei of even A and even Z have zero spin in their normal states.

Since the rotation of a charged particle produces a magnetic moment, nuclei with spin also have magnetic moments associated with them. For a particle of mass M, charge Ze, and angular momentum P the magnetic moment is, according to classical theory, $ZeP/2Mc$. For the electron [with $P = \frac{1}{2}(h/2\pi)$] this formula gives one-half of what is called the Bohr magneton (1 Bohr magneton $= 0.927 \times 10^{-20}$ erg per gauss). Since proton and electron have the same magnitude of charge and the same spin the proton magnetic moment calculated from the classical formula is 1/1835 of the electron moment; 1/1835 Bohr magneton is called a nuclear magneton and is used as the unit of nuclear magnetic moments. Actually neither the proton's nor the electron's magnetic moment agrees with this too simple theory. The electron has a magnetic moment of one (instead of one-half) Bohr magneton, and the proton has 2.79 (instead of one-half) nuclear magnetons. The magnetic moments of other nuclei also differ from the classical values. These moments are sometimes expressed in terms of nuclear g factors; the magnetic moment is then $g \cdot I$ nuclear magnetons. If the magnetic moment is in the direction of the spin, g is taken as positive; if magnetic moment and spin are opposed, g is negative. A negative g factor results from the presence of some neutrons arranged with unpaired spins. The negative magnetic moment of the neutron presumably results from a charge distribution with some negative charge (perhaps due to negative mesons) concentrated near the periphery and overbalancing the effect of an equal positive charge nearer the center.

Nuclear spins and magnetic moments can sometimes be determined from hyperfine structure in atomic spectra. Hyperfine structure arises from the fact that the energy of an atom is slightly different for different (quantized) orientations between nuclear spin and angular momentum of the electrons because of the interaction between the nuclear magnetic moment and the magnetic field of the electrons. From the number of lines in a spectroscopic "hypermultiplet" the nuclear spin I can be determined under suitable conditions. By this method many nuclear spins such as those of Bi^{209} ($I = 9/2$) and Pr^{141} ($I = 5/2$) have been measured.

Although the number of components in a hypermultiplet is determined by the nuclear spin, the amount of the splitting (which is usually of the order of 1 angstrom or less) depends on the value of the nuclear magnetic moment. This dependence is well enough understood to allow a calculation of the magnetic moment from the magnitude of the splitting provided that the nuclear spin is known. Thus the nuclear magnetic moments of Bi^{209} and Na^{23} have been determined by this method to be $+4.080$ and $+2.217$ nuclear magnetons, respectively.

Another method of determining nuclear spins is based on the alternating intensities found in rotational spectra of homonuclear diatomic molecules. Molecules in which the two nuclear spins are parallel and antiparallel, respectively, give rise to two sets of alternate lines in the rotational spectrum. The intensity ratio between successive lines is a measure of the abundance ratio for the two types of molecules, which can be shown to be $(I + 1)/I$ at equilibrium except at very low temperatures. For hydrogen the intensity ratio is 3:1, thus confirming the assignment of spin $I = 1/2$ to the proton. The two kinds of hydrogen, orthohydrogen (with spins parallel) and parahydrogen (with spins antiparallel), can actually be isolated. In normal hydrogen at moderate and high temperatures they are present in the ratio 3:1.

A second method for the determination of nuclear magnetic moments (and for the measurement of nuclear spin) is the atomic-beam method of I. I. Rabi and coworkers. In this method (which is an extension of the Stern-Gerlach experiment for the determination of magnetic moments of atoms) a beam of atoms is sent through an inhomogeneous magnetic field. The nuclear spin I, uncoupled from the electron angular momentum J by the external field, orients itself with respect to the field. This orientation is governed by the usual quantum conditions, and the beam is, therefore, split into $2I + 1$ components whose separations are dependent on the nuclear magnetic moment. The energies of these splittings may be found in terms of characteristic alternating-magnetic-field frequencies which induce transitions between components. Various modifications of this method, notably the addition of focusing devices and the adaptation to molecular rather than atomic beams, have greatly improved the accuracy of the results obtainable. The magnetic moment of the neutron has been directly determined by a suitable (and rather drastic) modification of this principle; it was found to be -1.91 nuclear magnetons.

A more recent technique for the study of nuclear spins, and especially of magnetic moments, uses nuclear resonance absorption. The magnetic dipoles of nuclei of spin I can align themselves with a strong external magnetic field in $2I + 1$ different orientations. The energy differences between the resulting $2I + 1$ energy states correspond to the radio-frequency region, and their magnitude depends on the so-called gyromagnetic ratio, that is, the ratio of magnetic moment to spin. Resonance absorption of radio-frequency radiation will, therefore, take place at a frequency corresponding to these transitions, and the resonance frequency is a measure of the gyromagnetic ratio and, if I is known, of the magnetic moment. In some cases I can be determined separately because the intensity of absorption is a function of I (and of other factors).

A very powerful tool for nuclear spin determinations is microwave spectroscopy. Many transitions, particularly between rotational states of molecules, occur in the microwave region (wavelengths of the order of 1 cm). The hyperfine structure of such transitions is quite analogous to that in atomic spectra and has been used for a number of nuclear spin determinations. Still a different type of hyperfine structure measurement which has found some application in this field uses the paramagnetic resonance method. What is observed here is the resonance absorption frequency for a paramagnetic substance in a radio-frequency field and the splitting of this frequency due to the interaction between nuclear spin and the electronic angular momentum of the molecule or ion.

A table of measured nuclear spins is given in appendix F. Information on spins of radioactive nuclei has been inferred from detailed studies of β- and γ-decay processes. This subject will be discussed in chapter 6.

In addition to its magnetic dipole moment a nucleus may have an electric quadrupole moment. This property may be thought of as arising from an elliptic charge distribution in the nucleus. The quadrupole moment q is given by the equation $q = \frac{2}{5}Z(a^2 - b^2)$, where a is the semiaxis of rotation of the ellipsoid, and b is the semiaxis perpendicular to a; q has the dimensions of an area. For the deuteron $q = +2.74 \times 10^{-27}$ cm^2, and the charge distribution is cigar-shaped. Quadrupole moments, including both positive and negative values, have been determined for quite a number of nuclei with $I > \frac{1}{2}$. (Nuclei with $I = 0$ or $I = \frac{1}{2}$ cannot have quadrupole moments.) Quadrupole moments give rise to abnormal hyperfine splittings in spectra, and the methods for quadrupole-moment measurements are therefore the ones already discussed: optical spectroscopy, microwave spectroscopy, nuclear resonance absorption, and some modified molecular-beam techniques.

Statistics. All nuclei and elementary particles are known to obey one of two kinds of statistics: Bose statistics or Fermi statistics. If the coordinates of two identical particles in a system can be interchanged without change in the sign of the wave function representing the system, Bose statistics applies. If the sign of the wave function does change with the interchange of the coordinates, the particles obey Fermi statistics. In Fermi statistics each completely specified quantum state can be occupied by only one particle; that is, the Pauli exclusion principle applies to all particles obeying Fermi statistics. For particles obeying Bose statistics no such restriction exists. Protons, neutrons, electrons (and some other elementary particles such as positrons, neutrinos, and some types of mesons) all obey Fermi statistics. A nucleus will obey Bose or Fermi statistics, depending on whether it contains an even or odd number of nucleons.

The statistics of nuclei can be deduced from the alternating intensities in rotational bands of the spectra of diatomic homonuclear molecules. With Bose statistics the even-rotational states and with Fermi statistics the odd-rotational states are more populated. This can be illustrated by the rotational spectra of hydrogen and deuterium. In normal hydrogen, H_2, the ratio of the populations in the states of odd- and of even-rotational quantum numbers is 3:1 corresponding to spin ½ and Fermi statistics; in deuterium, D_2, the ratio is 1:2 corresponding to spin 1 and Bose statistics.

The determination of the statistics of nuclei provides an important test of nuclear models. The demonstration in 1929 that N^{14} nuclei obey Bose statistics was one of the first clear-cut contradictions to

TABLE 2-3

PROPERTIES OF SOME ELEMENTARY PARTICLES

Symbol	Name	Charge *	Mass † Rest	Spin ‡	Magnetic Moment §	Statistics ‖
e^- or β^-	electron	−1	0.0005486	½	−1835	F
e^+ or β^+	positron	+1	0.0005486	½	+1835	F
γ	photon	0	0	1	0	B
ν	neutrino	0	<0.00002	½	<0.3	F
n	neutron	0	1.008982	½	−1.913	F
μ	mu-meson	+1, −1	0.115	½		F
π	pi-meson	+1, −1, 0	0.151	0		B
H^1 or p	proton	+1	1.008142	½	+2.793	F

* In units of $e = 4.8025 \times 10^{-10}$ esu.

† For the proton the mass of the neutral atom is listed. The unit is the physical atomic weight unit.

‡ In units of $h/2\pi$.

§ In units of the nuclear magneton $(eh/4\pi Mc)$, where M is the proton mass. Positive values indicate moment orientations with respect to spin orientations that would result from spinning positive charges.

‖ F means Fermi and B means Bose statistics.

the proton-electron model. According to that model the N^{14} nucleus would consist of 14 protons and 7 electrons, a total of 21 Fermi particles, and it should therefore obey Fermi statistics. On the proton-neutron model this nucleus is composed of 14 Fermi particles, which is consistent with the Bose statistics. All the information on statistics of nuclei is compatible with the proton-neutron rather than the proton-electron model. Quite similar arguments for the proton-neutron model can be made from the integral or half-integral nature of the measured nuclear spins.

Parity. Another nuclear property connected with symmetry properties of wave functions is parity. A system is said to have odd or even parity according to whether or not the wave function for the system changes sign when the signs of all the space coordinates are changed. We shall make some use of the concept of parity in our discussions of nuclear reactions and radioactive decay processes because the parity of an isolated system, like its total energy, momentum, angular momentum, and statistics, is conserved. We shall require merely the very simple rules of combination for parity. Two particles in states of even parity or two particles in states of odd parity can combine to form a state of even parity only. A particle of even parity and one of odd parity result in a system of odd parity. We may illustrate this by an example from atomic spectroscopy: allowed transitions in atoms occur only between an atomic state of even and one of odd parity, not between two even or two odd states, because the quanta of ordinary dipole radiation are characterized by odd parity.

In discussing nuclear energy states we shall make use of the fact that parity is connected with the angular momentum quantum number l. States with even l (s, d, g . . . states) have even parity, those with odd l (p, f, h . . . states) have odd parity.

D. ISOTOPY AND ISOTOPE SEPARATIONS

Occurrence of Isotopes in Nature. The phenomenon of isotopy was discovered when different radioactive bodies in the natural decay series, for example, RaB, AcB, and ThB, were found to exhibit identical chemical properties (in the case mentioned the properties are those of lead). This led to a search for the existence of isotopes in nonradioactive elements. In early experiments with ion deflections in magnetic and electric fields J. J. Thomson showed in 1913 that neon consisted of two isotopes of mass numbers 20 and 22 (now a third isotope Ne^{21} is known). Since that time the development of improved instruments, notably F. W. Aston's mass spectrograph and the various other mass-measuring devices mentioned on p. 32, has made possible very careful searches for isotopes in all the elements existing in stable form. As a result of these mass-spectrographic investigations we now know that the elements with atomic numbers between 1 and 83 have on the average more than three stable isotopes each. Some elements such as beryllium, phosphorus, arsenic, and bismuth have a single stable nuclear species each, whereas tin, for example, has as many as 10 stable isotopes.

The stable isotopes of a given element generally occur together in constant proportions. This accounts for the fact that atomic weight determinations on samples of a given element from widely different sources generally agree within experimental errors. However, there are some notable exceptions to this rule of constant isotopic composition. One is the variation in the abundances of lead isotopes, especially in ores containing uranium and thorium. Depending on the age and composition of such ores, the end products of the three radioactive families, Pb^{206}, Pb^{207}, and Pb^{208}, and the nonradiogenic Pb^{204} may occur in different proportions. Similarly the isotope Sr^{87} has been found to have an abnormally high abundance in rocks which contain rubidium; this is explained by the fact that Rb^{87} is a naturally occurring β emitter and decays to Sr^{87}.

Helium from gas wells probably has its origin in radioactive processes (α disintegrations) and contains a much smaller proportion of the rare isotope He^3 than does atmospheric helium. Water from various sources shows slight variations in the H^1/H^2 ratio. This is in some cases due to the fact that heavy water has a slightly lower vapor pressure than ordinary water and is, therefore, concentrated by evaporation. The enrichment of H^2 in the water of the Dead Sea and in certain vegetables is ascribed to this cause. The waters which show abnormally high H^2 concentrations usually also have slightly higher O^{18}/O^{16} ratios than normal. Another cause for small variations in isotopic composition is the fact that chemical equilibria are slightly dependent on the molecular weights of the reactants, and this may lead to isotopic enrichments in the course of reactions occurring in nature. For example, the slight enrichment of C^{13} in limestones relative to some other sources of carbon is explained by the fact that the equilibrium in the reaction between CO_2 and water to form carbonic acid lies somewhat further towards the side of carbonic acid for $C^{13}O_2$ than for $C^{12}O_2$.

Isotope Separations. Some of the principles involved in isotope fractionations in nature have been exploited for the artificial concentration and separation of isotopes. We stated earlier that chemical properties are determined by the nuclear charge, and it would follow from this that isotopes of a given element are completely identical in their chemical behavior. However, the isotopic mass does have a very slight effect on chemical equilibria and on rates of chemical reactions. In fact, for light elements such as carbon and nitrogen multistage exchange reactions have been used to produce separated isotopes on a commercial scale. These chemical effects become vanishingly small for isotopes of heavier elements because they depend essentially on percentage differences in mass.

Other methods for isotope separations should be mentioned briefly. Diffusion of gases or liquids through porous membranes results in separation, the lighter isotopes diffusing more rapidly. This is the method used for the large-scale separation of the uranium isotopes in the huge gaseous-diffusion plants in Oak Ridge, Tenn., and Paducah,

Ky. The thermal diffusion technique of K. Clusius and G. Dickel makes use of the fact that in a thermal gradient the heavy isotopic component concentrates at the cold end and, by means of vertical adjacent hot and cold walls, provides a very ingenious arrangement for obtaining multistage separations in simple apparatus through the combined actions of convection and thermal diffusion. Separations have also been effected by use of high-speed centrifugation. Differences in vapor pressure between compounds containing different isotopes lead to concentration of the heavy constituents in the residues from slow evaporations; this method has been used for the concentration of heavy water ($H^2{}_2O$ or D_2O). Heavy water is also produced by electrolysis, which enriches the heavy component in the residues. Finally the electromagnetic methods of separation deserve mention. Mass spectrographs have long been used to separate small quantities of isotopes, but during World War II the electromagnetic method was developed from a microgram to a kilogram scale for the purpose of separating U^{235} in quantity. Large electromagnetic separators (calutrons) at Oak Ridge, Tenn., are now used for the separation of isotopes of a large number of elements throughout the periodic table, and these are available through the Isotopes Division of the U. S. Atomic Energy Commission.

E. NUCLEAR SYSTEMATICS

Binding Energies. Numerous attempts have been made to account for the shape of the packing-fraction or binding-energy curve. On a semiempirical basis an expression for the binding energy of a nucleus as a function of its proton and neutron composition, that is, as a function of Z and $N = A - Z$, can be obtained. Several different expressions are given in the literature; one that gives rather good agreement with measured binding energies at least for $A > 80$ is

$$E_B = 14.1\,A - 13.1\,A^{2/3} - 0.585\,Z(Z-1)\,A^{-1/3} - 18.1(N-Z)^2\,A^{-1} + \delta\,A^{-1}, \quad (2\text{-}5)$$

where $\delta = 132$ for Z even and N even, $\delta = -132$ for Z odd and N odd, and $\delta = 0$ for A odd. The binding energy E_B is here expressed in million electron volts (Mev).

The first term in equation 2-5, and this is the most important term, is proportional to the number of nucleons A. This observation can be interpreted to mean that the nuclear forces have short ranges and act between a small number of nucleons only. The saturation of these forces is almost (but certainly not entirely) complete when four particles, two protons and two neutrons, interact, as is indicated by the large observed binding energies of He^4, C^{12}, O^{16}.

Those nucleons at the surface of a nucleus can be expected to have unsaturated forces, and, consequently, a reduction in the binding energy proportional to the nuclear surface should be taken into account. This is the second term, containing $A^{2/3}$, which is a measure of the surface since A is proportional to the volume.

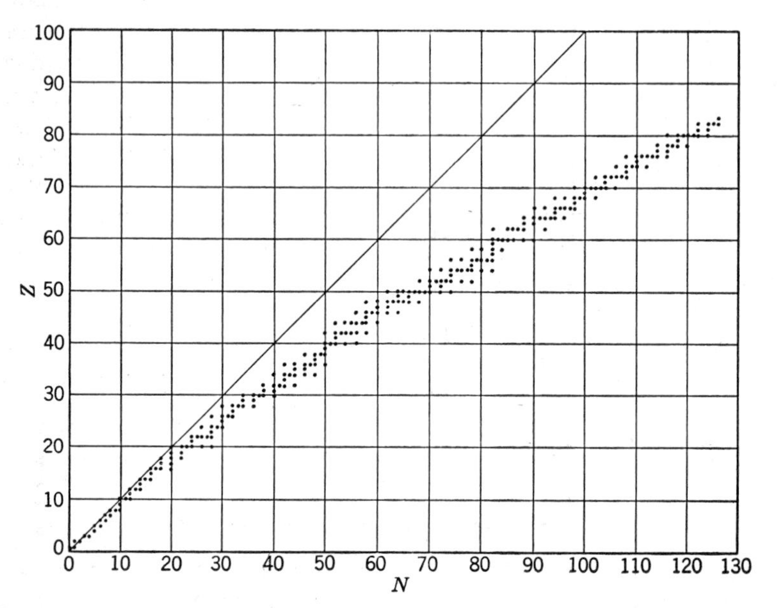

FIGURE 2-3. The known stable nuclei on a plot of Z versus N. Note the gradual increase in the neutron-proton ratio; the 45° line indicates a neutron-proton ratio of 1.

The Coulombic repulsive force between protons is, of course, not of the saturation type and is of sufficient range to be effective for all the protons in a nucleus. Therefore, each of the Z protons interacts with the other $Z - 1$ protons to reduce the binding energy as shown in the third term. The factor $A^{-1/3}$ enters this term because it measures the average separation distance for protons distributed in a volume proportional to A.

Other factors being equal, maximum stability, that is, maximum binding energy per nucleon, is found for nuclei with equal numbers of protons and neutrons (see figure 2-3). This would indicate that (except for the Coulombic energy effect) the protons and neutrons have similar energy-level spacings in nuclei. In this case the levels of lowest energy are occupied when $Z = N$; additional nucleons, most often neutrons, are by the Pauli exclusion principle required to go into levels of greater energy. This effect is expressed in quantitative (empirical) fashion by the fourth term.

Types of Nuclei. Nuclei can be classified according to whether they contain even or odd numbers of protons and neutrons. There are then four types of nuclei as shown in the following tabulation. The distribution of the known stable nuclear species among these four types and the corresponding values of δ in equation 2-5 are as follows:

164 even-even	(Z even, N even)	$\delta = +132$ [4]
55 even-odd	(Z even, N odd)	$\delta = 0$
50 odd-even	(Z odd, N even)	$\delta = 0$
4 odd-odd	(Z odd, N odd)	$\delta = -132$ [4]

A relation between the frequency of occurrence and the stability as measured by the binding energy is apparent. The striking preponderance of even-even nuclei and complete absence of odd-odd nuclei outside the region of the lightest elements (the four odd-odd nuclei are ${}_1H^2$, ${}_3Li^6$, ${}_5B^{10}$, and ${}_7N^{14}$) can be explained in terms of a tendency of two like particles to complete an energy level by pairing opposite spins. The δ term in the binding-energy equation is often called the pairing term.

The greater stability of nuclei with filled energy states is apparent not only in the larger number of even-even nuclei, but also in their greater abundance relative to the other types of nuclei. On the average, elements of even Z are much more abundant than those of odd Z (by a factor of about 10). For elements of even Z the isotopes of even mass (even N) account in general for about 70 to 100 per cent of the element (beryllium, xenon, and dysprosium being exceptions).

Nuclear Energy Surface. The binding energies of all nuclei can be represented as a function of A and Z by means of a three-dimensional plot of an equation such as 2-5. Without attempting to construct this nuclear energy surface in three dimensions, we can obtain useful information about some of its features.

[4] The quantity δ is actually not a constant but varies rather irregularly with A. The value given is an average for $A > 80$. For $A < 60$ a lower value, perhaps $\delta \sim \pm 65$, should be used, but in that region equation 2-5 does not give reliable results anyway. There is evidence that in some regions of A and Z, δ shows a slight systematic difference in odd A nuclei depending on whether the odd nucleon is a proton or a neutron. We disregard this small effect.

Equation 2-5 is seen to be quadratic in Z, apart from the pairing term. For constant A, the equation takes the form

$$E_B = aZ^2 + bZ + c + \delta/A, \tag{2-6}$$

where $a = -0.585A^{-1/3} - 72.4A^{-1}$,

$b = 0.585A^{-1/3} + 72.4$,

$c = -4.0A - 13.1A^{2/3}$.

Equation 2-6 represents a parabola (for a given value of δ). Thus we see that a section through the nuclear energy surface at any odd value

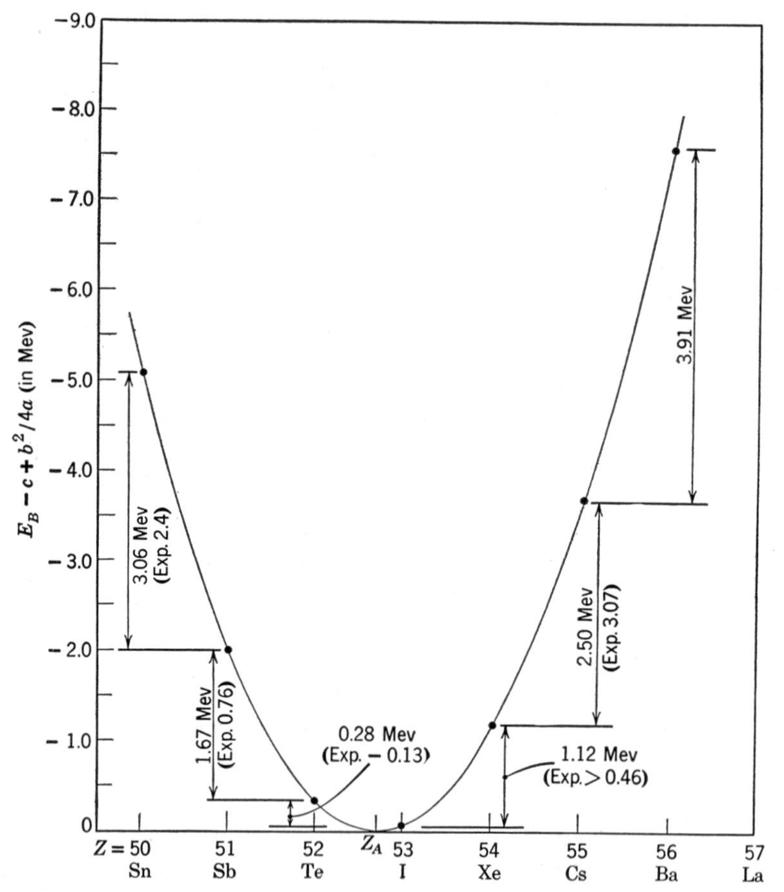

FIGURE 2-4. Binding-energy parabola for $A = 125$ as calculated from equation 2-8. The binding-energy differences (β-decay energies) between neighboring isobars as calculated with the constants of equation 2-6 are indicated; experimentally measured β-decay energies are shown in parentheses for comparison.

of A ($\delta = 0$) is a single parabola, and a section at an even value of A ($\delta = \pm 132$) results in two identical parabolas separated along the energy axis by $2\delta/A$. These binding-energy parabolas are very useful

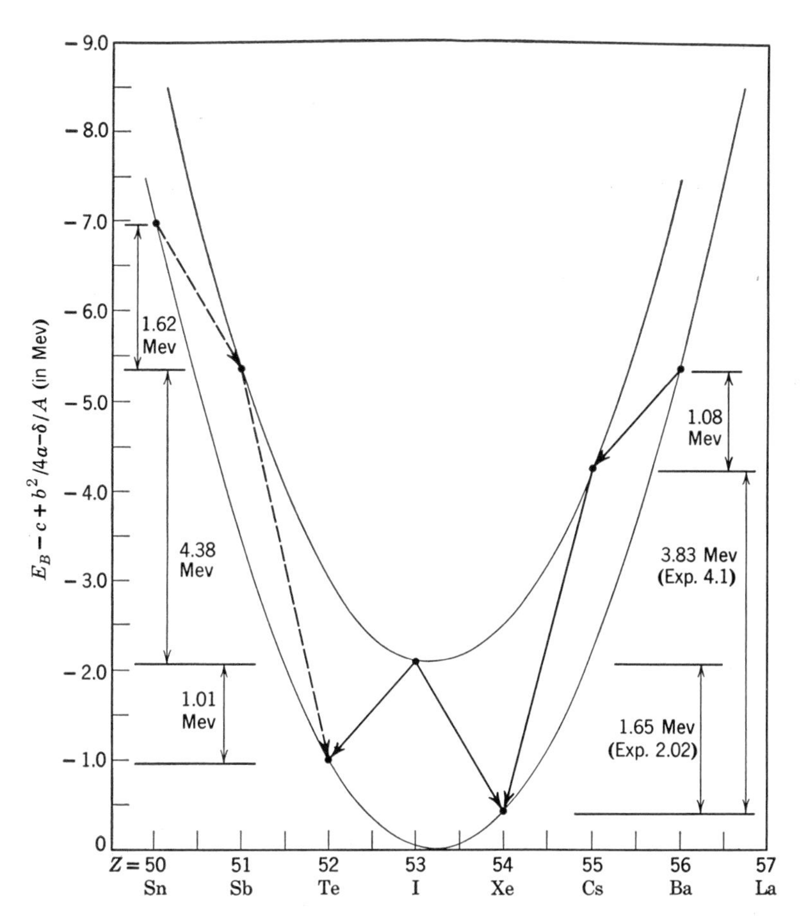

FIGURE 2-5. Binding-energy parabolas for $A = 128$ as calculated from equation 2-8. Experimentally measured as well as calculated β-decay energies are shown. The dotted lines indicate β-decay processes not yet experimentally observed.

in β-decay systematics, because approximate values of the energy available for β decay between neighboring isobars can be read directly from them. Parabolas for $A = 125$ and $A = 128$ as calculated from equation 2-6 are shown in figures 2-4 and 2-5. In these figures (and usually in the literature) the parabolas are plotted with their vertices (points of maximum stability) turned down. To find the value Z_A

corresponding to the maximum binding energy for a given A, we differentiate equation 2-6 with respect to Z, considering A constant, and set the derivative equal to zero:

$$\frac{\partial E_B}{\partial Z} = 2aZ_A + b = 0;$$

$$Z_A = -\frac{b}{2a} = \frac{0.585A^{2/3} + 72.4A}{2(0.585A^{2/3} + 72.4)}. \tag{2-7}$$

Note that for Z_A we may find nonintegral values, since we have treated Z as a continuous function. For $A = 125$, $Z_A = 52.7$; for $A = 128$, $Z_A = 53.2$. For the purpose of plotting energy parabolas we can now write equation 2-6 in a more convenient form often found in the literature:

$$E_B = a(Z - Z_A)^2 + \frac{\delta}{A} + \left(c - \frac{b^2}{4a}\right). \tag{2-8}$$

The last term, $c - (b^2/4a)$, is a function of A only, which we usually do not need to evaluate.

By considering the parabolic curves for a set of isobars we can draw several important conclusions about nuclear stability. For example, it is immediately clear that for any given odd A there can be only one β-stable nuclide,[5] that nearest the minimum of the parabola. For even A there are usually two and sometimes three possible β-stable isobars, all of the even-even type. In figure 2-5 both Te^{128} and Xe^{128} are stable. Strictly speaking, one of these, the figure indicates Te^{128}, is not really stable in the thermodynamic sense because it has a lower binding energy than does the other (Xe^{128}). However, the transition requires a so-called double β-decay process (involving simultaneous emission of two β particles or simultaneous capture of two electrons); such processes are expected to have exceedingly long half-lives, and none has been established with certainty.

In figures 2-4 and 2-5 the experimentally determined energy differences between neighboring isobars have been included for comparison with those obtained from the binding-energy equation. The agreement is seen to be within 1 Mev in the particular mass region considered. Considerably better agreement may be obtained by adjustment

[5] Apparent exceptions to this rule still exist at $A = 113$, with Cd^{113} and In^{113}, and at $A = 123$, with Sb^{123} and Te^{123}. One of the members of each of these pairs of seemingly stable isobars is undoubtedly radioactive but with a very long half-life. The same is presumably true for the odd-odd nuclides V^{50} and Ta^{180}, which occur in nature in small abundance.

of a and Z_A to fit known points in the particular region of Z and A. For example, according to our equations, Z_A for $A = 125$ is 52.7, and consequently I^{125} would be expected to be the stable nuclide of mass 125. Actually Te^{125} is stable and I^{125} is unstable by about 0.13 Mev with respect to electron capture. To obtain agreement with this experimental fact, we could empirically shift the parabola by 0.4 unit along the Z axis, using $Z_A = 52.3$; this would improve the agreement with the other experimentally known decay energies and would allow a more reliable prediction of the decay energy of the as yet undiscovered Ba^{125}. The maximum error in Z_A values as determined from our equations is approximately one unit.

Nuclear Shell Structure. In the preceding discussion we have treated nuclei essentially as statistical assemblies of neutrons and protons. This model, in which a nucleus is considered analogous to a liquid drop, is very successful in accounting for many properties of nuclei. However, there is also strong experimental evidence for some sort of shell structure in nuclei, analogous to the electron-shell structure in atoms, although not nearly as pronounced. That certain numbers of neutrons and protons seem to form particularly stable configurations was pointed out by W. Elsasser in 1934. However, except for attempts to account for the well-known special stability of light nuclei with N and Z values of 2, 8, and 20 (${}_2He^4$, ${}_8O^{16}$, and ${}_{20}Ca^{40}$), the subject of nuclear shell structure received little attention until in 1948 M. G. Mayer pointed out the strong evidence for the additional "magic numbers" 50 and 82 for protons, and 50, 82, and 126 for neutrons. Since then 28 has been recognized as an additional magic number. We shall briefly summarize some of the evidence.

Above $Z = 28$, the only nuclides of even Z which have isotopic abundances above 60 per cent are Sr^{88} (with $N = 50$), Ba^{138} ($N = 82$), and Ce^{140} ($N = 82$). No more than 5 isotones occur in nature for any N except $N = 50$, where there are 6, and $N = 82$, where there are 7. Similarly, the largest number of stable isotopes (10) occurs at tin, $Z = 50$, and both in calcium ($Z = 20$) and tin the stable isotopes span an unusually large mass range. The fact that all the heavy natural radioactive chains end in lead ($Z = 82$) is significant, as is the neutron number 126 of the two heaviest stable nuclides, Pb^{208} and Bi^{209}.

The particularly weak binding of the first nucleon outside a closed shell (analogous to the low ionization potential for the valence electron in an alkali atom) is shown by the fact that nuclides with $N = 50$, 80, and 126 have unusually low probabilities for reacting with neutrons. Also, in the nuclei Kr^{87} ($N = 51$) and Xe^{137} ($N = 83$)

one neutron is bound so loosely that it is emitted spontaneously when these nuclei are formed by β decay from Br^{87} and I^{137}, respectively.

The major discrepancies between the semi-empirical binding-energy equation and experimental decay energy and mass data occur in the regions of the magic numbers. Attempts to fit the isobaric parabolas to experimental β-decay data in these regions fail unless discontinuities of as much as 2 Mev in neutron and proton binding energies at the shell edges are taken into account. Similarly, careful mass measurements for nuclides in the neighborhood of $N = 50$, 82, and 126, and $Z = 28$, 50, and 82 have shown that the packing fraction curve (figure 2-1) is not really perfectly smooth in these regions but has slight breaks. Evidence for the weak binding of the first nucleon outside a closed shell may be found in tables 2-1 and 2-2. A great deal of evidence for the $N = 126$ shell has been accumulated in recent years from α-decay systematics. Alpha-decay energies are rather smooth functions of A for a given Z, but show striking discontinuities at $N = 126$. Finally, there are some very interesting correlations between the occurrence of nuclear isomerism and the magic numbers: so-called islands of isomerism occur for N and Z values just below 50, 82, and 126.

In chapter 6 we shall return to a discussion of nuclear shell structure and show how the magic numbers can be interpreted in terms of the filling of proton and neutron energy levels.

EXERCISES

1. Show that h ($= 6.624 \times 10^{-27}$ erg sec) has the dimensions of angular momentum.

2. Derive the expressions for the kinetic and potential energies of an electron in a Bohr orbit.

3. Show that the circumference of a stable Bohr orbit is always an integral multiple of the de Broglie wavelength of the electron in the orbit.

4. Calculate the packing fraction and the binding energy per nucleon for Li^6, P^{31}, Ni^{60}, Pd^{108}, Pt^{195}, and U^{238}.

5. Estimate the level width (in electron volts) of a quantum state whose lifetime is 10^{-15} sec.

6. From the masses given in appendix G, find (a) the binding energy for an additional neutron to O^{16}, V^{50}, Pu^{239}; (b) the binding energy for an additional proton to B^{10}, Mn^{52}, $Th^{234}(UX_1)$.

Answers: (a) Pu^{239} 6.4 Mev; (b) Mn^{52} 7.2 Mev.

7. Using the natural abundances of the oxygen isotopes from appendix G, compute the atomic weight of ordinary oxygen on the physical scale and the conversion factor between the physical and chemical scales of atomic weights.

8. What is the energy of (a) an electron, (b) a proton, (c) a pi-meson with a de Broglie wavelength of 1.5×10^{-13} cm? (You may want to refer to the relativistic relations in appendix B.) *Answer to part* (a): 830 Mev.

9. Without reference to tables, calculate the approximate charge and mass of the proton in familiar units (coulombs and grams, respectively).

10. The three fundamental mass doublets have been found to have the following separations:

$$(C^{12}H_4)^+ - (O^{16})^+ = 36.371 \text{ millimass units},$$

$$H_2^+ - D^+ = 1.550 \text{ millimass units},$$

$$D_3^+ - (C^{12})^{++} = 42.291 \text{ millimass units}.$$

Calculate the atomic masses of H, D, and C^{12}.

11. With the aid of the binding-energy equations estimate the β-decay energies of Mn^{53} (with respect to Cr^{53}) and Sc^{42} (with respect to Ca^{42}). Discuss possible reasons why the actual values might be lower or higher than those calculated. *Answer to first part:* 2.1 Mev.

12. Using the information you have on nuclear radii, estimate the minimum α-particle energy necessary to observe deviations from Rutherford scattering in silver. *Answer:* $\sim$14 Mev.

13. With the aid of equations 2-5 and 2-6 estimate: (*a*) the energy liberated when one additional neutron is added to U^{235}, (*b*) the energy liberated when one additional neutron is added to U^{238}, (*c*) the amount of energy by which I^{129} is unstable with respect to β decay to Xe^{129}.

Answer: (*a*) 7.3 Mev.

14. Determine from the binding-energy equations the atomic number Z_A corresponding to maximum stability for $A = 27$, $A = 131$, and $A = 204$. Compare your results with the experimental data as listed, for example, in appendix G.

15. What can you say about the intensities of alternate lines in the rotational spectrum of iodine?

REFERENCES

E. Rutherford, J. Chadwick, and C. D. Ellis, *Radiations from Radioactive Substances,* Cambridge University Press, 1930.

I. Kaplan, *Nuclear Physics,* Cambridge, Mass., Addison-Wesley Publishing Co., 1955.

D. Halliday, *Introductory Nuclear Physics,* New York, John Wiley & Sons, 1950.

R. E. Lapp and H. L. Andrews, *Nuclear Radiation Physics,* 2nd ed., New York, Prentice-Hall, Inc., 1954.

E. Fermi, *Nuclear Physics,* University of Chicago Press, 1950.

N. Feather, *An Introduction to Nuclear Physics,* Cambridge University Press, 1948.

H. A. Bethe and R. F. Bacher, "Nuclear Physics, A. Stationary States of Nuclei," *Revs. Mod. Phys.* **8,** 83–105 (1936).

F. K. Richtmyer and E. H. Kennard, *Introduction to Modern Physics,* 4th ed., New York, McGraw-Hill Book Co., 1947.

M. Born, *Atomic Physics,* London, Blackie, 1951.

E. Rutherford, "The Scattering of α and β Particles by Matter and the Structure of the Atom," *Phil. Mag.* **21,** 669 (1911).

N. Bohr, "On the Constitution of Atoms and Molecules," *Phil. Mag.* **26,** 1, 476, 857 (1913).

H. G. J. Moseley, "The High-Frequency Spectra of the Elements," *Phil. Mag.* **26,** 1024 (1913) and **27,** 703 (1914).

L. De Broglie, "Recherches sur la théorie des quanta," *Ann. phys.* **3,** 22 (1925).

E. Schroedinger, "An Undulatory Theory of the Mechanics of Atoms and Molecules," *Phys. Rev.* **28,** 1049 (1926).

G. E. Uhlenbeck and S. Goudsmit, "Spinning Electrons and the Structure of Spectra," *Nature* **117,** 264 (1926).

W. Pauli, Jr., "Ueber den Zusammenhang des Abschlusses der Elektronengruppen im Atom mit der Komplexstruktur der Spektren," *Z. Physik* **31,** 765 (1925).

W. Heisenberg, "Ueber den Anschaulichen Inhalt der Quantentheoretischen Kinematik and Mechanik," *Z. Physik* **43,** 172 (1927).

H. A. Bethe, *Elementary Nuclear Theory,* New York, John Wiley & Sons, 1947.

N. F. Ramsey, "Nuclear Two-Body Problems and Elements of Nuclear Structure," *Experimental Nuclear Physics* (E. Segrè, Editor), Vol. I, pp. 468–558, New York, John Wiley & Sons, 1953.

A. M. Thorndike, *Mesons, A Summary of Experimental Facts,* New York, McGraw-Hill Book Co., 1952.

A. O. Nier, "Mass and Relative Abundance of Isotopes," *Ann. Rev. Nuclear Sci.,* Vol. I, p. 137, Stanford, Annual Reviews Inc., 1952.

K. T. Bainbridge, "Charged Particle Dynamics and Optics, Relative Isotopic Abundances of the Elements, Atomic Masses," *Experimental Nuclear Physics* (E. Segrè, Editor), Vol. I, pp. 559–766, New York, John Wiley & Sons, 1953.

F. Bitter and H. Feshbach, "Nuclear Radii," *Phys. Rev.* **92,** 837 (1953).

G. P. Millburn, W. Birnbaum, W. E. Crandall, and L. Schecter, "Nuclear Radii from Inelastic Cross-Section Measurements," *Phys. Rev.* **95,** 1268 (1954).

N. F. Ramsey, "Nuclear Moments and Statistics," *Experimental Nuclear Physics* (E. Segrè, Editor), Vol. I, pp. 358–467, New York, John Wiley & Sons, 1953.

F. W. Aston, *Mass Spectra and Isotopes,* 2nd ed., New York, Longmans, Green, 1942.

C. P. Keim, "Electromagnetic Separation of Stable Isotopes," *Ann. Rev. Nuclear Sci.,* Vol. I, p. 263, Stanford, Annual Reviews Inc., 1952.

G. H. Clewett, "Chemical Separation of Stable Isotopes," *Ann. Rev. Nuclear Sci.,* Vol. I, p. 293, Stanford, Annual Reviews Inc., 1952.

D. W. Stewart, "Separation of Stable Isotopes," *Nucleonics* **1,** No. 2, 18 (October 1947).

E. Feenberg, "Semi-empirical Theory of the Nuclear Energy Surface," *Revs. Mod. Phys.* **19,** 239 (1947).

R. R. Williams, "Nuclear Energetics," *J. Chem. Educ.* **23,** 508 (1946).

M. G. Mayer, "On Closed Shells in Nuclei," *Phys. Rev.* **74,** 235 (1948).

M. G. Mayer and J. H. D. Jensen, *Elementary Theory of Nuclear Shell Structure,* New York, John Wiley & Sons, 1955.

N. Feather, *Nuclear Stability Rules,* Cambridge University Press, 1952.

C. D. Coryell, "Beta-Decay Systematics," *Ann. Rev. Nuclear Sci.,* Vol. II, p. 305, Stanford, Annual Reviews Inc., 1953.

H. W. Fulbright, "A Search for the Double Beta Decay of ^{124}Sn and ^{96}Zr," *Physica* **18,** 1026 (1952).

CHAPTER 3

NUCLEAR REACTIONS

A. THE NATURE OF NUCLEAR REACTIONS

A nuclear reaction is a process in which a nucleus reacts with another nucleus, an elementary particle, or a photon, to produce in a time of the order of 10^{-12} sec or less one or more other nuclei (and possibly other particles). Most of the nuclear reactions studied to date are of the type in which a nucleus reacts with a light particle (neutron, proton, deuteron, helium ion, electron, photon) and the products are a nucleus of a different species and again one or more light particles. The chief exception to this description is the fission reaction.

Notation. As an example of a nuclear reaction we may cite the first such process discovered, the disintegration of nitrogen by α particles. When Rutherford bombarded nitrogen with α particles from RaC′ he could observe scintillations on a zinc sulfide screen even with enough material interposed between the nitrogen and the screen to absorb all the α particles. Further experiments proved the long-range particles causing the scintillations to be protons, and the results were interpreted in terms of a nuclear reaction between nitrogen and α particles to give oxygen and protons, or, in the usual notation:

$$_7\mathrm{N}^{14} + {}_2\mathrm{He}^4 \rightarrow {}_8\mathrm{O}^{17} + {}_1\mathrm{H}^1.$$

Since 1919 thousands of different nuclear reactions have been studied. The recognition of reaction products is greatly facilitated when these are unstable because characteristic radioactive radiations can then be observed. The positron emitter P^{30} discovered by Joliot and Curie in the α-particle bombardment of aluminum is produced by the reaction

$$_{13}\mathrm{Al}^{27} + {}_2\mathrm{He}^4 \rightarrow {}_{15}\mathrm{P}^{30} + {}_0n^1.$$

The notation used for nuclear reactions is analogous to that in chemical reactions, with the reactants on the left- and the reaction products on the right-hand side of the equation. In all reactions so far observed (except those involving mesons) the total number of protons and the total number of neutrons (or total Z and total A) are conserved, just as in chemical reactions the number of atoms of each element is conserved. In addition other properties such as energy, momentum, angular momentum, statistics, and parity are conserved in nuclear reactions.

A short-hand notation is often used for the representation of nuclear reactions. The light bombarding particle and the light fragments (in that order) are written in parentheses between the initial and final nucleus; in this notation the two afore-mentioned reactions would read

$$N^{14}(\alpha, p)O^{17} \quad \text{and} \quad Al^{27}(\alpha, n)P^{30}.$$

The symbols n, p, d, α, e, γ, x are used in this notation to represent neutron, proton, deuteron, alpha particle, electron, gamma ray, and X ray.

Comparison of Nuclear and Chemical Reactions. Nuclear reactions, like chemical reactions, are always accompanied by a release or absorption of energy, and this is expressed by adding the term Q to the right-hand side of the equation. Thus a more complete statement of Rutherford's first transmutation reaction reads

$${}_7N^{14} + {}_2He^4 \rightarrow {}_8O^{17} + {}_1H^1 + Q.$$

The quantity Q is called the energy of the reaction or more frequently just "the Q of the reaction." Positive Q corresponds to energy release (exoergic reaction); negative Q to energy absorption (endoergic reaction).

Here an important difference between chemical and nuclear reactions must be pointed out. In treating chemical reactions we always consider macroscopic amounts of material undergoing reactions, and, consequently, heats of reaction are usually given per mole or occasionally per gram of one of the reactants. In the case of nuclear reactions we usually consider single processes, and the Q values are therefore given per nucleus transformed. If the two are calculated on the same basis, the energy release in a representative nuclear reaction is found to be many orders of magnitude larger than that in any chemical reaction. For example, the reaction $N^{14}(\alpha, p)O^{17}$ has a Q value of -1.20 Mev or $-1.20 \times 1.602 \times 10^{-6}$ erg or $-1.20 \times 1.602 \times 10^{-6} \times 2.390 \times 10^{-8}$ cal $= -4.60 \times 10^{-14}$ cal for a single process. Thus to convert 1 g atom of N^{14} to O^{17}, the energy required would be

$6.02 \times 10^{23} \times 4.60 \times 10^{-14}$ cal $= 2.77 \times 10^{10}$ cal. This is about 10^5 times as large as the largest values observed for heats of chemical reactions. On the other hand, one must keep in mind the fact that nuclear reactions are very rare events compared with chemical reactions; one reason is that the small sizes of nuclei make effective nuclear collisions quite improbable.

B. ENERGETICS OF NUCLEAR REACTIONS

The Q of a Reaction. It is clear from the foregoing discussion that the energy changes involved in nuclear reactions are of such magnitude that the corresponding mass changes in nuclear particles must be observable. (The mass changes accompanying chemical reactions are too small to be observable with the most sensitive balances available.) If the masses of all the particles participating in a nuclear reaction are known from mass spectrographic data, as is the case for the $N^{14}(\alpha, p)O^{17}$ reaction, the Q of the reaction can be calculated. The sum of the N^{14} and He^4 masses is 18.01139 mass units, and the sum of the O^{17} and H^1 masses is 18.01268 mass units; thus an amount of energy equivalent to 0.00129 mass unit has to be supplied to make the reaction energetically possible, or $Q = -0.00129 \times 931$ Mev $= -1.20$ Mev. When the Q value is known experimentally (from the kinetic energies of the bombarding particle and the reaction products), it is sometimes possible to compute the unknown mass of one of the participating nuclei. By this method the masses of a number of radioactive nuclei have been determined (see exercise 3).

It is often possible to calculate the Q value of a reaction even if the masses of the nuclei involved are not known, provided that the product nucleus is radioactive and decays back to the initial nucleus with known decay energy. Consider, for example, the reaction $Pd^{106}(n, p)Rh^{106}$. The product Rh^{106} decays with a 30-sec half-life and the emission of 3.53-Mev β particles to the ground state of Pd^{106}. We can write this sequence of events as follows:

$$_{46}Pd^{106} + {_0n^1} \rightarrow {_{45}Rh^{106}} + {_1H^1} + Q;$$

$$_{45}Rh^{106} \rightarrow {_{46}Pd^{106}} + \beta^- + 3.53 \text{ Mev}.$$

Adding the two equations we see that the net change is just the transformation of a neutron into a proton and an electron with accompanying energy change; or, symbolically,

$$_0n^1 \rightarrow {_1H^1} + \beta^- + Q + 3.53 \text{ Mev}.$$

Note that the symbol $_1H^1$ must here stand for a bare proton (evident from the charge conservation) whereas the listed "proton mass" includes the mass of one orbital electron.[1] For energy balance we therefore write

$$M_n = M_{H^1} + Q + 3.53 \text{ Mev},$$

where $M_n = 1.00898$ and $M_{H^1} = 1.00814$ mass units. Then

$$Q = (1.00898 - 1.00814) \times 931 - 3.53 = 0.78 - 3.53$$
$$= -2.75 \text{ Mev}$$

In the first example calculated we found the Q value of the reaction $N^{14}(\alpha, p)O^{17}$ to be -1.20 Mev. Does that mean that this reaction can actually be produced by α particles whose kinetic energies are just over 1.20 Mev? The answer is no, for two reasons. First, in the collision between the α particle and the N^{14} nucleus conservation of momentum requires that at least $4/18$ of the kinetic energy of the α particle must be retained by the products as kinetic energy; thus, only $14/18$ of the α particle's kinetic energy is available for the reaction. The threshold energy of α particles for the $N^{14}(\alpha, p)O^{17}$ reaction, that is, the kinetic energy of α particles just capable of making the reaction energetically possible, is $18/14 \times 1.20$ Mev $= 1.54$ Mev. The fraction of the bombarding particle's kinetic energy which is retained as kinetic energy of the products becomes smaller with increasing mass of the target nucleus (see exercise 5).

Barriers for Charged Particles. The second reason why the α particles must have higher energies than is evident from the Q value to produce the reaction $N^{14}(\alpha, p)O^{17}$ in good yield is the Coulomb repulsion between the α particle and the N^{14} nucleus. The repulsion increases with decreasing distance of separation until the α particle comes within the range of the nuclear forces of the N^{14} nucleus. This Coulomb repulsion gives rise to the potential barrier already mentioned in chapter 2. The height V of the potential barrier around a nucleus of charge Z_1e and radius R_1 for a particle of positive charge Z_2e and radius R_2 may be estimated as the energy of Coulomb repulsion when the two particles are just in contact: $V = Z_1Z_2e^2/(R_1 + R_2)$.

[1] In general, for negative-β-particle emission and electron-capture processes, the masses of electrons never have to be included in calculations when atomic masses are used. However, whenever emission of a positron is involved, two electron masses have to be taken into account: one for the positron and one for the extra electron that has to leave the electron shells to preserve electrical neutrality.

Obtaining the nuclear radii from the formula [2] $R = 1.5 \times 10^{-13} A^{1/3}$, we get for the barrier height between N^{14} and an α particle a value of about 3.4 Mev. According to classical theory then, an α particle must have at least $^{18}/_{14} \times 3.4 = 4.4$ Mev kinetic energy to enter a N^{14} nucleus and produce the α, p reaction, even though the energetic threshold for the reaction is only 1.54 Mev. In the quantum mechanical treatment of the problem there exists a finite probability for "tunneling through the barrier" by lower-energy particles, but this probability drops rapidly as the energy of the particle decreases. (The penetration of potential barriers is discussed in connection with α decay in chapter 6, section C.) Rutherford actually used α particles of over 7 Mev in his experiments.

The Coulomb barrier around a given nucleus for protons and for deuterons is about half as high as for α particles. The height of the barrier increases with increasing Z of the target nucleus; it is roughly proportional to $Z^{2/3}$ (not to Z, because the nuclear radius R increases approximately as $Z^{1/3}$). For the heaviest elements the potential barriers are about 15 Mev for protons and deuterons and about 30 Mev for α particles. In order to study nuclear reactions induced by charged particles, especially reactions involving heavy elements, it was therefore necessary to develop machines capable of accelerating charged particles to energies of many millions of electron volts. It is apparent that the entry of a neutron into a nucleus is not opposed by any Coulomb barrier, and even neutrons of very low energy react readily with even the heaviest nuclei.

In this discussion of the Coulomb barrier we have assumed that the incident particle collides head-on with the nucleus. Interactions do occur where the original direction of motion of the particle does not pass through the center of the target nucleus; such systems of projectile and target have angular momentum, and this angular momentum is quantized in integral multiples of the universal unit $h/2\pi$. In general the interactions are classified as s, p, d, etc., in the notation derived from atomic structure: s interactions correspond to $l = 0$, p interactions to $l = 1$, d interactions to $l = 2$, etc., where l is the value of the orbital angular momentum in units of $h/2\pi$. The resulting hindrance to the close approach of projectile to target is usually described as a centrifugal barrier, which is of course zero for s-wave interactions but is appreciable for higher l values. In crude approximation this barrier keeps any projectile just $l/2\pi$ de Broglie wave-

[2] For the lightest nuclei this formula for nuclear radii is actually a poor approximation; but for an estimate of barrier heights it is adequate.

lengths from the target center; the barrier is overcome at incident kinetic energies large enough to make this length as small as the sum of the nuclear radii of target and projectile. This approximation gives for the centrifugal barrier: $V = h^2l^2/[8\pi^2M(R_1 + R_2)^2]$, where M is the mass of the projectile. In the correct expression derived from wave mechanics l^2 is replaced by $l(l + 1)$:

$$V = \frac{h^2l(l + 1)}{8\pi^2M(R_1 + R_2)^2}.$$

For the reaction of an α particle and N^{14} the centrifugal barrier alone is $0.145\ l(l + 1)$ Mev, which is 0.29 Mev for p-wave and 0.87 Mev for d-wave interactions. The total barrier height is the sum of the Coulomb and the centrifugal barriers. Keep in mind, however, that of the two only the Coulomb barrier contributes to the minimum energy requirement for producing a nuclear reaction except in very special cases where s collisions may not lead to the reaction of interest.

It must be emphasized that potential barriers have an effect not only for particles entering, but also for particles leaving nuclei. For this reason a charged particle has to be excited to a rather high energy inside the nucleus before it can either go over the top of the Coulomb barrier or, according to the quantum mechanical picture, leak through the barrier with appreciable probability. Therefore, charged particles are usually emitted from nuclei with considerable energies (more than 1 Mev).

C. CROSS SECTIONS

Definitions. We now turn to a more quantitative consideration of reaction probabilities. The probability of a nuclear process is generally expressed in terms of a cross section σ which has the dimensions of an area. This originates from the simple picture that the probability for the reaction between a nucleus and an impinging particle is proportional to the cross-sectional target area presented by the nucleus. Although this picture certainly does not hold for reactions with charged particles which have to overcome Coulomb barriers or for slow neutrons (it does hold fairly well for the total probability of a fast neutron interacting with a nucleus), the cross section is a very useful measure of the probability for any nuclear reaction. For a beam of particles striking a thin target, that is, a target in which the beam is attenuated only infinitesimally, the cross section for a particular process is defined by the equation

$$N = \mathbf{I}n\sigma x, \tag{3-1}$$

where N is the number of processes of the type under consideration occurring in the target,
$\mathbf{I}$ is the number of incident particles,
n is the number of target nuclei per cubic centimeter of target,
σ is the cross section for the specified process, expressed in square centimeters, and
x is the target thickness in centimeters.

The total cross section for collision with a fast particle is never greater than the geometrical cross-sectional area of the nucleus, and therefore fast-particle cross sections are rarely much larger than 10^{-24} cm^2 (radii of the heaviest nuclei are about 10^{-12} cm). Hence, a cross section of 10^{-24} cm^2 is considered "as big as a barn" and 10^{-24} cm^2 has been named the barn, a unit generally used in expressing cross sections, and often abbreviated b. The millibarn (mb, 10^{-27} cm^2) and the microbarn (μb, 10^{-30} cm^2) are also used.

If instead of a thin target we consider a thick target, that is, one in which the intensity of the incident particle beam is attenuated, then the attenuation $-d\mathbf{I}$ in the infinitesimal thickness dx is given by the equation

$$-d\mathbf{I} = \mathbf{I}n\sigma\, dx,$$

where σ must be the total cross section. If we are able to neglect the variation in σ as the incident particles traverse the target, which is often the case for neutron reactions, we may obtain, by integration,

$$\mathbf{I} = \mathbf{I}_0 e^{-n\sigma x},$$

$$\mathbf{I}_0 - \mathbf{I} = \mathbf{I}_0(1 - e^{-n\sigma x}), \tag{3-2}$$

where $\mathbf{I}$ is the intensity of the beam after traversing a target thickness x, $\mathbf{I}_0$ is the incident intensity, and $\mathbf{I}_0 - \mathbf{I}$ is the number of reactions occurring.

As an illustration we shall calculate the number of radioactive Au^{198} nuclei produced per second in a sheet of gold 0.3 mm thick and 5 cm^2 in area exposed to a thermal neutron flux of 10^7 neutrons per cm^2 per sec. The capture cross section of Au^{197} for thermal neutrons is 94 barns, and we neglect any other reactions of neutrons with gold. The density of gold is 19.3 g cm^{-3}, and its atomic weight is 197.2; therefore,

$$n = \frac{19.3}{197.2} \times 6.02 \times 10^{23} = 5.89 \times 10^{22}\ \mathrm{Au}^{197} \text{ nuclei per cm}^3;$$

$$x = 0.03 \text{ cm};$$

$$\mathbf{I}_0 = 5 \times 10^7 \text{ incident neutrons per sec.}$$

Therefore, from equation 3-2,

$$\begin{aligned} \mathbf{I}_0 - \mathbf{I} &= 5 \times 10^7(1 - e^{-5.89\times10^{22}\times94\times10^{-24}\times0.03}) \\ &= 5 \times 10^7(1 - e^{-0.166}) \\ &= 7.6 \times 10^6\ \mathrm{Au}^{198} \text{ nuclei formed per sec.} \end{aligned}$$

Partial and Total Cross Sections. A cross section may be given for any particular nuclear process. For example, the total cross section for interaction of 10-Mev neutrons with a particular nuclear species may be measured by means of a transmission experiment in a collimated neutron beam, with the detector subtending a small solid angle with respect to the sample. In this case only those neutrons which have been neither absorbed nor scattered by the sample will be detected in the transmitted beam. The total cross section σ_t measured in this way is the sum of the cross sections for all the possible processes. Also we may define and measure cross sections for particular processes, such as n, γ or n, α reactions. We have already indicated that in equation 3-2 total cross sections must be used, and only the total number of reactions may be obtained directly. This may be multiplied by the ratio of a partial cross section to the total cross section to obtain the number of reactions of a particular kind. The partial cross section might be for an effect in one component of a mixture or compound or in a single isotope, but the total cross section must be that for the target substance; in such cases it is the product of cross section times number of effective nuclei that must be compared.

As an example, consider the irradiation of carbon tetrachloride to produce S^{35} by the reaction $Cl^{35}(n, p)S^{35}$. The sample is a 1-cm cube (1.46 g), and the thermal neutron flux normal to one face is 10^9 cm^{-2} sec^{-1}. How many S^{35} atoms are formed in 24 hours? According to appendix C the total absorption cross section for chlorine is 31.6 barns, that for carbon is only 0.0045 barn and may be neglected, and the isotopic cross section for the reaction $Cl^{35}(n,p)S^{35}$ is 0.17 barn. The number of chlorine atoms per cubic centimeter of sample is $(1.46/153.8) \times 4 \times 6.02 \times 10^{23} =$

2.28×10^{22}. Therefore, according to equation 3-2 the total number of neutrons absorbed in the sample in 24 hours is $24 \times 60 \times 60 \times 10^9(1 - e^{-2.28\times10^{22}\times31.6\times10^{-24}}) = 4.44 \times 10^{13}$. Since the isotopic abundance of Cl^{35} is 75.4 per cent, the fraction of neutrons absorbed that lead to n, p reactions in Cl^{35} is $(0.754 \times 0.17)/31.6 = 4.05 \times 10^{-3}$, and the number of S^{35} atoms formed is $4.05 \times 10^{-3} \times 4.44 \times 10^{13} = 1.8 \times 10^{11}$.

Sometimes the angular distribution of particles resulting from a particular process is of interest. In this case it is convenient to define a differential cross section $\frac{d\sigma}{d\Omega}$; this is the cross section for that part of the process in which the particles are emitted into unit solid angle at a particular angle Ω. Then the cross section for the over-all process under consideration is $\sigma = \int \frac{d\sigma}{d\Omega}\, d\Omega$.

Excitation Functions. Frequently the variation of a particular reaction cross section with incident energy is of interest; the relation between the two is called an excitation function. Examples of excitation functions are shown in figure 3-1. The determination of an absolute cross section requires a knowledge of the incident beam intensity and a measurement of the absolute number of reactions in the target. It is usually much simpler, and still frequently of considerable interest, to determine merely the relative yields of a reaction at different incident energies or the relative yields of different reactions at one energy. Most frequently the product radioactivity is used as a measure of the reaction yield.

D. BOHR THEORY OF NUCLEAR REACTIONS

Compound Nucleus. We have talked about nuclear reactions without considering in any detail the mechanisms by which such reactions may take place. In 1936 Bohr developed a theory of nuclear reactions which has been very successful in explaining many features of reactions induced by particles of moderate energies (at least up to 30 or 40 Mev). This theory was based on the liquid-drop model in which the nucleus is considered as a densely packed system with distances between nucleons of the same order of magnitude as the range of the nuclear forces and interaction energies between nucleons of the same order of magnitude as the kinetic energies of the incident particles. Bohr argued that an incident particle hitting such a system would lose much of its kinetic energy in the first few collisions with the nucleons and would then be held by the nuclear forces. Thus he postulated as the first step in any nuclear reaction the amalgamation of target nucleus and incident particle into a compound nucleus. In this compound nucleus the kinetic energy of the incident particle and the additional binding energy contributed by it are rapidly distributed among all the nucleons. The second step of the reaction, the breaking up of the compound nucleus into the reaction products, can take place only after a relatively long time because a large number of collisions is required before enough energy is likely to be "accidentally" concentrated on one nucleon to allow it to escape from the nuclear binding forces. The lifetimes of compound nuclei are of the order of 10^{-12} to 10^{-14} sec,[(3)] which is very long compared to the time required for a fast particle to traverse a distance equal to a nuclear diameter. For example, a 0.5-Mev neutron (velocity 10^9 cm per sec) would traverse a medium heavy nucleus (diameter 10^{-12} cm) in $10^{-12}/10^9 = 10^{-21}$ sec.

An essential feature of the Bohr picture is that the two steps of a nuclear reaction, the formation and the breaking up of a compound nucleus, are independent of each other. A given compound nucleus may be formed in different ways and may also be able to disintegrate in different ways (for example, by emission of a proton, a neutron, or an α particle). According to this model each mode of disintegration has a certain probability which is independent of the mode of formation of the compound nucleus.

Level Spacings and Level Widths. The Bohr picture is definitely statistical in nature and can therefore be expected to be valid only for nuclei containing a large number of nucleons and for excitation to high energies where the nuclear energy levels are closely spaced. Although there is at present little detailed knowledge of nuclear energy levels we can say that, in general, the level density increases with increasing mass number (that is, with increasing complexity of the nuclear system) and with increasing excitation energy.

Approximate formulas for the dependence of level density $W(E)$ on excitation energy E have been derived from statistical considerations and from empirical data. They are of the form

$$W(E) = Ce^{2\sqrt{aE}}, \tag{3-3}$$

[3] These times are too short to have been measured directly. By use of the uncertainty relation between time and energy ($\Delta E \cdot \Delta t \approx h/2\pi$) the lifetime of a compound nucleus in a particular energy state can be deduced from the width in energy of this state. This in turn can be determined experimentally (see p. 86).

where C and a are constants for a given A. With increasing A, C decreases and a increases.[4] Table 3-1 lists level densities (in

TABLE 3-1

Approximate Level Densities $W(E)$ in Mev^{-1} for Odd-A Nuclei

A	$E =$ 1 Mev	$E =$ 8 Mev	$E =$ 15 Mev	a (Mev^{-1})
27	2	20	90	0.45
63	5	9×10^2	2×10^4	2
115	6	2×10^5	6×10^7	8
181	6	6×10^5	4×10^8	10
231	5	2×10^6	2×10^9	12

Mev^{-1}) for several values of A and E as calculated from equation 3-3 and from the constants given by J. M. Blatt and V. F. Weisskopf for odd-A nuclei. For even-even nuclei the levels appear to be somewhat less dense, for odd-odd nuclei somewhat more dense, than for the odd-A group. It should be emphasized that the statistical treatment gives an extremely rough estimate of level density. For low excitation energies, within 3 or 4 Mev of the ground states, there is a good deal of experimental information on level spacings from γ-ray and α-particle transitions, and in this region the level densities are found to increase much less with energy than the exponential formula 3-3 would predict.

Most of the experimental evidence about level spacings at higher excitation energies comes from studies of nuclear reaction excitation functions. If the energy spread for the incident particles is smaller than the level spacing in the compound nucleus, the cross section for the formation of the compound nucleus will depend strongly on how nearly the excitation energy corresponds to one of the energy levels of the compound nucleus. The cross section may be orders of magnitude higher when the incident energy is such that a compound nucleus

[4] It is worth noting here that $k' \log W(E)$ may be considered as a nuclear entropy, where k' is the Boltzmann constant divided by 1.60×10^{-6} erg Mev^{-1}. We can then use standard thermodynamic relations to define a nuclear temperature T by the equation $\frac{1}{T} = k' \frac{d \log W(E)}{dE}$. From this, $T = (1/k')(E/a)^{1/2}$ degrees. For example, from the data in table 3-1 a nucleus of $A = 115$ excited to 8 Mev has $T = 1.2 \times 10^{10}$ degrees. Frequently nuclear "temperatures" are quoted in terms of $k'T$ in Mev rather than T in degrees; in our example, $k'T = 1.0$ Mev.

level is reached than it is for near-by energies. The condition of matching between excitation energy and a level energy of the compound nucleus is called resonance.

Very many resonances have been studied for slow-neutron reactions (section G) and also for charged-particle reactions with light nuclei. The spacing between the successive resonance peaks in an excitation function gives directly the spacing between levels in the compound nucleus. This information was used to evaluate the constants in equation 3-3. The energy widths of nuclear levels can be obtained from the observed breadths of the resonance peaks. In general the levels become wider with increasing excitation energy. As a result of the trends both in level densities and in level widths, levels show more and more overlapping at increasing energies, and at excitation energies of 12 or 15 Mev no level structure is discernible in medium and heavy nuclei.

Competition among Different Reactions. The Bohr theory suggests that a given compound nucleus may break up in several different ways. This is in agreement with the experimental observation that the bombardment of a given nuclide with one type of nuclear particle of one energy usually leads to a variety of products. For example, the bombardment of Al^{27} with fast neutrons (say 10 Mev) produces the radioactive products ${}_{13}Al^{26}$, ${}_{13}Al^{28}$, ${}_{12}Mg^{27}$, and ${}_{11}Na^{24}$. According to Bohr's picture this means that the compound nucleus ${}_{13}Al^{28*}$ is formed and that it may break up in any one of the following ways (the asterisk indicates a high state of excitation of the compound nucleus).

$$
{}_{13}\mathrm{Al}^{27} + {}_{0}n^{1} \longrightarrow {}_{13}\mathrm{Al}^{28*} \begin{cases} \nearrow {}_{13}\mathrm{Al}^{26} + 2\,{}_{0}n^{1} \\ \rightarrow {}_{13}\mathrm{Al}^{28} + \gamma \\ \rightarrow {}_{12}\mathrm{Mg}^{27} + {}_{1}\mathrm{H}^{1} \\ \searrow {}_{11}\mathrm{Na}^{24} + {}_{2}\mathrm{He}^{4} \end{cases}
$$

The Bohr picture permits some tentative predictions about the relative probabilities of various competing reaction types and their energy dependence, and, within the limitations to be discussed later, these predictions are in accord with experimental evidence. For example, the theory predicts that for a compound nucleus which has been formed by the entry of a thermal neutron into the target nucleus the probability of emission of any nuclear particle should be extremely low; for neutron emission the entire binding energy contributed by the incident neutron would have to be concentrated on one neutron again, and proton emission would require the concentration on one proton of a comparable binding energy plus the barrier energy. The compound nucleus from thermal-neutron capture generally gives up its excess energy in electromagnetic radiation (γ rays). Indeed almost the only reaction observed with slow neutrons is the n, γ process, often referred to as radiative capture. A few exceptions are found among reactions with the light nuclei in cases where the binding energy of a proton or α particle is appreciably lower than that of a neutron: the reactions $B^{10}(n, p)Be^{10}$, $N^{14}(n, p)C^{14}$, $Cl^{35}(n, p)S^{35}$, $B^{10}(n, \alpha)Li^7$, and $Li^6(n, \alpha)H^3$ occur with thermal neutrons.

As the excitation energy of the compound nucleus increases above the binding energy of the most loosely bound particle the probability for γ-ray emission becomes small relative to the probability for heavy-particle emission. For this reason radiative capture is much more important for neutrons (which can enter a nucleus without kinetic energy) than for charged particles. The relative cross sections for the emission of different heavy particles from a given compound nucleus depend on several factors. The principal ones are the binding energies for the various particles, the relative heights of Coulomb barriers, and the level densities of the product nuclei. For moderate excitation energies, potential barrier considerations favor the emission of neutrons over the emission of protons, and favor protons over α particles. For example, at moderate bombarding energies α, n reactions have much larger probabilities than α, p reactions. With increasing excitation energy the effect of the barrier becomes less pronounced. Occasionally, differences in the level densities of the product nuclei are determining factors in the competition between reactions. Apart from the other factors, a reaction for which many levels are available in the product nucleus is favored by purely statistical considerations.

At excitation energies above about 15 Mev the competition among different reactions becomes even more complex because the emission of a single particle (say a neutron) may leave the nucleus still in a sufficiently high state of excitation to "boil off" a second particle. Thus reactions of the types $(n, 2n)$, $(d, 2n)$, $(\alpha, 2n)$, (n, pn), (d, pn) will appear and compete with the simpler reactions (d, n), (α, n), (n, p), etc. At sufficiently high excitation energies one would expect the probability of single-particle emission to drop because of the competition of the two-particle emissions, and this again agrees with experimental results.

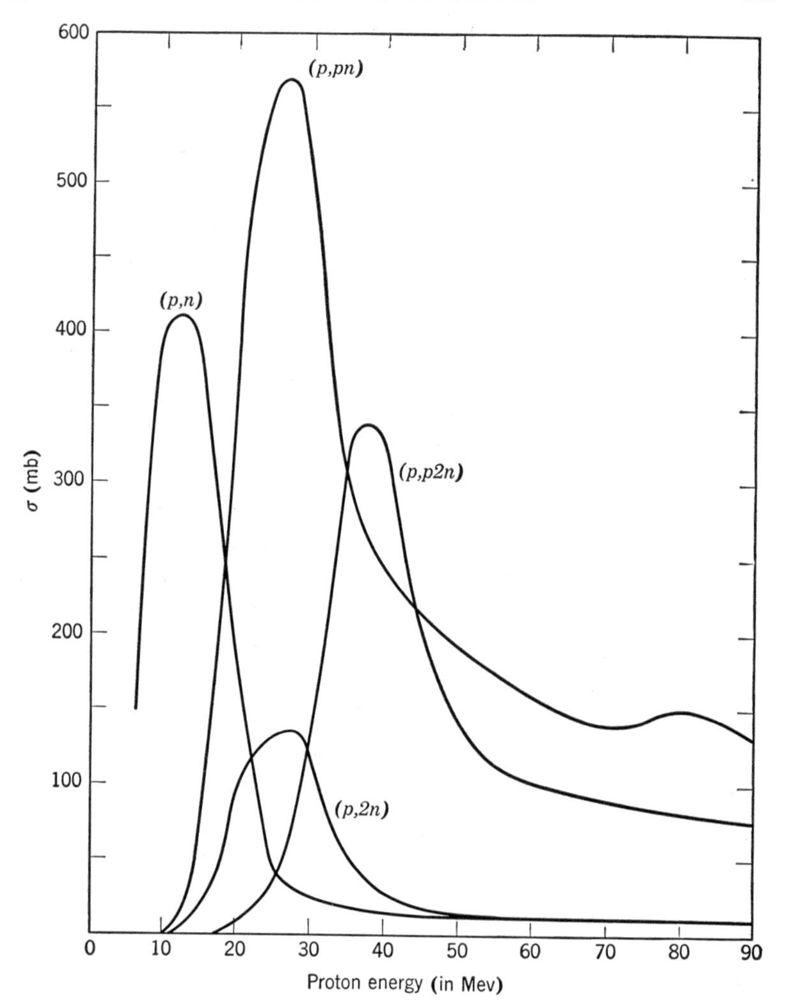

FIGURE 3-1. Excitation functions for proton-induced reactions on Cu^{63}. [From J. W. Meadows, *Phys. Rev.* **91,** 885 (1953).]

To illustrate the effect of competition, figure 3-1 shows the excitation functions of some reactions produced in the bombardment of Cu^{63} with protons up to 90 Mev. The reactions are

$$\mathrm{Cu}^{63}(p, n)\mathrm{Zn}^{63},$$

$$\mathrm{Cu}^{63}(p, 2n)\mathrm{Zn}^{62},$$

$$\mathrm{Cu}^{63}(p, pn)\mathrm{Cu}^{62},$$

$$\mathrm{Cu}^{63}(p, p2n)\mathrm{Cu}^{61}.$$

All the cross sections were determined from the yields of the radioactive products. The p, n cross section is seen to rise from a threshold energy (not measured in these experiments) to a peak at a proton energy of about 12 Mev. Its subsequent drop coincides with the rise of the p, pn and $p, 2n$ cross sections (thresholds at about 10 and 11 Mev, respectively). The excitation functions for these two reactions reach their peaks at 26- or 27-Mev proton energy and then drop, presumably because of competition from more complex reactions. One of these, the $p, p2n$ reaction, is seen to have a threshold at 17 Mev and a peak cross section of about 340 mb at 37 Mev. The slight bump in the curve labeled p, pn occurring in the region of 80-Mev proton energy probably is in reality an indication of the reaction $Cu^{63}(p, p5n)Cu^{58}$, since the half-life of Cu^{58} (8 min) is so similar to that of Cu^{62} (10 min) that the two were not distinguished in the measurements.

Several other features of the data in figure 3-1 are worth noting. In the first place we should remember that the four reactions investigated are not the only ones participating in the competition, even at energies below 40 or 50 Mev. The p, p; $p, 2p$; $p, 2pn$; $p, 3n$; and p, α reactions should undoubtedly be considered. That some of these reactions probably have appreciable cross sections is seen from the fact that the observed cross sections do not at any energy add up to the geometrical cross section of Cu^{63}, which by equation 2-4 is about 1100 mb. A comparison of the p, pn and $p, 2n$ cross sections is of interest. We see that, in spite of potential-barrier effects which would tend to favor $p, 2n$, the p, pn cross section is higher at all energies. This must be interpreted in terms of the greater level density in the odd-odd Cu^{62} compared to the even-even Zn^{62}. The ratio of the average level densities may actually be calculated from the cross-section ratios. A small contribution of p, d reactions to the curve labeled p, pn is likely.

Types of Reactions. Bombarding particles which have been used to effect nuclear reactions are neutrons, protons, deuterons, H^3, He^3, and He^4 nuclei, photons (γ and X rays), electrons, and π and μ mesons. All these, with the probable exception of electrons and μ mesons, occur among the fragments produced in nuclear reactions. In recent years bombardments have also been carried out with heavier ions such as C^{12}, C^{13}, and N^{14}. The fission process and the very-high-energy reactions are considered separately in sections E and F. In addition, a few reaction types deserve further discussion here.

The n, γ reaction has already been mentioned as the only type commonly occurring with slow neutrons. The reaction is always exoergic and occurs with very nearly every target. In well over 200 cases it is known to lead to radioactive products. This reaction type is particularly important for the production of radioactive isotopes, because of the relatively high reaction yields and because of the enormous neutron fluxes now available in the nuclear chain reactors.

Inelastic Scattering. Reactions in which the incident and emitted particles are of the same type—(n, n), (p, p), (γ, γ), etc.—lead to an excited state of the initial nucleus which usually reverts to the ground state by γ emission. The outgoing particle has less energy than the incident one, and, therefore, such a process is referred to as inelastic scattering. In general, this type of reaction is detected only by a measurement of the energy of the emitted (inelastically scattered) particle, but occasionally the residual nucleus is left in a metastable state of measurable lifetime; that is, an isomer of a stable nucleus is formed.

The n, n reaction is the most probable process with neutrons between a few hundred kev and a few Mev; in this region the n, γ reaction is no longer so important, and the n, p reaction cannot compete favorably because of the potential barrier. The p, p reaction is not very prevalent at any energy because of competition from the p, n reaction. For the same reason d, d and α, α reactions are rarely observed. Excitation to isomeric levels by γ, γ reactions and even by e^-, e^- reactions has been observed; in the latter case the excitation is not caused by an amalgamation of the electron with the nucleus, but by interaction between the nucleus and the electromagnetic field of the high-speed electron.

Oppenheimer-Phillips Process. The d, p reaction deserves special mention because it occurs very commonly and sets in at much lower energies than one would expect from the Bohr theory. In fact, the observed d, p thresholds are usually even lower than the corresponding d, n thresholds. This apparent anomaly has been explained by J. R. Oppenheimer and M. Phillips as being due to the polarization of the deuteron by the Coulomb field of the nucleus. As the deuteron approaches the nucleus, its "neutron end" is thought to be turned toward the nucleus, the "proton end" being repelled by the Coulomb force. Because of the relatively large neutron-proton distance in the polarized deuteron (several times 10^{-13} cm), the neutron reaches the surface of the nucleus while the proton is still outside most of the potential barrier. Since the binding energy of the deuteron is only 2.23 Mev, the action of the nuclear forces on the neutron tends to break up the deuteron, leaving the proton outside the potential barrier. The process just described is now generally called an Oppenheimer-Phillips (or O-P) process. An analogous mechanism appears to be responsible for the H^3, p reaction. An interesting feature of the O-P process is that the emergent protons have a spread of energies which includes values in excess of the incident deuteron energy, so that in a fraction of the cases the excitation of the compound nucleus is that which would result from the capture of a neutron of negative kinetic energy.

With increasing deuteron energy, the O-P mechanism becomes gradually less important, but there appears to be no energy range in which deuteron-induced reactions can be described completely by the simple compound nucleus picture. At higher energies, especially above about 50 Mev, a process called deuteron stripping becomes dominant: the proton (or neutron) is stripped off by collision with a nucleus, and the other nucleon continues essentially in the original direction of the deuteron and with its share of the deuteron momentum. The inverse reaction, called a pick-up process, is also observed: a fast proton picks up a neutron in traversing a nucleus and leaves as a high-energy deuteron in the forward direction.

Photonuclear Reactions. The excitation functions of γ, n and γ, p reactions look superficially not unlike those of other low-energy reactions; with increasing energy, they rise rather steeply to a maximum and then drop again. However, the drop in cross sections for these reactions is not accompanied by a corresponding rise in the cross sections for competing reactions. In other words, the total cross section for photon absorption itself appears to show a resonance behavior. This resonance absorption has been ascribed by M. Goldhaber and E. Teller to the excitation of dipole vibrations of all the neutrons moving collectively against all the protons; on this basis the magnitude, energy, and A-dependence of the resonance absorption have been accounted for quite well. Alternative mechanisms for the dipole absorption have been proposed.

The resonance peaks have widths of several Mev at half maximum, and the energy of the resonance peak decreases slowly with increasing A from about 24 Mev at O^{16} to about 14 Mev at Ta^{181}. The integrated cross sections under the resonance peaks vary from about 0.05 Mev-barn for the lightest elements to 2 or 3 Mev-barn for heavy elements. The energy of the dipole resonance is so low that mostly rather simple processes—such as γ, n; γ, p; and some $\gamma, 2n$ and photofission reactions—take place by this mechanism. A few reactions have been observed with low cross sections at energies below the dipole absorption (presumably due to quadrupole effects). At energies above the dipole resonance multiple particle emission is observed as in high-energy heavy-particle bombardments.

E. FISSION

Nature of the Process. By fission is meant the breakup of a heavy nucleus into two or more medium-heavy fragments. The process is usually accompanied by the emission of neutrons and much more rarely by the emission of α particles and possibly other light fragments. Fission has been produced in some nuclides (notably U^{235}, U^{238}, and Th^{232}) by neutrons, protons, deuterons, helium ions, and γ and X rays of moderate energies; and with higher bombarding energies (50 to 450 Mev) lighter elements such as bismuth, lead, gold, tantalum, and some rare earths have been shown to undergo fission. By far the most important of these reactions is neutron-produced fission. The species U^{232}, U^{233}, U^{235}, Pu^{239}, Am^{241}, and Am^{242} undergo fission with thermal or with fast neutrons, whereas fission of Th^{232}, Pa^{231}, U^{238}, and presumably other heavy nuclides requires fast neutrons.

The analogy between a nucleus and a liquid drop which Bohr used when he proposed the idea of the compound nucleus can be extended to explain fission at least in a qualitative way. A heavy nucleus is held together by nuclear forces analogous to the cohesive forces holding together a liquid drop. Just as a liquid drop tends to assume spherical shape under the action of surface tension, the unsaturation of the nuclear forces at the surface makes a sphere (which has the smallest surface for a given volume) the most stable configuration for a heavy nucleus. Bohr and J. A. Wheeler have shown that there will be a certain critical size for nuclei, depending on Z^2/A, above which the force of electrostatic repulsion will be greater than the surface forces holding the nucleus together. This critical size has been calculated to occur for Z somewhere near 100, and it is therefore reasonable that for a nucleus only slightly below this limit of stability a small excitation should be sufficient to induce breakup into two fragments. Bohr and Wheeler calculated the energetic conditions for fission of various heavy nuclear species on the basis of this model, and their theory is in fair agreement with the facts. They were able to predict the fission of Pa^{231} and to estimate its threshold energy before the reaction had been discovered.

Because nuclei of medium weight have much higher binding energies than those of the heaviest elements, the fission process is accompanied by a very large energy release, close to 200 Mev. The unique importance of the fission reaction is due to this energy release and especially to the fact that in each neutron-produced fission process more than one neutron is emitted, which makes a divergent chain reaction possible. The number ν of neutrons produced per thermal-neutron fission is 2.5 for U^{235} and 3.0 for Pu^{239}. It is to be noted, however, that not only fission but also radiative capture occurs with the heaviest elements. Therefore, to obtain the number η of neutrons produced per thermal neutron absorbed, the ν value has to be multiplied by the ratio of the thermal fission cross section to the total thermal-neutron absorption cross section. The resulting values of η are 2.1 for U^{235}, 1.3 for normal uranium, and 2.1 for Pu^{239}.

Fission Product Chains. The fission process may occur in many different modes, and a very large number of fission products are known, ranging from $Z = 30$ (zinc) to $Z = 65$ (terbium), and from $A = 72$ to $A = 161$ in the thermal-neutron fission of U^{235}. Fission into two equal fragments is by no means the most probable mode in thermal-neutron fission. Quite asymmetric modes are much more favored, the maximum fission product yields occurring at $A = 95$ and $A = 138$. The asymmetry appears to become less pronounced with increasing bombarding energy.

An enormous amount of radiochemical work was required to arrive at our present state of knowledge about fission products. It was necessary to develop chemical separation procedures, to analyze radioactive decay and growth patterns, to determine β- and γ-ray energies, to establish mass assignments of many previously unknown nuclides, and to measure the fission yields.[5]

As would be expected from the different neutron-proton ratios for U^{235} and for the stable elements in the fission product region, the primary products of fission are generally on the neutron-excess side of stability. Each such product decays by successive β^- processes to a stable isobar. Chains with as many as six β decays have been established, and undoubtedly some fission products still further removed from stability (higher up on the parabolic slope of the stability valley) have escaped detection because of their very short half-lives. No neutron-deficient nuclides have been found among the products of thermal-neutron fission; however, a few so-called shielded nuclides occur among the fission products. A shielded nuclide is one that has

[5] The fission yield of a nuclide is the fraction or the percentage of the total number of fissions which leads directly or indirectly to that nuclide.

a stable isobar one unit lower in Z so that it probably is not formed as a daughter product in a β-decay chain. The fission yield of such a nuclide is presumably due entirely to its direct formation as a primary product. The known fission chains are listed in table 3-2.

TABLE 3-2

Chains of Fission Products from Thermal-Neutron Fission of U^{235}

Mass Number	Elements
72	*Zn*, Ga, **Ge**
73	*Ga*, **Ge**
77	*Ge*, *As*, **Se**
78	*Ge*, *As*(0.09), **Se**
79	Se, **Br**
81	*Se*^{m}, *Se*, **Br**
82	*Br*(*s*, 1.6 × 10^{-4}), **Kr**
83	*Se*, *Br*(0.39), ***Kr***
84	Se, *Br*, ***Kr***
85	Br, Kr^m, *Kr*, **Rb**
86	*Rb*(*s*), **Sr**
87	Br*, Kr, **Rb**
88	Br, Kr, Rb, **Sr**
89	Br*, Kr, Rb, *Sr*, **Y**
90	Kr, (Rb), Sr, *Y*($<5 \times 10^{-4}$), **Zr**
91	Kr, (Rb), *Sr*, Y^m, *Y*, **Zr**
92	Kr, (Rb), *Sr*, Y, **Zr**
93	Kr, (Rb), Sr, Y, Zr, **Nb**
94	Kr, (Rb), Sr, *Y*, **Zr**
95	Kr, (Rb), (Sr), Y, *Zr*, Nb^m, Nb, **Mo**
97	Kr, (Rb), (Sr), (Y), *Zr*, Nb^m, Nb, **Mo**
99	*Mo*, Tc^m, Tc, **Ru**
101	Mo, Tc, **Ru**
(102)	Mo, (Tc), **Ru**
103	*Ru*, Rh^m, **Rh**
105	Mo, (Tc), *Ru*, Rh, **Pd**
106	*Ru*, Rh, **Pd**
107	Ru, Rh, Pd, **Ag**
109	*Pd*, Ag^m, **Ag**
111	Pd, *Ag*, **Cd**
111	Also Cd^m, **Cd**
112	*Pd*, Ag, **Cd**
113	Ag, **Cd**
113	Also Cd^m, **In**
114	Ag, **Cd**
115	Ag, *Cd*^{m}, In, **Sn**
115	Ag, *Cd*, In^m, In, **Sn**
117	*Cd*^{m}, Cd, In^m, In, **Sn**
121	*Sn*, **Sb**
123	*Sn*^{m}, **Sb**
125	*Sn*^{m}, Sb, Te^m, **Te**
126	*Sn*, Sb, **Te**
127	Sn, *Sb*, Te^m, Te, **I**
129	Sb, Te, I, **Xe**
129	Also *Te*^{m}, Te, I, **Xe**
130	Sb, **Te**
131	Sb, *Te*^{m}, Te, *I*, Xe^m, **Xe**
132	Sb, *Te*(0.36), I, **Xe**
133	*Sb*, *Te*^{m}, Te, *I*(0.19), *Xe*(<0.001), ***Cs***
134	(Sb), *Te*, *I*(0.16), ***Xe***
135	Te, *I*, Xe^m, *Xe*(0.035), Cs, **Ba**
136	*I*, ***Xe***, *Cs*(*s*, 0.001), **Ba**
137	I*, Xe, Cs, Ba^m, **Ba**
138	I, Xe, Cs, **Ba**
139	I, Xe, Cs, *Ba*, **La**
140	Xe, Cs, *Ba*, *La*(<0.03), **Ce**
141	Xe, (Cs), *Ba*, La, *Ce*, **Pr**
(142)	Cs, Ba, La, **Ce**
143	Xe, (Cs), (Ba), *La*, *Ce*, Pr, ***Nd***
144	Xe, (Cs), (Ba), (La), *Ce*, Pr, ***Nd***
145	Xe, (Cs), (Ba), (La), Ce, Pr, ***Nd***
(146)	Ce, Pr, ***Nd***
147	*Nd*, *Pm*, **Sm**
148	***Nd***
149	*Pm*, **Sm**
150	***Nd***
151	Pm, *Sm*, **Eu**
152	***Sm***
153	*Sm*, **Eu**
154	***Sm***
155	*Sm*, *Eu*, **Gd**
156	*Sm*, *Eu*, **Gd**
(157)	*Eu*, **Gd**
158	*Eu*, ***Gd***
159	*Gd*, **Tb**
160	***Gd***
161	*Tb*, **Dy**

A mass number in parentheses indicates an uncertain mass assignment.

An element name in parentheses indicates the particular nuclide has not been isolated but a precursor has.

For any nuclide in italics the fission yield has been determined.

The stable end product of each chain is given in bold face.

The letter *s* following an element symbol indicates a shielded nuclide (isobar of next lower Z is stable).

Where the independent primary fission yield of a chain member has been measured, it is given in parentheses as the fraction of the total chain yield.

The asterisk indicates an alternative mode of β^- decay followed by instantaneous neutron emission.

Charge Distribution. Direct information on the distribution of yields along any given chain is confined to the relatively few good measurements of independent fission yields of individual chain members and of the shielded nuclides. The hypothesis which appears to account best for the data is the postulate of "equal charge displacement." To state this we must make use of the quantity Z_A, the value of Z corresponding to the highest binding energy for a given A (chapter 2, p. 50). Furthermore, we define Z_p as the most probable charge for a primary fission fragment of mass number A. The postulate of equal charge displacement is that the two complementary fragments in a given fission event always have equal $Z_A - Z_p$ values, and furthermore that the probability distribution around Z_p is the same for all values of A. Remembering that on the average 2.5 neutrons are emitted per U^{235} fission we can write $Z_A - Z_p = Z_{233.5-A} - (92 - Z_p)$, or $Z_p = 46 + \frac{1}{2}(Z_A - Z_{233.5-A})$. From this formula and equation 2-7, Z_p can be calculated for any A. The calculated values for $Z_A - Z_p$ range from about 3.0 for the lightest and heaviest fission products to about 4.0 near $A = 115$. The measured independent yields indicate a probability distribution such that 50 per cent of the total chain yield occurs for $Z = Z_p$, about 25 per cent each for $Z = Z_p \pm 1$, about 2 per cent each for $Z = Z_p \pm 2$, and much less for other Z values.

The measured total yield of a particular fission product represents the sum of its independent yield and of the independent yields of all its precursors. Wherever fission yields have been measured for several isobars the results are in fair agreement with the postulate of equal charge displacement. We may therefore assume that the measured total fission yield of a nuclide which is only one or two units of Z from stability represents most of the total yield for its mass number.

Mass Distribution. When the total fission yield at each mass number is plotted against mass number, the curve shown in figure 3-2 results. The curve is essentially symmetrical about the minimum at $A = 233.5/2$ and has two rather broad maxima around mass numbers 95 and 138. The yields in each of the two peaks add up to approximately 100 per cent.

Sufficient information is available on the fission yields in the thermal-neutron fission of Pu^{239} to draw a yield-mass curve for this case. The general shape is very similar to the U^{235} curve, but there are certain significant differences. The yield at the minimum is not as low as for U^{235}; it is about 0.04 per cent fission yield at $A = 119$. The heavy peak appears not to be appreciably displaced as compared with U^{235} fission, but the light peak has its maximum at about $A = 99$.

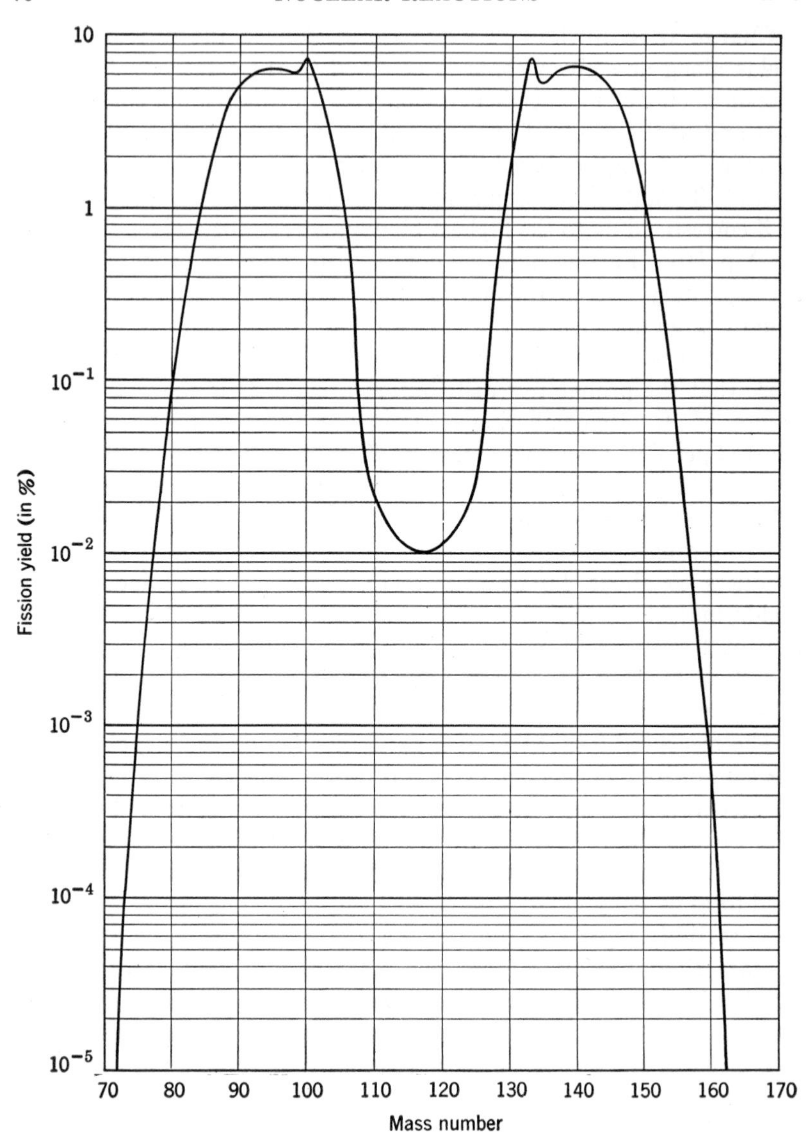

FIGURE 3-2. Yields of fission-product chains as a function of mass number for the slow-neutron fission of U^{235}.

Shell Effects. In recent years considerable attention has been given to some of the details of the fission yield curves. The most interesting result of these investigations was the discovery of the two "spikes" near the peaks of the yield-mass curve (figure 3-2). These have been studied both by mass-spectrographic and by radiochemical techniques. The effects are explained in terms of nuclear shell structure and appear to arise from three different causes.

In the first place there are among the fission products six delayed-neutron emitters, with half-lives of 55.6 sec, 22.0 sec, 4.51 sec, 1.52 sec, 0.43 sec, and 0.05 sec. These are actually β^- emitters which decay to nuclides that are unstable with respect to instantaneous neutron emission. The first two have been radiochemically identified as $_{35}Br^{87}$ and $_{53}I^{137}$. The daughters in these two cases, $_{36}Kr^{87}$ and $_{54}Xe^{137}$, have 51 and 83 neutrons, respectively, each just one neutron more than a "magic" number. Because of these delayed neutron emitters the yields of mass numbers 87 and 137 are expected to fall slightly below the smooth yield curve, with the yields at masses 86 and 136 correspondingly raised. Similar effects are expected from the other, as yet unassigned, neutron emitters. But from the yields of delayed neutrons it is clear that altogether these effects cannot account for the magnitude of the observed spikes.

A second possible cause for the observed phenomena might be the prompt boil-off of a neutron from primary fragments containing 51 or 83 neutrons. An analysis of this hypothesis shows that it would account reasonably well for the anomalies in the mass range 133–135, but it could not predict the almost complementary spike near $A = 100$.

The complementarity of the two spikes suggests that they are connected with the fission act itself. The assumption that in the primary process fragments with closed-shell configurations ($N = 82$ and $N = 50$) are formed preferentially leads to rather good agreement with the observations, not only for thermal-neutron fission of U^{235}, but also for several other fission reactions which yield "spikes" in somewhat different positions. However, there is still evidence for some contribution of post-fission neutron boil-off.

A number of attempts have been made to account theoretically for the observed fission yield distributions. The most successful of these has been a statistical theory based on the idea that the probabilities of various fission modes are determined by the level densities of the resulting excited fragments. According to this interpretation it would thus appear that the fission act itself is responsive to the structures of the fragments; the relation between closed-shell effects and fission yields points in the same direction.

F. REACTIONS AT VERY HIGH ENERGIES

Nuclear Transparency. For bombarding energies up to 40 or 50 Mev the Bohr compound-nucleus mechanism appears to account quite well for the observed features of nuclear reactions. However, at still

higher energies new phenomena are observed. As the bombarding energy is raised to several hundred million electron volts, reactions of the type predicted by the Bohr theory continue to occur, with the emission of a large number of fragments corresponding to a very highly excited compound nucleus. These have been termed spallation reactions. However, at the same time the whole spectrum of simpler reactions also occurs, with probabilities very much larger than the Bohr theory would permit.

An explanation for the observed phenomena in the high-energy region under discussion was first suggested by R. Serber. A nucleon with a kinetic energy of 100 Mev or more has a mean free path in nuclear matter comparable to nuclear dimensions and therefore has a finite chance of passing through a nucleus without making any collision. In other words, nuclei become somewhat transparent for bombarding particles at these energies, and the compound nucleus picture is not wholly applicable. Furthermore, the impinging nucleon may transfer only a small part of its kinetic energy to a nucleon struck by it and may then have more than enough energy left to escape from the nucleus.[6] Thus the particular mechanism depends on the size of the nucleus and on whether the impinging particle strikes the nucleus near the periphery (in which case it may escape after a single collision and transfer only about 25 Mev to the nucleus) or near the center (in which case it may be stopped in the nuclear matter by several collisions and transfer its entire kinetic energy to the nucleus). Clearly there are intermediate possibilities, and on this picture it is reasonable to expect a variety of modes of disintegration corresponding to the different possible excitation energies of the compound nucleus, all of which may have comparable probabilities. Rather simple reactions, such as p, pn or $p, 3n$, are then thought to come about by collisions in which the incident (or the struck) particle takes away most of the energy, leaving the nucleus sufficiently excited to boil off one or a few nucleons.

We have come to think of high-energy reactions as taking place in two distinct steps. The first is the so-called knock-on cascade in which the incoming particle makes one or more collisions, and some of its collision partners may make further collisions; this phase lasts of the order of 10^{-22} sec and ends when the kinetic energies of all the individual nucleons have dropped to a somewhat arbitrary lower

[6] A head-on collision in which the *struck* nucleon leaves the nucleus with almost the full kinetic energy of the incident nucleon is essentially equivalent to a glancing collision with very small energy transfer, except possibly for the charge of the outgoing particle.

limit, say 30 Mev, below which the energy remaining in the nucleus is considered as excitation. Then equipartition of energy in the compound nucleus sense and subsequent evaporation of particles takes place in the second phase of the reaction, which lasts several orders of magnitude longer than the first. The course of a particular reaction is thus determined first by the amount of excitation energy deposited during the knock-on phase, and second by the manner in which this excitation is given up during the evaporation phase—by the numbers and kinds of particles evaporated.

Spallation Products. A large number of radiochemical studies have been made of spallation reactions in the bombarding-energy region up to about 450 Mev. In summary of this rather complex field it is probably fair to say that essentially any spallation reaction which is energetically possible is believed to occur. However, the cross sections (or at least the relative yields) of different products from a given bombardment are of interest. In general the products in the immediate neighborhood of the target element, within perhaps 10 or 12 mass numbers on the low-mass side, are found in the highest yields. The yields for lower mass numbers then drop off rather rapidly. Thus the transfer of relatively small amounts of excitation, rather independent of incident energy, appears to be most probable, and this agrees with expectation from knock-on calculations.

The spallation yields tend to cluster quite strongly in the region of stability in the case of medium-weight targets, and somewhat more to the neutron-deficient side of stability for heavier elements. This is just what one would expect from evaporation theory. The considerations here are the same ones encountered in lower-energy competition: binding energies, Coulomb barriers, and level densities. It is interesting to note that the ratio of yields of two isobars from an evaporation cascade remains almost the same regardless of target element and bombarding energy.

High-Energy Fission. In addition to the spallation processes in which small fragments are emitted, fission processes are observed in the 100-to-400-Mev range. However, the characteristics of fission at these energies differ markedly from those of thermal-neutron fission. The familiar double hump in the fission product yield curve (figure 3-2) is at this energy replaced by a single broad peak, centered around a value of A somewhat less than half the mass number of the target nuclide. All the primary fission products tend to have a single proton-neutron ratio for a given target and given bombarding energy. (In contrast to low-energy fission, many neutron-deficient nuclides are therefore found, especially among the heavy products.) These observations have been interpreted as indicating that the excited nucleus formed after the knock-on phase of the reaction first evaporates a number of nucleons (mostly neutrons), and that after a sufficiently high value of Z^2/A is reached, fission competes with further evaporation. The fission process apparently occurs too rapidly to permit redistribution of neutrons and protons.

Fission has been observed for many elements of Z greater than about 70. In these elements the fission product region is rather definitely separated from the spallation products by a region of A with very low yields. For much lighter target elements fission has been reported, but in these cases the fission and spallation regions are not well separated, and the fission cross sections are extremely low (microbarns). Here the formation of certain products is ascribed to fission mainly on energetic arguments. For example, Cl^{38} was produced in proton bombardments of copper with a threshold of about 60 Mev, whereas the calculated threshold for the most economical spallation reaction $Cu^{63}(p, pn6\alpha)Cl^{38}$ is about 100 Mev. Therefore the investigators postulated a fission mechanism illustrated by ${}_{29}Cu^{63} + {}_{1}H^{1} \rightarrow {}_{17}Cl^{38} + {}_{13}Al^{25} + {}_{0}n^{1}$.

An interesting feature of high-energy reactions is the observation of small fragments heavier than α particles. Radiochemical studies have revealed the formation of Be^7 and Li^8, and photographic-emulsion studies have shown that various lithium, beryllium, and boron nuclei are among the products. Many of these particles are produced with sufficient energies to penetrate the Coulomb barriers of other target nuclei to make secondary reactions, as evidenced by the formation of radioactive products with atomic numbers two and three units greater than the target atomic number.

Higher and Higher? Before leaving the subject of very-high-energy reactions we should mention the further extension of this field into the billion-electron-volt (Bev) region. Some of the new effects observed here may well be connected with the greatly increased cross sections for meson production. For example, the spallation products closest to the target are no longer the most prevalent; rather, at 2-Bev proton bombarding energy the highest yields are found some 15 or 20 mass numbers below the target mass, and large excitation energies appear to be much more probable than expected from the 100- to 400-Mev data. Meson production and reabsorption within the same nucleus may be the mechanism for these large energy transfers. Another observation is that symmetric fission appears not to contribute very much to the total cross section of heavy elements in the 1- to 3-Bev range. Finally, light fragments such as Be^7 are formed with very significant cross sections—millibarns at 2 or 3 Bev from practically any target.

We should perhaps insert a reminder that this field of the very-high-energy reactions, although of great interest to the nuclear chemist and likely to produce much new information on nuclear-reaction mechanisms and nuclear properties, is not of primary concern to those interested in radioactive tracers. The production of practical amounts of radioactive tracers will undoubtedly continue to depend on relatively simple nuclear reactions at low energies. In particular, neutron-induced reactions will continue to play a dominant role in this connection. We therefore turn in the next section to a more detailed discussion of neutrons and some neutron-induced reactions.

G. NEUTRONS

Slow Neutrons. It should be evident from the discussion of Coulomb barriers in section B that it is much easier for neutrons than for charged particles to enter nuclei. Experiment has shown this to be so; in fact, the so-called thermal neutrons, that is, neutrons whose energy distribution is approximately that of gas molecules in thermal agitation at ordinary temperatures, have particularly high probabilities for reaction with target nuclei. This important effect was discovered at the University of Rome by E. Fermi, E. Amaldi, B. Pontecorvo, F. Rasetti, and E. Segrè in 1934 in experiments on the neutron irradiation of silver; they found that the neutron-induced radioactivity was much greater when a bulk of hydrogen-containing material such as paraffin was present to modify the neutron beam. Fermi reasoned correctly that fast neutrons would lose energy in collisions with protons, that repeated collisions might reduce the energy to the thermal range, and that such slow neutrons could show large capture cross sections. Other workers found the effect to be sensitive to the temperature of the paraffin, thus demonstrating that the neutrons were actually slowed to approximately thermal energies.

Our only sources of neutrons are nuclear reactions, in which neutrons are emitted from highly excited nuclei and, therefore, usually have initially rather high kinetic energies. Because of the great importance of slow or thermal neutrons in bringing about nuclear reactions, processes for slowing down fast neutrons to thermal energies have received much attention, both theoretically and experimentally. Fast neutrons may lose large amounts of energy in inelastic collisions, especially with heavy nuclei. This process ceases to be effective after intermediate energies are reached, and does not produce slow neutrons. Most slowing down is accomplished through a process of many successive elastic collisions with nuclei. Because of the conservation of momentum a neutron of energy E_0 making an elastic collision with a heavy nucleus bounces off with most of its original energy, giving up to the recoil nucleus no more energy than $4AE_0/(A+1)^2$, where A is the mass number of the target nucleus. The lighter the nucleus with which a neutron collides, the greater is the fraction of the neutron's kinetic energy that can be transferred in the elastic collision. For this reason hydrogen-containing substances such as paraffin or water are the most effective slowing-down media for neutrons.

When all possible elastic collisions are considered, with energy transfers ranging from the maximum (above) to zero (for the most trivial glancing collision), the average energy lost in a single collision is just half of the maximum, or $2AE_0/(A+1)^2$. (In the case of scattering by protons this is half of the neutron's original energy.) The ratio of the average energy retained to the original energy is of course $1 - \frac{2A}{(A+1)^2} = \frac{A^2+1}{(A+1)^2}$. This result may be obtained by an integration of $(E/E_0)\,dE$ between the minimum and maximum limits with the appropriate normalizing factors:

$$\overline{(E/E_0)} = \frac{(1+A)^2}{4AE_0}\int_{\left[1-\frac{4A}{(A+1)^2}\right]E_0}^{E_0} (E/E_0)\,dE = \frac{A^2+1}{(A+1)^2}.$$

The fraction is independent of energy so that in each successive collision the average amount of energy lost becomes smaller; on the average the logarithm of the neutron's energy, $\ln E$, decreases uniformly with each collision. Therefore the appropriate average is not the average change in energy but the average change in $\ln E$. The average of all possible values of $\ln (E/E_0)$ in a single collision is found by integration:

$$\overline{\ln (E/E_0)} = \frac{(1+A)^2}{4AE_0}\int_{\left[1-\frac{4A}{(A+1)^2}\right]E_0}^{E} \ln (E/E_0)\,dE$$

$$= \frac{(A-1)^2}{2A}\ln\left(\frac{A+1}{A-1}\right) - 1.$$

After n collisions the average result is

$$\overline{\ln (E_n/E_0)} = n\left[\frac{(A-1)^2}{2A}\ln\left(\frac{A+1}{A-1}\right) - 1\right].$$

For collisions with protons, $A = 1$, this reduces to $E_n = E_0e^{-n}$, and approximately 20 collisions are therefore necessary to reduce neutrons from a few million electron volts to thermal energies (about 0.04 ev at ordinary room temperature). Paraffin about 8 in. thick surrounding a neutron source is adequate for reducing most neutrons to the thermal energy distribution. The whole slowing-down process requires less than 0.001 sec.

The probable eventual fate of a thermal neutron in a hydrogenous medium like water or paraffin is capture by a proton to form a deuteron; but, since the cross section for this reaction is quite small compared with the cross section for scattering, a neutron after reaching thermal energies makes about 150 further collisions before being captured. Paraffin and water are good substances to use for the slowing down of neutrons because the capture cross sections of oxygen and carbon are even much smaller than the hydrogen capture cross section. Heavy water is better than ordinary water because of the low probability of neutron capture by deuterium. Carbon (graphite) is also useful as a slowing-down medium; many more (about 120) collisions are necessary to reduce neutrons to thermal energies in carbon than in hydrogen, but after reaching thermal energies the neutrons can exist longer in carbon. In either substance the lifetime of a neutron before capture is only a fraction of a second.

Even if neutrons could be kept in a medium where they would not eventually be captured, they would not exist very long. The systematics of β radioactivity predict that free neutrons are unstable and should decay rather quickly into protons and electrons. This decay was observed by A. H. Snell and by J. M. Robson in 1950. The neutrons, from nuclear reactors, were in free flight in vacuum. Robson measured the energy released in the disintegration, 780 kev, and the half-life, 13 min.

Thermal Distribution. It should be apparent that not all thermal neutrons have the same energy. After neutrons are slowed to energies comparable to thermal agitation energies they may either lose or gain energy in collisions, and the result is a Maxwellian distribution of velocities, in which the fraction of the total number of neutrons with velocity between v and $v + dv$ is given by

$$F(v)\, dv = 4\pi^{-\frac{1}{2}}(M/2kT)^{\frac{3}{2}}v^2e^{-Mv^2/2kT}\, dv.$$

Here the fraction is denoted by $F(v)\, dv$, M is the neutron mass, T is the absolute temperature, and k is the Boltzmann constant. Some properties of this distribution, usually derived in books on the kinetic theory of gases, are that the most probable velocity is

$$v_m = (2kT/M)^{1/2},$$

the average velocity is

$$\bar{v} = (8kT/\pi M)^{1/2} = 2v_m/\pi^{1/2},$$

and the average kinetic energy is $\bar{E} = \frac{3}{2}kT$. The average energy of the neutrons depends on the temperature of the slowing-down medium. At very low temperatures the Maxwellian distribution function becomes a poor approximation because of the discrete energy levels of the bound atoms of the medium. At all temperatures the approximation can be poor if the neutron path in the medium is too short, or if the distribution is seriously altered by neutron absorption or leakage from the surface.

A significant point is the distinction between the velocity distribution present in a medium and that felt by a sample placed in the medium. The two distributions are different because the probability that a particular neutron strike the sample in a given time is proportional to v. It is this altered or weighted distribution, denoted here by $F'(v)\,dv$, which is significant in any transmutation or cross section computation:

$$F'(v)\,dv = 2(M/2kT)^2 v^3 e^{-Mv^2/2kT}\,dv.$$

Slow-Neutron Reaction Cross Sections. Although all the remarks in preceding sections on nuclear reaction cross sections are applicable to neutrons, there are some special features apparent in slow-neutron reactions that deserve special mention. For fast-particle reactions the total cross section is of the order of the geometrical cross section of the target nucleus, πR^2. In reactions with slow particles, particularly slow neutrons, the area of the target nucleus is negligible in comparison with the cross-sectional area of the incident particle estimated from its de Broglie wavelength λ. The measured cross sections for thermal-neutron reactions are often much greater than πR^2, but are never greater than $\lambda^2 = (h/mv)^2 \cong 10^{-16}$ cm^2 = 10^8 barns at room temperature. Some of the largest thermal-neutron capture cross sections observed among ordinary target nuclides are for Cd^{113} (19,500 barns), Sm^{149} (50,000 barns), Gd^{155} (70,000 barns), and Gd^{157} (160,000 barns). Cross sections for some radioactive nuclides have been measured, and the record value is 3.5×10^6 barns for Xe^{135}.

It is not to be assumed that most, or even many, nuclides have such large thermal-neutron cross sections. Nor does the cross section vary in any smooth or regular way from element to element or from one isotope to another. For example, the capture cross sections (in barns) for a number of gadolinium isotopes are: $Gd^{152} < 125$, Gd^{155} 70,000, Gd^{157} 160,000, Gd^{158} 4, Gd^{160} 1.5. The observed cross section for ordinary gadolinium is the weighted average of these values, about 44,000 barns. Of the cadmium isotopes Cd^{113} is the only one with an unusually large cross section, and ordinary cadmium has a thermal-neutron cross section of about 2400 barns. Cadmium is often used as an absorber of thermal neutrons, and even a thin sheet of cadmium will effectively shield a sample or instrument from all neutrons of energy less than a few tenths of an electron volt.

A compilation of thermal-neutron cross sections is given in appendix C. Because the values have been determined by a variety of experimental methods it is not easy to find a common basis for listing them. Many have been measured for the neutron spectrum present in a particular nuclear reactor. Some have been measured in a thermal-neutron flux characterized to good approximation by the velocity distribution functions already given, usually at approximately 20°C. Others have been measured at particular neutron velocities by the use of neutron monochromators (described in chapter 4, section C). Following the usual practice, we have tabulated all thermal-neutron reaction cross sections for the discrete neutron velocity of 2.20×10^5 cm sec^{-1} (corresponding to the discrete energy 0.025 ev and being the most probable velocity in a Maxwellian distribution at 20°C). Values may be converted from one basis to the other, provided that the variation of cross section with neutron energy is known; rarely is the difference greater than 30 per cent. For the many nuclides whose absorption cross sections are inversely proportional to the neutron velocity, the value for a 20°C spectrum is just $\pi^{1/2}/2 = 0.89$ times the value for neutrons at 2.20×10^5 cm sec^{-1}, which is often within the experimental uncertainty.

In chapter 4, section C, we give several numerical values of thermal-neutron fluxes. The neutron flux is the product of the number n of neutrons diffusing in the medium per unit volume and their average velocity $\bar{v}$. However, it is common practice to give all neutron fluxes (nv) as n times 2.20×10^5 cm sec^{-1}, regardless of the temperature of the neutrons. Therefore a thermal distribution at 20°C will have a true flux which is just $2/\pi^{1/2} = 1.13$ times the quoted flux. Clearly, for those cases in which the cross section varies inversely with the neutron velocity, the rate of nuclear reaction per target nucleus is given correctly by the product of the quoted (2.20×10^5 cm sec^{-1})

flux times the tabulated (2.20×10^5 cm sec^{-1}) cross section. This result is independent of the temperature of the neutrons.

One-over-v Law and Resonance Processes. Apart from the specific properties of a particular target nuclide, there are general features of slow-neutron reactions that appear in every case although frequently more or less obscured by the specific features. We have already implied that the cross sections should bear a relation to λ^2, and indeed the general theory for reaction cross sections contains this factor λ^2. Among the many other variables in this theory of neutron-capture cross sections is a factor called the neutron width. This factor (its name should be apparent from the uncertainty relation) is a measure of the a priori probability for emission or absorption of a neutron of energy E, and is proportional to $E^{1/2}$. It is essentially a statistical factor, since the number of available possibilities for emission or capture of neutrons varies directly as their (linear) momentum. Consequently it is a general expectation that neutron cross sections should be proportional to

$$\lambda^2 E^{1/2} = (h^2/M^2v^2)(Mv^2/2)^{1/2} = \text{constant} \times 1/v.$$

This variation of cross section with the reciprocal of the neutron velocity, known as the one-over-v law, is valid over a considerable energy range for some light elements. For example, up to at least 10 kev the cross section for $B^{10}(n, \alpha)$ is well represented by $\sigma = 8.8 \times 10^8(1/v)$, with σ in barns and v in centimeters per second.

For most slow-neutron reactions the $1/v$ dependence is modified or even completely concealed by the existence of resonance peaks at particular energies. Figure 3-3 shows on log-log coordinates the total cross section of silver for neutrons of energies from 0.01 to 100 ev. A $1/v$ dependence, indicated by the dotted line, is shown at thermal energies, and its extension is suggested in a rough way by the minima between resonances at the higher energies. This curve, with nine resolved resonance peaks, is not entirely typical but does illustrate a fairly complex case for which good data are available. The highest peak, at 5.1 ev, reaches a height of almost 10,000 barns; its width at half maximum is approximately 0.2 ev, indicating a lifetime for the particular state of the compound nucleus of roughly $h/2\pi\,\Delta E = 3 \times 10^{-15}$ sec.

Some representative neutron resonances in other elements are at 1.21 ev in rhodium (2700 barns), at 1.44 ev in indium (In^{115}; 27,600 barns), at 4.8 ev in gold, at 3000 ev in sodium (550 barns), and at 250,000 ev in lithium. The large thermal-neutron cross section of cadmium is due to a resonance at 0.176 ev (Cd^{113}; 58,000 barns), which is wide enough to overlap the thermal region. In many elements (including indium and rhodium) resonance capture leads to the formation of radioactive isotopes, and such substances are useful as

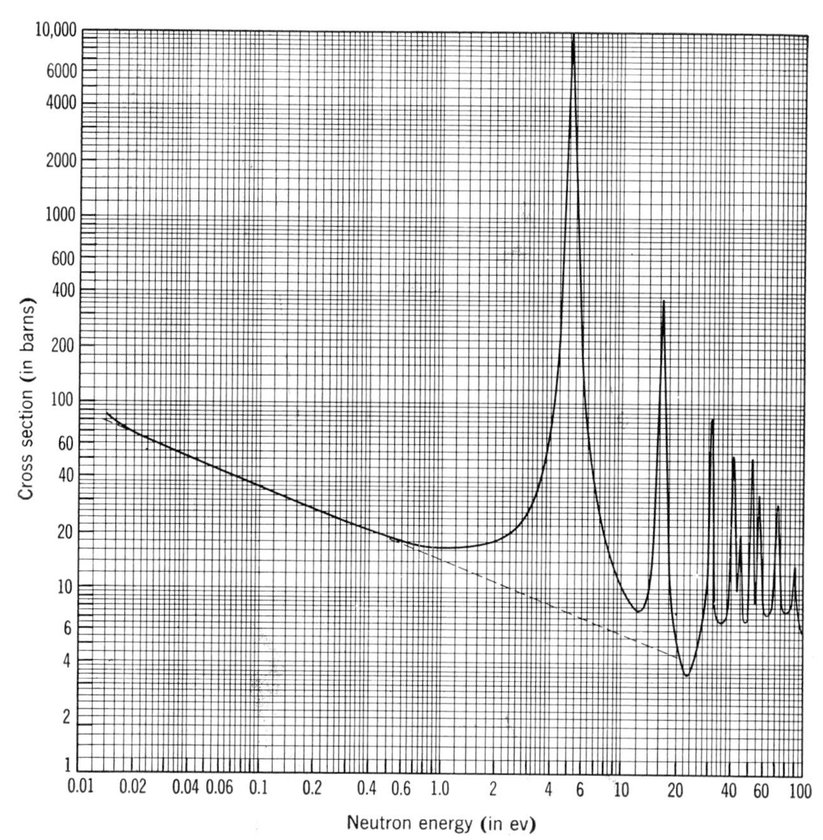

FIGURE 3-3. Neutron cross section of silver as a function of energy in the region of 0.01 to 100 ev. (From Atomic Energy Commission Document AECU-2040 and its supplements.)

detectors for neutrons of particular energies. Because of the very large cross sections at resonance, neutrons of the resonance energy do not penetrate deeply into these substances, and the activation is confined to a very thin surface layer.

Resonances occur not only for capture but also for scattering processes. Another consequence of the general considerations mentioned earlier is that the cross section for scattering of neutrons is expected to be independent of neutron energy except near specific resonance peaks.

EXERCISES

1. Compute, from masses in appendix G, the Q values for the following reactions: (*a*) $Mg^{24}(d, p)Mg^{25}$; (*b*) $B^{10}(n, \alpha)Li^{7}$.

2. Would the $Ca^{43}(n, \alpha)$ reaction go with thermal neutrons? Justify your answer. *Answer:* No.

3. The reaction $S^{33}(n, p)P^{33}$ is exoergic by 0.51 Mev. What is the mass of P^{33}?

4. Estimate the Coulomb barrier and the centrifugal barrier for p-wave interaction between protons and Be^{9}. *Answer:* 1.25 Mev, 1.9 Mev.

5. Show from conservation of momentum that in any nuclear reaction $A(a, b)B$ the fraction of the kinetic energy of the bombarding particle a which goes into kinetic energy of the products is $M_a/(M_a + M_A)$, where M_a and M_A are the masses of a and A, respectively.

6. Calculate the approximate heights of the Coulomb barriers around ${}_{13}Al^{27}$, ${}_{26}Fe^{56}$, ${}_{47}Ag^{107}$, ${}_{73}Ta^{181}$, and ${}_{92}U^{238}$ for protons.
Answers to first two: 3.1, 5.2 Mev.

7. Calculate the de Broglie wavelength of a neutron of (*a*) 1 ev, (*b*) 1 kev, (*c*) 1 Mev kinetic energy. *Answer:* (*b*) 0.9×10^{-10} cm.

8. What are the average energies (in electron volts) of thermal neutrons at 25°C and at −196°C (liquid nitrogen temperature)?

9. Estimate the total energy release and (from Coulomb barrier considerations) the minimum total kinetic energy (in Mev) of the two fission fragments when a U^{235} nucleus captures a thermal neutron and splits into (*a*) Kr^{90} and Ba^{143}, (*b*) Rh^{113} and Ag^{121}.

10. Using appendix G, decide what reactions would be practical for the production of (*a*) Mn^{53}, (*b*) Gd^{159}, (*c*) Mg^{28}, (*d*) Tc^{100}, if you had at your disposal 12-Mev deuterons, 6-Mev protons, 24-Mev α particles, and neutrons up to 16 Mev.

11. Approximately what thickness of cadmium is necessary to reduce a beam of thermal neutrons to 0.1 per cent of its intensity?

12. At room temperature (say 27°C) a beam of neutrons is brought to thermal equilibrium in graphite. This beam then falls on a thin boron absorber and is reduced to 90 per cent of its original intensity by the absorber. What would have been the intensity reduction if the entire experiment had been performed at 327°C? *Answer:* To 93 per cent.

13. The nuclide Cl^{33} can be produced by the reaction $S^{33}(p, n)Cl^{33}$. The Cl^{33} emits positrons with an upper energy limit of 4.13 Mev. What is the Q value of the reaction? What is the height of the potential barrier around the S^{33} nucleus for the proton? Estimate the minimum proton energy required to produce the reaction.
Answer: Minimum proton energy = 6.1 Mev.

14. With the very crude assumption that in the highly excited compound nucleus the energy partition between nucleons is the same as in an ideal gas, estimate the temperature of a heavy nucleus (say $A = 150$) after the capture of a 10-Mev neutron. Compare with an estimate made from the data in table 3-1. *Answer:* About 10^{9}°K.

15. A 16 mg cm^{-2} foil of gadolinium is exposed to a pile neutron flux of 1×10^{13} cm^{-2} sec^{-1} for 24 hours. What will be the approximate isotopic composition of the sample after irradiation?

16. (*a*) The measured cross section for absorption of thermal neutrons in B^{10} is 3500 barns at 300°K. Assuming the $1/v$ law to hold and using the distribution function on p. 84, find the discrete velocity v' at which $\sigma = 3500$ barns.

(*b*) Using the answer to (*a*) estimate the mean life of a thermal neutron in 0.1 M borax ($Na_2B_4O_7 \cdot 10H_2O$) solution. You may assume B^{10} to be the only capturing material.

Answer: (*a*) 2.51×10^5 cm per sec; (*b*) 2.5×10^{-5} sec.

17. On the basis of the postulate of equal charge displacement, what are the most probable primary fission products in thermal-neutron fission of Pu^{239} at $A = 81, 117, 140$?

18. In the bombardment of chromium with 30-Mev α particles the ratio of number of Mn^{52} atoms to number of Fe^{52} atoms formed is about 25. What are the reactions leading to these two nuclides, and how can you account for the above result?

19. Estimate the minimum proton energy necessary to produce K^{42} from Nb^{93} (*a*) by a fission process, (*b*) by a spallation process involving the emission of nucleons and He^4 ions only.

REFERENCES

P. Morrison, "Introduction to the Theory of Nuclear Reactions," *Am. J. Phys.* **9,** 135 (1941).

P. Morrison, "A Survey of Nuclear Reactions," *Experimental Nuclear Physics* (E. Segrè, Editor), Vol. II, New York, John Wiley & Sons, 1953.

H. A. Bethe, "Nuclear Physics, B. Nuclear Dynamics, Theoretical," *Revs. Mod. Phys.* **9,** 69 (1937).

M. S. Livingston and H. A. Bethe, "Nuclear Physics, C. Nuclear Dynamics, Experimental," *Revs. Mod. Phys.* **9,** 245 (1937).

J. M. Blatt and V. F. Weisskopf, *Theoretical Nuclear Physics,* New York, John Wiley & Sons, 1952.

W. J. Whitehouse and J. L. Putman, *Radioactive Isotopes. An Introduction to Their Preparation, Measurement and Use.* Oxford, Clarendon Press, 1953.

H. H. Barschall, "Methods for Measuring Fast Neutron Cross Sections," *Revs. Mod. Phys.* **24,** 120 (1952).

N. Bohr, "Transmutation of Atomic Nuclei," *Science* **86,** 161 (1937).

V. F. Weisskopf and D. H. Ewing, "On the Yield of Nuclear Reactions with Heavy Elements," *Phys. Rev.* **57,** 472 (1940).

D. C. Peaslee, "Deuteron-Induced Reactions," *Phys. Rev.* **74,** 1001 (1948).

K. Strauch, "Recent Studies of Photonuclear Reactions," *Ann. Rev. Nuclear Sci.,* Vol. II, p. 105, Stanford, Annual Reviews Inc., 1953.

J. S. Levinger, "Theories of Photonuclear Reactions," *Ann. Rev. Nuclear Sci.,* Vol. IV, p. 13, Stanford, Annual Reviews Inc., 1954.

O. Hahn and F. Strassmann, "Ueber den Nachweis und das Verhalten der bei der Bestrahlung des Urans mittels Neutronen Entstehenden Erdalkalimetalle," *Naturwiss.* **27,** 11 (1939).

L. Meitner and O. R. Frisch, "Disintegration of Uranium by Neutrons: A New Type of Nuclear Reaction," *Nature* **143,** 239 (1939).

N. Bohr and J. A. Wheeler, "The Mechanism of Nuclear Fission," *Phys. Rev.* **56,** 426 (1939).

W. J. Whitehouse, "Nuclear Fission," *Progress in Nuclear Physics,* Vol. 2 (O. R. Frisch, Editor), London, Pergamon Press, 1953.

C. D. Coryell and N. Sugarman, *Radiochemical Studies: The Fission Products,* National Nuclear Energy Series Div. IV, Vol. 9, New York, McGraw-Hill Book Co., 1951. (Particularly Book 1, Part IV, "Studies of the Fission Process.")

D. J. Hughes, J. Dabbs, A. Cahn, and D. Hall, "Delayed Neutrons from the Fission of U^{235}," *Phys. Rev.* **73,** 111 (1948).

A. C. Pappas, "A Radiochemical Study of Fission Yields in the Region of Shell Perturbations and the Effect of Closed Shells in Fission," Atomic Energy Commission Unclassified Document AECU-2806 (1953).

L. E. Glendenin and E. P. Steinberg, "Fission Radiochemistry," *Ann. Rev. Nuclear Sci.,* Vol. IV, p. 69, Stanford, Annual Reviews Inc., 1954.

P. Fong, "Asymmetric Fission," *Phys. Rev.* **89,** 232 (1953).

R. Serber, "Nuclear Reactions at High Energies," *Phys. Rev.* **72,** 1114 (1947).

D. H. Templeton, "Nuclear Reactions Induced by High Energy Particles," *Ann. Rev. Nuclear Sci.,* Vol. II, p. 93, Stanford, Annual Reviews Inc., 1953.

R. W. Spence and G. P. Ford, "High Energy Fission," *Ann. Rev. Nuclear Sci.,* Vol. II, p. 399, Stanford, Annual Reviews Inc., 1953.

G. Friedlander, J. M. Miller, R. Wolfgang, J. Hudis, and E. Baker, "Nuclear Reactions of Copper with 2.2-Bev Protons," *Phys. Rev.* **94,** 727 (1954).

E. Amaldi, O. D'Agostino, E. Fermi, B. Pontecorvo, F. Rasetti, and E. Segrè, "Artificial Radioactivity Produced by Neutron Bombardment—II," *Proc. Roy. Soc.* **149A,** 522 (1935).

D. J. Hughes, *Pile Neutron Research,* Cambridge, Mass., Addison-Wesley Publishing Co., 1953.

AEC Neutron Cross Section Advisory Group, *Neutron Cross Sections,* Atomic Energy Commission Document AECU-2040 (1952) (available from office of Technical Services, U. S. Department of Commerce, $1.00). Also Supplements 1, 2, and 3 to AECU-2040.

B. T. Feld, "The Neutron," *Experimental Nuclear Physics,* Vol. II (E. Segrè. Editor), New York, John Wiley & Sons, 1953.

B. B. Kinsey, G. A. Bartholomew, and W. H. Walker, "Neutron Capture γ-Rays from Phosphorus, Sulfur, Chlorine, Potassium and Calcium," *Phys. Rev.* **85,** 1012 (1952).

CHAPTER 4

PRODUCTION AND STUDY OF NUCLEAR REACTIONS

A. CHARGED-PARTICLE ACCELERATORS

From the discovery of nuclear transmutations in 1919 until 1932 the only known sources of particles which would induce nuclear reactions were the natural α emitters. In fact the only type of nuclear reaction known during that period of 13 years was the α, p reaction. The natural α-particle sources most frequently used in transmutation experiments were Po^{210} (5.30 Mev, $t_{1/2} = 138$ days) and RaC′ (7.68 Mev, $t_{1/2} = 1.6 \times 10^{-4}$ sec) used in equilibrium with its β-emitting parent RaC. Today natural α-particle sources for nuclear reactions are chiefly of historical interest because of the much higher intensities and higher energies now available from man-made accelerators for charged heavy particles. The acceleration of ions to sufficiently high energies for the production of nuclear transmutations was first achieved with high potentials applied across an accelerating tube. Among the devices of this type are the voltage-multiplying rectifier of J. D. Cockcroft and E. T. Walton, still widely used for ion acceleration up to about 1 Mev, and the cascade transformer developed by C. C. Lauritsen and his coworkers at the California Institute of Technology.

Electrostatic (Van de Graaff) Generator. The adaptation of the electrostatic machine to the production of high potentials for the acceleration of positive ions was pioneered by R. J. Van de Graaff of the Massachusetts Institute of Technology, beginning in 1931. In the Van de Graaff machine a high potential is built up and maintained on a conducting sphere by the continuous transfer of static charges from a moving belt to the sphere. This is illustrated in figure 4-1. The belt, made of silk, rubber, paper, or some other suitable insulator, is driven by a motor and pulley system. It passes through the gap AB, which is connected to a high-voltage source (10,000 to 30,000 volts d-c) and adjusted so that a continuous discharge is maintained from the sharp point B. Thus positive (or negative) charges are sprayed from B onto the belt which carries them to the interior of the insulated metal sphere; there another sharp point or sharp-toothed comb C connected to the sphere takes off the charges and distributes them to the surface of the sphere. The sphere will continue to charge up until the loss of charge from the surface by corona discharge and by leakage along its insulating support balances the rate of charge transfer from the belt. The continuous current that can be maintained with an electrostatic generator depends on the rate at which charge can be supplied to the sphere.

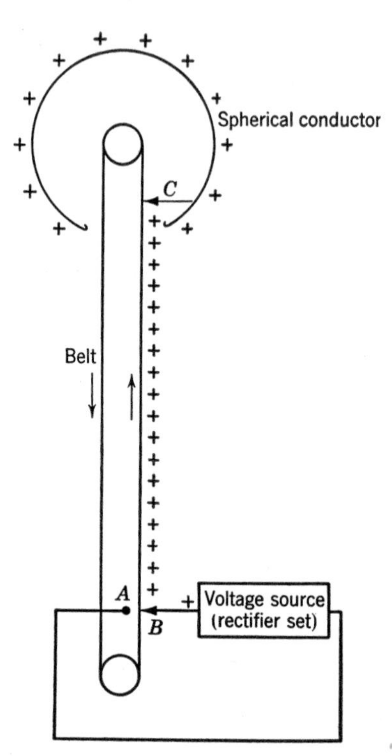

FIGURE 4-1. Schematic representation of the charging mechanism of a Van de Graaff generator.

Van de Graaff's first installation consisted of two spheres, each 2 ft in diameter, one charged to a positive potential of about 750,000 volts above ground and the other to an equal negative potential. All recent electrostatic generators use a single electrode, with acceleration of the ions between that electrode and ground potential, because considerable practical advantages are gained if much of the auxiliary equipment can be operated at ground potential.

Since the voltage of an electrostatic generator is limited by the breakdown of the gas surrounding the charged electrode it is desirable to use conditions under which the breakdown potential is as high as possible. The breakdown potential is a function of pressure and goes through a minimum at a rather low pressure (small fraction of an atmosphere). It is therefore advantageous to operate an electrostatic generator either in a high vacuum, which presents formidable difficulties, or in a high-pressure atmosphere. Most electrostatic generators are completely enclosed in steel tanks in which pressures of several atmospheres are maintained. A further improvement is the use of gases which have higher breakdown potentials than air. Nitrogen is most commonly used, and sulfur hexafluoride has been very successful.

Pressure-type electrostatic generators capable of accelerating protons or other positive ions to energies of 2 to 6 Mev are in operation.

A variety of models for positive-ion and electron acceleration up to 5.5 Mev are commercially available. Proton currents of 5 to 100 μa and even larger electron currents are common. The chief application of electrostatic generators is in nuclear physics work requiring high precision because, unlike other machines such as cyclotrons, they supply ions of precisely controllable energies (constant to about 0.1 per cent).

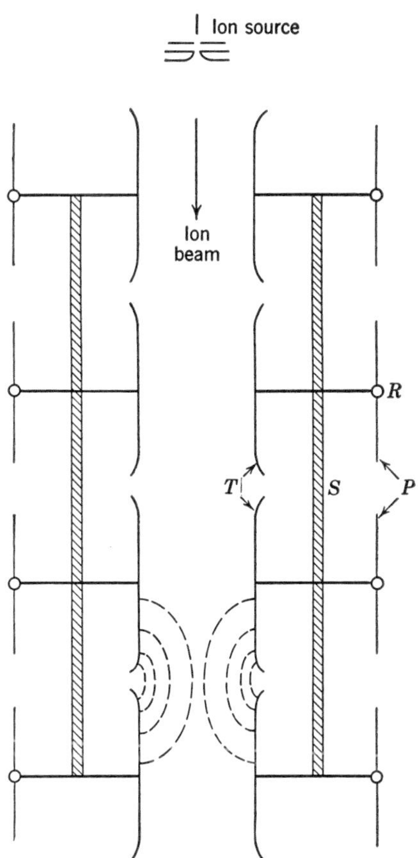

FIGURE 4-2. Schematic diagram of a portion of an accelerating tube.

Accelerating Tubes. Any machine for the acceleration of ions by the application of a high potential requires an accelerating tube across which the potential is applied. A source of ions near the high-voltage end, a system of accelerating electrodes, and a target at the low-voltage end must be provided and enclosed in a vacuum tube connected to the necessary pumping system. The ion source is essentially an arrangement for ionizing the proper gas (hydrogen, deuterium, helium) in an arc or electron beam; the ions are drawn through an opening into the accelerating system. A typical accelerating tube (figure 4-2) is built of glass or porcelain sections *S*. Inside this tube, sections of metal tube *T* define the path of the ion beam. Each metal section is supported on a disk which passes between two sections of insulator out into the gas-filled space to a corona ring *R* equipped with corona points *P*. The purpose of the corona rings and points is to carry the corona discharge from the high- to the low-voltage end of the tube and to distribute the voltage drop uniformly along the tube. Depending on the number of sections used, a potential difference somewhere between ten and several hundred kilovolts exists between successive sections. Each gap between successive sections has both a focusing and a defocusing action on the ions traveling down the tube. The ions tend to travel along the electric lines of force (see figure 4-2 for the pattern of these lines between a pair of sections). In entering the gap the ions are therefore focused, and in leaving it they are defocused; but because the ions move more slowly on entering the gap than on leaving it the focusing effect is stronger than the subsequent defocusing. Well-focused beams (cross-sectional area less than 0.1 cm^2) can be obtained. It should be mentioned that from hydrogen gas in an ion source not only protons but also hydrogen molecule ions (H_2^+) and H_3^+ ions are obtained; these are also accelerated in the tube but can be separated from the protons before striking the target by means of a magnetic analyzer.

In a pressure electrostatic generator the charging system, high-voltage electrode, and accelerating tube are all enclosed in the steel tank containing the high-pressure gas. The high-potential electrode is often more like a cylinder than a sphere.

Linear Accelerator. In all the devices for accelerating ions mentioned so far, the full high potential corresponding to the final energy of the ions must be provided, and the limitations of this type of device are introduced by the insulation problems. These problems are very much reduced in machines which employ repeated acceleration of ions through relatively small potential differences, as in the linear accelerator. In this machine a beam of ions from an ion source is injected into an accelerating tube containing a number of coaxial cylindrical sections (see figure 4-3 for a schematic diagram). Alternate sections are connected together, and a high-frequency alternating voltage from an oscillator is applied between the two groups of electrodes. An ion traveling down the tube will be accelerated at a gap between electrodes if the voltage is in the proper phase. By choosing the frequency and the lengths of successive sections correctly one can arrange the system so that the ions arrive at each gap at the proper phase for acceleration across the gap. The successive electrode lengths have to be such that the ions spend just one half cycle in each electrode. Acceleration takes place at each gap, and the focusing action is the same as in the accelerating tubes of high-voltage sets.

In early models of the linear accelerator, mercury ions were accelerated to 2.85 Mev with an input voltage of about 80 kv. However, because the cyclotron was developed almost simultaneously and had

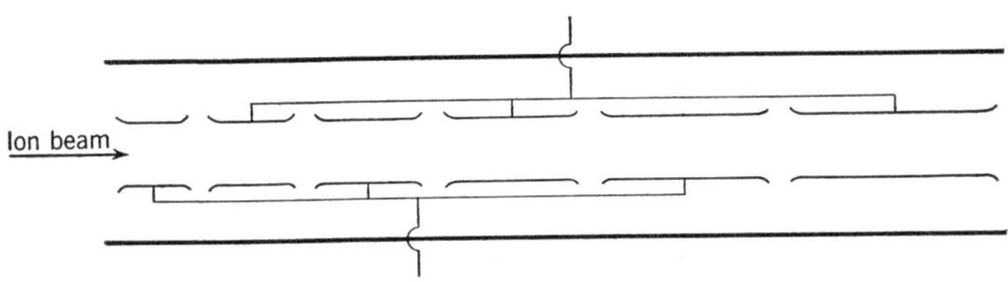

FIGURE 4-3. Schematic diagram of the accelerating tube of a linear accelerator.

obviously great advantages, the linear accelerator did not receive much further attention from about 1934 until after World War II, when the availability of high-power microwave oscillators made possible acceleration to high energies in relatively small linear accelerators. A linear accelerator employing a single 40-ft wave-guide cavity with drift tubes for the acceleration of protons to 32 Mev has been in operation at the University of California in Berkeley. The protons are injected from a 4-Mev electrostatic generator.

A number of linear accelerators for electrons with various maximum energies up to 50 Mev have been constructed both in the United States and abroad. The largest electron linear accelerator is the 1-Bev machine at Stanford University. It is 220 ft long, and the radio-frequency power is fed into its wave guide by 22 klystrons, each delivering 17 megawatts at a frequency of about 3000 megacycles. For electron acceleration to billion-electron-volt energies the linear accelerator ("lineac") is probably the most promising type because it avoids the huge energy losses by radiation common to all the circular types of electron accelerators (figure 4-8). For the production of very-high-energy positive ions, on the other hand, linear accelerators almost certainly cannot compete with synchrotrons.

Cyclotron. By far the most successful device to date for accelerating positive ions to millions of electron volts is the cyclotron proposed by E. O. Lawrence in 1929. A remarkable development has taken place from the first working model which produced 80-kev protons in 1930 to the giant synchrocyclotrons built in recent years which accelerate protons to energies as high as about 500 Mev.

In the cyclotron, as in the linear accelerator, multiple acceleration by a radio-frequency (r-f) potential is used. But the ions, instead of traveling along a straight tube, are constrained by a magnetic field to move in a spiral path consisting of a series of semicircles with increasing radii. The principle of operation is illustrated in figure 4-4. Ions are produced in an arc ion source P near the center of the gap between two hollow semicircular electrode boxes A and B called "dees." The dees are enclosed in a vacuum tank, which is located between the circular pole faces of an electromagnet and is connected to the necessary vacuum pumping system. A high-frequency potential supplied by an oscillator is applied between the dees. A positive ion starting from the ion source is accelerated toward the dee which is at negative potential at the time. As soon as it reaches the field-free interior of the dee, the ion is no longer acted on by electric forces, but the magnetic field perpendicular to the plane of the dees constrains the ion to a semicircular path. If the frequency of the alternating potential is such that the field has reversed its direction just at the time the ion again reaches the gap between dees, the ion again is accelerated, this time toward the other dee. Now its velocity is greater than before, and it therefore describes a semicircle of larger radius; however, as we shall see from the equations of motion, the time of transit for each semicircle is independent of radius. Therefore, although the ion describes larger and larger semicircles it continues to arrive at the gap when the oscillating voltage is at the right phase for acceleration. At each crossing of the gap the ion acquires an amount of kinetic energy equal to the product of the ion charge and the voltage difference between the dees. Finally, as the ion reaches the periphery of the dee system it is removed from its circular path by a negatively

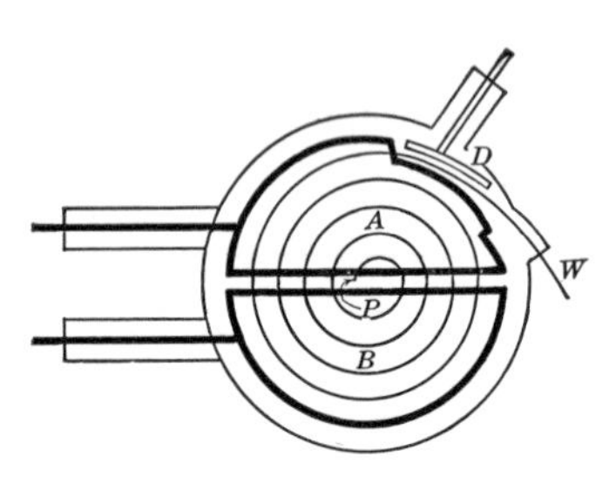

FIGURE 4-4. Cyclotron vacuum chamber. The ions originate at the ion source P and follow a spiral path. The dees A and B, the deflector D, and the exit window W are shown. Reproduced from E. Pollard and W. L. Davidson, *Applied Nuclear Physics*, 2nd ed., New York, John Wiley and Sons, 1951.)

charged deflector plate D and is allowed to emerge through a window W and to strike a target.

The equation of motion of an ion of mass M, charge e, and velocity v in a magnetic field H is given by the necessary equality of the centripetal magnetic force Hev and the centrifugal force Mv^2/r, where r is the radius of the ion's orbit:

$$Hev = \frac{Mv^2}{r} \quad \text{and} \quad r = \frac{Mv}{He}. \tag{4-1}$$

Remembering that the angular velocity $\omega = v/r$, we see that

$$\omega = \frac{He}{M}. \tag{4-2}$$

From this equation it is evident that the angular velocity is independent of radius and ion velocity and that the time required for half a revolution is constant for ions of the same e/M, provided that the magnetic-field strength is constant. In practice, the magnetic field is kept constant, e/M is a characteristic of the type of ion used, and therefore ω is constant. The radio frequency has to be chosen such that its period equals the time it takes for the ions to make one revolution. For $H = 15{,}000$ gauss, and e/M for a proton, the revolution frequency $\omega/2\pi$ and therefore the necessary oscillator frequency turns out (from equation 4-2) to be about 23×10^6 cycles per sec. For deuterons or helium ions (He^{++}) at the same H the frequency is half that value. Most cyclotrons are operated as deuteron sources, and they often use r-f oscillators tuned to about 11 or 12 megacycles.

It is clear from equation 4-2 that in a given cyclotron both the magnetic field and the oscillator frequency can be left unchanged when different ions of the same e/M, such as deuterons and α particles, are accelerated. Equation 4-1 shows that the velocity reached at a given radius is the same for ions of the same e/M; therefore, α particles are accelerated to the same velocity and, hence, twice the energy as deuterons. To accelerate protons in a cyclotron designed for deuterons either the frequency must be approximately doubled (which is usually impractical) or H must be about halved. Although the latter method makes inefficient use of the magnet, it is occasionally used, and the final velocity is again the same as for deuterons (equation 4-1); therefore, protons are accelerated to half the energy available for deuterons.

By squaring equation 4-1, we get

$$r^2 = \frac{M^2v^2}{H^2e^2} \quad \text{or} \quad \frac{1}{2}Mv^2 = \frac{H^2e^2}{2M}r^2.$$

Thus the final energy attainable for a given ion varies with the square of the radius of the cyclotron. With $H = 15{,}000$ gauss the deuteron energy $E = 0.035r^2$ for E in million electron volts and r in inches. The size of a cyclotron is usually given in terms of its pole-face diameter.

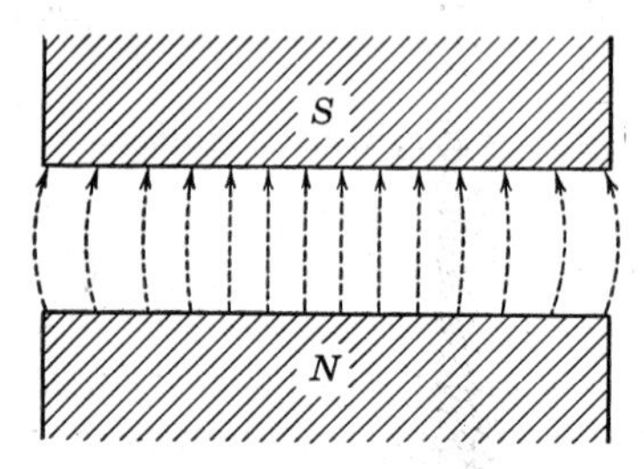

FIGURE 4-5. Shape of magnetic field in the gap of a cyclotron magnet. The curvature of the lines of force gives rise to the focusing action.

From the equations of motion it is clear that an ion can reach the dee gap at any phase of the dee potential and still be in resonance with the radio frequency. As we have just derived, the final energy acquired by an ion is entirely independent of the energy increment the ion receives at each crossing of the dee gap. However, in practice only ions which enter the first gap in a favorable phase of the radio frequency (perhaps during about one-third of the cycle) contribute to the beam current. To avoid difficulties due to excessively long paths for the ions, rather high dee voltages (20,000 to 200,000 volts) are generally used.

A very important feature of the cyclotron is the focusing action it provides for the ion beam. The electrostatic focusing at the dee gap is entirely analogous to that in the high-voltage accelerating tubes. However, as the energy of the ions increases, this effect becomes almost negligible. Fortunately a magnetic focusing effect becomes more and more pronounced as the ions travel towards the periphery. This can be seen from the shape of the magnetic field as shown in figure 4-5. Near the edge of the pole faces the magnetic lines of force are curved, and therefore the field has a horizontal component which provides a restoring force toward the median plane to an ion either below or above that plane. The focusing is so good that a cyclotron beam generally covers less than 1 cm^2 at the target.

One difficulty we have so far neglected is presented by the relativistic mass increase of the ions as they reach high energies. This increase is about ½ per cent for a 10-Mev deuteron and about 5 per cent for a 100-Mev deuteron. It is clear from equation 4-2 that if the revolution frequency is to be kept constant the increase in mass must be compensated by a proportional increase in field strength. When the relativity effects are small this increase of the magnetic field toward the periphery can be readily achieved by slight radial shaping or shimming of the pole faces.[1] Notice, however, that this

FIGURE 4-6. View of the 45-in. cyclotron at Washington University. The target chamber is indicated by an arrow near the center. (Courtesy A. A. Schulke.)

shaping of the field creates regions of magnetic defocusing. For moderate relativistic mass increases this difficulty has been overcome, mainly by the use of higher dee voltages and correspondingly shorter ion paths.

More than twenty cyclotrons in the United States and an approximately equal number abroad are now operating; among these are several of about 60-in. pole-face diameter that accelerate deuterons

[1] In a given cyclotron the field should be shaped slightly differently for protons and for deuterons because of the different relativity effects. For this reason deuteron cyclotrons do not give very good proton beams without major readjustments.

to about 20 Mev and helium ions to about 40 Mev. The largest standard cyclotrons in operation in 1954 are the 86-in. machine at Oak Ridge (20-Mev protons) and the 89-in. cyclotron at the Nobel Institute in Stockholm (25-Mev deuterons). Present-day cyclotrons may have circulating beams of hundreds of microamperes; the deflected external beams are somewhat smaller. The large beam currents available have made target cooling a rather severe problem. The power dissipation in a target receiving 100 μa of 20-Mev particles is 2000 watts, and even iron targets are melted unless water cooling is provided.

Synchrocyclotron. The relativity limitation in cyclotrons can be overcome by modulation of the oscillator frequency to compensate for the mass increase of the ions. Since World War II about a dozen frequency-modulated (FM) cyclotrons, or synchrocyclotrons as they are usually called, have been constructed in several countries. Maximum energies range from 17 Mev (for the converted Princeton and UCLA machines) to 450 Mev (for the University of Chicago's 170-in. synchrocyclotron). Most of the existing synchrocyclotrons are used for proton acceleration; however, the 184-in. cyclotron at Berkeley can be used interchangeably for protons (340 Mev), deuterons (190 Mev), or helium ions (380 Mev) by a change in oscillator frequency.

To accelerate protons to 450 Mev, the frequency has to be decreased during each acceleration to about 63 per cent of its initial value. In most synchrocyclotrons the frequency modulation is brought about by means of a rotating condenser in the oscillator circuit. Obviously, for successful acceleration ions have to start their spiral path at or near the time of maximum frequency. Because ions are accepted into stable orbits only during about 1 per cent of the FM cycle the beam consists of successive pulses. Average beam currents of 0.1 to 1 μa and pulse rates between 50 and 500 cycles per second are rather common. Focusing presents less of a problem than in standard cyclotrons because the relativity effects need not be compensated for by the shape of the magnetic field. The magnetic field can actually be decreased near the edges of the pole faces so as to increase the magnetic focusing. Most FM cyclotrons have but one working dee, and the dee voltage is relatively low; that for the 184-in. Berkeley cyclotron is 15 kv, which means that the deuterons make about 10^4 revolutions for a total path length of the order of 10^5 meters, and take about a millisecond to reach the target.

Betatron. The cyclotron which has been so successful for the acceleration of positive ions is not practical for the acceleration of electrons because of the high frequencies that would be required and because of the enormous relativistic mass increase of electrons even at moderate energies. (See appendix B; at 1 Mev the total mass is three times the rest mass.) The first device for producing electron energies above 2 or 3 Mev was the betatron suggested by a number of investigators and first developed by D. W. Kerst in 1940. The betatron may be thought of as a transformer in which the secondary winding is replaced by a stream of electrons in a vacuum "doughnut." The acceleration is supplied by the electromotive force induced at the position of the doughnut by a steadily increasing magnetic flux perpendicular to and inside the electron orbit. In order for the electrons to move in a fixed orbit it is necessary that the field at the orbit

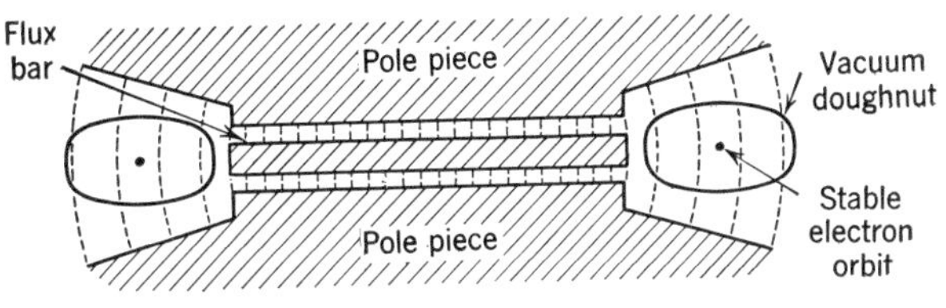

FIGURE 4-7. Cross section through central region of a betatron (schematic), with the magnetic lines of force indicated.

change proportionally with the momentum of the electrons. This condition is fulfilled if the field at the orbit increases at just half the rate at which the average magnetic flux inside the orbit increases; this may be achieved by the proper tapering of the pole faces as indicated schematically in figure 4-7. The radial variation of the field in the region of the electron orbit is important in the focusing problem. It turns out that, if the field falls off as the inverse nth power of the radius in the region of the orbit and if $0 < n < 1$, the electrons will describe damped oscillations about the equilibrium orbit. Betatrons are generally designed with $n = 0.75$, and the focusing is excellent, permitting the electrons to make hundreds of thousands of revolutions.

Electrons for acceleration are pulse-injected into the doughnut at 20 to 50 kev from an electron gun when the field at the orbit is zero. Alternating-current magnets constructed of laminated iron and operating between about 60 and 1800 cycles per second are used in betatrons. The energy obtainable with a given betatron is limited by the saturation of the central flux bars. As they begin to saturate, the orbit begins to shrink. The electron beam can then be allowed to strike a target (often tungsten wire) mounted in the doughnut inside the equilibrium orbit. Or by the use of auxiliary coils the orbit can be expanded, raised, lowered, or contracted toward a suitably placed target, at any electron energy.

Several 20- to 50-Mev betatrons and a few larger ones are in operation. The largest betatron (in 1954) is the 340-Mev machine at the University of Illinois. The ultimate limitation on the energy attainable in betatrons and any other circular electron accelerators is presumably set by the radiation of energy by electrons under centripetal acceleration; the radiative energy loss at a given radius increases with the fourth power of the electron energy and is quite prohibitive above about 1 Bev.

Synchrotron. This device, proposed independently in 1945 by V. I. Veksler and by E. M. McMillan, has been successful for the acceleration of both electrons and protons. As in the betatron the radius of the orbit is kept approximately constant by a magnetic field which increases proportionally with the momentum of the particles. However, the acceleration (or rather the increase in energy since the velocity must remain essentially constant at $v \approx c$) is provided not by a changing central flux but (more nearly as in the cyclotron) by a r-f oscillator which supplies an energy increment every time the particles cross a gap in a resonator which forms part of the vacuum doughnut. It turns out that with this arrangement phase stability is obtained at the orbit, because the particles tend to cross the gap at a time when the field changes from accelerating to decelerating. Particles arriving at the gap too early gain energy, and, therefore, their mass and period of revolution increase, and they will arrive relatively later at the next revolution. Those particles which arrive too late have their mass and period of revolution decreased and are more nearly "on time" the next time around. As the magnetic field is steadily increased, a slight phase difference is maintained between the particle orbits and the resonator voltage, and on the average the particles gain some energy at each passage of the gap.

For electron acceleration the synchrotron is much more economical than the betatron because no large central magnetic flux is required and therefore magnet costs are much lower. Most electron synchrotrons actually use betatron acceleration by means of small central flux bars until the electrons have almost reached the velocity of light (at 2 Mev $v = 0.98c$). Then the r-f circuits are turned on for further acceleration by synchrotron action, and in this way no frequency modulation is required. Injection, targeting, and beam ejection in electron synchrotrons present essentially the same problems as in betatrons. Approximately twenty electron synchrotrons with maximum energies between 20 and 330 Mev are in operation or nearing completion; about half of these are in the United States. Figure 4-8 shows the 70-Mev synchrotron at the General Electric Company. At

FIGURE 4-8. Seventy-Mev synchrotron, Research Laboratory, General Electric Company, Schenectady, N. Y. Notice the light spot near the left edge of the magnet gap. This light emerging tangentially from the doughnut is caused by the energy loss of the accelerating electrons in their circular path. (Courtesy E. E. Charlton.)

the California Institute of Technology a synchrotron is in operation at about 500 Mev, and its energy may eventually be raised to about 1 Bev. The orbit radius in this machine is 11.5 ft.

For proton (or other positive-ion) acceleration to energies in the billion-electron-volt range the synchrotron has proved to be the first practical device. Requiring a ring-shaped magnet only, a proton synchrotron is very much cheaper to construct for these energies than would be a synchrocyclotron with its solid magnet structure. The chief difference between proton and electron synchrotrons arises from the fact that protons do not approach the speed of light until they have energies of billions of electron volts (at 3.8 Bev $v = 0.98c$).

FIGURE 4-9. General view of the Brookhaven Cosmotron. The Van de Graaff injector is partially visible in the background. Three of the vacuum pump stations and some concrete shielding are in the foreground. The two straight sections of the vacuum chamber at left and right are shown open to the atmosphere. (Courtesy Brookhaven National Laboratory.)

Therefore, for a constant orbit radius the revolution frequency of the protons changes by a large factor during the acceleration (a factor of 12 for acceleration from 4 Mev to the limiting velocity). The frequency of the r-f accelerating voltage must be modulated over this very wide range, and in most of the present machines this is accomplished electronically rather than by rotating condensers as in the FM cyclotrons.

Three proton synchrotrons were in operation in 1954: the 1.0-Bev machine at Birmingham, England, the 3-Bev Cosmotron at Brookhaven National Laboratory, and the 6-Bev Bevatron at the Berkeley Radiation Laboratory. A fourth machine, designed for 2 Bev, is under construction at Canberra, Australia. Injection is accomplished in different ways. At Birmingham, a 2-Mev voltage multiplier set is used, at Brookhaven a 4-Mev electrostatic generator, at Berkeley a 10-Mev linear accelerator, and at Canberra the protons will be accelerated to 200 Mev by synchrocyclotron operation.

Figure 4-9 shows a view of the Cosmotron, and we give here a few of its design features. The orbit radius is 30 ft, and the total magnet weight is about 2000 tons (to be compared with the 4300-ton magnet of the Berkeley 184-in. synchrocyclotron). The vacuum chamber is about 6 by 25 in. in cross section and has a total volume of about 300 cu ft. Normal operation is at 12 pulses per minute, and the total acceleration time for each pulse is one second. Each proton travels about 150,000 miles to reach maximum energy. Beam intensities of a few times 10^{10} protons per pulse have been achieved, and these are quite ample for radiochemical studies of nuclear reactions as well as for many types of cloud chamber, emulsion, and counter experiments.

It is worth noting that with increasing particle energies it becomes more and more difficult to obtain external beams by magnetic or electrostatic deflection. Much of the experimentation with synchrocyclotrons and proton synchrotrons is therefore done with targets in the circulating ion beam. Targeting then presents some special problems. One interesting observation is that the fractional energy loss in a metal foil may be so small that the same ions can traverse the target dozens or even hundreds of times in successive revolutions.

Strong-Focusing Synchrotron. The weight and cost of the magnet for a synchrotron of a given orbit radius are largely determined by the size of the aperture in which the magnetic field has to be supplied. This in turn depends on the radial and vertical oscillations of the particles around their equilibrium orbit. These oscillations, caused by spread in angle and in energy at injection, by gas scattering at low energies, by inhomogeneities in the magnetic field, and by inadequate r-f control, must be kept small enough relative to the size of the vacuum chamber to avoid excessive loss of particles from the beam by collisions with the walls. For economy it is clearly desirable to reduce the amplitudes of these oscillations and thereby to reduce the required aperture. Now the magnetic restoring forces for these oscillations are related to the radial variation of the magnetic field B, and more specifically to the quantity $n = -\dfrac{d \log B}{d \log r}$, which must have a value between 0 and 1 for orbit stability in ordinary synchrotrons and betatrons. For a given angular deviation from the orbit, the vertical amplitude is proportional to $n^{-1/2}$, the radial amplitude proportional to $(1 - n)^{-1/2}$. Thus in a synchrotron the vertical dimension of the aperture can be reduced only at the expense of the radial dimension, and vice versa.

From the above discussion it may be seen that the amplitudes of vertical oscillations could be made very small in a magnet section of large positive $n(\gg 1)$, and the radial oscillations could be similarly reduced in a magnet section of large negative $n(\ll -1)$. That a ring magnet design with alternate sections of large positive and large negative n values leads to strong focusing and therefore small aperture requirements, while still preserving phase stability for synchrotron acceleration, was first pointed out by N. Christophilos in 1950 and independently discovered by E. D. Courant, M. S. Livingston, and H. S. Snyder in 1952.

Strong-focusing (alternating-gradient) synchrotrons are in advanced design stages at Brookhaven and at Geneva, Switzerland, for proton acceleration to about 25 or 30 Bev. Other designs based on the same principle are under study elsewhere. A 1-Bev strong-focusing electron synchrotron has been constructed and put into operation at Cornell University. The Brookhaven design calls for a 300-ft orbit radius, a 2½- by 5-in. aperture, and 240 alternating magnet sections with n values of ± 350.

B. GAMMA-RAY AND X-RAY SOURCES

Radioactive Sources. Since nucleons are bound in most nuclei with binding energies of 6 to 8 Mev, photons having energies less than 6 Mev cannot be expected to induce many nuclear reactions. No γ rays emitted in radioactive processes (except from a few short-lived, low-Z nuclides such as N^{16}) have energies as high as that; nor do the X rays from conventional X-ray tubes. The only γ-ray- or X-ray-induced [2] nuclear reactions produced with such sources are, there-

TABLE 4-1

Some Typical Radioactive Gamma-Ray Sources

Source	Half-life	Energy (Mev)	Number of Quanta per Disintegration
ThC″	3.1m	2.62	1
Na^{24}	14.8h	2.76	1
		1.38	1
Y^{88}	105d	0.91	1
		1.85	1

[2] For convenience we shall speak of γ-ray-induced reactions even when the electromagnetic radiation used is not of nuclear origin but is produced by the deceleration of electrons in a target in the manner of continuous X rays.

fore, excitations of nuclei to isomeric levels and the "photodisintegrations" of the deuteron (threshold 2.23 Mev) and of Be^9 (threshold 1.67 Mev). Some of the radioactive γ-ray sources that have been used are listed in table 4-1.

Nuclear Reactions as Sources. In a number of nuclear reactions, especially with the lightest elements (which have large nuclear level spacings), very energetic γ rays are emitted. These in turn have been used to induce other nuclear reactions. Such sources are of particular value if the γ rays are monoenergetic. The most important sources of this type are listed in table 4-2. With these reactions relatively

TABLE 4-2

HIGH-ENERGY GAMMA-RAYS FROM NUCLEAR REACTIONS

Reaction	γ-Ray Energy (Mev)	Remarks
$Li^7(p, \gamma)Be^8$	17.6, 14.8	Resonance at 440 kev proton energy. Other components, at ~15 Mev and at lower energies, also found.
$B^{11}(p, \gamma)C^{12}$	11.8, 16.6	11.8 Mev has 7 times intensity of 16.6 Mev; also low-energy component (~4 Mev) found.
$H^3(p, \gamma)He^4$	21.6	Monoenergetic.

high intensities of γ rays (of the order of 10^6 quanta per sec) can be obtained from rather moderate high-voltage sets operating at 500 to 1000 kev.

Bremsstrahlung. The continuous X rays produced when electrons are decelerated in the Coulomb fields of atomic nuclei are called bremsstrahlung (German for "slowing-down radiation"). This type of radiation is produced whenever fast electrons pass through matter, and the efficiency of the conversion of kinetic energy into bremsstrahlung goes up with increasing electron energy and with increasing atomic number of the material. In tungsten, for example, a 10-Mev electron loses about 50 per cent of its energy by radiation, whereas a 100-Mev electron loses over 90 per cent of its energy by that mechanism (see chapter 7, section B).

The spectrum of bremsstrahlung from a monoenergetic electron source extends from the electron energy down to zero, with approximately equal amounts of energy in equal energy intervals; in other words, the number of quanta in a narrow energy interval is about inversely proportional to the mean energy of the interval.

The stopping of fast electrons in matter thus produces a continuous spectrum of X rays, and any electron accelerator also serves as an X-ray source. Van de Graaff machines, betatrons, and synchrotrons have all been used as sources of X rays for producing nuclear reactions. In fact, unless special devices are used to bring the electron beam out of betatron or synchrotron doughnuts, the X rays are the only radiation available outside the vacuum systems of these machines. The higher the energy of an electron producing bremsstrahlung, the more the X-ray emission is concentrated in the forward direction; with a 100-Mev betatron, for example, about half the intensity of the X-ray beam is contained in a 2° cone. The chief disadvantage of bremsstrahlung sources for nuclear work is their spectral distribution. However, they are capable of producing electromagnetic radiation in energy and intensity ranges not accessible by other means.

C. NEUTRON SOURCES

Radioactive Sources. Our only sources of neutrons are nuclear reactions. There are several naturally occurring and several artificially produced α and γ emitters which can be combined with a

TABLE 4-3

ALPHA- AND GAMMA-RAY NEUTRON SOURCES

Source	Main Reaction	Q (Mev)	Neutron Energy (Mev)	Neutron Yield (per 10^6 disintegrations)
Ra + Be (mixed)	$Be^9(\alpha, n)C^{12}$	5.65	up to 13	460
Rn + Be (mixed)	$Be^9(\alpha, n)C^{12}$	5.65	up to 13	400
Po + Be (mixed)	$Be^9(\alpha, n)C^{12}$	5.65	up to 11, av. 4	80
Ra + B (mixed)	$B^{11}(\alpha, n)N^{14}$	0.28	up to 6	180
$RaBeF_4$ (pure)	$\begin{cases} Be^9(\alpha, n)C^{12} \\ F^{19}(\alpha, n)Na^{22} \end{cases}$	5.65	up to 13	68.5
Ra + Be (separated)	$Be^9(\gamma, n)Be^8$ *	−1.67	<0.6	0.8 †
Ra + D_2O (separated)	$H^2(\gamma, n)H^1$	−2.23	0.1	0.03 †
Na^{24} + Be	$Be^9(\gamma, n)Be^8$ *	−1.67	0.8	3.5 †
Na^{24} + D_2O	$H^2(\gamma, n)H^1$	−2.23	0.2	7.3 †
Y^{88} + Be	$Be^9(\gamma, n)Be^8$ *	−1.67	0.16	2.7 †
Y^{88} + D_2O	$H^2(\gamma, n)H^1$	−2.23	0.3	0.08 †
Sb^{124} + Be	$Be^9(\gamma, n)Be^8$ *	−1.67	0.02	5.1 †
La^{140} + Be	$Be^9(\gamma, n)Be^8$ *	−1.67	0.6	0.08 †
La^{140} + D_2O	$H^2(\gamma, n)H^1$	−2.23	0.15	0.2 †
MsTh + Be	$Be^9(\gamma, n)Be^8$ *	−1.67	0.8	0.9 †
MsTh + D_2O	$H^2(\gamma, n)H^1$	−2.23	0.2	2.6 †

* The product Be^8 is unstable and decomposes in less than 10^{-14} sec into two He^4 nuclei.

† The photoneutron yields are given for 1 g of target (D_2O or Be) at 1 cm from the γ-ray source.

suitable light element to make useful neutron sources. Because of the short ranges of the α particles, α emitters must be intimately mixed with the light element (usually beryllium, because it gives the highest yield). Such sources necessarily give neutrons with energies spread over a wide range. A γ emitter may be enclosed in a capsule surrounded by a beryllium or deuterium oxide target. (Only beryllium and deuterium have γ, n thresholds below 5 Mev.) Some of these sources can in principle give monoenergetic neutrons, but because of neutron and γ-ray scattering in targets of practical thickness the actual spectrum usually has an energy spread of about 30 per cent, with the average energy roughly 20 per cent below the expected maximum value. Some useful sources are listed in table 4-3.

Neutron-Producing Reactions with Accelerators. Much more copious sources of neutrons than can be obtained with radioactive α and γ emitters are available with ion accelerators. The reaction $H^2(d, n)He^3$ (often called a D, D reaction) is exoergic ($Q = +3.27$ Mev), and, because the potential barrier is very low, good neutron yields can be obtained with deuteron energies as low as 100 to 200 kev. With thick targets of solid D_2O, the yields are about 0.7, 3, and 80 neutrons per 10^7 deuterons at 100 kev, 200 kev, and 1 Mev deuteron energy, respectively. High-voltage sets and electrostatic generators are often used to produce the D, D reaction. The neutrons are monoenergetic if monoenergetic deuterons of moderate energies (up to a few million electron volts) fall on a sufficiently thin target.

A very interesting reaction for neutron production is $H^3(d, n)He^4$. The hydrogen isotope H^3 (tritium) is radioactive, half-life about 12 years, but has become available in useful quantities. For use as a target it is usually adsorbed on zirconium or titanium. Such targets have been reported to give about 150 neutrons per 10^7 deuterons at 200 kev. The reaction has a strong resonance at 100 kev deuteron energy and can be a remarkable source of neutrons from very-low-energy deuterons. The reaction is very exoergic, $Q = 17.6$ Mev, and monoenergetic neutrons of about 14 Mev are produced from a thin target.

For a controlled source of monoenergetic neutrons of very low energy (down to about 30 kev) the $Li^7(p, n)Be^7$ reaction is suitable, especially when produced with the protons of well-defined energy available from electrostatic generators. The reaction is endoergic ($Q = -1.646$ Mev) and has a threshold of 1.88 Mev. Advantage may be taken of the differences in neutron energy in the forward and backward (and intermediate) directions.

With X rays from electrostatic generators, betatrons, and the like, neutrons can be produced by means of the $Be^9(\gamma, n)$ or $H^2(\gamma, n)$ reactions. The yields of these reactions go up quite sharply with energy. With an electrostatic generator operating at 2.5 Mev with 100 μa electron current the neutron yield per gram of beryllium is equivalent to that from about 4 g of radium mixed with beryllium; at 3.2 Mev energy the corresponding figure is 26 g of radium.

Where high-energy deuterons are available, the most prolific neutron source is obtained by bombarding beryllium with deuterons. The reaction $Be^9(d, n)B^{10}$ has a positive Q value of 3.79 Mev, but the neutrons are far from monoenergetic. When a beryllium target is bombarded with deuterons of E Mev energy, neutrons with a distribution of energies up to about $(E + 3.5)$ Mev are emitted. The neutron yield goes up rapidly with deuteron energy; it is about 10^8 neutrons per sec per μa for 1-Mev deuterons, about 10^{10} neutrons per sec per μa for 8-Mev deuterons, and about 3×10^{10} neutrons per sec per μa for 14-Mev deuterons.

With a given deuteron source a lithium target gives the highest neutron energies [3] because the $Li^7(d, n)$ reaction is exoergic by 15.0 Mev. The neutron yield is only about one-third that for the $Be^9(d, n)B^{10}$ reaction. Neutrons are also obtained in the bombardment of practically any element with fast protons, deuterons, or α particles. The yields and energies vary from reaction to reaction, but if a neutron bombardment is needed for the activation of some substance it is often sufficient to place the sample near a cyclotron target which is being bombarded by deuterons, even if the target is not beryllium or lithium.

In the bombardment of targets with deuterons of much higher energy (for example the 190-Mev deuterons of the 184-in. synchrocyclotron in Berkeley) high-energy neutrons are emitted in a rather narrow cone in the forward direction as a result of the deuteron stripping mechanism mentioned on page 71. The energy distribution of these neutrons is approximately Gaussian, with the maximum at half the deuteron energy. The highest-energy machines in operation today accelerate protons to several billions of electron volts. Such protons in striking target nuclei presumably will knock forward by essentially elastic collisions neutrons of about the same maximum energy. The 2.2-Bev proton beam of the Brookhaven cosmotron is known to produce a neutron beam of average energy about 1.4 Bev.

[3] An exception is the tritium target which gives slightly more energetic neutrons.

Neutrons from all nuclear reactions initially are fast neutrons. The slowing down of neutrons and some properties of thermal neutrons have already been discussed in chapter 3, section G.

Nuclear Chain Reactors. By far the most prolific sources of neutrons known are the nuclear chain reactors. A nuclear reactor is an assembly of fissionable material (such as uranium, enriched U^{235}, Pu^{239}, or U^{233}) arranged in such a way that a self-sustaining chain reaction is maintained. In each fission process about three neutrons are emitted. The requirement common to all reactors is that at least one of these neutrons must be available to produce another fission rather than escape from the assembly or be used up in some other type of nuclear reaction. Therefore, for a given type of reactor there is a minimum (or critical) size, below which the chain reaction cannot be self-sustaining. In most of the nuclear reactors now in operation thermal neutrons are used for the propagation of the chain reaction. Since the neutrons produced in fission are emitted with kinetic energies averaging about 1.5 Mev, such reactors contain moderators, that is, materials whose function it is to slow down the neutrons to thermal energies. Moderators should, of course, be of low mass number and have low cross sections for neutron absorption. Graphite, heavy water, and ordinary water have been used. Reactors providing neutron fluxes of the order of 10^{12} neutrons cm^{-2} sec^{-1} are not uncommon. Table 4-4 compares the thermal neutron fluxes available from portable laboratory sources, from common types of particle accelerators, and from representative nuclear reactors. More information on reactors and on their neutron fluxes will be found in chapter 12.

The flux generally falls off from the center towards the outside of a reactor. In most reactors, especially in those designed primarily for research purposes (such as the Brookhaven and Harwell reactors), facilities are available for exposure of samples in holes or channels in the interior. The neutron energy distribution in these spots depends, of course, on the type of reactor; in graphite-uranium reactors thermal neutrons predominate, but the flux of neutrons even up to several million electron volts energy is not negligible. To provide pure thermal-neutron sources so-called thermal columns are often attached to reactors. A thermal column is a column of graphite (or some other moderator) of sufficient length to insure a thermal-energy distribution for the neutrons which have passed through it. The neutron flux at the end of a thermal column is, of course, several orders of magnitude smaller than that available inside the associated reactor. Especially large ratios of fast-neutron to slow-neutron fluxes can be obtained inside uranium-walled containers placed in a reactor.

TABLE 4-4

THERMAL NEUTRON FLUXES

Source	Conditions	Thermal Flux (cm^{-2} sec^{-1})
1 g Ra mixed with Be	immersed in a large volume of water or paraffin; flux measured 4 cm from source	1×10^5
Po + Be, 3.7×10^{10} α particles sec^{-1}	immersed in large volume of water or paraffin; flux estimated 4 cm from source	2×10^4
Van de Graaff, 10 μa of 1-Mev deuterons on Be	target surrounded with paraffin; flux estimated in paraffin near target	1×10^7
Cyclotron, 100 μa of 8-Mev deuterons on Be	target backed up with large paraffin block; flux estimated in paraffin near target	1×10^9
Cyclotron, 100 μa of 14-Mev deuterons on Be	target backed up with large paraffin block; flux estimated in paraffin near target	3×10^9
Nuclear reactor, Oak Ridge, graphite-U	in center of core	2×10^{12}
	in hole in shield	1×10^7
Nuclear reactor, MTR, Arco, Idaho, H_2O-U^{235}	in reflector (maximum)	5×10^{14}
Nuclear reactor, NRX, Chalk River, D_2O-U	in center of core	6×10^{13}
	in hole in shield	4×10^7
	in thermal column	1×10^9
Nuclear reactor, North Carolina State College, Raleigh, H_2O-U^{235}		5×10^{11}

Neutron Monochromators. A number of means have been devised for the conduct of experiments with neutrons selected to have a particular energy. One of these, the crystal spectrometer, is analogous to an optical grating monochromator. A thermal neutron with a velocity of 2.2×10^5 cm sec^{-1} (the most probable velocity at 20°C) has a wavelength $\lambda = h/mv = 1.8 \times 10^{-8}$ cm. This length is in the range of common X-ray wavelengths (1.54×10^{-8} cm for copper K_α radiation), and the spacing between crystal planes is about the proper "grating" spacing for slow-neutron diffraction as it is for X-ray diffraction. Considerably higher-energy (shorter-wavelength) neutrons may be diffracted successfully by the crystal at grazing incidence angles. With an intense source of slow neutrons available, such as a nuclear reactor, the crystal and slit system may be arranged to select neutrons from the spectrum with good resolution from about 0.02 to about 10 ev.

The other common means for selecting monoenergetic neutrons from a spectrum depend upon control of the time of flight of the neutrons over a measured course. A burst of neutrons, containing all energies in the spectrum of the source, may be selected mechanically by interposing in the beam a rotating "chopper." Timing devices activate the detector circuits at a chosen time in each "chopping" cycle. Thus neutrons which traverse the distance between chopper and detector in the chosen time lag and produce a practically instantaneous response in the detector may be studied. (Reactions involving only a delayed detector response, such as the production of radioactivity of conventional half-life periods, cannot be investigated by the time-of-flight technique.) A neutron of energy $E = 0.025$ ev has a velocity $v = 1.38 \times 10^6 E^{1/2} = 2.2 \times 10^5$ cm sec^{-1} and so traverses a distance of 10 meters in 4.55×10^{-3} sec. Monochromators with burst times and response times of a few microseconds give very good energy resolution for neutrons of this energy and are useful from about 0.001 to perhaps 10,000 ev when operated in conjunction with nuclear reactors.

If the source of neutrons is an accelerator, such as a cyclotron, the bursts of neutrons for time-of-flight studies can be generated directly by suitable modulation of the accelerator ion beam. The modulated-cyclotron velocity selector at Columbia University is effective from 0.001 to about 1000 ev. The pulsed electron beams from electron accelerators are well suited for this application; if the electron energy is about 15 Mev, the bremsstrahlung can give by γ, n reaction more than 100 neutrons per 10^6 electrons. The Harwell electron-accelerator monochromator has a wide useful range, from 0.001 ev to several thousand electron volts.

An interesting possibility for future development is the use of precision neutron spectroscopy, in a way analogous to optical absorption spectroscopy, for qualitative and quantitative chemical analysis. Elementary analysis for many elements may be possible without destruction of the sample.

D. TARGET CHEMISTRY

We now turn to the chemical problems of purifying and isolating radioactive species following their production in nuclear reactions. In this connection the radiochemist may be confronted with one of two tasks. He may need to prepare a known reaction product free from other radioactive contaminants and sometimes free from certain inactive impurities and in a specified chemical form for use in subsequent experimentation or for determination of its yield in a nuclear reaction. Or he may wish to identify a hitherto unknown or unidentified radioactive species as to its atomic number, mass number, half-life, and radiation characteristics. In both cases chemical separations are usually required for two reasons: (1) in almost any nuclear bombardment more than one type of reaction occurs, and therefore the reaction products have to be separated; (2) impurities present in the target material usually give rise to radioactive products. Apart from the ordinary chemical impurities, further contamination is often introduced in the bombardment procedure; particularly in cyclotron bombardments, where for cooling purposes the target material is usually soldered, pressed, or bolted onto a copper, brass, or aluminum backing plate, transmutation products of the sample container, backing material, solder, and fluxes must be considered.

In a slow-neutron bombardment the only type of reaction produced in almost any target element is the n, γ reaction. Therefore, if an element of sufficient purity is bombarded with slow neutrons, chemical separations are often not required. However, in this case the radioactive product is isotopic with the target, and it is sometimes desirable to free the product isotope from the bulk of the target material in order to obtain high specific activities. Special techniques developed for this purpose are discussed in chapter 11, p. 332. Here we confine our attention to the separation of products not isotopic with the target material.

Comparison with Ordinary Analytical Practice. In many respects the chemical separations which the radiochemist carries out on irradiated targets are very similar to ordinary analytical procedures. However, there are a number of important differences. One of these is the time factor which is often introduced by the short half-lives of the species involved. An otherwise very simple procedure such as the separation of two common cations may become quite difficult when it is to be performed, and the final precipitates are to be dried and mounted, in a few minutes. Where the usual procedures involve long digestions, slow filtrations, or other slow steps, completely different separation procedures must be worked out for use with short-lived activities. Ingenious chemical isolation procedures taking as little as a few seconds have been developed.

In radiochemical separations, at least those subsequent to bombardments with projectiles of moderate energies, we usually are concerned with several elements of neighboring atomic numbers. Thus the procedures given in complete schemes of qualitative analysis can often be modified and shortened. On the other hand, the separation of neighboring elements often presents considerable difficulties as can readily be seen by considering such groups as Ru, Rh, Pd or Hf, Ta, W or any sequence of neighboring rare earths. In very-high-energy reactions and in fission the products are spread over a wide range of atomic numbers. In these cases the separation procedures either become more akin to general schemes of analysis or, more frequently, are designed for the isolation of one or a few elements free from all the others; the latter type of procedure is required particularly when a short-lived substance is to be isolated, and for such cases many specialized techniques have been developed.

High yields in radiochemical separations are not always of great importance, provided that the yields can be evaluated. It may be more valuable to get 50 per cent (or perhaps even 10 per cent) yield of a radioactive element separated in 10 min than to get 99 per cent yield in 1 hr (this is certainly so if the activity has a half-life of 10 or 20 min). High *chemical* purity may or may not be required for radioactive preparations, depending on their use. For identification and study of radioactive species and for many chemical tracer applications it is not important; for most biological work it is. On the other hand *radioactive* purity is usually required and often has to be extremely good.

Some specific effects of the radiations from radioactive substances on the separation procedures may be noted. In case of very high activity levels (say 10^{12} β disintegrations per min per ml of solution) the chemical effects of the radiations, such as decomposition of water and other solvents, and heat effects, may affect the procedures. However, this is generally not so important as the fact that even at much lower activity levels, especially in the case of γ-ray emitters, the person carrying out the separation receives dangerous doses of radiation unless protected by shielding or distance. For this reason it is often necessary to carry out separations behind lead shields and to perform operations with the use of tongs and other tools; for very high activity levels (say in excess of about 10^{12} γ quanta per min) more elaborate remote-control methods are necessary. It is obvious that separation procedures are more difficult under these conditions and in many cases have to be modified considerably to adapt them for remote-control operation. References to discussions of the safe handling of radioactive materials and of appropriate health-protection measures may be found at the end of this chapter.

Carriers. The mass of radioactive material produced in a nuclear reaction is generally very small. Notice, for example, that a sample of 37-min Cl^{38} undergoing 10^8 disintegrations per sec weighs about

2×10^{-11} g; a sample of 53-day Sr^{89} of the same disintegration rate weighs 1×10^{-7} g. Thus the substance to be isolated in a radiochemical separation may often be present in a completely impalpable quantity.[4] It is clear that ordinary analytical procedures involving precipitation and filtration or centrifugation may fail for such minute quantities. In fact, solutions containing the very minute concentrations of solutes which can be investigated with radioactive tracers behave in many ways quite differently from solutions in ordinarily accessible concentration ranges; this subject is treated in chapter 11, section D. Usually some inactive material isotopic with the radioactive transmutation product is deliberately added to act as a carrier for the active material in all subsequent chemical reactions. Most often it is not sufficient to add carrier only for the particular transmutation product to be isolated; frequently it is necessary to add carriers also for other activities which are known or assumed to be formed, including those which derive from target impurities.

It is in many cases not necessary to add carriers for all active species present, because several elements may behave sufficiently alike under given conditions so that traces of one will be carried by macroscopic quantities of another. For example, an acid-insoluble sulfide such as CuS can usually be counted on to carry traces of ions such as Hg^{++}, Bi^{+++}, Pb^{++}, which also form acid-insoluble sulfides. On the other hand, since many precipitates (such as $BaSO_4$ or $Fe(OH)_3$) tend to occlude or adsorb many foreign substances, it is usually necessary to add carriers not only for ions to be precipitated but also for ions to be held in solution when other ions are precipitated. For example, if a zinc activity is to be separated from a ferric solution by ferric hydroxide precipitation with excess ammonia, all the zinc will not be left in solution unless zinc carrier is present. The carrier in such cases is sometimes referred to as hold-back carrier. We shall later discuss cases where carriers are unnecessary.

We have mentioned before that extreme radioactive purity is often very important. Frequently the desired product has an activity that constitutes only a very small fraction of the total target activity; yet this product may be required completely free of the other activities. Such extreme purification is usually quite readily attained by repeated removal of the impurities with successive fresh portions of carrier, until the fractions removed are sufficiently inactive. This so-called "washing-out" principle may be illustrated by the separa-

[4] Actually the mass of an element formed in a nuclear reaction is often exceeded by that of the inactive isotopes of the same element present as an impurity in the target and in the reagents used in the separation procedure.

tion of a weak cobalt activity from radioactive copper contamination. Cobalt and copper carriers are added to a 0.3 *f* HCl solution of the activities, CuS is precipitated, and filtered or centrifuged off, excess H_2S removed by boiling, then fresh copper carrier added to the filtrate, and the procedure repeated until a final CuS precipitate no longer shows an objectionable amount of activity. The same principle can be applied to other than precipitation reactions. Radioactive iron impurity might be removed by repeated extraction of ferric chloride from 9 *f* HCl into isopropyl ether, with fresh portions of $FeCl_3$ carrier added after each extraction. In applying the washing-out method one must, of course, make sure that the desired product is not partially removed along with the impurity in each cycle. If the washing out works properly, the activities of successive impurity fractions should decrease by large and approximately constant factors, provided that the conditions in each step are about the same.

In order that an added inactive material serve as a carrier for an active substance, the two must generally be in the same chemical form. For example, inactive iodide can hardly be expected to be a carrier for active iodine in the form of iodate ion; sodium phosphate would not carry radioactive phosphorus in elementary form. The chemical form in which a transmutation product emerges from a nuclear reaction is usually very hard to predict and has been investigated in only a few cases. However, it is often possible to treat a target in such a way that the active material of interest is transformed to a certain chemical form. For example, if a zinc target is dissolved in a strongly oxidizing medium (say, HNO_3, or HCl + H_2O_2), any copper present as a transmutation product is found afterwards in the Cu^{++} form. If there is any uncertainty about the chemical form of the transmutation product—as to its oxidation state or presence in some complex or undissociated compound, for example—the only method which can be relied on to avoid difficulties is the addition of carrier in the various possible forms and a subsequent procedure for the conversion of all of these into one form. To go through such a procedure prior to the addition of carrier may not be adequate. In fact, it appears that it may not always be sufficient to add the carrier element (say, iodine) in its highest oxidation state (IO_4^-) and carry through a reduction to a low oxidation state (I_2). In the case of the iodine compounds this procedure does not seem to reduce all the active atoms originally present in intermediate oxidation states.

So far we have not spoken of the amounts of carriers used. For manipulative reasons it is often convenient to use about 10 or 20 mg of each carrier, and less than about 1 mg is used only rarely. In separations from large bulks of target material larger amounts of carrier (perhaps 100 to 500 mg) are sometimes useful.[5] The amount of carrier frequently has to be measured at various stages of a chemical procedure to determine the chemical yield in the different steps, or at least in the over-all process. In such cases very small amounts of carrier are inconvenient. On the other hand, it is necessary to keep the quantities of carrier small in the preparation of sources of high specific activity. The specific activity of a sample of an element is sometimes expressed as the ratio of the number of radioactive atoms to the total number of atoms of the element in the sample; more conveniently it is often expressed in terms of the disintegration rate per unit weight. High specific activities are essential particularly in many biological and medical applications of radioactive isotopes, and also are often very desirable in samples to be used in physical measurements or chemical tracer studies, to insure small absorption of the radiations in the sample itself or to permit high dilution factors.

Often it is possible to prepare samples of very high specific activities by the use of a nonisotopic carrier in the first stages of the separation; this may later be separated from the active material. In the isolation of radioyttrium (104-day Y^{88}) from deuteron-bombarded strontium targets, ferric ion can be used as a carrier for the active Y^{+++}; ferric hydroxide is then precipitated, centrifuged, washed, redissolved, and, after the addition of more strontium as hold-back carrier, it is reprecipitated several more times to free it of strontium activity. Finally the ferric hydroxide which carries the yttrium activity is dissolved in 9 *f* HCl, and ferric chloride is extracted into isopropyl ether, leaving the active yttrium in the aqueous phase almost carrier-free. The use of nonisotopic carriers is particularly important in cases where no stable isotopes of the active material have been found in nature; these cases are treated in chapter 11, section F. Criteria for the choice of nonisotopic carriers also are discussed in chapter 11 in connection with the behavior of substances at very small concentrations.

Not all chemical procedures require the use of carriers. Particularly procedures which do not involve solid phases may sometimes be carried out at tracer concentrations without the addition of carriers. Because of the great importance of high specific activities, considerable work has been done on the preparation of carrier-free sources of many radioactive species. In the course of the following

[5] In a radiochemical laboratory it is convenient to have carrier solutions for a large number of elements on hand. These may, for example, be made up to contain 1 or 10 mg of carrier element per milliliter, or possibly 1 mg per drop.

brief discussion of the various types of separation techniques we shall, therefore, point out those which lend themselves to the production of carrier-free preparations.

Precipitation. In most radiochemical separations, as in conventional analytical schemes, precipitation reactions play a dominant role. The chief difficulties with precipitations arise from the carrying down of other materials. Some precipitates such as manganese dioxide and ferric hydroxide are so effective as "scavengers" that they are sometimes used deliberately to carry down foreign substances in trace amounts. Some other precipitates, such as rare-earth fluorides precipitated in acid solution, cupric sulfide precipitated in acid solution, or elementary tellurium brought down by reduction with sulfur dioxide, have little tendency to carry substances not actually insoluble under the same conditions, and, therefore, can sometimes be brought down without the addition of hold-back carriers for activities that are to be left in solution. Most precipitates have an intermediate behavior in this regard.

A radionuclide capable of existence in two oxidation states can be effectively purified by precipitation in one oxidation state followed by scavenging precipitations for impurities while the element of interest is in another oxidation state. For example, a useful procedure for cerium decontamination from other activities uses repeated cycles of ceric iodate precipitation, reduction to Ce(III), zirconium iodate precipitation (with Ce(III) staying in solution), and re-oxidation to Ce(IV).

The use of nonisotopic carrier has already been illustrated in the case of high-specific-activity yttrium carried on $Fe(OH)_3$. The same technique can, of course, be applied to many other di- and trivalent cations which coprecipitate with $Fe(OH)_3$, for example, Be^{++}, Cr^{+++}, Bi^{+++}, rare earths, and even some anions such as phosphate. Other coprecipitation reactions may often be found useful, especially if the subsequent separation of the radionuclide from the nonisotopic carrier can be accomplished by some technique other than precipitation.

Adsorptions on the walls of glass vessels and on filter paper, which are sometimes bothersome, have been put to successful use in special cases. Carrier-free yttrium activity has been quantitatively adsorbed on filter paper from an alkaline strontium solution at yttrium concentrations at which the solubility product of yttrium hydroxide could not have been exceeded.

Ion Exchange. An exceedingly useful separation technique closely related to adsorption chromatography has been developed for use both with and without carriers. This technique involves the adsorption of a mixture of ions on an ion-exchange resin followed by selective elution from the resin. Both cation- and anion-exchange resins have been used very successfully. Most of the cation resins (such as Amberlite IR-1 or Dowex-50) are synthetic polymers containing free sulfonic acid groups. The anion exchangers (such as Dowex-1) usually contain quaternary amine groups with replaceable hydroxyl ions. The distribution of any given ionic species between a solution and the resin depends on the composition of the solution, and for practically any pair of ions conditions can be found under which they will show some difference in distribution.

In practice a solution containing the ions to be separated is run through a column of the finely divided resin, and conditions (solution composition, column dimensions, and flow rate) are chosen such that the ions to be adsorbed will appear in a narrow band near the top of the column. In the simplest kind of separation, some ionic species will run through the column while others are adsorbed. For example, Ni(II) and Co(II) may be separated very readily by passing a 12 *f* HCl solution of the two elements through a Dowex-1 column; the Co(II) forms negatively charged chloride complexes and is held on the column, while Ni(II) apparently does not form such complexes and appears in the effluent.

More commonly a number of ionic species may be adsorbed together on the column and separated subsequently by the use of eluting solutions differing in composition from the original input solution. Frequently, complexing agents which form complexes of different stability with the various ions are used as eluents. There exists then a competition between the resin and the complexing agent for each ion, and if the column is run close to equilibrium conditions each ion will be exchanged between resin and complex form many times as it moves down the column.[6] The number of times an ion is adsorbed and desorbed on the resin in such a column is analogous to the number of theoretical plates in a distillation column. The rates with which different ionic species move down the column under identical conditions are different, because the stabilities of both the resin compounds and the complexes vary from ion to ion; separations are particularly efficient if both these factors work in the same direction,

[6] Slow flow rate, high resin-to-ion ratio, and fine resin particle size favor close approach to equilibrium. In practice, a compromise has to be made between high separation efficiency on the one hand and good yield and speed on the other.

that is, if the complex stability increases as the metal-resin bond strength decreases. As the various adsorption bands move down the column their spatial separations increase, until finally the ion from the lowest band appears in the effluent. The various ions can then be collected separately in successive fractions of the effluent.

The most striking application of cation-exchange columns is in the separation of rare earths from each other, both on a tracer scale and in gram or hundred-gram lots. The eluting solution in this case may be 5 per cent citric acid solution buffered with ammonia to a *p*H somewhere between 2.5 and 8, depending on the resin used and other conditions. The rare earths are eluted in reverse order of their atomic numbers, and yttrium falls between dysprosium and holmium. Very clean separations can be obtained, with impurities in some cases reduced to less than one part per million. By continuously recording the specific activity of the effluent solution as a function of time one obtains separate sharp peaks for the activities of the various rare earths when a mixture of rare-earth radioactivities is run through the column. This method led to the definite assignment of several decay periods to isotopes of element 61.

For rather rapid target chemistry, anion exchange is often more useful than cation exchange, because larger flow rates can usually be used with anion columns. A large number of elements form anionic complexes under some conditions, and available data make it appear likely that a general scheme of analysis based entirely on ion-exchange-column separations could be worked out for these elements. If all the transition elements from manganese to zinc are present in a 12 *f* HCl solution, all but Ni(II) are adsorbed on Dowex-1. Then they may be successively eluted, Mn(II) with 6 *f* HCl, Co(II) with 4 *f* HCl, Cu(II) with 2.5 *f* HCl, Fe(III) with 0.5 *f* HCl, and Zn with 0.005 *f* HCl. With milligram quantities of the elements and a column a few millimeters in diameter and about 10 cm long, this entire separation can be carried out in about half an hour. Another interesting separation is that of palladium, rhodium, iridium, and platinum on Dowex-50 cation-exchange resin. From a dilute $HClO_4$ solution free of halide ions, palladium, rhodium, and iridium are adsorbed while platinum runs through. Subsequently palladium is eluted with 0.1 *f* HCl, then rhodium with 2 *f* HCl, and finally iridium with 5 *f* HCl. In this case cations are adsorbed, and the differences between the chloride complex constants are used to obtain the selective elution.

All ion exchange separations so far investigated work as well with carrier-free radioactivities as with carriers.

Volatilization. Other separation methods avoiding the difficulties inherent in precipitations have frequently been used in radiochemical work. Among these are volatilization, solvent extraction, electrodeposition, and leaching. In special cases all these techniques lend themselves to the preparation of carrier-free tracers. Radioactive noble gases can be swept out of aqueous solutions or melts with some inert gas. The volatility of such compounds as $GeCl_4$, $AsCl_3$, $SeCl_4$ can be used to effect separations from other chlorides by distillation from HCl solutions. Similarly, osmium, ruthenium, rhenium, and technetium can be separated from other elements and from each other by procedures involving distillations of their oxides OsO_4, RuO_4, Re_2O_7, and Tc_2O_7. Carrier-free palladium (Pd^{103}) has been prepared from a rhodium target by a method involving coprecipitation of palladium with selenium (by reduction of H_2SeO_3 with SO_2), followed by removal of selenium by a perchloric acid distillation.

Distillation and volatilization methods often give very clean separations provided that proper precautions are taken to avoid contamination of the distillate by spray or mechanical entrapment. Most volatilization methods can be done without specific carriers, but some nonisotopic carrier gas may be required. Precautions are sometimes necessary to avoid loss of volatile radioactive substances during the dissolving of irradiated targets or during the irradiation itself.

Solvent Extraction. Under certain conditions compounds of some elements can be quite selectively extracted from an aqueous solution into an organic solvent, and often the partition coefficients are approximately independent of concentration down to tracer concentrations (say 10^{-12} or 10^{-15} f). In other cases, particularly if dimerization occurs in the organic phase (as in the ethyl ether extraction of ferric chloride), carrier-free substances are not extracted. Solvent extractions often lend themselves particularly well to rapid and specific separations. In most cases the extraction can be followed by a "back-extraction" into an aqueous phase of altered composition.

Extractions of the chlorides of Fe(III), Ga(III), and Tl(III) into various ethers are frequently used by radiochemists. The partition coefficients vary quite rapidly with HCl concentration. Extraction from 6 f HCl into ethyl ether or from 8 to 9 f HCl into isopropyl ether gives very good separations from practically all other metal chlorides. The separation of gallium from iron and thallium can be achieved by ether extraction of $GaCl_3$ in the presence of reducing agents so that the reduced ions Fe(II) and Tl(I) are present.

Gold nitrate and mercuric nitrate can be extracted into ethyl acetate from nitric acid solutions. The extraction of uranyl nitrate by ethyl ether from a nitric acid solution of high nitrate concentration is sufficiently specific to serve as an excellent first step in the isolation of carrier-free fission products from the bulk of irradiated uranium. The basic acetate of beryllium is very soluble in chloroform, and a chloroform solution of this compound may be shaken with water to separate beryllium from many impurities. The extraction into ethyl ether of the blue peroxychromic acid formed when H_2O_2 is added to a dichromate solution is an excellent radiochemical decontamination step for chromium although it tends to give low yields. Copper dithizonate extraction into carbon tetrachloride, cadmium thiocyanate extraction into chloroform, and many other examples could be cited.

Several organic substances such as thenoyltrifluoroacetone (TTA) have been found to form chelate complexes with a large number of metal ions. These complexes are preferentially soluble in nonpolar solvents such as benzene, and, since the dissociation constants of the different metal chelates show different *p*H dependence, specific separation procedures can sometimes be devised using several extraction steps at different *p*H values.

Occasionally it may be possible to leach an active product out of a solid target material. This has been done successfully in the case of neutron- and deuteron-bombarded magnesium oxide targets; radioactive sodium is separated rather efficiently from the bulk of such a target by leaching with hot water.

Electrochemical Methods. Electrolysis or electrochemical deposition may be used either to plate out the active material of interest or to plate out other substances leaving the active material in solution. For example, it is possible to separate radioactive copper from a dissolved zinc target by an electroplating process. Carrier-free radioactive zinc may be obtained from a deuteron-bombarded copper target by solution of the target and electrolysis to remove all the copper.

Chemical displacement may sometimes be used for the separation of carrier-free substances from bulk impurities. The separation of polonium from lead by deposition on silver is a classical example. Similarly, bismuth activity obtained in lead bombardments may be separated practically quantitatively from the lead by plating on nickel powder from hot 0.5 *f* HCl solution. This method for lead-bismuth separations is sufficiently rapid to permit isolation of the 0.8-sec Pb^{207m} isomer from its bismuth parent.

EXERCISES

1. See p. 109. Explain the difference between the Q value and the threshold of the $Li^7(p, n)Be^7$ reaction.

2. Estimate (*a*) the percentage frequency modulation and (*b*) the pole diameter required for an FM cyclotron designed to accelerate protons to 350 Mev. Assume $H = 16{,}000$ gauss.

3. What would be the minimum n, γ cross section detectable by means of the product activity in a sample of 10 cm^2 area containing 1 mg-equivalent of target isotope, with a mixed Ra–Be source containing 1 g radium? Assume that the bombardment is continued to saturation and that 1 per cent of the neutrons emitted by the source strike each square centimeter of the target sample as slow neutrons. Consider 30 disintegrations per min as the minimum detectable activity.

4. Suppose you want to prepare some 5.2-year Co^{60} with a cyclotron and have the choice of bombarding a cobalt sample directly with 14-Mev deuterons for 2 hr or of surrounding it with paraffin and placing it near a beryllium target bombarded with 14-Mev deuterons for a total of 100 hr. Which is more advantageous from the point of view of total activity obtained? Use data in appendices C and E, and make reasonable assumptions about the solid angle subtended by the neutron-irradiated sample.

5. Suggest methods for the chemical identification of (*a*) V^{52} produced in the fast-neutron bombardment of a chromate solution, (*b*) Mn^{52} produced in the deuteron bombardment of iron, (*c*) O^{14} produced in the proton bombardment of nitrogen gas.

6. (*a*) What would be the approximate neutron energy from a beryllium target bombarded with Ni^{57} γ rays? (*b*) What would be the energy difference between neutrons in the forward and in the reverse directions?

Answer: (*a*) 0.21 Mev; (*b*) 8.7 kev.

7. A sample of sodium iodide is irradiated with fast neutrons to produce 115-day Te^{127}. Suggest a chemical procedure for the isolation of the tellurium. How would you modify this procedure if you knew that the sodium iodide contained some sodium bromide impurity?

8. Estimate (*a*) the equilibrium quantity of Ba^{140} present in a uranium-graphite reactor operating at 1000 kw, and (*b*) the total amount of Ce^{140} accumulated in the same reactor after 1 year's operation followed by 2 months' shutdown. *Answer:* (*a*) 0.70 g.

9. What time would be required to convert 2 per cent of the Cd^{113} in a thin cadmium foil to Cd^{114} if the foil were placed in a reactor with a thermal neutron flux of 5×10^{11} neutrons per cm^2 per sec? *Answer:* 24d.

10. A 60-in. cyclotron capable of accelerating deuterons to 20 Mev and helium ions to 40 Mev is to be used for the preparation of the following nuclides: (*a*) 34-day Rb^{84} in high specific activity and as free as possible from other rubidium activities; (*b*) carrier-free Ce^{139}; (*c*) radiochemically pure As^{77}; (*d*) Ba^{140}. For each case outline a method of preparation, including a statement about target material, bombarding particle, and approximate bombarding energy to be used, and the chemical procedures following bombardment. Justify all your choices of conditions.

11. In a study of the reactions of cobalt with 300-Mev protons the activities associated with the iron, manganese, chromium, and chlorine fractions are to be investigated. Outline procedures for the isolation of each of these, bearing in mind that products of any $Z \leqq 28$ may be formed in the bombardment.

REFERENCES

E. Pollard and W. L. Davidson, *Applied Nuclear Physics,* 2nd ed., New York, John Wiley & Sons, 1951.

D. Halliday, *Introductory Nuclear Physics,* New York, John Wiley & Sons, 1950.

W. J. Whitehouse and J. L. Putman, *Radioactive Isotopes, An Introduction to Their Preparation, Measurement and Use,* Oxford, The Clarendon Press, 1953.

M. S. Livingston, "Particle Accelerators," *Advances in Electronics,* Vol. I, p. 269, New York, Academic Press Inc., 1948.

M. S. Livingston, "High Energy Accelerators (Standard Cyclotron, Synchrocyclotron, Proton Synchrotron)," *Ann. Rev. Nuclear Sci.,* Vol. I, pp. 157–174, Stanford, Annual Reviews Inc., 1952.

J. E. Thomas, Jr., W. L. Kraushaar, and I. Halpern, "High Energy Accelerators (Synchrotron)," *Ann. Rev. Nuclear Sci.,* Vol. I, p. 175, Stanford, Annual Reviews Inc., 1952.

J. C. Slater, "High Energy Accelerators (Linear Accelerator)," *Ann. Rev. Nuclear Sci.,* Vol. I, p. 199, Stanford, Annual Reviews Inc., 1952.

E. L. Chu and L. I. Schiff, "Recent Progress in Accelerators," *Ann. Rev. Nuclear Sci.,* Vol. II, p. 79, Stanford, Annual Reviews Inc., 1953.

M. H. Blewett (Editor), Collected papers on the design, construction and initial operation of the Cosmotron, *Rev. Sci. Instr.* **24,** 723–870 (1953).

E. D. Courant, M. S. Livingston, and H. S. Snyder, "The Strong-Focusing Synchrotron—A New High Energy Accelerator," *Phys. Rev.* **88,** 1190 (1952).

D. T. Green, R. F. Errington, F. C. Boyd, and N. J. Hopkins, "Production of Multicurie Gamma-Ray Teletherapy Sources," *Nucleonics* **11,** No. 5, 29 (May 1953).

R. West, "Low-Energy Gamma-Ray Sources," *Nucleonics* **11,** No. 2, 20 (February 1953).

H. V. Argo, H. T. Gittings, A. Hemmendinger, G. A. Jarvis, and R. F. Taschek, "Properties of the $T^3(p, \gamma)He^4$ Reaction," *Phys. Rev.* **78,** 691 (1950).

F. Ajzenberg and T. Lauritsen, "Energy Levels of Light Nuclei. IV," *Revs. Mod. Phys.* **24,** 321 (1952).

L. H. Lanzl and A. O. Hanson, "Z Dependence and Angular Distribution of Bremsstrahlung from 17-Mev Electrons," *Phys. Rev.* **83,** 959 (1951).

B. T. Feld, "The Neutron," *Experimental Nuclear Physics,* Vol. II (E. Segrè, Editor), New York, John Wiley & Sons, 1953.

A. C. Graves, R. L. Walker, R. F. Taschek, A. O. Hanson, J. H. Williams, and H. M. Agnew, "Neutron Sources," *Miscellaneous Physical and Chemical Techniques of the Los Alamos Project,* Div. V, Vol. 3 of National Nuclear Energy Series, New York, McGraw-Hill Book Co., 1952.

D. J. Hughes, *Pile Neutron Research,* Cambridge, Mass., Addison-Wesley Publishing Co., 1953.

I. Kaplan, *Nuclear Physics,* Cambridge, Mass., Addison-Wesley Publishing Co., 1955.

"Research Reactors: What You Need to Know to Build One," *Nucleonics* **12,** No. 4, 7 (April 1954).

T. I. Taylor and W. W. Havens, Jr., "Neutron Spectroscopy for Chemical Analysis," *Nucleonics* **5,** No. 6, 4 (May 1949); **6,** No. 2, 66 (February 1950); and **6,** No. 4, 54 (April 1950).

G. B. Cook and J. F. Duncan, *Modern Radiochemical Practice,* Oxford, Clarendon Press, 1952.

A. A. Noyes and W. C. Bray, *A System of Qualitative Analysis for the Rare Elements,* New York, The Macmillan Co., 1927.

P. C. Stevenson and H. G. Hicks, "Separation Techniques Used in Radiochemistry," *Ann. Rev. Nuclear Sci.,* Vol. III, p. 221, Stanford, Annual Reviews Inc., 1953.

H. L. Finston and J. Miskel, "Radiochemical Separation Techniques," *Ann. Rev. Nuclear Sci.,* Vol. V, Stanford, Annual Reviews Inc., 1955.

"Collected Radiochemical Procedures," Atomic Energy Commission Report LA-1566, Available from Office of Technical Services, U. S. Department of Commerce, Washington 25, D. C. ($1.25).

W. W. Meinke, "Chemical Procedures Used in Bombardment Work at Berkeley," Atomic Energy Commission Report AECD-2738. Available from Office of Technical Services, U. S. Department of Commerce, Washington 25, D. C. ($0.90).

C. D. Coryell and N. Sugarman, *Radiochemical Studies: The Fission Products,* National Nuclear Energy Series, Div. IV, Vol. 9, New York, McGraw-Hill Book Co., 1951.

W. M. Garrison and J. G. Hamilton, "Production and Isolation of Carrier-Free Radioisotopes," *Chem. Revs.* **49,** 237 (1951).

K. A. Kraus and G. E. Moore, "Anion Exchange Studies VI. The Divalent Transition Elements Manganese to Zinc in Hydrochloric Acid," *J. Am. Chem. Soc.* **75,** 1460 (1953).

P. C. Stevenson, A. A. Franke, R. Borg, and W. Nervik, "The Separation of the Four Platinum Group Metals Palladium, Rhodium, Iridium and Platinum," *J. Am. Chem. Soc.* **75,** 4876 (1953).

Collected Papers on Ion Exchange, *J. Am. Chem. Soc.* **69,** 2769–2881 (1947).

Discussions of safety and health protection in the handling of radioactive sources may be found in the following references.

E. Bleuler and G. J. Goldsmith, *Experimental Nucleonics,* New York, Rinehart, 1952.

"Radiological Protection—International Commission Recommendations," *Nucleonics* **8,** No. 1, 31 (January 1951).

S. Warren and A. M. Brues, "Protection Against Radiation Hazards," *Nucleonics* **7,** No. 4, 70 (October 1950).

S. Kinsman, *Radiological Health Handbook,* U. S. Department of Health, Education, and Welfare, Sanitary Engineering Center, Cincinnati, Ohio, 1954.

H. A. Levy, "Some Aspects of the Design of Radiochemical Laboratories," *Chem. Eng. News* **24,** 3168 (1946).

H. E. Skipper, "The Hazards Involved in the Use of Carbon-14," *Nucleonics* **10,** No. 2, 40 (February 1952).

CHAPTER 5

EQUATIONS OF RADIOACTIVE DECAY AND GROWTH

A. EXPONENTIAL DECAY

Half-life. We have seen (in chapter 1) that a given radioactive species decays according to an exponential law: $N = N_0e^{-\lambda t}$ or $\mathbf{A} = \mathbf{A}_0e^{-\lambda t}$, where N and $\mathbf{A}$ represent the number of atoms and the measured activity, respectively, at time t, and N_0 and $\mathbf{A}_0$ the corresponding quantities when $t = 0$, and λ is the characteristic decay constant for the species. The half-life $t_{1/2}$ is the time interval required for N or $\mathbf{A}$ to fall from any particular value to one-half that value. The half-life is conveniently determined from a plot of log $\mathbf{A}$ versus t when the necessary data are available and is related to the decay constant:

$$t_{1/2} = \frac{\ln 2}{\lambda} = \frac{0.69315}{\lambda}.$$

Average Life. We may determine the average life expectancy of the atoms of a radioactive species. This average life is found from the sum of the times of existence of all the atoms divided by the initial number; if we consider N to be a very large number we may approximate this sum by an equivalent integral, finding for the average life τ:

$$\tau = -\frac{1}{N_0}\int_{t=0}^{t=\infty} t\,dN = \frac{1}{N_0}\int_0^{\infty} t\lambda N\,dt = \lambda\int_0^{\infty} te^{-\lambda t}\,dt$$

$$= -\left[\frac{\lambda t + 1}{\lambda}e^{-\lambda t}\right]_0^{\infty} = \frac{1}{\lambda}.$$

We see that the average life is greater than the half-life by the factor $1/0.693$; the difference arises because of the weight given in the averaging process to the fraction of atoms that by chance survive for a long time. It may be seen that during the time $1/\lambda$ an activity will be reduced to just $1/e$ of its initial value.

Mixtures of Independently Decaying Activities. If two radioactive species, denoted by subscripts 1 and 2, are mixed together, then the observed total activity is the sum of the two separate activities: $\mathbf{A} = \mathbf{A}_1 + \mathbf{A}_2 = c_1\lambda_1 N_1 + c_2\lambda_2 N_2$. The detection coefficients c_1 and

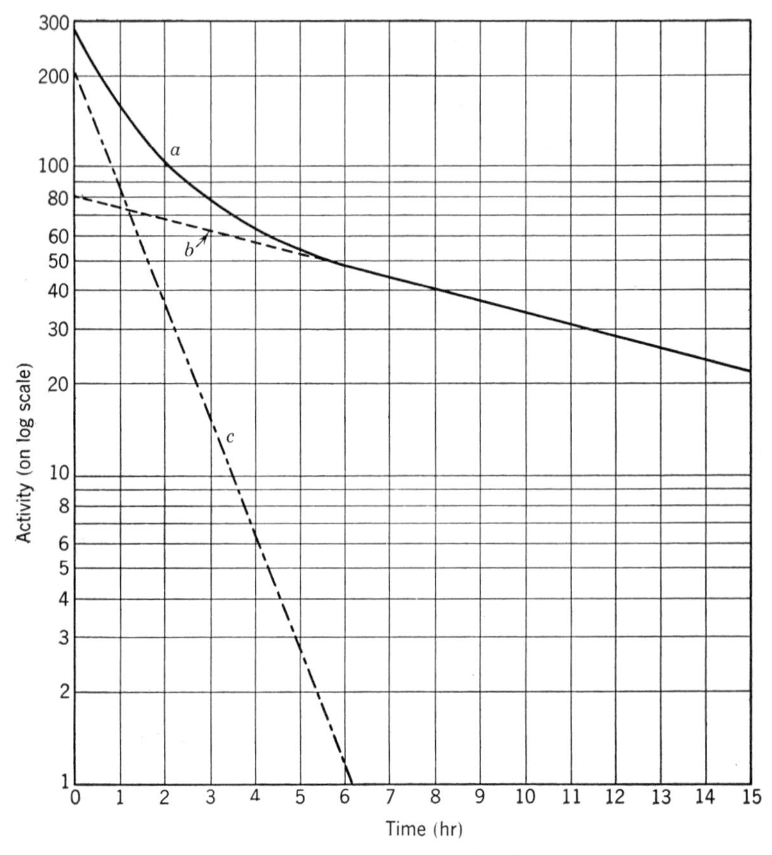

FIGURE 5-1. Analysis of composite decay curve.
(a) Composite decay curve.
(b) Longer-lived component ($t_{1/2} = 8.0$ hr).
(c) Shorter-lived component ($t_{1/2} = 0.8$ hr).

c_2 are by no means necessarily the same and often are very different in magnitude. In general, $\mathbf{A} = \mathbf{A}_1 + \mathbf{A}_2 + \cdots \mathbf{A}_n$ for mixtures of n species.

For a mixture of several *independent* activities the result of plotting log $\mathbf{A}$ versus t is always a curve concave upward (convex toward the origin). This curvature results because the shorter-lived components become relatively less significant as time passes. In fact, after sufficient time the longest-lived activity will entirely predominate, and its half-life may be read from this late portion of the decay curve. Now, if this last portion, which is a straight line, is extrapolated back to $t = 0$ and the extrapolated line subtracted from the original curve, the residual curve represents the decay of all components except the longest-lived. This curve may be treated again in the same way, and in principle any complex decay curve may be analyzed into its components. In actual practice experimental uncertainties in the observed data may be expected to make it most difficult to handle systems of more than three components, and even two-component curves may not be satisfactorily resolved if the two half-lives differ by less than about a factor of two. The curve shown in figure 5-1 is for two components with half-lives differing by a factor of 10.

B. GROWTH OF RADIOACTIVE PRODUCTS

General Equation. In chapter 1 we considered briefly a special case in which a radioactive daughter substance was formed in the decay of the parent. Let us take up the general case for the decay of a radioactive species, denoted by subscript 1, to produce another radioactive species, denoted by subscript 2. The behavior of N_1 is just as has been derived; that is, $-\frac{dN_1}{dt} = \lambda_1 N_1$, and $N_1 = N_1^0 e^{-\lambda_1 t}$, where we use the symbol N_1^0 to represent the value of N_1 at $t = 0$. Now the second species is formed at the rate at which the first decays, $\lambda_1 N_1$, and itself decays at the rate $\lambda_2 N_2$. Thus,

$$\frac{dN_2}{dt} = \lambda_1 N_1 - \lambda_2 N_2$$

or

$$\frac{dN_2}{dt} + \lambda_2 N_2 - \lambda_1 N_1^0 e^{-\lambda_1 t} = 0. \tag{5-1}$$

For this linear differential equation of the first order we assume a solution of the form $N_2 = uv$, where u and v are functions of t. Differentiating, we obtain

$$\frac{dN_2}{dt} = u\frac{dv}{dt} + v\frac{du}{dt}.$$

Substituting in equation 5-1, we have

$$u\frac{dv}{dt} + v\frac{du}{dt} + \lambda_2 uv - \lambda_1 N_1^0 e^{-\lambda_1 t} = 0,$$

which may be rearranged to give

$$u\left(\frac{dv}{dt} + \lambda_2 v\right) + v\frac{du}{dt} - \lambda_1 N_1^0 e^{-\lambda_1 t} = 0. \tag{5-2}$$

We may choose the arbitrary function v so that the term in parenthesis is zero,

$$\frac{dv}{dt} + \lambda_2 v = 0,$$

$$v = e^{-\lambda_2 t}.$$

By substitution of this result in equation 5-2 a differential equation in u is obtained:

$$e^{-\lambda_2 t}\frac{du}{dt} - \lambda_1 N_1^0 e^{-\lambda_1 t} = 0,$$

$$du = \lambda_1 N_1^0 e^{(\lambda_2 - \lambda_1)t}\, dt,$$

$$u = \frac{\lambda_1}{\lambda_2 - \lambda_1} N_1^0 e^{(\lambda_2 - \lambda_1)t} + C;$$

and

$$N_2 = uv = \frac{\lambda_1}{\lambda_2 - \lambda_1} N_1^0 e^{-\lambda_1 t} + C e^{-\lambda_2 t}. \tag{5-3}$$

The constant C is evaluated from the condition $N_2 = N_2^0$ at $t = 0$:

$$C = N_2^0 - \frac{\lambda_1}{\lambda_2 - \lambda_1} N_1^0.$$

Substituting in equation 5-3 and rearranging, we obtain the final solution for N_2 as a function of time:

$$N_2 = \frac{\lambda_1}{\lambda_2 - \lambda_1} N_1^0 (e^{-\lambda_1 t} - e^{-\lambda_2 t}) + N_2^0 e^{-\lambda_2 t}. \tag{5-4}$$

Notice that the first group of terms shows the growth of daughter from the parent and the decay of these daughter atoms; the last term gives the contribution at any time from the daughter atoms present initially.

Transient Equilibrium. In applying equation 5-4 to considerations of radioactive (parent and daughter) pairs we can distinguish two general cases, depending on which of the two substances has the longer half-life. If the parent is longer-lived than the daughter ($\lambda_1 < \lambda_2$) a state of so-called radioactive equilibrium is reached; that is, after a certain time the ratio of the numbers of atoms and, consequently, the ratio of the disintegration rates of parent and daughter become con-

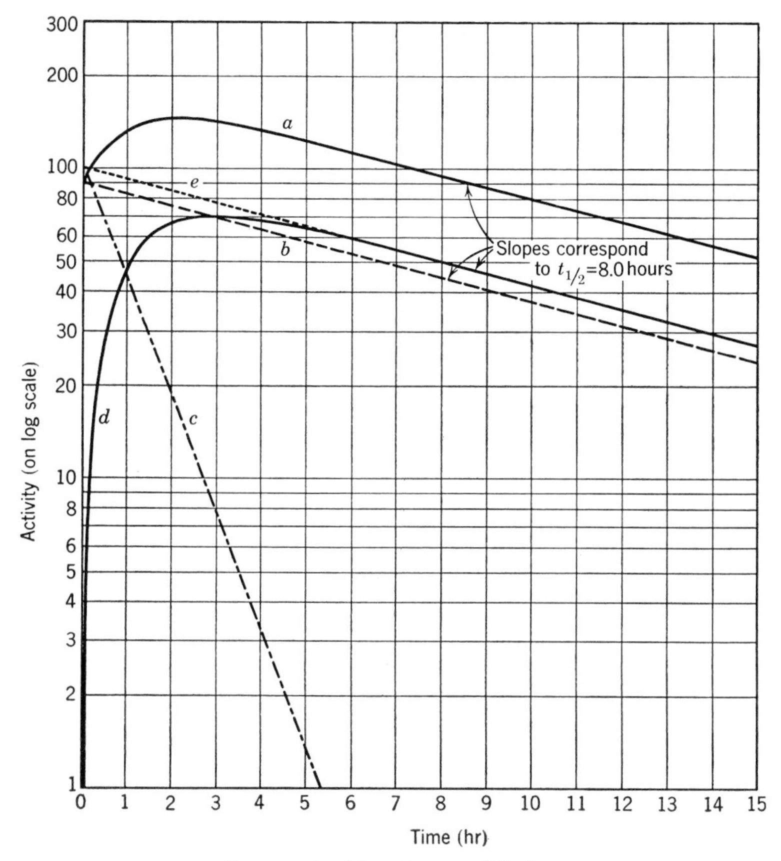

FIGURE 5-2. Transient equilibrium.

(a) Total activity of an initially pure parent fraction.
(b) Activity due to parent ($t_{1/2} = 8.0$ hr).
(c) Decay of freshly isolated daughter fraction ($t_{1/2} = 0.80$ hr).
(d) Daughter activity growing in freshly purified parent fraction.
(e) Total daughter activity in parent-plus-daughter fractions.

stant. This can be readily seen from equation 5-4; after t becomes sufficiently large $e^{-\lambda_2 t}$ is negligible compared with $e^{-\lambda_1 t}$, and $N_2^0 e^{-\lambda_2 t}$ also becomes negligible; then

$$N_2 = \frac{\lambda_1}{\lambda_2 - \lambda_1} N_1^0 e^{-\lambda_1 t},$$

and, since $N_1 = N_1^0 e^{-\lambda_1 t}$,

$$\frac{N_1}{N_2} = \frac{\lambda_2 - \lambda_1}{\lambda_1}. \tag{5-5}$$

The relation of the two measured activities is found, from $\mathbf{A}_1 = c_1\lambda_1 N_1$, $\mathbf{A}_2 = c_2\lambda_2 N_2$, to be

$$\frac{c_2\mathbf{A}_1}{c_1\mathbf{A}_2} = \frac{\lambda_2 - \lambda_1}{\lambda_2}. \tag{5-6}$$

Notice that the right-hand sides of equations 5-5 and 5-6 are not the same. In the special case of equal detection coefficients ($c_1 = c_2$) the ratio of the two activities, $\mathbf{A}_1/\mathbf{A}_2 = 1 - (\lambda_1/\lambda_2)$, may have any value between 0 and 1, depending on the ratio of λ_1 to λ_2; that is, in equilibrium the daughter activity will be greater than the parent activity by the factor $\lambda_2/(\lambda_2 - \lambda_1)$. In equilibrium both activities decay with the parent's half-life.

Secular Equilibrium. A limiting case of radioactive equilibrium in which $\lambda_1 \ll \lambda_2$ and in which the parent activity does not decrease measurably during many daughter half-lives is known as secular equilibrium. We illustrated this situation in chapter 1 and now may derive the equation presented there, as a useful approximation of equation 5-5:

$$\frac{N_1}{N_2} = \frac{\lambda_2}{\lambda_1}, \quad \text{or} \quad \lambda_1 N_1 = \lambda_2 N_2.$$

In the same way equation 5-6 reduces to

$$\frac{c_2\mathbf{A}_1}{c_1\mathbf{A}_2} = 1, \quad \text{or} \quad \frac{\mathbf{A}_1}{\mathbf{A}_2} = \frac{c_1}{c_2},$$

and the measured activities are equal if $c_1 = c_2$.

The production of a radioactive substance (daughter) by any steady source, for example, steadily operating nuclear chain reactors or cyclotrons, presents a situation analogous to the approach to secular equilibrium. We may obtain the growth formula for N_2 as a function of time from equation 5-4, setting $N_2^0 = 0$ at $t = 0$, using $\lambda_1 \ll \lambda_2$ and $e^{-\lambda_1 t} = 1$, and replacing $\lambda_1 N_1^0$ by the rate $\mathbf{R}$ of production of the active atoms:

$$N_2 = \frac{\mathbf{R}}{\lambda_2}(1 - e^{-\lambda_2 t}). \tag{5-7}$$

As t becomes long compared to the half-life of the activity, N_2 approaches $\mathbf{R}/\lambda_2$ as a maximum limiting value, and we may rewrite equation 5-7 in this way:

$$N_2 = (N_2)_{\text{max}}(1 - e^{-\lambda_2 t}). \tag{5-8}$$

Thus if an activity with a 20-min half-life (say C^{11}) is being steadily produced, one-half the maximum attainable yield is reached after 20 min, three-fourths after 40 min, seven-eighths after 60 min, fifteen-sixteenths after 80 min, and so on. If you must pay by the hour for

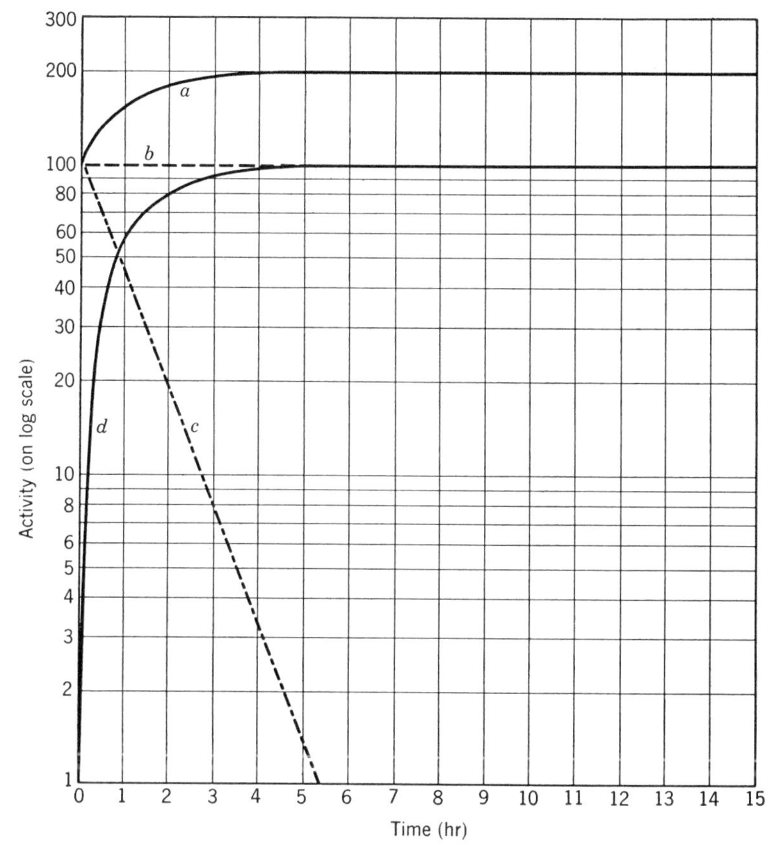

FIGURE 5-3. Secular equilibrium.

(a) Total activity of an initially pure parent fraction.

(b) Activity due to parent ($t_{1/2} = \infty$); this is also the total daughter activity in parent-plus-daughter fractions.

(c) Decay of freshly isolated daughter fraction ($t_{1/2} = 0.80$ hr).

(d) Daughter activity growing in freshly purified parent fraction.

cyclotron running time, you would want to irradiate for not more than about two half-lives of the desired product.

Figure 5-2 presents an example of the transient equilibrium with $\lambda_1 < \lambda_2$ (actually with $\lambda_1/\lambda_2 = 1/10$); the curves represent variations with time of the parent activity and the activity of a freshly isolated daughter fraction, the growth of daughter activity in a freshly purified parent fraction, and other relations; in preparing the figure we have taken $c_1 = c_2$. Figure 5-3 is a similar plot for secular equilibrium; it is apparent that as λ_1 becomes smaller compared to λ_2 the curves for transient equilibrium shift to approach more and more closely the limiting case shown in figure 5-3.

The Case of No Equilibrium. If the parent is shorter-lived than the daughter ($\lambda_1 > \lambda_2$), it is evident that no equilibrium is attained at any time. If the parent is made initially free of the daughter, then as the parent decays the amount of daughter will rise, pass through a maximum, and eventually decay with the characteristic half-life of the daughter. This is illustrated in figure 5-4; for this plot we have taken $\lambda_1/\lambda_2 = 10$, and $c_1 = c_2$. In the figure the final exponential decay of the daughter is extrapolated back to $t = 0$. This method of analysis is useful if $\lambda_1 \gg \lambda_2$ for then this intercept measures the activity $c_2\lambda_2N_1^0$: the N_1^0 atoms give rise to N_2 atoms so early that N_1^0 may be set equal to the extrapolated value of N_2 at $t = 0$. The ratio of the initial activity, $c_1\lambda_1N_1^0$, to this extrapolated activity gives the ratios of the half-lives if the relation between c_1 and c_2 is known:

$$\frac{c_1\lambda_1N_1^0}{c_2\lambda_2N_1^0} = \frac{c_1}{c_2} \cdot \frac{\lambda_1}{\lambda_2} = \frac{c_1}{c_2} \cdot \frac{(t_{1/2})_2}{(t_{1/2})_1}.$$

If λ_2 is not negligible compared to λ_1, it can be shown that the ratio λ_1/λ_2 in this equation should be replaced by $(\lambda_1 - \lambda_2)/\lambda_2$, and the expression involving the half-lives changed accordingly.

Both the transient-equilibrium and the no-equilibrium cases are sometimes analyzed in terms of the time t_m for the daughter to reach its maximum activity when growing in a freshly separated parent fraction. This time we find from the general equation 5-4 by differentiating,

$$\frac{dN_2}{dt} = -\frac{\lambda_1^2}{\lambda_2 - \lambda_1} N_1^0 e^{-\lambda_1 t} + \frac{\lambda_1\lambda_2}{\lambda_2 - \lambda_1} N_1^0 e^{-\lambda_2 t},$$

and setting $dN_2/dt = 0$ when $t = t_m$:

$$\frac{\lambda_2}{\lambda_1} = e^{(\lambda_2 - \lambda_1)t_m}, \quad \text{or} \quad t_m = \frac{2.303}{\lambda_2 - \lambda_1} \log \frac{\lambda_2}{\lambda_1}.$$

At this time the daughter decay rate, $\lambda_2 N_2$, is just equal to the rate of formation, $\lambda_1 N_1$ (this is obvious from equation 5-1); and in figures 5-2, 3, 4, where we assumed $c_1 = c_2$, we have the parent activity $\mathbf{A}_1$

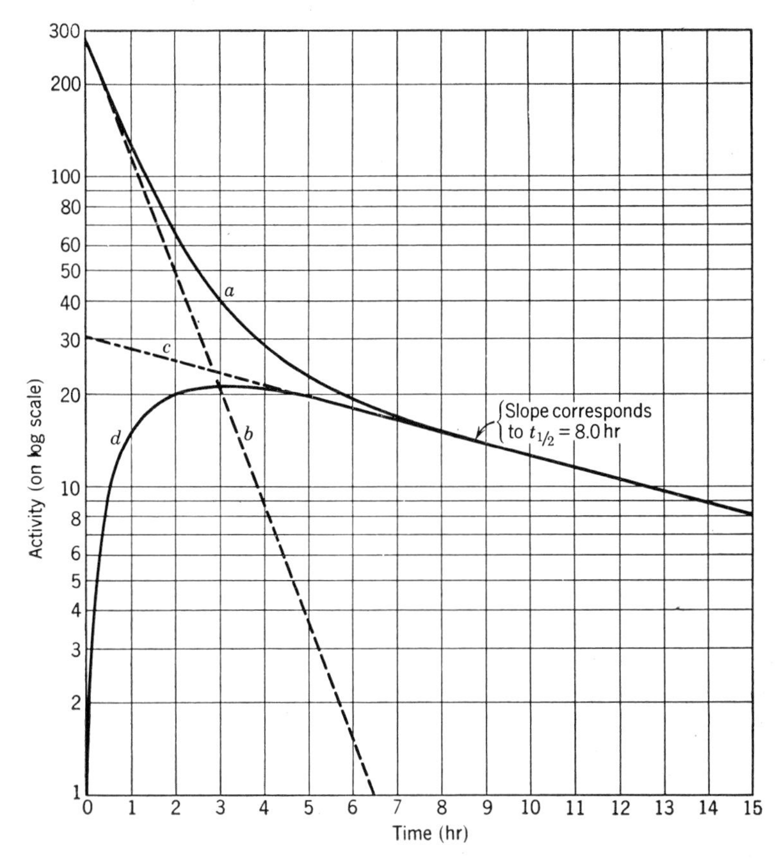

FIGURE 5-4. The case of no equilibrium.

(a) Total activity.
(b) Activity due to parent ($t_{1/2}$ = 0.80 hr).
(c) Extrapolation of final decay curve to time zero.
(d) Daughter activity in initially pure parent.

intersecting the daughter growth curve d at the time t_m. (The time t_m is infinite for secular equilibrium.)

Many Successive Decays. If we consider a chain of three or more radioactive products it is clear that the equations already derived for N_1 and N_2 as functions of time are valid, and N_3 may be found by solving the new differential equation:

$$\frac{dN_3}{dt} = \lambda_2 N_2 - \lambda_3 N_3. \tag{5-9}$$

This is entirely analogous to the equation for dN_2/dt, but the solution calls for more labor since N_2 is a much more complicated function than N_1. The next solution, for N_4, is still more tedious. H. Bateman has given the solution for a chain of n members with the special assumption that at $t = 0$ the parent substance alone is present, that is, that $N_2{}^0 = N_3{}^0 = \cdots N_n{}^0 = 0$. This solution is

$$N_n = C_1 e^{-\lambda_1 t} + C_2 e^{-\lambda_2 t} + \cdots C_n e^{-\lambda_n t},$$

$$C_1 = \frac{\lambda_1 \lambda_2 \cdots \lambda_{n-1}}{(\lambda_2 - \lambda_1)(\lambda_3 - \lambda_1) \cdots (\lambda_n - \lambda_1)} N_1{}^0,$$

$$C_2 = \frac{\lambda_1 \lambda_2 \cdots \lambda_{n-1}}{(\lambda_1 - \lambda_2)(\lambda_3 - \lambda_2) \cdots (\lambda_n - \lambda_2)} N_1{}^0, \quad \text{etc.}$$

If we do require a solution to the more general case with $N_2{}^0$, $N_3{}^0 \cdots N_n{}^0 \neq 0$, we may construct it by adding to the Bateman solution for N_n in an n-membered chain, a Bateman solution for N_n in an $(n - 1)$-membered chain with substance 2 as the parent, and, therefore, $N_2 = N_2{}^0$ at $t = 0$, and a Bateman solution for N_n in an $(n - 2)$-membered chain, etc.

Branching Decay. Another variant that is met in general decay schemes is the branching decay, illustrated by

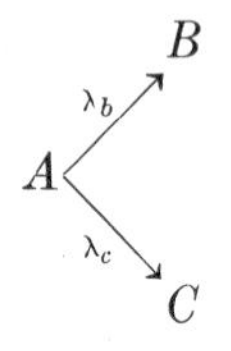

Here the two partial decay constants, λ_b and λ_c, must be considered when the general relations in either branch are studied because, for example, the substance B is formed at the rate $\lambda_b N_A$, but A is consumed at the rate $(\lambda_b + \lambda_c)N_A$. Notice that A can have but one half-life, given in this case by $t_{1/2} = 0.693/(\lambda_b + \lambda_c)$. By definition the half-life is related to the total rate of disappearance of a substance regardless of the mechanism by which it disappears.

If the Bateman solution is to be applied to a decay chain containing branching decays, the λ's in the numerators of the equations defining C_1, C_2, etc., should be replaced by the partial decay constants. That is, λ_i in the numerators should be replaced by $\lambda_i{}^*$, where $\lambda_i{}^*$ is the decay constant for the transformation of the ith chain member to the

$(i + 1)$th member. If a decay chain branches, and subsequently the two branches are rejoined, as in the natural radioactive series, the two branches are treated by this method as separate chains; the production of a common member beyond the branch point is the sum of the numbers of atoms formed by the two paths.

C. EQUATIONS OF TRANSFORMATION IN A NEUTRON FLUX

When nuclear reactions are induced in a radioactive nuclide, the rate of disappearance of the substance is no longer governed by the law of radioactive transformation alone, but by a modified law which takes into account the disappearance by transmutation reactions also. Under most practical bombardment conditions the rate of transformation of radioactive species by nuclear reactions is negligible compared to the rate of radioactive decay. However, in the case of long-lived nuclides and with the large neutron fluxes available in nuclear reactors, transformations by both mechanisms sometimes have to be considered. We shall state the modified transformation equations for the case of a neutron flux; they are equally applicable for any other bombarding particle. The treatment given here follows that developed by W. Rubinson.

Consider N atoms of a single radioactive species of decay constant λ (in reciprocal seconds) and total neutron reaction cross section σ (in square centimeters) in a constant neutron flux nv (neutrons cm^{-2} sec^{-1}). The rate of radioactive transformation is λN, the rate of transformation by neutron reactions is $nv\sigma N$, and the total rate of disappearance is

$$-\frac{dN}{dt} = (\lambda + nv\sigma)N = \Lambda N, \tag{5-10}$$

where Λ may be considered as a modified decay constant. Equation 5-10 has the same form as the standard differential equation of radioactive decay, and is integrated to give

$$N = N_0 e^{-\Lambda t}. \tag{5-11}$$

If we consider a parent-daughter pair, the parent disappears by both transmutation and decay: $-\dfrac{dN_1}{dt} = (\lambda_1 + nv\sigma_1)N_1 = \Lambda_1 N_1$; but the daughter grows by decay of the mother only and disappears by both processes: $\dfrac{dN_2}{dt} = \lambda_1 N_1 - \Lambda_2 N_2$, or, in more general notation,

$$\frac{dN_{i+1}}{dt} = \lambda_i N_i - \Lambda_{i+1} N_{i+1}.$$

Actually we may want to consider chains in which the transformation from one member to the next may occur by nuclear reaction as well as by radioactive decay. Then λ_i must be replaced by a modified decay constant, $\Lambda_i^* = \lambda_i^* + nv\sigma_i^*$, where the asterisks serve as a reminder that if either the decay or reaction of the parent does not always lead to the next chain member, then λ_i^* must be the partial decay constant and σ_i^* must be the partial reaction cross section leading from the ith member to the $(i + 1)$th member of the chain. With this notation the general solution is written as in the Bateman equations, for $N_2^0 = N_3^0 = \cdots N_n^0 = 0$:

$$N_n = C_1 e^{-\Lambda_1 t} + C_2 e^{-\Lambda_2 t} + \cdots C_n e^{-\Lambda_n t}, \tag{5-12}$$

where
$$C_1 = \frac{\Lambda_1^* \Lambda_2^* \cdots \Lambda_{n-1}^*}{(\Lambda_2 - \Lambda_1)(\Lambda_3 - \Lambda_1) \cdots (\Lambda_n - \Lambda_1)} N_1^0,$$

$$C_2 = \frac{\Lambda_1^* \Lambda_2^* \cdots \Lambda_{n-1}^*}{(\Lambda_1 - \Lambda_2)(\Lambda_3 - \Lambda_2) \cdots (\Lambda_n - \Lambda_2)} N_1^0, \quad \text{etc.}$$

As an illustration we compute the amount of 3.15-day Au^{199} formed by two successive n, γ reactions when 1 g Au^{197} is exposed for 30 hr in a neutron flux of 1×10^{14} cm^{-2} sec^{-1}. The chain of reactions is

$$Au^{197} \xrightarrow[n,\,\gamma]{\sigma = 94b} Au^{198} \xrightarrow[n,\,\gamma]{\sigma = 35{,}000b} Au^{199}$$
$$\beta^- \downarrow t_{1/2} = 2.7\text{d} \qquad \beta^- \downarrow t_{1/2} = 3.15\text{d}$$

We use equation 5-12 for this three-membered chain:

$$N_{199} = \Lambda_{197}^* \Lambda_{198}^* N_{197}^0 \left[\frac{e^{-\Lambda_{197} t}}{(\Lambda_{198} - \Lambda_{197})(\Lambda_{199} - \Lambda_{197})} + \frac{e^{-\Lambda_{198} t}}{(\Lambda_{197} - \Lambda_{198})(\Lambda_{199} - \Lambda_{198})} + \frac{e^{-\Lambda_{199} t}}{(\Lambda_{197} - \Lambda_{199})(\Lambda_{198} - \Lambda_{199})} \right].$$

The numerical values to be substituted are

$$t = 1.08 \times 10^5 \text{ sec},$$

$$nv = 10^{14} \text{ cm}^{-2} \text{ sec}^{-1},$$

$$\sigma_{197} = 9.4 \times 10^{-23} \text{ cm}^2,$$

$$\sigma_{198} = 3.5 \times 10^{-20} \text{ cm}^2$$

$$N_{197}^0 = \frac{6.02 \times 10^{23}}{197} = 3.05 \times 10^{21},$$

$$\Lambda_{197}^* = \Lambda_{197} = nv\sigma_{197} = 9.4 \times 10^{-9}\ \text{sec}^{-1},$$

$$\Lambda_{198} = \lambda_{198} + nv\sigma_{198} = 3.0 \times 10^{-6} + 3.5 \times 10^{-6}$$
$$= 6.5 \times 10^{-6}\ \text{sec}^{-1},$$

$$\Lambda_{198}^* = nv\sigma_{198} = 3.5 \times 10^{-6}\ \text{sec}^{-1}, \quad \text{and}$$

$$\Lambda_{199} = \lambda_{199} = 2.55 \times 10^{-6}\ \text{sec}^{-1}.$$

Using these values, we get

$$N_{199} = 1.0 \times 10^8 \left(\frac{e^{-0.0010}}{6.5 \times 10^{-6} \times 2.55 \times 10^{-6}} + \frac{e^{-0.702}}{6.5 \times 10^{-6} \times 3.95 \times 10^{-6}} - \frac{e^{-0.275}}{2.55 \times 10^{-6} \times 3.95 \times 10^{-6}} \right)$$
$$= 1.0 \times 10^8 (6.0 \times 10^{10} + 1.9 \times 10^{10} - 7.5 \times 10^{10})$$
$$= 4 \times 10^{17}.$$

The disintegration rate of Au^{199} at the end of the irradiation is $\lambda_{199}N_{199} = 1 \times 10^{12}\ \text{sec}^{-1}$. For comparison we compute the disintegration rate of Au^{198} in the sample (again from equation 5-12, for a two-membered chain):

$$\lambda_{198}N_{198} = \lambda_{198}nv\sigma_{197}N_{197}^0 \left(\frac{e^{-\Lambda_{197}t}}{\Lambda_{198} - \Lambda_{197}} + \frac{e^{-\Lambda_{198}t}}{\Lambda_{197} - \Lambda_{198}} \right)$$
$$= 8.6 \times 10^7 \frac{1 - 0.495}{6.5 \times 10^{-6}} = 6.7 \times 10^{12}\ \text{sec}^{-1}.$$

Thus about 13 per cent of the radioactive disintegrations in the sample occur in Au^{199}.

D. UNITS OF RADIOACTIVITY

A familiar unit of radioactivity is the curie. Originally the term referred to the quantity of radon in equilibrium with one gram of radium. Later it came to be used as a unit of disintegration rate for any radioactive preparation, defined as that quantity of the preparation which undergoes the same number of disintegrations per second as one gram of pure radium. With this definition the value of the curie varied with successive refinements in the measurement of the decay constant or atomic weight of radium. In 1950 a Joint Commission of the International Union of Pure and Applied Chemistry and the International Union of Pure and Applied Physics adopted the following definition: "The curie is a unit of radioactivity defined as the quantity of any radioactive nuclide in which the number of disintegrations per second is 3.700×10^{10}." The millicurie (mc) and the microcurie (μc) are practical units also in common use, and the megacurie finds use in reactor technology.[1]

As an illustration we calculate the weight in grams W of 1.00 mc of C^{14} from its half-life of 5570 years:

$$\lambda = \frac{0.693}{5570 \times 365 \times 24 \times 60 \times 60} = 3.95 \times 10^{-12} \text{ sec}^{-1};$$

$$-\frac{dN}{dt} = \lambda N = \lambda \frac{W}{14} \times 6.02 \times 10^{23} = 1.70W \times 10^{11} \text{ sec}^{-1}.$$

With $-\dfrac{dN}{dt} = 3.700 \times 10^{7}$ disintegrations per second (1 mc),

$$W = \frac{3.700 \times 10^{7}}{1.70 \times 10^{11}} = 0.218 \times 10^{-3} \text{ g}.$$

E. DETERMINATION OF HALF-LIVES

Decay Curves. Half-lives in the range from several seconds to several years are usually determined experimentally by measurements of the activity with an appropriate instrument at a number of suitable successive times. Then log **A** is plotted versus time, and the half-life is found by inspection, provided that the activity is sufficiently free of other radioactivities that a straight line (exponential decay) is found, preferably extending over several half-life intervals. As we have already discussed, the decay curve resulting from a mixture of independent activities may often be analyzed to yield the half-lives of the various components. When difficulties arise in this analysis it is often adequate to measure separately decay curves through several different thicknesses of absorbing material to obtain curves with some components relatively suppressed; even better is the

[1] A different unit of radioactive disintegration rate was proposed by the National Bureau of Standards. This unit, the rutherford (rd), is defined as that amount of a radioactive substance which undergoes 1,000,000 disintegrations per second.

use of selective detection equipment which will measure separately the radiations from the several activities in the sample. Our treatments of the more general equations have already suggested methods of finding half-lives from more complicated growth and decay curves.

The manipulations necessary for activity measurements become difficult as the time scale to be investigated becomes short. The use of electronic and photographic recording devices can extend the working region to half-lives well below 0.1 sec. With short-lived gaseous products, or products in solution, a method that has been particularly useful for fission products with half-lives of the order of a few seconds is to measure the activity at different points along a tube through which the fluid flows at a measured rate. The ordinary decay curve is then found on a plot of log **A** versus distance along the tube. A method based on a similar principle, using a rapidly rotating wheel, has been employed for solid samples; the half-life (0.022 sec) of B^{12} was determined in this way. In these procedures the limitation usually arises not in the activity measurements but in the rapid preparation, and possibly isolation, of the short-lived sample. The possible use of a modulated source, such as a betatron or synchrotron, or a cyclotron modified to produce periodic pulses of accelerated ions, may be mentioned. Appropriate electric circuits will divide the time between pulses into an arbitrary number of intervals and measure the average resulting activity in each interval.

Variable-Delay Coincidences. When a body of very short half-life results from a radioactive decay with moderate or long half-life the method of variable-delay coincidences can be used. In one form of apparatus the electric pulse produced in a detection instrument by a ray from the parent is electrically delayed by a time t and then recorded in coincidence with any ray from the daughter that may produce a pulse in a detector at that time, or more correctly at that time within the limits of the resolving time τ of the coincidence equipment. Now as t is varied by electrical means the coincidence counting rate—coincidences per unit τ—will vary; the effect is essentially to record disintegrations over the period τ at a time t after formation of the short-lived nucleus. The very short half-life is determined from the typical decay curve with the logarithm of the coincidence rate plotted against t. So long as Geiger counters were used as the detection instruments the lower limit of measurable half-lives was a few tenths of a microsecond because of inherent response times in these counters. With scintillation detectors (described in chapter 8, section C) the method has more recently been extended down to about 0.0002 μsec. Some half-lives reported are 1.57×10^{-9} sec for Tm^{170m} and

1.9×10^{-10} sec for Te^{123m_1}. In this region the delay time t is provided by the time required for the electric impulse to travel along a few centimeters of connecting wire.

In an earlier form of delayed-coincidence apparatus no provision was made for the introduction of a delay time, and coincidences C were recorded as τ was varied. Clearly, with τ very short (compared to the half-life sought) no coincidences would result; with τ long (compared to $t_{1/2}$) a maximum number of coincidences C_{max} would be observed. The expected relation, $C = C_{max}(1 - e^{-\lambda\tau})$, is analogous to the formula for radioactive growth, equation 5-8, and the half-life is obtained from the semilog plot of $(C_{max} - C)$ versus τ. The half-lives of the C′ bodies in the three natural decay series were measured by this method.

Specific Radioactivity. If the half-life, or disintegration constant, is to be determined for a substance of very long half-life (very small λ), the activity $\mathbf{A} = c\lambda N$ may not change measurably in the time available for observation. In such cases λ may be found from the relation $\lambda N = -\frac{dN}{dt} = \frac{\mathbf{A}}{c}$, provided that N is known and $-\frac{dN}{dt}$ may be determined in an absolute way (through knowledge of the detection coefficient c). This method is most accurate for α emitters, and the absolute rates of emission of α particles from uranium samples have been investigated with great care to measure the half-life of U_I. In an accurate determination of the half-life of Pu^{239} the value of $-\frac{dN}{dt}$ was established in a calorimetric measurement of the heating effect, with the α-particle energy known from the α-particle range.

In some instances the distintegration rate is better obtained from a measurement of the equal disintegration rate of a daughter in secular equilibrium. Early determinations of the half-life of U^{235} were based on the α-particle counting rate of Pa^{231} obtained in known yield from old uranium ores; the U^{235} α particles were not measurable in a direct way because of the much larger number of α disintegrations occurring in the U^{238} and U^{234}.

Decay Systematics. The knowledge that has been gained of decay systematics often permits useful estimates of half-lives from decay-energy and other information, especially in the case of α radioactivity. This is discussed in chapter 6. The earliest empirical relationship for α emitters was the Geiger-Nuttall rule: $\log R = a \log \lambda + b$, where R is the range of the α particles, a is a general constant, and b is a constant characteristic of the particular radioactive series. The Sargent relation was the first and even less precise attempt to correlate the disintegration energy and the disintegration constant for β emitters.

EXERCISES

1. The following experimental data were obtained when the activity of a certain beta-active sample was measured at the intervals shown.

Time (in hours)	Activity (in counts/min)	Time (in hours)	Activity (in counts/min)
0	7300	4.0	481
0.5	4680	5.0	371
1.0	2982	6.0	317
1.5	1958	7.0	280
2.0	1341	8.0	254
2.5	965	10.0	214
3.0	729	12.0	181
3.5	580	14.0	153

Plot the decay curve on semilog paper and analyze it into its components. What are the half-lives and the initial activities of the component activities?

2. Compute (*a*) the weight of 1 curie of radon; (*b*) the weight of 1 curie of P^{32} (see appendix G for the half-life); (*c*) the disintegration rate of 1 cm^3 of tritium (H^3) at STP. *Answer:* (*a*) 6.47 μg.

3. What was the rate of production, in atoms per second, of I^{128} during a constant 1-hr cyclotron (neutron) irradiation of an iodine sample, if the sample is found to contain 2.00 mc of I^{128} activity at 15 min after the end of the irradiation?

4. From data in appendix G, calculate the total rate of emission of α particles from 1 mg of ordinary uranium. Calculate this answer also for the case of 1 mg of very old uranium, in secular equilibrium with all its decay products. *Answer to first part:* 25.0 per sec.

5. A 0.100 mg sample of pure $_{94}Pu^{239}$ (an α-particle emitter) was found to undergo 1.40×10^7 disintegrations per min. Calculate the half-life of this isotope. Pu^{239} is formed by the β decay of Np^{239}. How many curies of Np^{239} would be required to produce a 0.100-mg sample of Pu^{239}?

Answer to second part: 23.5 curies.

6. To determine the thermal-neutron capture cross section of 31-hr Os^{193}, a 100-mg sample of osmium metal is placed in a thermal-neutron flux of 2×10^{12} cm^{-2} sec^{-1} for 30 days. The amount of 700-day Os^{194} activity formed is found from subsequent decay measurements to be 210 disintegrations per second at the end of irradiation. From the known activation cross section of Os^{192} (1.6b) and the half-lives of Os^{193} and Os^{194}, compute the capture cross section of Os^{193}. *Answer:* See appendix C.

7. A sample of 1.00×10^{-10} g of RaE is freshly purified at time $t = 0$. (*a*) If this sample is left without further treatment, when will the amount of Po^{210} in it be a maximum? (*b*) At that time of maximum growth, what will be the weight of Po^{210} present, the α activity in disintegrations per second, the beta activity of the sample in disintegrations per second, the number of microcuries of Po^{210} present? (*c*) Sketch on semilog paper a graph of α activity and β activity versus time.

8. In the slow-neutron activation of a sample of separated Mo^{100} isotope some 14.6-min Mo^{101} is produced; this decays to 14.3-min Tc^{101}. A sample of Mo^{101} is chemically freed of technetium and then immediately placed under a counter. Sketch the activity as a function of time, assuming the detection coefficient to be the same for the Tc^{101} as for the Mo^{101} radiation.

9. Carry out the solution of the differential equation 5-9. Compare your result with the Bateman solution for this case with $N_2{}^0$ and $N_3{}^0$ not equal to 0.

10. A sample of an activity whose half-life is known to be 7.50 min was measured from 10:03 to 10:13. The total number of counts recorded in this 10-min interval was 34,650. What was the activity of the sample (in counts per min) at 10:00? *Answer:* 7012.

11. A bombardment of cerium with 380-Mev protons is carried out to determine the cross sections for the reactions $Ce^{142}(p, pn)Ce^{141}$ and $Ce^{142}(p, 2p)La^{141}$. The target consists of 61.4 mg ceric oxide (CeO_2). The beam current is steady at 5.0×10^{13} protons cm^{-2} min^{-1} for the entire 120-min bombardment. After bombardment the target is dissolved, lanthanum carrier is added, and suitable chemical separations are performed. The separation of the cerium and lanthanum fractions takes place 80 min after the end of bombardment. Subsequent counting and decay measurements show that, at the time of this separation, the disintegration rates are 1.74×10^7 min^{-1} of 3.7-hr La^{141} in the lanthanum fraction, and 2.19×10^5 min^{-1} of 33-day Ce^{141} in the cerium fraction. (Assume 100 per cent chemical yields in the separation.) Calculate the cross sections for the $Ce^{142}(p, pn)$ and $Ce^{142}(p, 2p)$ reactions. Note that La^{141} decays to Ce^{141}, and that the length of bombardment and the time from bombardment to chemical separation are not negligible compared to the half-life for this decay.

Answers: $\sigma_{p,pn} = 83$ mb; $\sigma_{p,2p} = 60$ mb.

REFERENCES

G. Hevesy and F. A. Paneth, *A Manual of Radioactivity,* Oxford University Press, 1938.

E. Rutherford, J. Chadwick, and C. D. Ellis, *Radiations from Radioactive Substances,* Cambridge University Press, 1930.

G. B. Cook and J. F. Duncan, *Modern Radiochemical Practice,* Oxford, Clarendon Press, 1952.

H. Bateman, "Solution of a System of Differential Equations Occurring in the Theory of Radio-active Transformations," *Proc. Cambridge Phil. Soc.* **15,** 423 (1910).

W. Rubinson, "The Equations of Radioactive Transformation in a Neutron Flux," *J. Chem. Phys.* **17,** 542 (1949).

F. A. Paneth, "Radioactive Standards and Units," *Nature* **166,** 931 (1950).

S. Rowlands, "Methods of Measuring Very Long and Very Short Half-lives," *Nucleonics* **3,** No. 3, 2 (September 1948).

Papers 64 to 68 (on short-lived krypton and xenon fission products) in *Radiochemical Studies: The Fission Products,* Div. IV, Vol. 9, Book 2 of National Nuclear Energy Series, New York, McGraw-Hill Book Co., 1951.

R. E. Bell, R. L. Graham, and H. E. Petch, "Design and Use of a Coincidence Circuit of Short Resolving Time," *Can. J. Phys.* **30,** 35 (1952).

CHAPTER 6

NUCLEAR STATES AND RADIOACTIVE PROCESSES

A. STATIONARY STATES OF NUCLEI

In concluding chapter 2 we presented the empirical evidence for some sort of shell structure in the arrangements of nucleons within nuclei. The shell concept has long been the basis for any discussion of atomic structure, and it may appear surprising that the nuclear shell model came so slowly to its present-day successes. Therefore we discuss, in a very qualitative way, some of the aspects that have in the past discouraged and that still complicate nuclear shell theory.

Much of the success of atomic shell theory is attributed to the very open structure of the atom, in which the several particles move almost independently and pretty well keep out of each other's way. Even an additional electron, shot at high speed through the atom from outside, usually encounters no resistance and creates no disturbance. This permits a very important simplification in that the rather intractable mathematical equations for the motions of many bodies may be reduced to an equation for the motion of two bodies only, one of these bodies being any particular electron and the other being the remainder of the atom. Such approximate methods are likely to be much less useful in dealing with the nuclear many-body problem. In contrast to the open atmosphere in the outer parts of the atom, the nucleus is a very crowded place. The nucleons are pressed very closely together—the nuclear density attests to this—and a nucleon projectile shot into the nucleus at several million electron volts energy has almost no chance of avoiding a major collision. How then can there be any reality in a model that expects the constituent nucleons to move unhindered in their appointed orbits?

The paradox becomes somewhat less puzzling if we think of the nucleons as occupying not only space but also particular quantum states in the nucleus. In the ground state of the nucleus the nucleons will be in the lowest possible energy states, and on account of the exclusion principle will fill the lowest-lying levels completely up to the levels containing the proton and the neutron of smallest binding energy. Under these circumstances any tendency toward nucleon-nucleon collisions is frustrated except when a projectile brings in from outside enough energy to knock nucleons up into higher-lying, unoccupied states.

Interactions between Nucleons. The forces acting between nucleons must be of very short effective range as is shown by the evidence from neutron and proton scattering experiments. The deflections produced in a beam of fast neutrons by passage through hydrogen are interpreted in terms of the presence of a very strong attraction between the particles when their separation is less than about 2×10^{-13} cm and an absence of any perceptible mutual force at appreciably larger separations. The magnitude of the attractive force is so great that the energy of binding amounts to many millions of electron volts in the bound region. That the deuteron, which consists of superposed neutron and proton waves, has a relatively small binding energy (2.23 Mev) comes about because the region of strong attraction is smaller than the wavelength so that the full binding is not achieved. In large nuclei it seems almost certain that individual nucleons are attracted strongly only by their nearest neighbors.

In other scattering experiments, apart from the addition of the Coulomb interaction in proton-proton scattering and the absence of any direct neutron-neutron experiments, the evidence is that the nuclear force is about the same between two nucleons of any kind, strongly attractive and of very short range. Exceptions are suggested at the very high energies recently available; these energies permit penetration of the centrifugal barrier for other than s interactions and reveal that the p interaction is a weak repulsion.

Much more information on nucleon-nucleon forces is wanted before any attempt to formulate a nuclear shell theory can appear straightforward. And whereas the information available so far reveals too little about what holds nucleons together in the nucleus, it leaves even more obscure the question of what holds them apart. No two-nucleon experiments performed up to 1954 have given any indication of strong repulsive forces, analogous to those with which we are familiar in the interactions of two atoms or of two automobiles. The meson-exchange theory of nuclear forces, mentioned on page 27, makes provision for repulsive as well as attractive forces, in order to account for the proportionality of volume and of binding energy to the number of nucleons. It may be that the repulsion is characteristic of assemblies of more than two nucleons, and an interesting possibility is that nucleons may be found to exhibit valence properties.

Closed Shells in Nuclear Structure. With the hope that the preceding discussion will help us not to expect too much quantitative precision, we are ready to consider the proposed configurations of the closed shells in nuclear structure. The evidence for the existence of closed shells at $Z = 2, 8, 20, 28, 50$, and 82 and at $N = 2, 8, 20, 28, 50, 82$, and 126 was summarized in chapter 2, section E. Of current interest are the designations of the quantum states which when filled give this sequence of magic numbers.

The supposition that the first nuclear shell is $1s$, like the first (K) atomic shell, is universal. The order of levels of successively higher energy (lower binding energy) has been computed for a variety of nuclear models. For example, the order for a nucleus inside which the nucleons are held by a large and uniform potential, the so-called deep rectangular well, is not far from $1s$, $2p$, $3d$, $2s$, $4f$, $3p$, $5g$, $4d$, $3s$, $6h$, $5f$, $4p$, $7i$ . . . . This order indicates immediately a system of closed shells which fits satisfactorily the sequence of magic numbers up to 20. The most popular scheme for extending the fit to the higher numbers involves splitting the levels with larger l values as proposed by M. G. Mayer and by O. Haxel, J. H. D. Jensen, and H. E. Suess. The splitting is attributed to a coupling between the particle's spin and its orbital angular momentum such that the state with resultant angular momentum $l + \frac{1}{2}$ lies much lower in energy than that with $l - \frac{1}{2}$. In more descriptive language, a nucleon moving in an orbit of high angular momentum has a strong preference for the orientation of its intrinsic spin in the direction that will make the two angular momenta add rather than subtract. For the f, g, h, and i states the splitting is so great that usually it marks the end of a closed shell. This scheme is shown in table 6-1. The notation for the levels is taken from that for atomic structure; for example, the $3d_{5/2}$ state has $n = 3$, $l = 2$, and resultant angular momentum $j = 2 + \frac{1}{2} = \frac{5}{2}$. The number of neutrons or of protons in each level is limited by the exclusion principle to a maximum of $2j + 1$. The last column in the table gives the sum of the number of neutrons or of protons in each filled level plus those in all (filled) lower-lying levels; these are the magic numbers. Those levels between each successive pair of magic numbers constitute a shell.

There are several important features of the energy level table. First, the level order given is to be applied independently to neutrons and to protons. Thus the nucleus ${}_2\mathrm{He}^4$ contains 2 protons and 2 neutrons, all in the $1s_{1/2}$ level; ${}_4\mathrm{Be}^9$ contains 4 protons, 2 in $1s_{1/2}$ and 2 in $2p_{3/2}$

TABLE 6-1

NUCLEAR ENERGY LEVELS

Level Designation	Neutron or Proton Capacity	Cumulative Number of Neutrons or Protons
$1s_{1/2}$	2	
		2
$2p_{3/2}$	4	
$2p_{1/2}$	2	
		8
$3d_{5/2}$	6	
$3d_{3/2}$	4	
$2s_{1/2}$	2	
		20
$4f_{7/2}$	8	
		28
$4f_{5/2}$	6	
$3p_{3/2}$	4	
$3p_{1/2}$	2	
$5g_{9/2}$	10	
		50
$5g_{7/2}$	8	
$4d_{5/2}$	6	
$4d_{3/2}$	4	
$3s_{1/2}$	2	
$6h_{11/2}$	12	
		82
$6h_{9/2}$	10	
$5f_{7/2}$	8	
$5f_{5/2}$	6	
$4p_{3/2}$	4	
$4p_{1/2}$	2	
$7i_{13/2}$	14	126

(indicated more briefly by $1s_{1/2}{}^2 2p_{3/2}{}^2$), and 5 neutrons, $1s_{1/2}{}^2 2p_{3/2}{}^3$. On an absolute energy scale the proton levels are increasingly higher than neutron levels as Z increases. This is the familiar Coulomb repulsion effect, and in first approximation it does not change the order of the levels for a particular kind of nucleon. But there is a small tendency for the proton levels in nuclei of large Z to shift in order, those levels with maximum orbital angular momentum ($4f$, $5g$, $6h$, $7i$) appearing at relatively lower energies, apparently because the proton suffers less from Coulombic repulsion when traveling in the outermost region of the nucleus.

Second, the order given within each shell is essentially schematic and may not represent the exact order of filling; indeed this order may differ slightly in different nuclides, depending on the number of nucleons in the outermost shell. (Similar level shifts are quite familiar in the atomic structure of the heavier elements.) The order written in the table, within each shell, is chosen mostly because of its relation to the rectangular-well solution and because it is easy to remember as indicated in the next paragraph.

Except for the effect of splittings due to spin-orbit coupling, which shift the $4f_{7/2}$, $5g_{9/2}$, $6h_{11/2}$, and $7i_{13/2}$ levels into a shell of lower energy, each shell contains only states of the same parity. (Remember that s, d, g, i . . . states have even parity, often denoted by a plus sign (+), and that p, f, h, j . . . states have odd (−) parity.) This fact gives an easy way to remember the order of the states. Without the spin designation, the order is determined by increasing n, keeping l a maximum, and following each new n value by the succession of states with n decreasing by 1 and l decreasing by 2 units. Thus the lowest-energy state is $1s$; since there are no states of lower n the next state must have $n = 2$; and for maximum l this is $2p$; there is no state of lower n with l decreased by 2, and the next state must be $3d$; this state is followed by $n = 3 - 1$, $l = 2 - 2$, or $2s$; etc. All the states obtained in this way (except s states) are then split into $j = l + \frac{1}{2}$, followed by $j = l - \frac{1}{2}$. The shell boundaries are just before each increase in j until the $4f_{7/2}$ state is reached, and just after each increase in j beyond $4f_{7/2}$.

Single-Particle Model. If a nucleus contains 2, 8, 20, 28, 50, 82, or 126 neutrons the level scheme just described permits a good prediction of the quantum states occupied by the neutrons. Thus $_{38}Sr^{88}$ has its 50 neutrons filling the five shells: $(1s^2)$, $(2p^6)$, $(3d^{10}2s^2)$, $(4f_{7/2}{}^8)$, $(4f_{5/2}{}^6 3p^6 5g_{9/2}{}^{10})$. Similarly, the proton structure is obvious for nuclides with magic atomic numbers: He, O, Ca, Ni, Sn, and Pb. It is a well-known theorem in atomic structure that filled shells are spherically symmetric and have no spin or orbital angular momentum and no magnetic moment. Although the corresponding theorem may be more difficult to prove for the somewhat arbitrary nuclear shells, an even more sweeping postulate is made in the extreme single-particle nuclear model, that not only filled nucleon shells but any even number of neutrons or protons have no net angular momentum and no magnetic moment. Thus we expect $I = 0$ (and $\mu = 0$ and even parity) not only for $_2He^4$ and $_8O^{16}$ but also for $_{38}Sr^{88}$, $_{76}Os^{192}$, $_{92}U^{238}$, and all the other even-even nuclei.

In any nucleus of odd A, all but one of the nucleons are considered to have their angular momenta paired off, forming an even-even "core"; the single odd nucleon is thought to move essentially independently in (or outside) this core, and the net angular momentum of the entire nucleus is determined by the quantum state of this nucleon. For example, consider the even-odd nucleus $_6C^{13}$. The 6 protons and 6 of the 7 neutrons are paired up (in the configuration $1s^2 2p_{3/2}{}^4$); the odd neutron is in the $2p_{1/2}$ level, and the entire nucleus in its ground state is characterized by the $p_{1/2}$ designation. The nuclear spin of C^{13} has been measured, and the value $I = 1/2$ corresponds to the resultant angular momentum indicated as the subscript in $p_{1/2}$. As a second example consider $_{23}V^{51}$. The odd nucleon in this case is the twenty-third proton; it belongs in the $4f_{7/2}$ level; the ground state of the nucleus is expected to be $f_{7/2}$. The measured spin of this nucleus is $7/2$. Without going into details we may say that the measured magnetic moments for C^{13} and V^{51} lend some support to the spin evidence for the correct assignment of these ground states. For a given spin the magnitude of the magnetic moment of a nucleus depends on whether the spin and orbital angular momenta of the odd nucleon are parallel or antiparallel. An $s_{1/2}$ and a $p_{1/2}$ nucleus will, for example, have quite different magnetic moments, and the differences can be at least qualitatively predicted.

For nuclei in general the situation is not nearly so simple as is indicated in the examples just cited. The order of the levels within each shell very often may be different from that in table 6-1, especially for two or three adjacent levels which differ in n or l. In such a case we conclude from the single-particle model only that several particular states of the nucleus are close together in energy without knowing which is the lowest, or ground, state. (Sometimes this information alone is very useful.) As an example, the odd nucleon in $_{56}Ba^{137}$ is the eighty-first neutron, and table 6-1 may be said to indicate that the ground state is probably $h_{11/2}$, $s_{1/2}$, or $d_{3/2}$, depending on the order of filling of these three levels. For Ba^{135} the ground state is probably $h_{11/2}$ or $d_{3/2}$. For each of these nuclei the measured spin is $I = 3/2$.

What can be said about the states of odd-odd nuclides? Most of these are radioactive (the stable ones known are $_1H^2$, $_3Li^6$, $_5B^{10}$, $_7N^{14}$, $_{23}V^{50}$, and $_{73}Ta^{180}$), and there are fewer directly measured data on spins and magnetic moments. The single-particle-model assumption of pairing leaves in every case one odd proton and one odd neutron, each producing an effect on the nuclear moments. No universal rule can be given to predict the resultant ground state; however, the following rules proposed by L. W. Nordheim are very helpful. If for the two odd nucleons $j_1 + j_2 + l_1 + l_2 =$ *an even number*, the resultant spin is $I = |j_1 - j_2|$. To this rule there is one known exception, K^{40}. If $j_1 + j_2 + l_1 + l_2 =$ *an odd number*, I is probably large, approaching $j_1 + j_2$. For example, in $_{23}V^{50}$, both the twenty-seventh neutron and the twenty-third proton are expected to be in $4f_{7/2}$ levels (for the proton this is confirmed by the measured spin $7/2$ of $_{23}V^{51}$). Since $j_1 + j_2 + l_1 + l_2 = 13$, Nordheim's rule predicts a high resultant spin for V^{50}, the maximum possible being $7/2 + 7/2 = 7$. The measured spin of V^{50} is 6. Even (+) parity is predicted unambiguously for this nucleus in its ground state, since each of the two odd nucleons is in an f state and therefore has odd parity.

For very many nuclides the single-particle model is certainly an oversimplification. As an illustration of one kind of evidence for this statement, $_{11}Na^{23}$ would be expected to have a $d_{5/2}$ ground state, and the only other reasonable single-particle-model possibility is $s_{1/2}$. The measured spin is $3/2$. This is not to be attributed to an odd proton in the $3d_{3/2}$ level because $3d_{3/2}$ certainly should lie higher than $3d_{5/2}$; moreover, the magnetic moment is definitely in disagreement with the $d_{3/2}$ interpretation. Another such case is $_{25}Mn^{55}$, where the odd nucleon clearly should be $4f_{7/2}$ and yet the measured spin is $5/2$. A better model for these nuclei is one in which all the protons outside the closed shells are unpaired and contribute to moments and parity much as in the case of two nucleons in odd-odd nuclei. This possibility exists whenever a level contains an odd number of nucleons which is more than one and less than the level capacity minus one. The extreme single-particle predictions should thus be used with some caution, and the likelihood of low-lying states due to such multiple-particle configurations should be kept in mind.

Excited States. The concept of closed shells and the single-particle model have applications in the study of excited states of nuclei, particularly for low excitation energies. Generally, where the model predicts several possible low-lying configurations, all except the one which happens to be energetically favored are eligible for existence as excited states. Partly because in the next section we consider certain aspects of the excited states, especially for odd-nucleon nuclides, and partly because our knowledge of the excited states is less than of the ground state, we shall here give only a brief summary, and that directed toward the even-even nuclei.

G. Scharff-Goldhaber has assembled some informative statistics on the lower excited states of even-even nuclides. (It may be noted that possibly odd-nucleon nuclides have a similar pattern of excited states plus additional, interlocking states involving excitation of the odd particle only.) Of her conclusions the most striking is that almost all the first excited states (the first excited state is the one nearest the ground state in energy) have spin $I = 2$ and even parity, denoted 2+. Most second excited states are 2+ or 4+, although there are many exceptions. There is reason to believe that for the nth excited state $I \leq 2n$.

The energies of the first excited states (of even-even nuclides) generally vary smoothly with mass number, except for maxima at shell closures, especially neutron shell closures, and strong maxima at the doubly magic nuclides $_2He^4$, $_8O^{16}$, $_{20}Ca^{40}$, and $_{82}Pb^{208}$. Usually the addition of two neutrons to a nucleus hardly affects the first excitation energy. Apart from the maxima, the energies usually fall between 0.5 and 2.0 Mev, except that between $N = 82$ and $N = 126$ the energies do not exceed about 0.4 Mev, and for $N > 136$ they fall in the range of 40 to 80 kev.

Collective Models. We have already illustrated or implied several deficiencies of the single-particle model in regard to the spins of nuclear ground states, and although the nuclear magnetic moment values give some support to this model the situation is not as happy as it might be. When nuclear electric quadrupole moments are considered, the failure of the single-particle model is hardest to repair. Even in nuclides with just one nucleon more than a closed shell or just one nucleon less than a closed shell (one nucleon "hole"), where the single-particle model should be at its best, the measured quadrupole moments are several times larger than can reasonably be attributed to the odd nucleon.

Moreover, the single-particle model does not take full advantage of the powerful successes of the liquid-drop model, as embodied in the binding-energy equation 2-5 and discussed in some detail in section E of chapter 2, and as employed in the Bohr theory of nuclear reactions (chapter 3, section D). The introduction into the single-particle theory of states containing several nucleons outside a core of closed shells, and of interactions between odd nucleons and the core, is a step in the direction of a wider theory. The trend is towards a hybrid single-particle–liquid-drop model that contains the best features of both; the name "collective model" has been used in this connection.

A model proposed by Aage Bohr retains most of the single-particle features, but provides a relatively ponderous rotational surface oscillation in a liquid-drop core with which the odd nucleon's angular momentum may be coupled. The predictions of the single-particle model for ground-state spins remain unchanged. However, the magnetic-dipole-moment data are fitted better by the collective model than by the single-particle model. Also the rotational motion in the core, involving many nucleons in an arrangement of appreciable spherical asymmetry, can provide the observed magnitude of electric quadrupole moments. On this model the low excited states may be classified approximately according to whether they arise by excitation of the individual nucleons or by excitation of higher surface oscillation modes. In regions far from shell closures the latter are expected to be low-lying. They may constitute the unusually low first excited states in the lanthanides and actinides. The order of such excited states would be $I = 2+, 4+, 6+$, etc. (The same order has been derived by extension of the single-particle theory.) The energies of these rotational states above the ground state should be proportional to $I(I + 1)$. The excitation energies of the first, second, and third excited states of even spin in a number of even-even actinide nuclides are found to approach closely to the ratio 1:3.33:7 as predicted for $I = 2$, 4, and 6.

B. GAMMA TRANSITIONS AND ISOMERISM

Gamma Transitions. A nucleus in an excited state may give up its excitation energy and return to the ground state in a variety of ways. The most obvious, and the most common, transition is by the emission of electromagnetic radiation. Such radiation is called γ radiation; the γ rays have a frequency determined by their energy, $E = h\nu$. Frequently the transition does not proceed directly from an upper state to the ground state, but may go in several steps involving intermediate excited states. Any event which leaves nuclei in an excited state, and this is true of many α- and β-decay processes, is usually accompanied—more accurately, followed—by γ radiation. Gamma rays with energies from about 10 kev up to about 7 Mev have been observed in radioactive processes.

Gamma-ray emission may be accompanied, or even replaced, by another process, the emission of internal-conversion electrons. Internal conversion has been pictured as a photoelectric effect produced by a γ ray in the electron shell surrounding the γ-emitting nucleus. An extranuclear electron is emitted with a kinetic energy equal to the difference between the γ energy and the binding energy of the electron in the atom. Actually the emission of internal-conversion electrons is better regarded as an additional, alternative process for the de-excitation of a nucleus. It is a common process, of special significance in nuclear isomerism.

A third process for the de-excitation of a nucleus is possible if the available energy exceeds 1.02 Mev. This energy is equivalent to the mass of two electrons. It is possible for the excited nucleus to create simultaneously one new electron and one positron and to emit these with kinetic energies which total the excitation energy minus 1.02 Mev. This is a very uncommon mode of de-excitation; it is the mode of decay of the first excited state of O^{16}, $E = 6.05$ Mev, $t_{1/2} = 7 \times 10^{-11}$ sec.

All the processes just described we call γ transitions, although only in the first is a γ ray emitted by the nucleus. All are characterized by a change in energy without change in Z and A.

In a number of instances a nuclide in an excited state decays predominantly by α- or β-decay. A conceivable possibility, though it certainly is not expected, is that such a β decay might be followed by another β process leading back to the original nucleus in its ground state. (We would not be inclined to describe this sequence as a γ transition.)

Selection Rules for Gamma Transitions. The γ transitions, like the other spontaneous nuclear changes, proceed in accordance with the exponential decay law, although in most cases the γ decays occur so quickly that the half-lives have not been measured. Indirect evidence from competition between γ and α decay and from the energy widths of γ-emitting levels indicates that many of the lifetimes are as short as 10^{-13} sec. By modern electronic techniques the exponential decay has been measured for γ transitions with half-lives as short as 10^{-9} or 10^{-10} sec. At the other extreme, long-lived excited states are known; Sn^{119m} has a half-life of 250 days, and Cd^{113m} is even longer-lived.

The theoretical expectations and the experimental evidence are in agreement that the γ-transition lifetimes should depend upon the energy of the transition (E), on the nuclear spin change ($|I_i - I_f| = \Delta I$), on the degree of internal conversion, and on the mass number of the nucleus (A). The selection rules for γ transitions, on which the appearance of long lifetimes for high spin changes ultimately depends, are summarized in an abbreviated [1] form in table 6-2.

The greater the value of ΔI, at least above $\Delta I = 1$ or 2, the greater is the degree of forbiddenness of the transition, and thus the greater is the lifetime, other factors being equal. The role of the parity change is primarily to determine the classification of the transition as electric ($E1$, $E2$, $E3$ . . .) or magnetic ($M1$, $M2$, $M3$ . . .) multipole radia-

[1] We omitted most of the following information. If the number used with E or M to denote the type is represented by l, the selection rules require that $I_i + I_f \geq l \geq \Delta I$. The exceptions noted in the table follow from this statement of the rules. Also apparent is that the l value tabulated for a given ΔI is in most cases the minimum of several allowed l values. This is because for $\Delta I > 1$ the smallest l value is usually the only one that need be considered, since transition probabilities fall off very rapidly with increasing l. Theoretical predictions that $E(l + 1)$ transitions should compete with Ml transitions are not borne out by experimental facts for $\Delta I > 1$.

TABLE 6-2

SELECTION RULES FOR GAMMA TRANSITIONS

ΔI	Parity Change?	Type
0	yes	$E1$ (except for $I_i = I_f = 0$) *
0	no	$M1$ (except for $I_i = I_f = 0$) *
		or $E2$ (except for $I_i = I_f = 0$)
1	yes	$E1$
1	no	$M1$
		or $E2$ (except for I_i or $I_f = 0$)
2	yes	$M2$
2	no	$E2$
3	yes	$E3$
3	no	$M3$
4	yes	$M4$
4	no	$E4$
5	yes	$E5$
5	no	$M5$
6	yes	$M6$
6	no	$E6$
7	yes	$E7$
7	no	$M7$
etc.		

* Selection rules for the transition $\Delta I = 0$,no permit de-excitation by internal conversion or by positron-electron pair creation. For $\Delta I = 0$,yes de-excitation is permitted only by the simultaneous emission of two photons (or two conversion electrons).

tion.[2] If for the moment we simplify the considerations by discussing only the half-life the nuclide would have due to γ emission if internal conversion and other modes of decay were absent, calling this the partial half-life [3] t_γ, we may represent the general trends of experimental and theoretical information by the equation

[2] We need not concern ourselves here with the significance of the various multipole radiations beyond the relations with spins and parities expressed in the selection rules. It should be emphasized that once a γ ray is well removed from the region and frame of reference of the nucleus where it originated, it bears no recognizable mark of the multipole character of the transition which gave rise to its emission.

[3] We shall make further use of the partial-half-life terminology. In general we define a partial half-life as ln 2 divided by the partial decay constant for any particular decay process. Remember that the rate of disappearance of any nuclide is determined by *the* half-life, which is ln 2 divided by the sum of all its partial decay constants.

$$t_\gamma = \frac{(2I_i + 1)10^{(6\Delta I - 20)}}{E^{(2\Delta I+1)}A^{\frac{2}{3}(\Delta I-1)}}, \tag{6-1}$$

where t_γ is in seconds, E is in Mev, I_i is the spin in the initial state, and ΔI is the absolute magnitude of the difference between the spins of initial and final states. This equation gives values of t_γ with an accuracy that is usually within a factor of 100. It is generally adequate to establish the spin change. The greatest deviations, amounting to perhaps a factor of 1000, occur for $\Delta I < 2$; in this region irregularities including competition between $E2$ and $M1$ are recognized and may eventually be interpreted in terms of a collective nuclear model. For the very common $M4$ transitions equation 6-1 reduces to an empirical law given by M. Goldhaber and A. W. Sunyar.

Nuclear Isomerism. We have seen that γ transitions, especially where ΔI is large and E is small, can have appreciable lifetimes. Before these principles were suggested the phenomenon of nuclear isomerism had been discovered, and several pairs of nuclear isomers, including UZ-UX_2 and Br^{80}-Br^{80m}, had been identified. The γ transitions between isomeric pairs are now known as isomeric transitions. One member of each pair of isomers must be an excited state of the particular nucleus, and for its lifetime to be measurably long the γ transitions producing de-excitation must be sufficiently restricted by the selection rules. An important aspect of nuclear shell structure has been the correlation of nuclear spins and isomer lifetimes.

E. Feenberg in 1949 called attention to the fact that there were abundant groupings of isomers with odd Z or odd N just below the magic number values 50, 82, and 126. (Above $Z = 50$ most isomers are of the odd-N type.) This phenomenon is connected with the appearance, just before shell closure at these numbers, of a new level of very high spin ($5g_{9/2}$ before 50, $6h_{11/2}$ before 82, $7i_{13/2}$ before 126). As an illustration consider $_{48}Cd^{113}$; its odd nucleon—the sixty-fifth neutron—is assigned to the $3s_{1/2}$ state to accord with the measured ground-state spin $I = 1/2$. Other possible unfilled states within the same shell, all probably low-lying, are $4d_{3/2}$ and $6h_{11/2}$. If $6h_{11/2}$ happens to be the first excited level, which is the case for this nuclide, then the γ transition to ground is $h_{11/2} \rightarrow s_{1/2}$, $\Delta I = 5$,yes (the parity changes), an $E5$ transition which should be very long-lived. The isomer actually observed, Cd^{113m}, has $t_{1/2} = 5.1$ years; it decays predominantly by β decay so that t_γ is probably greater than 50 years.

For Cd^{111}, to choose a related example, the situation is similar. For the ground state $I = 1/2$ and the sixty-third neutron is $3s_{1/2}$. The $6h_{11/2}$ state is 0.396 Mev above the ground state, and its half-life (Cd^{111m_2}) is 49 min. The γ transition is not directly to the ground state, but to a $4d_{5/2}$ state which happens to lie between at 0.246 Mev above ground; therefore $\Delta I = 3$,yes, and the classification is $E3$. The $4d_{5/2}$ state in turn decays to the ground state; for this transition $\Delta I = 2$,no, and the half-life of this $E2$ transition is measured as 8×10^{-8} sec.

The large number of even-odd isomers from $_{48}Cd^{111}$ to $_{56}Ba^{137}$, with 63 to 81 neutrons, have similar explanations. In all but $_{50}Sn^{125}$ the long-lived state is $6h_{11/2}$, and the corresponding isomeric transition in most is $h_{11/2} \rightarrow d_{3/2}$, $\Delta I = 4$,yes, classification $M4$, often followed by the $M1$ transition $d_{3/2} \rightarrow s_{1/2}$. When the next neutron shell (82 to 126) is partly filled in the even-odd nuclei such as $_{78}Pt^{195}$, Pt^{197}, $_{80}Hg^{197}$, Hg^{199}, and $_{82}Pb^{207}$, the long-lived isomeric level is $7i_{13/2}$; the transition is generally $i_{13/2} \rightarrow f_{5/2}$, which is again $M4$. Another group of $M4$ isomeric transitions is between $g_{9/2}$ and $p_{1/2}$ states in the region of odd nucleon numbers just below 50. Several-particle states enter in $_{45}Rh^{105}$, for which the ground state appears to contain a combination of several $5g_{9/2}$ protons giving $I = 7/2+$; the isomeric transition is $p_{1/2} \rightarrow 7/2+$, giving $\Delta I = 3$,yes, and the type $E3$. In $_{47}Ag^{107}$ and Ag^{109} (and in many other nuclides in this region) the several-proton state $7/2+$ is the upper isomeric state with $E3$ transitions to $p_{1/2}$ ground states.

There are a sizable number of odd-odd isomers, but because of the difficulties in assignment of configurations to the two-nucleon states these are not easy to classify in any organized way. There are some very interesting even-even isomers. In one, $_{32}Ge^{72m}$, $t_{1/2} = 3 \times 10^{-7}$ sec, $E = 0.84$ Mev, the ground and the first excited state both have $I = 0+$; the transition is thus of the $0 \rightarrow 0$ type. All even-even isomers have very short half-lives except $_{72}Hf^{180m}$ (5.5 hr, type unknown) and $_{82}Pb^{204m_2}$ (68 min, probably $E5$). Those from $_{66}Dy^{160}$ to $_{76}Os^{186}$ constitute a series, all $2+ \rightarrow 0+$, $E2$, with smoothly decreasing half-lives from 2×10^{-9} to 0.8×10^{-9} sec; these excited states may represent rotational levels of the core as mentioned on page 152.

A few remarks may be in order on the usual definition of nuclear isomers, namely, two or more energy levels of a nucleus with half-lives not too short to be measured. Directly measurable half-lives now extend into the 10^{-10}-sec region. The much shorter, indirectly measured half-lives have been excluded, but border-line measuring techniques, based on decay in flight (for O^{16m}) and on Doppler broadening (for Li^{7m}, $t_{1/2} = 5 \times 10^{-14}$ sec), are tending to make this definition either arbitrary or trivial. Some workers are now using the terms "long-lived isomers" ($t_{1/2} > \backsim 1$ sec) and "short-lived isomers" ($t_{1/2} \ll \backsim 1$ sec). (Lifetimes in the millisecond range appear to be extremely rare for γ transitions.) Chemists with some chemical experiment in mind are likely to think mostly of the "long-lived" isomers.

Internal Conversion. The emission of an extranuclear electron from an atom as a means of de-excitation for its nucleus is known as internal conversion. This alternative to γ-ray emission results in a half-life for the nuclide shorter than t_γ. The ratio of the rate of the internal conversion process to the rate of γ-ray emission is known as

TABLE 6-3

K-Shell Conversion Coefficients

[From Rose, Goertzel, Spinrad, Harr, and Strong, *Phys. Rev.* **83,** 79 (1951).]

Z	Transition Type	$E\gamma =$ 0.15 Mev	0.25 Mev	0.50 Mev	0.90 Mev
	$E1$	5.62×10^{-3}	1.18×10^{-3}	1.72×10^{-4}	4.52×10^{-5}
	$M1$	4.31×10^{-3}	1.25×10^{-3}	2.58×10^{-4}	7.69×10^{-5}
	$E2$	0.0489	6.85×10^{-3}	5.94×10^{-4}	1.08×10^{-4}
	$M2$	0.0316	6.14×10^{-3}	8.03×10^{-4}	1.74×10^{-4}
20	$E3$	0.358	0.0339	1.82×10^{-3}	2.37×10^{-4}
	$M3$	0.227	0.0294	2.39×10^{-3}	3.76×10^{-4}
	$E4$	2.49	0.160	5.34×10^{-3}	5.02×10^{-4}
	$M4$	1.63	0.141	7.01×10^{-3}	7.94×10^{-4}
	$E5$	17.0	0.740	0.0154	1.05×10^{-3}
	$M5$	11.8	0.674	0.0205	1.66×10^{-3}
	$E1$	0.0564	0.0140	2.48×10^{-3}	7.14×10^{-4}
	$M1$	0.232	0.0583	9.97×10^{-3}	2.47×10^{-3}
	$E2$	0.308	0.0583	7.32×10^{-3}	1.73×10^{-3}
	$M2$	1.52	0.267	0.0309	6.01×10^{-3}
54	$E3$	1.41	0.212	0.0194	3.68×10^{-3}
	$M3$	8.38	1.09	0.0846	0.0127
	$E4$	6.25	0.749	0.0500	7.51×10^{-3}
	$M4$	45.2	4.36	0.227	0.0257
	$E5$	27.8	2.64	0.128	0.0150
	$M5$	243	17.5	0.606	0.0512
	$E1$	0.114	0.0322	6.71×10^{-3}	2.12×10^{-3}
	$M1$	2.08	0.503	0.0799	0.0181
	$E2$	0.320	0.0924	0.0181	5.50×10^{-3}
	$M2$	9.88	1.76	0.201	0.0381
	$E3$	0.810	0.259	0.0458	0.0121
78	$M3$	32.5	5.27	0.463	0.0721
	$E4$	2.10	0.742	0.112	0.0246
	$M4$	98.6	15.6	1.06	0.133
	$E5$	5.73	2.19	0.272	0.0482
	$M5$	291	46.0	2.42	0.241

the internal conversion coefficient α; it may be found to have any value between 0 and ∞. The half-life is then given by $t_{1/2} = t_\gamma/(1 + \alpha)$.

Computations of precise coefficients for internal conversion in the K shell only (α_K) have been published, and some of the numerical results are shown in table 6-3. In general the coefficients increase with decreasing energy, increasing ΔI, and increasing Z.

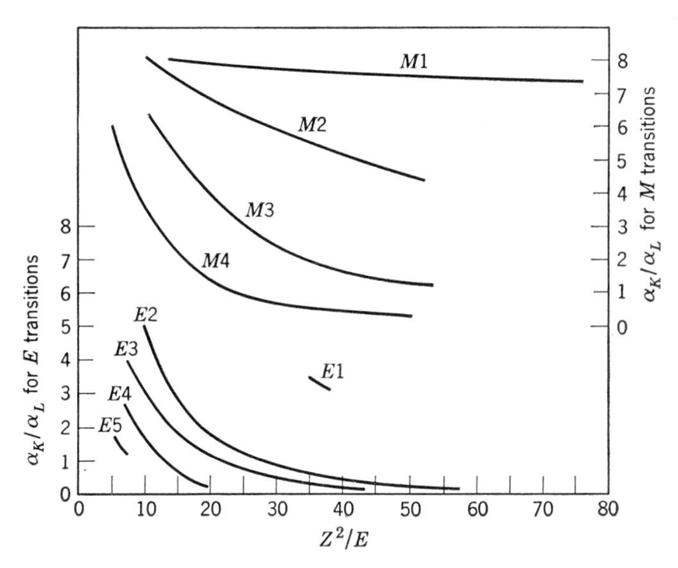

FIGURE 6-1. Approximate curves for conversion coefficient ratios α_K/α_L for various transition types, on the basis of empirical information. The scale at the left applies to the electric multipole transitions, that at the right to the magnetic multipole transitions. [From M. Goldhaber and A. W. Sunyar, *Phys. Rev.* **83**, 906 (1951).]

Internal conversion electrons, examined in an electron spectrograph, show a line spectrum with lines corresponding to the γ-transition energy minus the binding energies of the K, L, M . . . shells in which conversion occurs. The differences in energy between successive lines serve to identify Z and to classify groups of lines resulting from different γ transitions. The ratios of the intensities of the lines measure the ratios of the conversion coefficients α_K, α_L, α_M, etc. Experimentally these ratios can be determined more accurately than any individual coefficient. Precisely computed values of the ratios, when available, will be of great assistance in the classification of isomeric transitions; empirical α_K/α_L ratios for common transition types are plotted in figure 6-1 as a function of Z^2/E (where E is the transition energy in kiloelectron volts).

An internal conversion process leaves the atom with a vacancy in one of its shells. Especially for the emission of a K electron from an

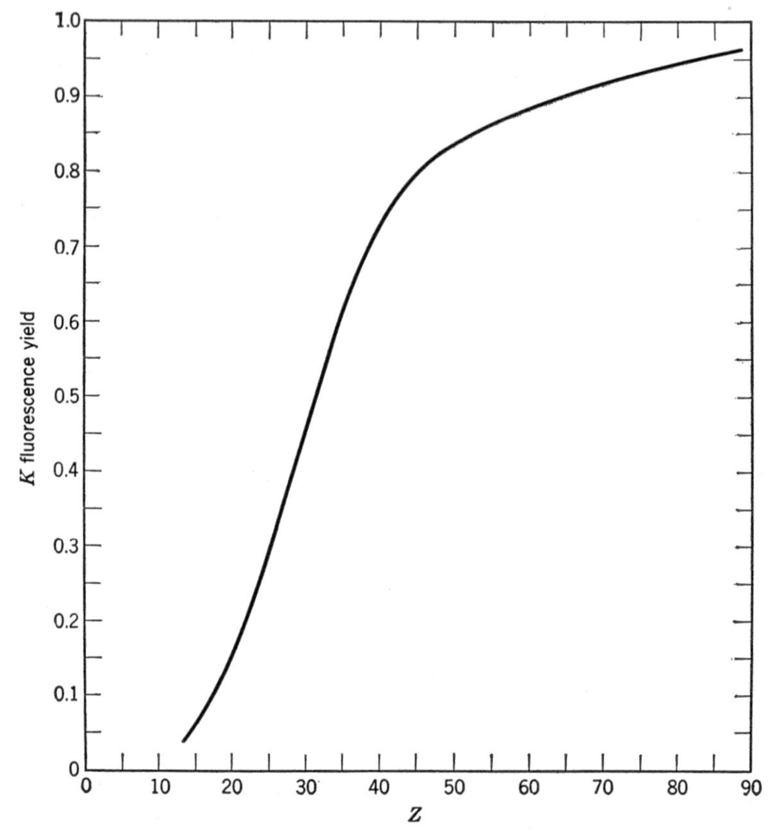

FIGURE 6-2. K-shell fluorescence yields as a function of atomic number. [From C. D. Broyles, D. A. Thomas, and S. K. Haynes, *Phys. Rev.* **89,** 715 (1953).]

atom of high Z the resulting atomic excitation is appreciable. The vacancy is filled most frequently by an electron from the next higher shell. If an L electron falls into the K shell, the difference between the K- and L-binding energies may be emitted as a characteristic X ray or may be used in an internal photoelectric process analogous to internal conversion. In the latter case an additional extranuclear electron from the L, or M, etc., shell is emitted with a kinetic energy equal to the characteristic X-ray energy minus its own binding energy.

Such electrons are called Auger electrons. The whole process of readjustment in a heavy atom may involve many X-ray emissions and Auger processes in successively higher shells. The fraction of vacancies in a given shell that are filled with accompanying X-ray emission is called the fluorescence yield, and the fraction that are filled by Auger processes is the Auger yield. The K-shell fluorescence yields are plotted as a function of Z in figure 6-2. The L-shell fluorescence yield varies with Z in a similar manner, but is several times smaller than the K coefficient for a given Z or about the same as the K coefficient for a given electron binding energy.

Angular Correlations. A very powerful tool for the determination of γ-transition types is the measurement of angular correlations between successive γ rays. If the nuclear spins of all the atoms in a sample of a γ-emitting nuclide could be lined up in a given direction (this has been achieved in a few cases by the application of strong external fields at temperatures near 0°K), the angular distribution of γ-ray intensity would depend on the nuclear spin and on the multipole character of the γ rays. Normally the spins are randomly oriented, and therefore γ rays are emitted isotropically. However, if the first γ ray of a cascade is observed in a given direction this in effect selects a preferred direction for the spin orientation of the emitting nucleus, and therefore the direction of emission of the second γ ray may be correlated with that of the first, and coincidence measurements with different angles between the two sample-detector axes will reveal the anisotropy. The angular correlation between successive γ rays depends on the multipole character of the two radiations and on the spin of the intermediate level, and correlation functions have been calculated and tabulated for various situations, so that experimental measurements of angular correlations can be used to identify transition types.

It is interesting to note that an angular correlation may be altered by the interaction of external electric and magnetic fields with the electric and magnetic moments of the emitting nucleus. The dependence of an angular correlation on the magnitude of an applied magnetic field has been used to determine the magnetic moment of the intermediate level of the γ cascade investigated. The fact that an angular correlation may vary with the physical and chemical form of the sample because of the effects of molecular and crystalline electric and magnetic fields sometimes causes difficulties. On the other hand, this fact may be used to advantage for the investigation of molecular and crystal structure.

C. BETA DECAY

Electrons and Positrons. Electrons had been recognized as the ultimate units of negative electricity, and their properties had begun to be investigated, by the time radioactivity was discovered. The existence of positrons or positive electrons was first postulated by P. A. M. Dirac on the basis of his relativistic quantum theory of the electron. Solutions of the relativistic wave equations reveal possible states of electrons with energies always larger than mc^2 (where m is the electron mass), but with either positive or negative signs. As to the physical meaning of the unobserved negative-energy states of electrons Dirac suggested that normally all the negative-energy states are filled. The raising of an electron from a negative- to a positive-energy state (by the addition of an amount of energy necessarily greater than $2mc^2$) should then be observable not only through the appearance of an ordinary electron, but also through the simultaneous appearance of a "hole" in the infinite "sea" of electrons of negative energy. This hole would have the properties of a positively charged particle, otherwise identical with an ordinary electron. The subsequent discovery of positrons, first in cosmic rays and then in radioactive disintegrations, was soon followed by discoveries of the processes of pair production and positron-electron annihilation, which may be regarded as experimental verifications of Dirac's theory.

Pair production is the name for a process which involves the creation of a positron-electron pair by a photon of at least 1.02 Mev ($2mc^2$). It can be shown that in this process both momentum and energy cannot be conserved in empty space; however, the pair production may take place in the field of a nucleus which can then carry off some momentum and energy. The cross section for pair production goes up with increasing Z and with increasing photon energy. Pair production may be thought of as the lifting of an electron from a negative- to a positive-energy state. The reverse process, the falling of an ordinary electron into a hole in the sea of electrons of negative energy, with the simultaneous emission of the corresponding amount of energy in the form of radiation, is observed in the so-called positron-electron annihilation process. This process accounts for the very short lifetime of positrons; whenever a hole in the sea of electrons is created it is quickly filled again by an electron. The energy corresponding to the annihilation of a positron and electron is released either in the form of two γ quanta emitted in nearly opposite directions (to conserve momentum) or, much more rarely, in the form of a single quantum if the electron involved in the annihilation is strongly bound (say, in an inner shell of an atom) so that a nucleus is available to carry off the excess momentum. (The latter process, although theoretically possible, has not been definitely established experimentally.) The two-quantum annihilation occurs principally with very slow positrons, that is, positrons which have almost come to rest by ionization processes. It is then accompanied by the emission of two γ quanta, each of energy equal to mc^2 (0.51 Mev); this radiation is often referred to as annihilation radiation.

Selection rules for the two-quantum annihilation require that the electron and positron have opposite spin orientations. Ordinarily there are so many electrons available that this causes no inconvenience to a positron seeking annihilation. However, when positrons are stopped in some gases (for example, CCl_2F_2) a few of them form neutral "atoms" with individual electrons of parallel spin as discovered by M. Deutsch. Essentially these "atoms," each consisting of one positive and one negative electron circling each other, constitute a hydrogen isotope of mass number zero, usually called positronium. Annihilation occurs by the simultaneous emission of three γ quanta (of variable energies); the half time for the unimolecular process is about 10^{-7} sec. In the presence of small concentrations of the odd-electron gas NO the positronium electron spins become mixed, presumably by electron-exchange reaction, and the annihilation proceeds by the two-quantum mechanism with much shorter ($\backsim 10^{-10}$ sec) lifetime.

The Neutrino. The β particles [4] from a given radioactive species are emitted with a continuous energy distribution extending from zero up to a maximum value. Beta-ray spectra have been studied in some detail by magnetic-deflection methods. Some typical shapes of β spectra are shown in figure 6-3. The average energy is usually about one-third the maximum energy. Maximum energies ranging approximately from 15 kev to 15 Mev occur among known β emitters. Since its discovery by Chadwick in 1914 the continuous spectrum of β rays has presented a very puzzling problem. Studies of the α- and γ-ray spectra have revealed that nuclei exist in definite energy states. Yet in every known β-decay process the transition from one such definite energy state to another takes place with the emission of β particles of variable kinetic energy. It was proved by calorimetric measurements

[4] By β particles we shall mean any electrons, positive or negative, emitted from nuclei. Whenever necessary, negative β particles or negatrons (β^-) and positive β particles or positrons (β^+) will be distinguished. Electrons originating in the extranuclear shells should not be referred to as β particles; they are often represented by the symbol e^-. In the early literature any electrons emitted in radioactive processes were usually called β particles.

that when all the β particles are absorbed in a calorimeter the measured energy per β particle is the average and not the maximum energy of the β spectrum. Thus the law of the conservation of energy might appear to be violated in β decay.

Furthermore, the observations show discrepancies with other conservation laws also. As we have seen in chapter 2, all nuclei of even mass number have integral spins and obey Bose statistics; all nuclei of odd mass number have half-integral spins and obey Fermi statistics. Since the mass number remains unchanged in β decay the spins of initial and final nuclei should belong to the same class, either integral

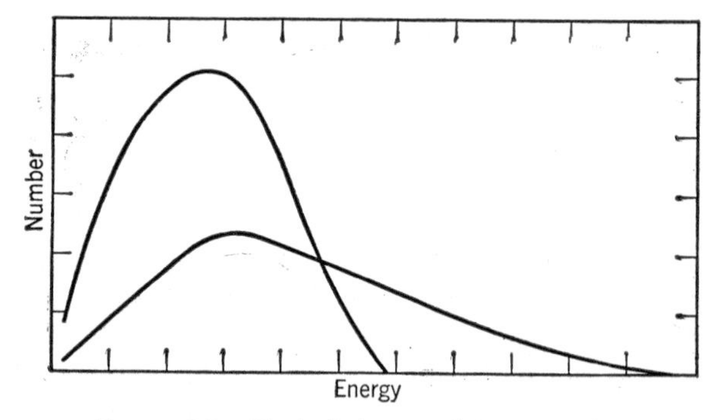

FIGURE 6-3. Typical shapes of β-ray spectra.

or half-integral, and the statistics should remain the same. Yet electrons (and positrons) have one-half unit of spin and obey Fermi statistics. Thus angular momentum and statistics appear not to be conserved in β decay. Finally, experiments in which the recoil momenta of nuclei as well as the corresponding β-particle momenta were measured seem to indicate that conservation of linear momentum also is violated in β decay.

To avoid the necessity of abandoning all these conservation laws for the case of β-decay processes, Pauli postulated that in each β disintegration an additional unobserved particle is emitted. The properties attributed to this hypothetical particle which has come to be known as the neutrino are such that the conservation difficulties are eliminated. The neutrino is supposed to have zero charge, spin $\frac{1}{2}$, and Fermi statistics, and it is thought to carry away the appropriate amount of energy and momentum in each β process to conserve these quantities. To account for the fact that neutrinos are almost undetectable, it is in addition necessary to assume that they have a very small or zero rest mass and a very small or zero magnetic moment. By careful measurements of the maximum energy of a β spectrum and determination of the masses of the corresponding β emitter and product nucleus, experimenters have set an upper limit to the rest mass of the neutrino at about 0.05 electron mass (or 25 kev). Moreover, the close agreement between the measured and predicted β-ray spectrum of H^3 sets an indirect limit of only 0.0005 electron mass.

The difficulties with respect to conservation laws in positron decay are entirely analogous to those in negatron decay. In some theories the neutrino emitted in positron decay is distinguished from that in negatron decay, and the latter is called an antineutrino. Since the properties of neutrino and antineutrino make them almost indistinguishable we shall speak only of neutrinos.

Electron Capture. In the sense of the Dirac theory, positron emission is the capture of an electron from the continuum of negative-energy states. This suggests that a possible alternative way for a nucleus to accomplish the result of decreasing Z by one unit without changing A is by the capture of any convenient electron (of positive energy). As the K electrons in an atom are, on the average, closest to the nucleus (quantum-mechanically the wave functions of the K electrons have larger amplitudes at the nucleus than those of the L, M, etc., electrons) the capture probability should ordinarily be greatest for a K electron. In 1938 L. Alvarez first established the existence of this mode of decay. In electron capture, as in other β-decay processes, conservation of momentum, angular momentum, and statistics require that a neutrino be emitted. However, since the electron is captured from a definite energy state, the neutrinos emitted in this process are presumably monoenergetic.

The electron-capture process can be more difficult to observe than positron or negatron emission because it is not accompanied by the emission of detectable nuclear radiation, except in cases where the product nuclei are left in excited states and γ rays are emitted.[5] The most characteristic radiations accompanying electron capture are the X rays and Auger electrons emitted as a consequence of the vacancy created in the K (or L, etc.) shell. The atomic rearrangement processes

[5] A continuous spectrum of electromagnetic radiation of very low intensity is found to be emitted in electron-capture processes and in fact in all β-decay processes. The quanta of this so-called inner bremsstrahlung have part or all of the energy ordinarily carried away by the neutrino. The total number of quanta per electron-capture disintegration is approximately $7.4 \times 10^{-4}E_0^2$, where E_0 is the transition energy in Mev of the electron-capture process. When nuclear γ rays are emitted, the inner bremsstrahlung usually escapes detection because of its low intensity. However, for electron-capture transitions not accompanied by γ emission, measurement of the upper energy limit of the inner-bremsstrahlung spectrum is a very useful method for the determination of the transition energy.

following electron capture are quite similar to those following internal conversion (p. 160). It is sometimes important to know the ratio of K capture to capture in the other shells, especially if only K X rays are measured and the total disintegration rate is wanted. Calculations of the L-capture to K-capture ratio have been published; from $Z = 14$ to $Z = 90$ the result is very nearly $L/K = (0.06 + 0.0011Z)(E_L{}^0/E_K{}^0)^2$, where $E_L{}^0$ and $E_K{}^0$ are the neutrino energies accompanying the two processes ($E_L{}^0$ exceeds $E_K{}^0$ by the difference between the binding energies of the two shells). For electron captures of small energy release the ratio $E_L{}^0/E_K{}^0$ is appreciably different from unity, and a direct measurement of the L- to K-capture ratio then permits an estimation of the decay energy by use of the relation given above.

It is clear that a nucleus stripped of all extranuclear electrons cannot undergo orbital-electron capture. By the same reasoning it is evident that it should be possible to change the half-life for an electron-capture process by chemical changes which alter the electron density near the nucleus. E. Segrè, and others, have demonstrated this effect in the 53-day electron-capture decay of Be^7; the half-life in BeF_2 is 0.08 per cent greater than in Be metal.[(6)]

Selection Rules. Fermi in 1934 constructed a theory of β decay, somewhat analogous to the theory of emission of radiation from atoms. In this theory β emission is treated as the transition of a nucleon from the neutron state to the proton state (or the reverse) with the simultaneous creation of an electron (or positron) and a neutrino. The theory makes possible predictions of the shape of the β-particle spectrum and the half-life of the β emitter in relation to the maximum energy E_0, the atomic number Z, and the change in nuclear spin ΔI. Some ambiguity remains in the predictions because of a lack of detailed knowledge about the forces between nucleons, electrons, and neutrinos; from the most recent evidence this interaction is described as a mixture of rather complex nature. The interaction types determine the selection rules. In table 6-4 are tabulated the rules which give the best interpretation of existing data; this table will require considerable discussion.

It will be seen that there is an assortment of types; dependence on spin change is evident; and the parity change has a stronger role than in γ transitions. Within each main group (allowed, first forbidden,

[6] Isomeric transitions which decay by internal conversion are similarly dependent upon the electron density at the nucleus. The finding for 6-hr Tc^{99m} is a 0.27 per cent greater half-life in Tc_2S_7 than in $KTcO_4$. The 1.8-kev isomeric transition in Tc^{99m} takes place largely by emission of M- and N-conversion electrons.

TABLE 6-4

SELECTION RULES FOR BETA DECAY

Type	ΔI	Parity Change?	Log ft	Log $[(W_0^2-1)^{\Delta I-1}ft]$	Examples
Allowed (favored)	0 or 1	no	3		H^3, Mg^{23}
Allowed (normal)	0 or 1	no	4 to 7		S^{35}, Zn^{69}
Allowed (l-forbidden)	1	no	6 to 9		C^{14}, P^{32}
First forbidden	0 or 1	yes	6 to 8		Ag^{111}, Ce^{143}
First forbidden (unique)	2	yes	(~9)	~10	Cl^{38}, Sr^{90}
Second forbidden	2	no	10 to 14		Cl^{36}, Cs^{135}
Second forbidden (unique)	3	no	(~14)	~15	Be^{10}, Na^{22}
Third forbidden	3	yes	18		Rb^{87}
Third forbidden (unique)	4	yes	(~20)	~21	K^{40}
Fourth forbidden	4	no	~23		In^{115}
Fourth forbidden (unique)	5	no		~28	
Fifth forbidden	5	yes			
Fifth forbidden (unique)	6	yes			

etc.) there is a special category having the maximum allowed ΔI; these are the "l-forbidden allowed," the "unique first forbidden," etc., transitions. The extent to which the various types are forbidden (or allowed) is indicated in a rough way by the ft values (log ft appears in table 6-4). The significance of the quantity ft may be seen in the following very brief discussion of the simplest features of β-decay theory.

In Fermi's theory the decay constant for β decay can be represented as the product of three factors. The first consists of a combination of universal constants including a new one characteristic of β decay, the second contains the matrix elements determined by the particular form of the interaction and by the spins and parities of initial and final states. The third factor f takes account of the energy distribution of electrons and neutrinos. The probability of emission of each of the particles with a particular energy is taken as proportional to the corresponding momentum, and, integrating over all possible energies, one obtains for β^- and β^+ emission [7]

$$f = \int_1^{W_0} F(\pm Z, W_0) W (W^2 - 1)^{1/2} (W_0 - W)^2 \, dW,$$

[7] For electron capture $f = (W_0 + 1 - W_B)^2$, where W_B is the electron binding energy in units of mc_2 and $W_0 = \frac{E_0}{0.51} - 1$, with E_0 the neutrino energy in Mev.

where W is defined as the kinetic energy of an electron (β^- or β^+), in units of mc^2, plus its rest energy (1 in this unit), and $W_0 = \frac{E_0}{0.51} + 1$ is the maximum possible value of W. (Here E_0 is the maximum kinetic energy in the electron spectrum in Mev.) The function $F(\pm Z, W_0)$ is a measure of the effect of the nuclear Coulomb barrier on the momentum distribution.

Writing for the decay constant

$$\frac{\ln 2}{t} = \lambda = \text{constants} \times \text{matrix elements} \times f,$$

we see that the product ft should be nearly constant for each type of transition, since the matrix elements are expected to remain essentially constant for a given type. The time t is the partial half-life in seconds, that is, the half-life the nuclide would have if it decayed only by the particular β transition considered, and the ft product is often called the "comparative half-life" for the transition.

The log ft values corresponding to the various types of transition are shown in table 6-4. It is apparent that even for transitions of a single type ft is not exactly constant; log ft values show a range of about 3 for each type. Even so, the ranges hardly overlap, and ft values do aid in the classification of β transitions as to type.

Practical application of the ft concept calls for a method for evaluation of the integral f. Although the function $F(\pm Z, W_0)$ is known and tabulated, the integration requires too much labor for routine use. Tables, graphs, and a convenient nomograph for the evaluation of f have been published (see references). Sufficient accuracy for most purposes can be had with the appropriate one of the following three equations, one for β^-, one for β^+, and one for electron capture:

$$\log f_{\beta^-} = 4.0 \log E_0 + 0.80 + 0.02\,Z - 0.005\,Z \log E_0; \qquad (6\text{-}2)$$

$$\log f_{\beta^+} = 4.0 \log E_0 + 0.80 - 0.007\,Z - 0.009\,Z \left(\log \frac{E_0}{3}\right)^2; \qquad (6\text{-}3)$$

$$\log f_{\text{EC}} = 2.0 \log E_0 + 3.5 \log Z - 5.6. \qquad (6\text{-}4)$$

The approximations contained in these equations lead to errors no greater than about 0.3 unit in $\log f$ for $0 < Z < 100$ and 0.1 Mev $< E_0 <$ 10 Mev, except that for electron capture the lower limit of E_0 should be nearer 0.5 Mev at high Z. In these equations Z is the atomic number of the parent nuclide. We repeat that E_0 is kinetic energy, in Mev, for the spectrum upper limit in β^- and β^+ emission and for the neutrinos in electron capture.

In the group of allowed transitions there is a very special type, the "favored" allowed transitions. Many of these occur between "mirror nuclei," that is, a pair of nuclei each of which has as many protons as the other has neutrons. Examples are ${}_1H^3 \rightarrow {}_2He^3 + \beta^-$ and ${}_{12}Mg^{23} \rightarrow {}_{11}Na^{23} + \beta^+$. The β decay of the neutron is allowed and favored; the *ft* value is the same as for H^3. Favored transitions are

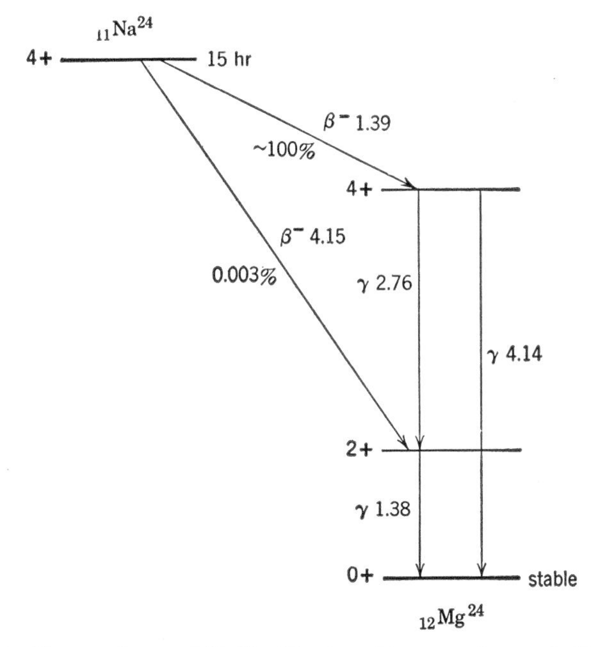

FIGURE 6-4. Decay scheme of Na^{24}. The transition energies are in Mev. Spins (I) and parities ($+$ or $-$) are shown.

not found above about ${}_{22}Ti^{43}$; recall that the heaviest stable nucleus with $Z = N$ is ${}_{20}Ca^{40}$. Other favored transitions, again in light elements only, are members of triads; a triad is a group of three isobaric nuclei with $Z = N + 2$, $Z = N$, and $Z + 2 = N$ (for example ${}_8O^{14}$, ${}_7N^{14}$, ${}_6C^{14}$). Not all β transitions among triads are allowed.

While the "unique" forbidden types can be characterized very roughly by *ft* values, the generalized β-decay theory predicts that a more nearly constant characteristic for each of these types only is $(W_0^2 - 1)^{\Delta I - 1} ft$. This is found to be true, and values of $\log [(W_0^2 - 1)^{\Delta I - 1} ft]$ are given for these types in table 6-4.

Beta-unstable nuclei can have several competing modes of decay; these may include β^-, β^+, EC (electron capture), γ, and α transitions. Each individual mode of decay, connecting specific states in the parent and daughter nuclides, is considered separately for application of the selection rules. The appropriate t value for each application is the partial half-life for that mode of decay (see footnote 3 on p. 155).

An illustration of these concepts may be seen in figure 6-4, which shows the decay scheme of ${}_{11}Na^{24}$. Almost all the β^- decays are to the second excited state of ${}_{12}Mg^{24}$ at 4.14 Mev. Thus, for this transition, $t = 15 \times 60 \times 60 = 5.4 \times 10^4$ sec. From equation 6-2, $\log f = 1.6$, and $\log ft = 6.3$, which agrees with the "normal allowed" classification for $4+ \rightarrow 4+$, $\Delta I = 0$,no. For the rare 4.15-Mev β^- transition we compute $t = 5.4 \times 10^4 \times \dfrac{100}{0.003} = 1.8 \times 10^9$ sec, $\log ft = 12.7$; again the value is consistent with the level assignments, $4+ \rightarrow 2+$, the transition being second forbidden, $\Delta I = 2$,no. The fourth forbidden β^- transition directly to the ground state is not observed. For it we compute $\log f = 4.0$, and, taking $\log ft \cong 23$, obtain as an estimate $\log t \cong 19$. Thus the half-life of Na^{24} if it decayed only to the Mg^{24} ground state might be $\sim 3 \times 10^{11}$ years. The expected branching ratio for this mode of decay is $\sim 5 \times 10^{-15}$, which is quite unobservable.

Beta Spectra. Figure 6-3 shows at least the qualitative features of typical β-ray spectra. The Fermi theory and its later modifications contain predictions as to the shape of the spectrum. For transitions with $\Delta I = 0$ or 1, the allowed and the ordinary first forbidden transitions, the expected shape is approximately that already written in the integral for evaluation of f; the probability of energies between W and $W + dW$ is

$$P(W)\,dW = \text{constants} \times \text{matrix elements} \times F(\pm Z, W)W(W^2 - 1)^{1/2}(W_0 - W)^2\,dW.$$

In β-ray spectrometers the quantity ordinarily measured is the β-ray momentum η. Using the appropriate relativistic relations (see appendix B) and remembering that W is in units of m_0c^2 and η in units of m_0c, we convert the energy distribution to the momentum distribution:

$$P(\eta)\,d\eta = \text{constants} \times \text{matrix elements} \times F(\pm Z, \eta)\eta^2(W_0 - W)^2\,d\eta. \tag{6-5}$$

For spectra with this distribution a plot of $\left[\dfrac{P(\eta)}{\eta^2 F(\pm Z, \eta)}\right]^{1/2}$ against $(W_0 - W)$ is a straight line, intercepting the energy axis at W_0. Such plots, with $P(\eta)$ from spectrometer data, are known as Kurie plots or

Fermi plots. The expectation of a straight-line plot is fully confirmed for decays with $\Delta I = 0$ or 1, at all energies for which good data are obtainable (usually > 25 kev). The Coulomb function $F(\pm Z, \eta)$ corrects the simple probability-proportional-to-momentum distribution, $\eta^2(W_0 - W)^2$, to account for the effect of the Coulomb barrier on the outgoing electron. For β^- decay the result is a retardation giving more weight to electrons of low energies. For β^+ decay the result is a reduction in the probability of emission of low-energy positrons. In figure 6-3, the curve of lower maximum energy is a representation of $P(E)\,dE$ at very low Z, where the Coulomb correction is negligible.

For β decays with $\Delta I > 1$, the unique first forbidden and all the higher forbidden transitions, the electron and neutrino are required to carry away orbital angular momentum. For these cases there exists a centrifugal barrier as well as the Coulomb barrier, and additional correction factors must be applied to the distribution functions. Qualitatively, the effect is to emphasize both the low- and the high-energy ends of the distribution, because almost equal sharing of the energy between electron and neutrino in the middle region produces on the average the smallest net momentum transfer. Ordinary Kurie plots are not straight lines for transitions with $\Delta I > 1$; but straight-line plots may be obtained by the use of correction functions characteristic of each type of forbiddenness.

Typical β-decay schemes are likely to involve transitions to more than one energy level in the product nuclide. For each transition between particular energy levels there is a β spectrum of the types just described, either the "allowed" shape or one of the "forbidden" shapes. A conventional spectrometer would record the sum of these spectra. In favorable cases the individual spectra may be resolved in the Fermi plot, in a manner analogous to the resolution of complex radioactive decay curves.

D. ALPHA DECAY

Alpha-Particle Spectra. The α particles from a given isotope either all have the same energy or are distributed among a few monoenergetic groups. Where a single α-particle energy occurs, for example, in the decays of AcA(Po^{215}) and Rn^{222}, the transition evidently takes place to a single energy level (generally the ground state) of the product nucleus. The emission of α particles of several different energies by one nuclide occurs when the product nucleus can be left in different states of excitation which subsequently transform to the

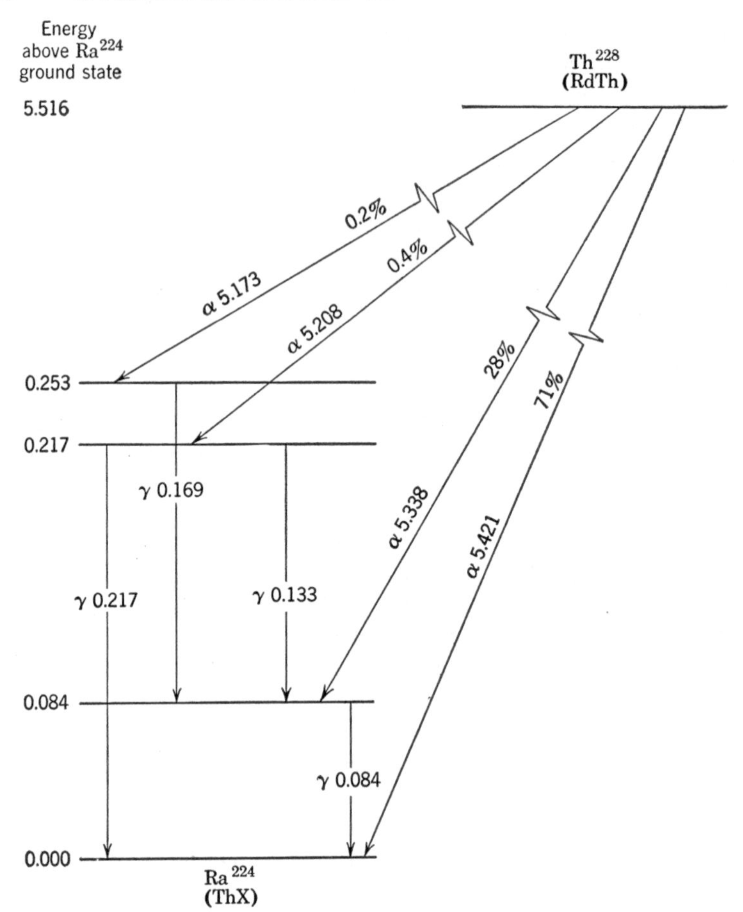

FIGURE 6-5. Energy-level diagram for $_{88}Ra^{224}$ as obtained from the observed α and γ radiations of $_{90}Th^{228}$. All energies are in Mev. The α-particle energies are the kinetic energies, not total disintegration energies.

ground state by γ emission. Each γ-ray energy observed is then as a rule equal to the energy difference between the disintegration energies associated with two of the α-particle groups.[8] From a complete knowledge of the α and γ energies, an energy-level diagram of the

[8] The total disintegration energy associated with an α-particle emission is larger than the α-particle energy by the recoil energy of the nucleus, which for the heavy α emitters is of the order of magnitude of 0.1 Mev. Since in nonrelativistic mechanics the momentum p and kinetic energy E of a particle of mass M are related by the equation $p^2 = 2ME$, it follows from the conservation of momentum that $M_\alpha E_\alpha = M_{\text{nucleus}} E_{\text{nucleus}}$. For example, for the 6.083-Mev α particles of Bi^{212} the recoil energy is $6.083 \times 4/208 = 0.117$ Mev.

product nucleus can often be constructed, as illustrated in figure 6-5 for the α decay of radiothorium to thorium X. Which γ transitions actually occur from the levels populated by α decay is determined by the selection rules for γ transitions.[9]

Penetration of Potential Barriers. The 10.54-Mev α particles of ThC′ are the most energetic α particles known from radioactive sources. Near the other extreme are the 2.0-Mev α particles of samarium. Most of the naturally occurring α particles are emitted with energies between 4 and 8 Mev. Before the advent of quantum mechanics, the fact that α particles could be emitted with such low energies from nuclei which were known to have much higher potential barriers was very puzzling. For example, scattering experiments with 8.78-Mev α particles (from ThC′) on uranium show that around a uranium nucleus no deviation from the Coulomb law exists at least up to 8.78 Mev; yet U^{238} emits 4.2-Mev α particles. How do these α particles get outside the potential barrier, which is at least 8.78 Mev high (and actually quite a bit higher)?

This question was answered by the wave-mechanical treatment of the problem which was first presented in 1928 independently by G. Gamow and by R. W. Gurney and E. U. Condon. In this treatment the Schroedinger wave equation for an α particle of energy E inside the nuclear potential well is set up and solved. The wave function representing the α particle does not go abruptly to zero at the wall of the potential barrier (R_0 in figure 6-6) and has small but finite values outside the radial distance R_0. By applying the boundary conditions that the wave function and its first derivative must be continuous at R_0 and R_1, one can solve the wave equation for the region between R_0 and R_1, that is, inside the barrier where the potential energy $U(r)$ is greater than the total energy E. The probability P for the α particle of mass M to be in that region is given by the square of the wave function and turns out to be

$$P = e^{-\frac{4\pi}{h}\sqrt{2M}\int_{R_0}^{R_1}\sqrt{U(r)-E}\,dr}.$$

It is clear from this expression that the probability for barrier penetration decreases with increasing value of the integral in the exponent,

[9] An interesting and somewhat different situation occurs in the ThC and RaC β-decay branches. Here some of the excited states of ThC′(Po^{212}) and RaC′(Po^{214}) are so unstable with respect to α emission that α decay from these states can compete with γ emission. This is the origin of the so-called long-range α particles of ThC′ and RaC′ with energies up to 10.5 Mev. The α- to γ-branching ratio and a knowledge of the partial half-lives for α decay have been used to obtain partial γ-half-lives for the ThC′ and RaC′ states involved.

that is, with increasing barrier height and width. (The higher the barrier, the larger is the difference $U(r) - E$; and the wider the barrier, the greater is the difference between the limits of integration R_0 and R_1.)

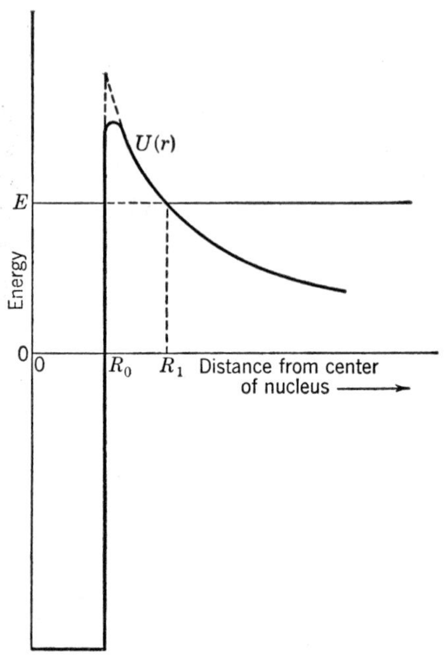

FIGURE 6-6. Potential energy in the neighborhood of a nucleus.

The decay constant λ may be considered as the product of P and the frequency f with which an α particle strikes the potential barrier; the order of magnitude of f may be estimated as follows. The de Broglie wavelength h/Mv of the α particle of velocity v and momentum Mv inside the nucleus is taken comparable to R_0, thus

$$\frac{h}{Mv} \approx R_0, \quad \text{or} \quad v \approx \frac{h}{MR_0}.$$

If the α particle is considered as bouncing back and forth between the potential walls,

$$f = \frac{v}{2R_0}, \quad \text{or} \quad f \approx \frac{h}{2MR_0^2}.$$

Therefore, the decay constant

$$\lambda \approx \frac{h}{2MR_0^2} e^{-\frac{4\pi}{h}\sqrt{2M}\int_{R_0}^{R_1}\sqrt{U(r)-E}\,dr}. \tag{6-6}$$

By a more elaborate treatment more accurate expressions for f and λ are obtained. If a simple shape is assumed for $U(r)$ (for example, a Coulomb law up to R_0 as indicated by a dotted line in figure 6-6), it is possible to evaluate the integral in the exponent and thus to obtain an explicit expression for λ in terms of R_0, Z, and E.

Alpha Lifetimes. The Gamow-Gurney-Condon theory does not permit precise calculations of the decay constants for α emitters; however, in view of the very large range of known half-lives (24 powers of ten) the approximate quantitative results are gratifying, especially for the even-even α-emitting nuclides.[10] Figure 6-7 shows the dependence of partial α half-life t_α (see footnote 3, p. 155) on the disintegration energy for even-even isotopes of a number of heavy elements. Plotted as the ordinate in figure 6-7 is $\log t_\alpha$, and included among the experimental points are α transitions both to ground (0+) states and first excited (2+) states. Each curve is for one value of Z, and the lifetimes corresponding to a given α energy increase regularly from curve to curve with increasing height of the potential barrier. The shapes of the individual curves conform to the theoretical equation, with the value of R_0 set equal to $1.51 \times 10^{-13} A^{1/3}$. (The partial α half-lives are very sensitive to R_0, and this result constitutes one of the better measurements of nuclear radii.) Alpha transitions to second and higher excited states were omitted from figure 6-7 because most such values would not accord with the respective curves by factors up to several hundred in t_α. These α transitions are said to be hindered, but no full explanation is known.

Among the even-odd, odd-even, and odd-odd nuclides practically all α transitions are hindered by factors that may be as high as 1000, as judged by comparison with the curves of figure 6-7. This is especially true of transitions to the daughter ground state, and frequently the chief decay mode for these nuclides is to an excited state. For example, the α transitions of Am^{241} to the ground and first excited states of Np^{237} have hindrance factors of $\sim 10^3$ and the main, almost unhindered, transition is to the second excited state at 60 kev above ground. The even-odd U^{235} is entered as an isolated point in figure 6-7; except for the obvious hindrance this isotope would not be found on earth. I. Perlman, A. Ghiorso, and G. T. Seaborg, who pointed out most of these correlations, have advanced an explanation for the hin-

[10] In recent years the enormous increase in experimental information on α decay has made possible a much more complete check of the theory and much more fruitful attempts at systematization of both lifetimes and decay energies. In 1940 only about two dozen α emitters were known. In 1954 the number has grown to about 150, most of the additions being artificially produced nuclides from $Z = 83$ to $Z = 100$.

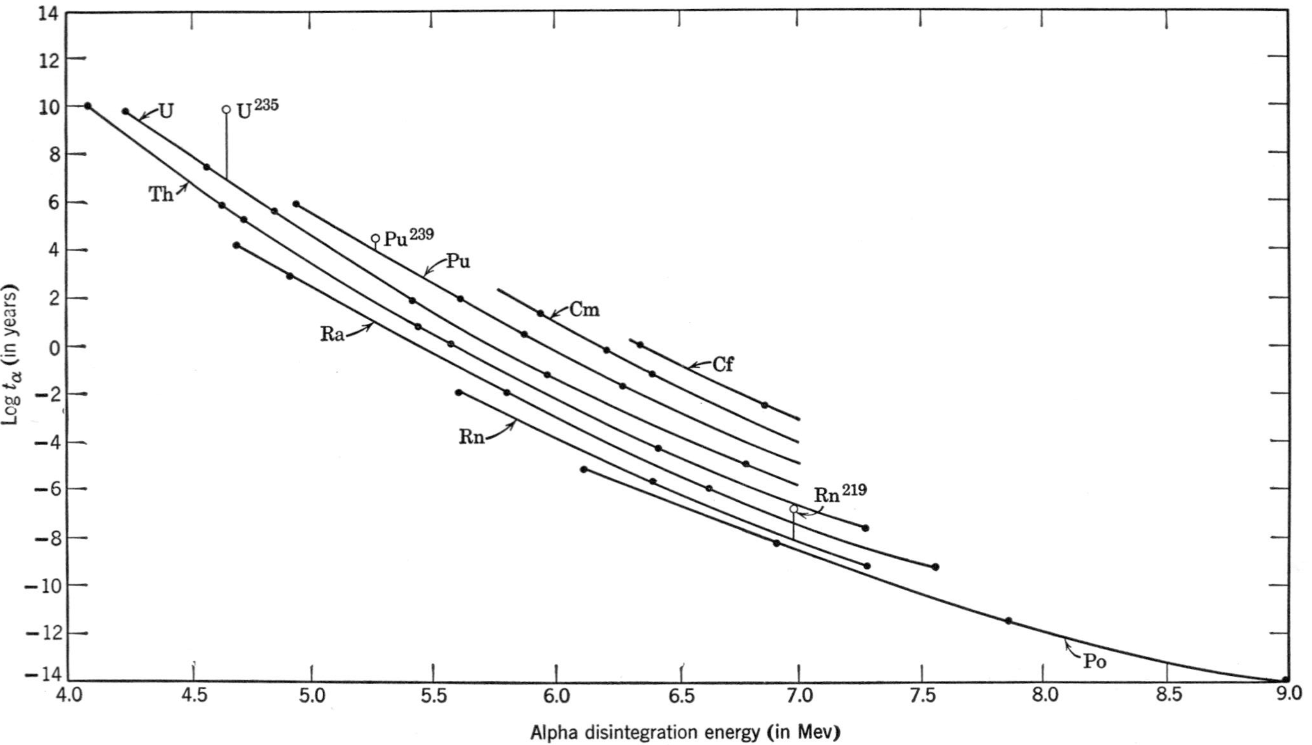

FIGURE 6-7. Relation between partial α half-life and α-disintegration energy for even-even α emitters. [After I. Perlman, A. Ghiorso, and G. T. Seaborg, *Phys. Rev.* **77,** 26 (1950).] Experimental points for each element are connected by a curve. A few even-odd species are shown also.

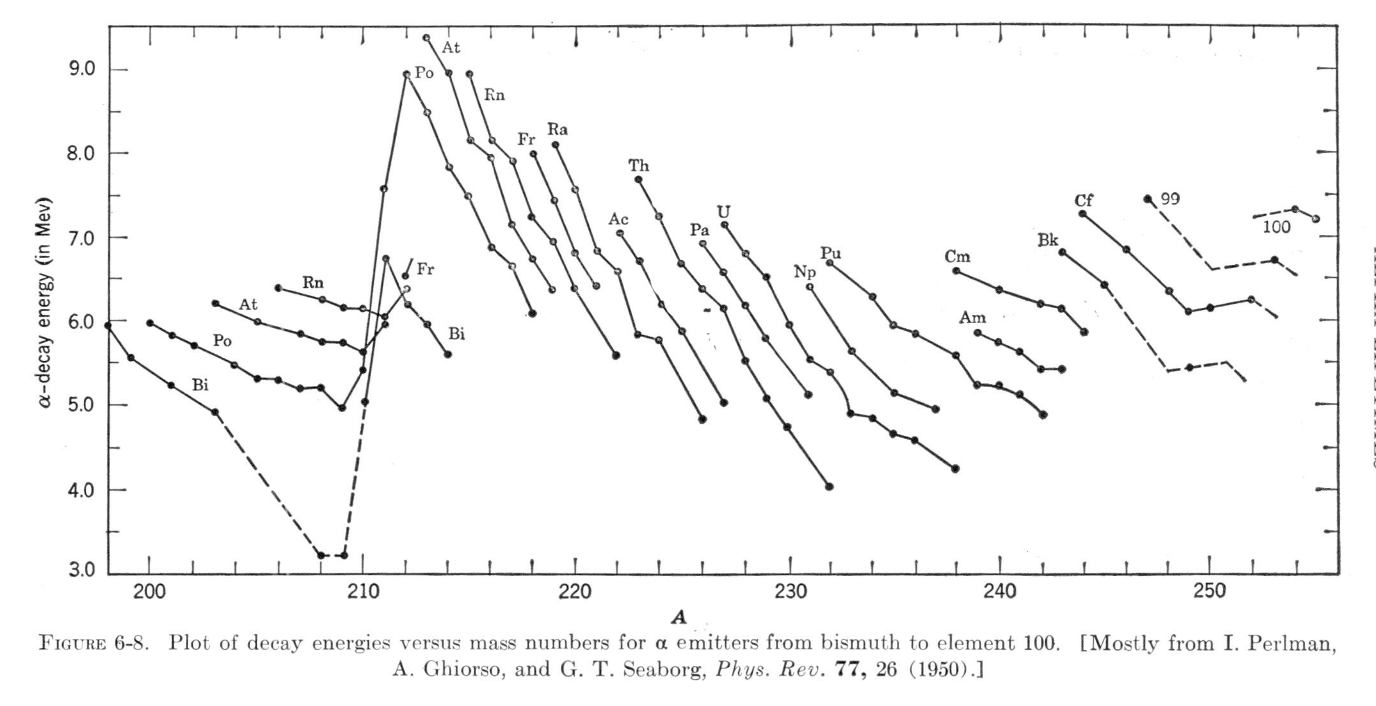

FIGURE 6-8. Plot of decay energies versus mass numbers for α emitters from bismuth to element 100. [Mostly from I. Perlman, A. Ghiorso, and G. T. Seaborg, *Phys. Rev.* **77**, 26 (1950).]

drance in odd-nucleon nuclides, as follows. It is implicit in the α-decay theory that the particle exists inside the nucleus prior to its emission. It is easy to believe that the assembly of an α particle which includes the odd nucleon might be difficult, and of course the emission of an α particle from the core leaving the odd nucleon in its quantum level leads to an excited state of the final nucleus.

Also omitted from the smooth curves of figure 6-7 are those nuclides which have neutron numbers near 126. The α lifetimes of the lighter isotopes (even even-even isotopes) of radon, astatine, and polonium and of all the bismuth isotopes are lengthened by factors beyond expectations for any odd-nucleon effects. The interpretation suggested is that there is an abrupt increase of about 10 per cent in nuclear radii on the addition of the first nucleon beyond the closed shells.

Alpha-Decay Energies. In addition to the regularities in lifetimes there are some interesting systematic trends in α-decay energies. Still following the work of the Berkeley group, we plot in figure 6-8 most of the known α-disintegration energies against the mass number of the α emitter. Points belonging to one element are joined. The energies shown are the energy differences between the ground states. A few of the points were obtained not by direct measurements but by the method of closed decay cycles, which is illustrated for Am^{242} in figure 6-9.

One of the striking features of a plot such as that in figure 6-8 is the nearly linear decrease of α energy with A for almost every element. The application to the prediction of decay energies of new α emitters is obvious. The slopes of the lines appear to go through a minimum in the region of atomic number 95.

In one sense, the information revealed in figure 6-8 is more a reflection of the nuclear binding energies than a specific property of α decay, and some of the general regularities can be derived from the binding-energy equation 2-5. But the very pronounced drop in decay energy below Po^{212} and Bi^{211} is clearly related to the closed neutron shell at $N = 126$ which stabilizes the product nuclei Pb^{208} and Tl^{207}.[(11)] The full shape of the bismuth curve in this region is not known because the α-decay energies become so low that α emission cannot compete successfully with electron capture in $Bi^{204-207}$. The unusually large difference in decay energies between the heavy polonium and the heavy bismuth isotopes presumably has to do with the closed proton shell

[11] For astatine and radon the corresponding discontinuities undoubtedly occur just below At^{213} and Rn^{214}, respectively. The indications of smaller discontinuities at Cf^{252}, and probably 99^{253} and 100^{254}, have been interpreted as evidence for a closed neutron subshell at $N = 152$.

at $Z = 82$. For elements below atomic number 83 the available α-decay energies evidently become so low that the lifetimes are generally immeasurably long. In the rare-earth region, just above neutron number 82, an "island" of α emitters has been found, including the naturally occurring $_{62}Sm^{147}$ and $_{60}Nd^{144}$ and about ten artificially produced nuclides, most of them very neutron-deficient relative to the stable isotopes.

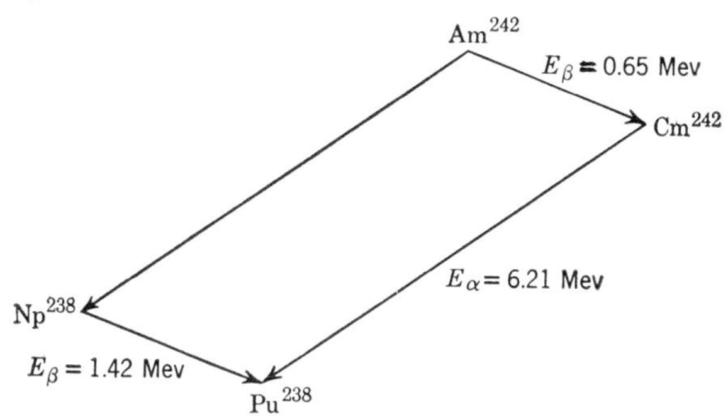

FIGURE 6-9. Closed decay cycle for determination of Am^{242} α-decay energy. From the measured decay energies shown the α-decay energy of Am^{242} is computed to be $0.65 + 6.21 - 1.42 = 5.44$ Mev.

Proton Emission. It may be appropriate to say a few words about the fact that proton decay has not been observed. Protons are emitted by nuclei in less than about 10^{-12} sec or not at all. The explanation of the difference in behavior between α particles and protons is as follows. The proton barrier is half as high as the α-particle barrier and therefore also narrower, and for high excitation energies the lifetimes for proton emission are thus much smaller than for α emission. For lower excitation energies α emission is more probable because the energy balance is much more favorable than for proton emission: the nucleons in the α particle are still about as tightly bound as in the original nucleus, whereas a proton to be emitted must be supplied with an energy of several million electron volts (its binding energy).

E. SPONTANEOUS FISSION

The explanation of the fission reaction in terms of the liquid-drop model naturally leads one to inquire whether a nucleus that can be split by the addition of a relatively small amount of excitation energy may not have a finite probability of undergoing fission spontaneously. This process of spontaneous fission does indeed take place in a number of the heaviest nuclides. It was first discovered in uranium by

K. A. Petrzhak and G. N. Flerov in 1940. Since then the spontaneous fission rates for over 20 nuclides have been measured, and upper limits have been set for several others. The observed rates extend from about 4×10^{-5} fissions g^{-1} sec^{-1} for Th^{232} to about 10^{14} fissions

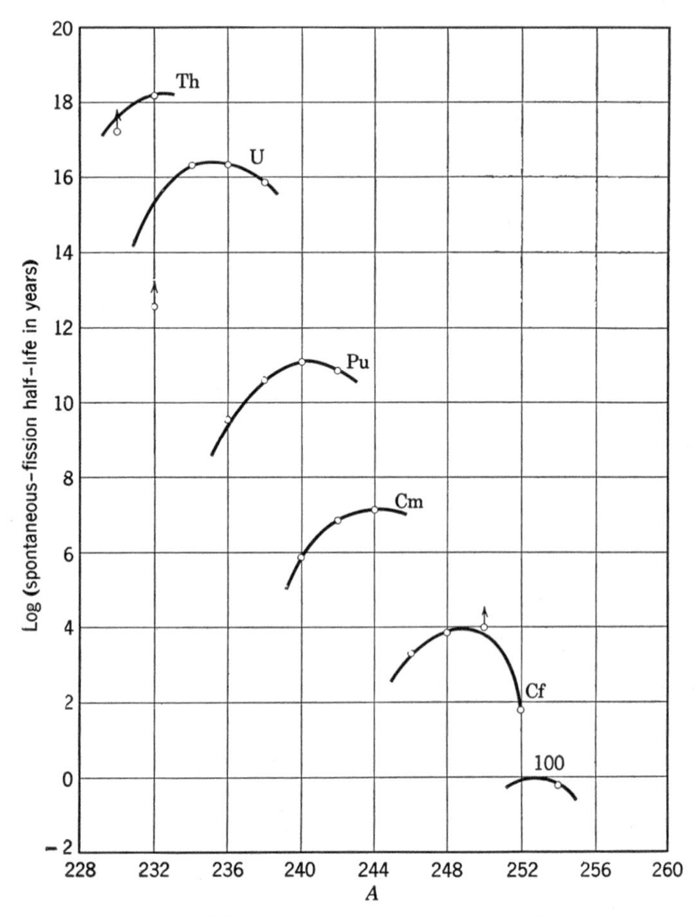

Figure 6-10. Partial half-lives for spontaneous fission of even-even nuclides plotted against A. The points marked ↥ indicate lower limits.

g^{-1} sec^{-1} for element 100 of mass 254. In the latter α-emitting nuclide of half-life 3.3 hr there is about one spontaneous fission for every 1600 α disintegrations. An even higher fission-to-alpha ratio, about 1 to 30, has been reported for 2-year Cf^{252}.

We may define a partial half-life t_f for spontaneous fission in the presence of other decay processes, just as we defined t_γ and t_α. A number of attempts have been made to account quantitatively for the partial spontaneous-fission half-lives on the basis of the liquid-drop model. In these calculations spontaneous fission is treated as a barrier penetration problem analogous to α decay, and the relation between partial half-life and barrier height ΔE should then have the general form $t_f = k_1 e^{-k_2 \Delta E}$, where k_1 and k_2 are constants. From liquid-drop-model calculations together with empirical data Seaborg has derived an expression for ΔE as a function of the Bohr-Wheeler parameter Z^2/A:

$$\Delta E = (19.0 - 0.36\, Z^2/A) \text{ Mev.}$$

The difference between this calculated barrier height ΔE for spontaneous fission of the nucleus Z^A and the binding energy for an added neutron to the nucleus Z^{A-1} correlates remarkably well with the cross section for thermal-neutron fission of Z^{A-1}.

If the equations of the preceding paragraph were strictly correct, there should be a linear relation between $\log t_f$ and Z^2/A. Actually the relation is found to be approximately linear for even-even nuclides only. J. R. Huizenga has pointed out that for each element the partial spontaneous-fission half-lives of even-even nuclides go through a maximum when plotted as a function of A, as in figure 6-10. That useful predictions of t_f for unknown nuclides can be made from such empirical relations is obvious. The partial spontaneous-fission half-lives for odd-nucleon nuclides are significantly longer than would correspond to interpolations from figure 6-10. The available data for odd-A nuclides are given in table 6-5. The general trends of spontaneous-fission rates indicate that at sufficiently high Z fission instability may well become the limiting factor for the synthesis of new elements and new isotopes.

TABLE 6-5

PARTIAL SPONTANEOUS-FISSION HALF-LIVES FOR ODD-A NUCLIDES

Nuclide	Partial Spontaneous-Fission Half-life (years)	Principal Mode of Decay	Half-life
$_{91}Pa^{231}$	10^{16}	α	3.4×10^4 y
$_{92}U^{233}$	$>3 \times 10^{17}$	α	1.6×10^5 y
$_{92}U^{235}$	1.9×10^{17}	α	7.1×10^8 y
$_{93}Np^{237}$	$\gtrless 4 \times 10^{16}$	α	2.2×10^6 y
$_{93}Np^{239}$	$>5 \times 10^{12}$	β^-	2.33 d
$_{94}Pu^{239}$	5.5×10^{15}	α	2.44×10^4 y
$_{95}Am^{241}$	1.2×10^{13}	α	470 y
$_{97}Bk^{249}$	$>10^7$	β^-	$\sim$1 y
$_{98}Cf^{249}$	$>10^6$	α	$\sim$400 y
$_{99}?^{253}$	$>10^5$	α	19 d

EXERCISES

1. What do you expect the ground state spins and parities to be for (*a*) A^{39}; (*b*) Pt^{196}; (*c*) Zr^{89}; (*d*) Co^{55}; (*e*) N^{16}? *Answer:* (*a*) $\frac{7}{2}-$; (*b*) $0+$; (*e*) $2-$.

2. From the measured spin values of Na^{24} and Rb^{86} listed in appendix F, and from Nordheim's rules, what are the level assignments of the odd neutron and of the odd proton in each of these nuclides? Compare with the predictions of the single-particle model. What are the parities of Na^{24} and Rb^{86}?

3. The 104-day isomer Te^{123m_2} decays by an 88-kev isomeric transition to Te^{123m_1}, which in turn decays with a 1.9×10^{-10}-sec half-life to the Te^{123} ground state. For the 88-kev step the internal conversion coefficient is very large ($\gg$100), and $\alpha_K/\alpha_L = 0.68$. The second transition has an energy of 159 kev, $\alpha_K = 0.18$, and $\alpha_K/\alpha_L = 8.9$. On the basis of these data, select the most likely transition types for the two steps. Then, with the help of the single-particle model, assign spins and parities to the three states of Te^{123} involved. Finally check the partial γ half-lives of the two transitions against the approximate formula 6-1.

4. Show that the production of a positron-electron pair by a photon in vacuum is impossible. (*Note:* Set up the conditions for momentum and energy conservation, using relativistic expressions, and show that they lead to a contradiction, for example to the inequality $\cos\theta > 1$, where θ is the angle between the directions of motion of positron and electron.)

5. A sample of 79-hr Zr^{89} is found to emit positrons (of 0.905 Mev maximum energy) and yttrium K X rays in the intensity ratio 0.38:1. No γ-ray emission in coincidence with the positrons or X rays is observed. (*a*) What is the ratio of electron capture to positron decays? (Include the contribution of L-electron capture!) (*b*) Estimate the $\log ft$ values for the two branches and the degree of forbiddenness of the transition.

6. The β^+ and EC decay of Zr^{89} (see exercise 5) lead to the 14-sec isomer Y^{89m} rather than to the stable Y^{89} of spin $I = \frac{1}{2}$. The isomer is de-excited by a 913-kev transition with $\alpha_K \approx 0.01$ and $\alpha_K/\alpha_L = 7.0$. (*a*) Using these data and shell structure considerations, assign spins and parities to Y^{89m} and to the 79-hr Zr^{89}. (*b*) Estimate the partial half-life for direct decay of Zr^{89} to the ground state of Y^{89}. (*c*) The 1.463-Mev β^- spectrum of 53-day Sr^{89} is not accompanied by γ radiation and has the unique first-forbidden shape. What is the $\log ft$ value for this transition and the spin and parity of Sr^{89}? (*d*) Estimate the fraction of Sr^{89} decays that might lead to Y^{89m}. *Answer:* (*d*) $\sim 10^{-5}$.

7. In the decay of AcC(Bi^{211}) to AcC″(Tl^{207}) the following α- and γ-ray energies have been observed: α 6.618, 6.272 Mev; γ 0.353 Mev. Construct a reasonable decay scheme for this disintegration. Indicate the *total* energy difference between each energy state involved and the ground state of AcC″.

8. From figure 6-8, estimate the α-decay energies of Bk^{245} and Cm^{245}. Use these data, together with information from appendix G, to decide which of these isobars is β unstable with respect to the other and by what energy.
Answer: Bk^{245} is β unstable by 0.70 Mev.

9. The α transition from Am^{241} to the ground state of Np^{237} takes place in only about 0.3 per cent of all Am^{241} decays. Estimate the "hindrance factor" for this transition relative to the curves of figure 6-7.

10. What is the approximate rate of neutron emission from 1 curie of Cf^{252}? Compare this with the neutron emission rate of 1 curie of Po^{210} mixed with beryllium (see chapter 4).

11. From data in appendix G and from α-decay systematics, give the energies of the first excited states of Ra^{222}, Th^{226}, and Pu^{240} and the approximate abundances of the α branches leading to these states.

12. (*a*) What neutron number do you expect to be the next magic number after 126? (*b*) On the basis of data in appendix F, what neutron levels might be filled at neutron number 152 (which may correspond to a closed subshell; see footnote 11, p. 178)? *Answer:* (*a*) 184.

REFERENCES

J. M. Blatt and V. F. Weisskopf, *Theoretical Nuclear Physics,* New York, John Wiley & Sons, 1952.

F. Rasetti, *Elements of Nuclear Physics,* New York, Prentice-Hall, Inc., 1936.

I. Kaplan, *Nuclear Physics,* Cambridge, Mass., Addison-Wesley Publishing Co., 1955.

E. Fermi, *Nuclear Physics,* University of Chicago Press, 1950.

G. Gamow and C. L. Critchfield, *Theory of Atomic Nucleus and Nuclear Energy Sources,* Oxford, Clarendon Press, 1949.

D. Halliday, *Introductory Nuclear Physics,* New York, John Wiley & Sons, 1950.

W. J. Whitehouse and J. L. Putman, *Radioactive Isotopes. An Introduction to their Preparation, Measurement and Use,* Oxford, Clarendon Press, 1953.

N. Feather, *Nuclear Stability Rules,* Cambridge University Press, 1952.

P. B. Moon, *Artificial Radioactivity,* Cambridge University Press, 1949.

H. A. Bethe, "Mesons and Nuclear Forces," *Physics Today* **7,** No. 2, 5 (February 1954).

M. G. Mayer, "Nuclear Configurations in the Spin-Orbit Coupling Model," *Phys. Rev.* **78,** 16, 22 (1950).

E. Feenberg, *The Shell Theory of the Nucleus,* Princeton University Press, 1954.

M. G. Mayer and J. H. D. Jensen, *Elementary Theory of Nuclear Shell Structure,* New York, John Wiley & Sons, 1955.

B. H. Flowers, "Nuclear Shell Model," *Progress in Nuclear Physics,* Vol. 2 (O. R. Frisch, Editor), London, Pergamon Press, 1953.

P. F. A. Klinkenberg, "Tables of Nuclear Shell Structure," *Revs. Mod. Phys.* **24,** 63 (1952).

G. Scharff-Goldhaber, "Excited States of Even-Even Nuclei," *Phys. Rev.* **90,** 587 (1953).

A. Bohr, "On the Quantization of Angular Momenta in Heavy Nuclei," *Phys. Rev.* **81,** 134 (1951).

A. Bohr and B. R. Mottelson, "Collective and Individual Particle Aspects of Nuclear Structure," Kgl. Danske Videnskab. Selskab, Mat-fys. Medd. **27,** No. 16 (1953).

M. Goldhaber and A. W. Sunyar, "Classification of Nuclear Isomers," *Phys. Rev.* **83,** 906 (1951).

M. Goldhaber and R. D. Hill, "Nuclear Isomerism and Shell Structure," *Revs. Mod. Phys.* **24,** 179 (1952).

M. E. Rose, G. H. Goertzel, B. I. Spinrad, T. Harr, and P. Strong, "The Internal Conversion Coefficients. I: The *K*-Shell," *Phys. Rev.* **83,** 79 (1951).

E. H. S. Burhop, *The Auger Effect and Other Radiationless Transitions,* Cambridge University Press, 1952.

H. Frauenfelder, "Angular Correlations of Nuclear Radiation," *Ann. Rev. Nuclear Sci.,* Vol. II, p. 129, Stanford, Annual Reviews Inc., 1953.

L. C. Biedenharn and M. E. Rose, "Theory of Angular Correlation of Nuclear Radiations," *Revs. Mod. Phys.* **25,** 729 (1953).

N. R. Crane, "The Energy and Momentum Relations in the Beta Decay, and the Search for the Neutrino," *Revs. Mod. Phys.* **20,** 278 (1948).

C. W. Sherwin, "The Neutrino," *Nucleonics* **2,** No. 5, 16 (May 1948).

M. Deutsch, "Annihilation of Positrons," *Progress in Nuclear Physics,* Vol. 3 (O. R. Frisch, Editor), London, Pergamon Press, 1953.

C. E. Anderson, G. W. Wheeler, and W. W. Watson, "Inner Bremsstrahlung Associated with K Capture in A^{37}," *Phys. Rev.* **90,** 606 (1953).

T. B. Novey, "Experimental Energy and Angular Distributions of Inner Bremsstrahlung," *Phys. Rev.* **89,** 672 (1953).

M. E. Rose and J. L. Jackson, "The Ratio of L_I to K Capture," *Phys. Rev.* **76,** 1540 (1949).

J. J. Kraushaar, E. D. Wilson, and K. T. Bainbridge, "Comparison of the Values of the Disintegration Constant of Be^7 in Be, BeO, and BeF_2," *Phys. Rev.* **90,** 610 (1953).

K. T. Bainbridge, M. Goldhaber, and E. Wilson, "Influence of the Chemical State on the Lifetime of a Nuclear Isomer, Tc^{99m}," *Phys. Rev.* **90,** 430 (1953).

E. Feenberg and G. Trigg, "The Interpretation of Comparative Half-lives in the Fermi Theory of Beta-Decay," *Revs. Mod. Phys.* **22,** 399 (1950).

S. A. Moszkowski, "Rapid Method of Calculating Log(ft) Values," *Phys. Rev.* **82,** 35 (1951).

C-S. Wu, "Recent Investigations of the Shapes of β-Ray Spectra," *Revs. Mod. Phys.* **22,** 386 (1950).

M. G. Mayer, S. A. Moszkowski, and L. W. Nordheim, "Nuclear Shell Structure and β-Decay," *Revs. Mod. Phys.* **23,** 315 (1951).

A. de Shalit and M. Goldhaber, "Mixed Configurations in Nuclei," *Phys. Rev.* **92,** 1211 (1953).

T. P. Kohman, "Limits of Beta-Stability," *Phys. Rev.* **73,** 16 (1948).

I. Perlman, A. Ghiorso, and G. T. Seaborg, "Systematics of Alpha-Radioactivity," *Phys. Rev.* **77,** 26 (1950).

I. Kaplan, "On the Systematics of Even-Even Alpha Emitters," *Phys. Rev.* **81,** 962 (1951).

J. O. Rasmussen, Jr., S. G. Thompson, and A. Ghiorso, "Alpha-Radioactivity in the 82-Neutron Region," *Phys. Rev.* **89,** 33 (1953).

I. Perlman and F. Asaro, "Alpha Radioactivity," *Ann. Rev. Nuclear Sci.,* Vol. IV, p. 157, Stanford, Annual Reviews Inc., 1954.

E. Segrè, "Spontaneous Fission," *Phys. Rev.* **86,** 21 (1952).

A. Ghiorso, G. H. Higgins, A. E. Larsh, G. T. Seaborg, and S. G. Thompson, "Spontaneous Fission of U^{234}, Pu^{236}, Cm^{240}, and Cm^{244}," *Phys. Rev.* **87,** 163 (1952).

J. R. Huizenga, "Spontaneous Fission Systematics," *Phys. Rev.* **94,** 158 (1954).

G. T. Seaborg, "Activation Energy for Fission," *Phys. Rev.* **88,** 1429 (1952).

CHAPTER 7

INTERACTION OF RADIATIONS WITH MATTER

A. ALPHA PARTICLES AND OTHER IONS

Processes Responsible for Energy Loss. Nuclear radiations, both corpuscular and electromagnetic, are detectable only through their interactions with matter. If this interaction is sufficiently small, as in the case of the neutrino, the radiation remains undetected. For an understanding of the methods and instruments used for the detection, measurement, and characterization of nuclear radiations it is necessary to consider the manner in which these radiations interact with matter.

In passing through matter α particles lose energy chiefly by interaction with electrons.[1] This interaction may lead to the dissociation of molecules or to the excitation or ionization of atoms and molecules. The effect which is most easily measured and most often used for the detection of α particles is ionization. The details of the ionization processes and other effects associated with α-particle passage are more readily investigated in gases than in liquids or solids, although the processes are presumably about the same. We shall therefore speak mostly of phenomena observed in the passage of α particles through gases.

Because α particles have relatively short ranges a known number of α particles of known initial energy can be made to spend their entire energy inside an ionization chamber, and thus the total ionization produced per α particle is readily measured. These experiments show that on the average about 35 ev (35 electron volts of energy) are dissipated for each ion pair formed in air. The energy required to form an ion pair is listed for a number of other gases in table 7-1,

[1] The interactions of α particles with nuclei (scattering and nuclear reactions) have been discussed in previous chapters. The contribution of these processes to energy loss of helium ions in passing through matter is entirely negligible except at very high energies.

TABLE 7-1

AVERAGE ENERGY LOST BY ALPHA PARTICLES IN PRODUCING ONE ION PAIR IN VARIOUS GASES

Gas	Energy per Ion Pair W (ev)	First Ionization Potential I (ev)	Fraction of the Energy Used in Ionization (I/W)
H_2	36.3	15.6	0.43
He (very pure)	43	24.5	0.58
He (tank)	30		
N_2	36.5	15.5	0.42
O_2	32.5	12.5	0.38
Air	35.0		
Ne (very pure)	36.8	21.5	0.58
Ne (tank)	28		
A	26.4	15.7	0.59
Kr	24.1	13.9	0.58
Xe	21.9	12.1	0.55
CH_4	30	14.5	0.48
C_2H_4	29	10.5	0.36
CO	34	14.3	0.42
CO_2	34		
CS_2	26	10.4	0.40
CCl_4	27		
NH_3	39	10.8	0.28

together with the first ionization potentials of these gases. In the noble gases the fraction of the α-particle energy spent in ionization processes is larger than it is in the diatomic and polyatomic gases, where dissociation of molecules is also possible. Most of the values tabulated were determined for α particles from Po^{210}, but the energy per ion pair is surprisingly insensitive to the energy and the nature of the radiation; almost identical values for several of the gases have been obtained with 340-Mev protons. A very good way to measure the energy of an α particle or similar ion is to measure electrically the total number of ions produced when it is stopped in a gas-filled ionization chamber.

A large part of the energy loss of α particles and other ions is accounted for by the kinetic energy given to the electrons removed from atoms or molecules in close collisions with the α particle. It can easily be shown from conservation of momentum that the maximum velocity which an α particle of velocity v can impart to an electron is about $2v$; therefore, the maximum energy which an electron can receive from the impact of a 6-Mev α particle, for example, is about 3 kev. The average energy imparted to electrons by α particles in their passage through matter is of the order of 100 to 200 ev. Many of these secondary electrons or δ rays are fast enough to ionize other atoms. In fact about 60 to 80 per cent of the ionization produced by α particles is due to secondary ionization; the exact ratio of primary to secondary ionization is difficult to determine. Delta-ray tracks are often seen in cloud-chamber pictures of α-particle tracks.

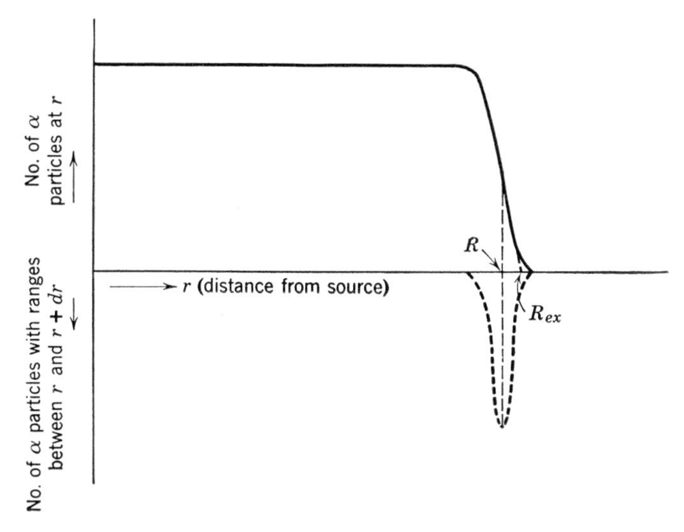

FIGURE 7-1. Number of α particles from a point source as a function of the distance from the source (full curve). The derivative of that function is also shown (dotted curve); the latter represents the distribution in ranges.

Range. Because an α particle loses only a very small fraction of its energy in a single collision with an electron and is not appreciably deflected in the collision, α-particle paths are very nearly straight lines. Furthermore, because of the very large number of collisions (of the order of 10^5) necessary to bring an α particle of a few million electron volts initial energy to rest, the ranges of all α particles of the same initial energy are the same within narrow limits. Ranges of α particles are generally determined by absorption methods, either with solid absorbers or, more accurately, with a gaseous absorber at variable pressures. Ranges may be determined with a precision of about one part in 5000.

In figure 7-1 the number of α particles found in a gas at a distance r from the source is plotted against r for the case of a source which emits α particles of a single energy. It is seen that the ranges of all the particles in a given medium are not exactly the same but show a small spread of about 3 or 4 per cent. This phenomenon, called the straggling of α-particle ranges, is caused by the statistical fluctuations in the number of collisions and in the energy loss per collision. The

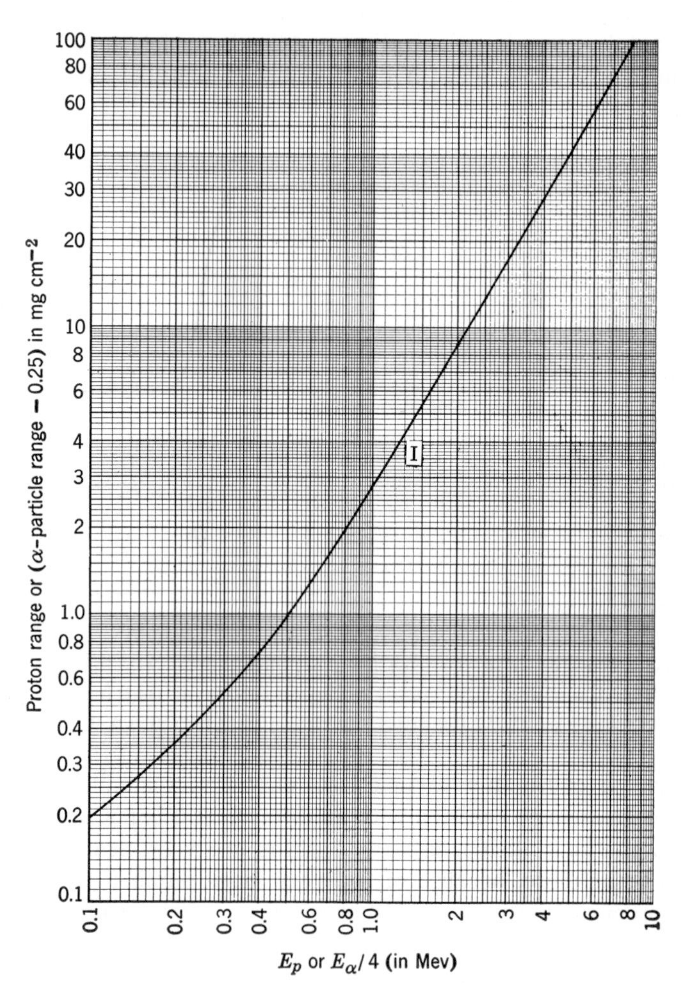

Figure 7-2. Range-energy relations for protons and helium ions in air.

dotted curve in figure 7-1 is obtained by differentiation of the other (integral) curve and represents the distribution of ranges or the amount of straggling; it is approximately a Gaussian curve. The distance r corresponding to the maximum of the differential curve (point of inflection of the integral curve) is called the mean range R of the α particles. The distance r obtained by extrapolating to the abscissa the approximately straight portion of the integral curve is the extrapolated range R_{ex}. The mean range is now generally used in range tables and in range-energy relations. Extrapolated ranges were

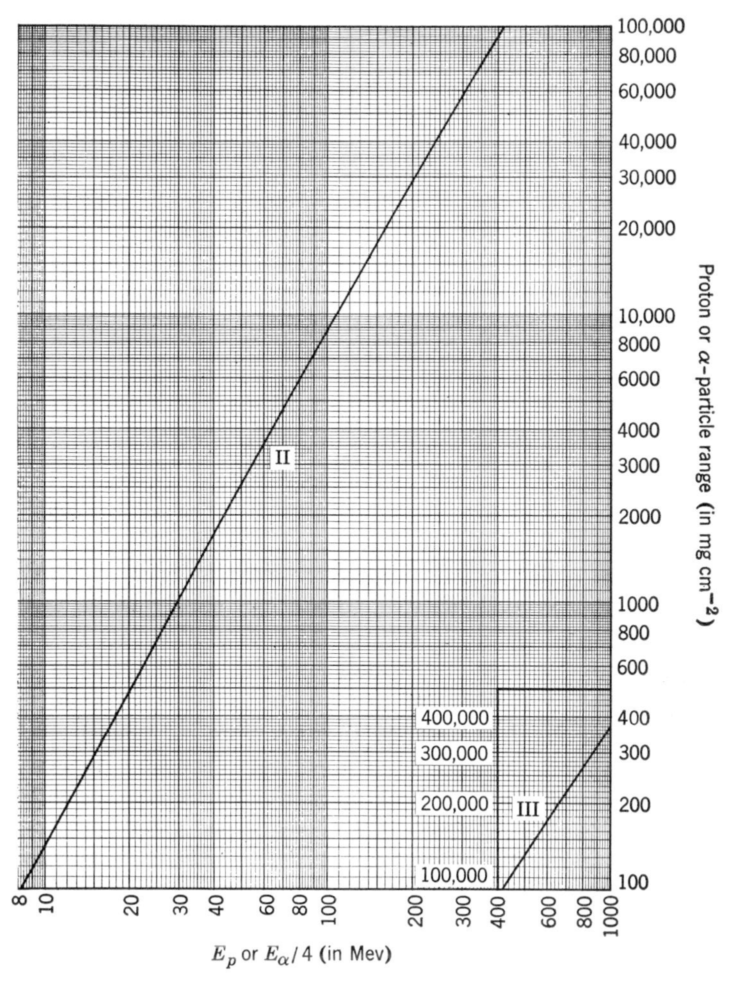

FIGURE 7-2 (*continued*).

often given in the older literature and are more easily determined experimentally. Relations between the two ranges are available; the difference is approximately 1.1 per cent for α particles of ordinary energies.

Range-Energy Relation. Figure 7-2 gives the ranges in dry air of protons and of helium ions (α particles) as functions of their kinetic energy. These curves, taken from the literature (see references), are based more on theoretical calculations than on experiment because the calculated values are believed to be more accurate over most of the energy region. The only energy losses considered were those due to electronic collisions. At very high energies other mechanisms may become relatively important; for example, 2-Bev protons are appreciably (approximately 15 per cent) attenuated in intensity by nuclear reactions in a lead absorber 1 in. thick while losing relatively little (less than 3 per cent) of their energy by ionization processes.

The ranges in figure 7-2 are expressed in milligrams of air per square centimeter in the absorption path. The range can be expressed as the length of the absorption path in centimeters provided that the density of the air is specified. Dry air at 15°C and 760 mm pressure (the standard for range values) has a density of 1.226 mg cm^{-3}, and for such air the range in centimeters is given by the range in milligrams per square centimeter divided by 1.226. Obviously the range in centimeters for air at other temperatures and pressures is readily computed by use of the corresponding density. Even in liquid air, the ranges in milligrams per square centimeter are unchanged from those given in figure 7-2.

The ranges of α particles and other ions in absorbing materials other than air are often wanted. Data can hardly be accumulated for all substances, and again theoretical computations are resorted to. These computations are very time-consuming and have been carried through for relatively few elementary substances (see references at the end of the chapter). Several approximate rules, now chiefly of historical significance, have been given for estimating ranges in an absorber of atomic number Z and mass number A; one which is easy to remember is that the range in milligrams per square centimeter is proportional to $A^{1/2}$ (Bragg's rule). Actually the range in an absorber, compared to the range in air for the same ray, is a complicated function of Z, A, and the radiation energy E. The following equation approximates this function well enough to be useful, within the limits indicated below, for protons, deuterons, and helium ions with initial energies from about 0.1 Mev to about 1000 Mev and for any elementary absorber:

$$\frac{R_Z}{R_a} = 0.90 + 0.0275\,Z + (0.06 - 0.0086\,Z)\log\frac{E}{M}. \tag{7-1}$$

Here R_Z is the range in element Z in milligrams per square centimeter, R_a is the range of the same ray in air in the same unit, M is the mass number of the particle (1 for protons, 4 for α particles, etc.), and E is the initial particle energy in million electron volts. As written, the equation is applicable to absorbers with $Z > 10$. For lighter elements, replace $(0.90 + 0.0275\,Z)$ by 1.00, except for helium and hydrogen use 0.82 and 0.30, respectively. (For deuterium as absorber, double the range computed for hydrogen.) For elements heavier than air the results are improved by replacement of R_Z by $R_Z + (0.01\,Z/z)$, where z is the atomic number of the particle; this correction is quite negligible except for very large Z or very low E. With these modifications, where indicated, the equation 7-1 fits available calculated range-energy curves for the light-element absorbers and for aluminum, copper, silver, and lead to within a few per cent, at least from 1 Mev to 100 Mev.

In many actual cases, indeed for air, the stopping substance is not a single element but rather is a compound or mixture of elements. For practical purposes we make the further approximation that the stopping effect of a molecule or of a mixture of atoms or molecules is given by the sum of the stopping effects of all the component atoms (another rule due to Bragg).[2] Therefore, if R_1, R_2, R_3 . . . denote the ranges (in milligrams per square centimeter) of a particular ray in each of several elements, the range R_t of that ray in a compound or in an essentially homogeneous mixture of these elements with respective weight fractions w_1, w_2, w_3 . . . is given by

$$\frac{1}{R_t} = \frac{w_1}{R_1} + \frac{w_2}{R_2} + \frac{w_3}{R_3} + \cdots \qquad (7\text{-}2)$$

Because the relative stopping effects of various elements are functions of the energy of the α particle or other ion, equation 7-2 is not to be applied to grossly heterogeneous absorbers, which contain separate phase regions large enough to produce serious changes in the particle energy.

As an example we shall determine the range of 20-Mev α particles in polyethylene, $(CH_2)_x$. From figure 7-2 the range in air is 41.3 mg cm^{-2}. Using equation 7-1 (modified), we get for the range in hydrogen

$$R_H = 41.3(0.30 + 0.051 \log \tfrac{20}{4}) = 13.9 \text{ mg cm}^{-2},$$

[2] In view of the fact that a considerable fraction of the α-particle energy is expended in molecular excitation and dissociation processes, this simple additivity relation is somewhat surprising. The stopping power of water vapor has been measured to be about 3 per cent less than that of the equivalent mixture of hydrogen and oxygen; range measurements in a number of organic isomers show that ranges in them are the same within less than 1 per cent.

and for the range in carbon

$$R_C = 41.3(1.00 + 0.012 \log \tfrac{20}{4}) = 41.6 \text{ mg cm}^{-2}.$$

Polyethylene is 85.6 per cent by weight carbon, 14.4 per cent hydrogen, and hence by equation 7-2,

$$\frac{1}{R_{CH_2}} = \frac{0.856}{41.6} + \frac{0.144}{13.9},$$

and $R_{CH_2} = 32.3$ mg cm^{-2}.

Suppose now that a beam of 20-Mev α particles is incident on a polyethylene absorber 15 mg cm^{-2} thick. At what energy E' will the α particles emerge, and how much farther will they travel in air? The emerging α particles would have a residual range in polyethylene of $32.3 - 15.0 = 17.3$ mg cm^{-2}. Therefore their range in air R_a' is given by

$$\frac{1}{17.3} = \frac{0.856}{R_a'\left(1.00 + 0.012 \log \dfrac{E'}{4}\right)} + \frac{0.144}{R_a'\left(0.30 + 0.051 \log \dfrac{E'}{4}\right)}.$$

As a first approximation we neglect the small log terms in the denominators and get $R_a' = 23.1$ mg cm^{-2}. According to figure 7-2 this corresponds to $E' = 16$ Mev, and, using this value, we obtain as a second (and evidently sufficiently accurate) approximation $R_a' = 22.2$ mg cm^{-2} and $E' = 15.6$ Mev.

Specific Ionization. The specific ionization for any radiation is usually defined as the number of ion pairs formed per millimeter of path in air (15°C and 760 mm pressure). At energies above about 1 Mev, for α particles and similar light ions, the specific ionization is approximately inversely proportional to the particle velocity. (In the nonrelativistic region the velocity of an α particle of energy E Mev is $6.9 \times 10^8 E^{1/2}$ cm sec^{-1}.) For any particle there is a maximum specific ionization; for an individual α particle the maximum occurs about 3.0 mm from the end of its range, where its energy is about 0.37 Mev and its velocity 4.2×10^8 cm sec^{-1}. As the energy is reduced further, the specific ionization falls rapidly to zero. For a beam of initially homogeneous α particles the maximum of the specific ionization occurs at about 4.7 mm from the extrapolated range. A plot of specific ionization versus distance from the source is called a Bragg curve (figure 7-3). For α particles of different energies the Bragg curves are almost identical over corresponding regions measured from the end of the range. It may be noted that for a given

α-particle source the extrapolated range obtained from a Bragg curve is not exactly the same as that obtained from a number-versus-distance curve, the latter being a few tenths of 1 per cent larger.

The straggling in specific ionization is complicated by the fact that near the end of their ranges the α particles frequently pick up electrons (becoming He^+ or even He) and subsequently lose them in later collisions. Several thousand such fluctuations in charge occur for each α particle, but they are almost completely confined to the

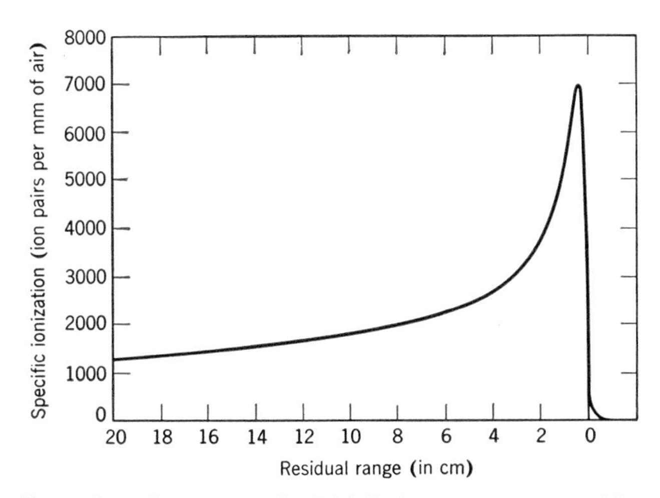

FIGURE 7-3. Bragg curve for initially homogeneous α particles.

last few millimeters of the range where the velocity of the α particle becomes comparable to the orbital-electron velocities in helium atoms. An α particle spends over 90 per cent of its entire path as He^{++}. The relative abundances of He^{++}, He^+, and He at various energies were studied by magnetic-deflection measurements with various thicknesses of absorbers between source and measuring device.

The ionization produced along the paths of protons and α particles (helium ions) are given in table 7-2 for a number of energies. In this table the quantity listed is the number of ion pairs produced per 1.00 mg cm^{-2} of air, which is just the specific ionization divided by 0.1226.[(3)]

[3] These values may be obtained from the slope of a range-versus-energy plot, which gives the energy loss ΔE Mev per mg cm^{-2}, and are just $10^6\Delta E/W$, where $W = 35$ ev per ion pair. (*Caution:* The range-energy curves of figure 7-2 are on logarithmic scales.) The values for other gaseous absorbers should be given by $10^6\Delta E/W$, where W has the appropriate value (table 7-1) and ΔE is the reduction in energy per 1.00 mg cm^{-2} of the gas.

TABLE 7-2

IONIZING EFFECTS OF PROTONS AND ALPHA PARTICLES IN AIR

Energy (Mev)	Ion Pairs Produced per 1.00 mg cm^{-2} by	
	Protons	α Particles
0.2	16,000	40,000
0.5	11,000	56,000
1.0	6,500	54,000
1.5	5,100	46,000
2.0	4,400	41,000
3.0	2,900	32,000
4.0	2,400	26,000
5.0	2,000	22,000
6.0	1,700	20,000
8.0	1,300	16,000
10.0	1,100	13,000
14.0	860	10,300
25.0	560	6,500
70	400	2,900
100	180	2,200
1,000	56	400
10,000	59	210

Except at low energies the ionization produced by any light particle at a given velocity is proportional to z^2, where z is the charge of the particle. Therefore, the ionization (per mg cm^{-2}) produced by an α particle of energy E is very nearly $z^2 = 4$ times as great as that produced by a proton of energy $E/4$, which is to say by a proton of the same velocity. This may be verified by inspection of table 7-2. Also the specific ionization produced by a deuteron is very closely the same as that produced by a proton of half the energy.

Ranges of Other Ions. Any ion moving at high speed through matter loses its energy by essentially the same mechanism. We have already stated that at a given velocity the energy loss (measured by the specific ionization) is proportional to z^2 (z is the *net* charge on the ion). Therefore α particles and protons of the same velocity have almost equal ranges because the α particle loses energy at four times the rate for the proton and has just four times as much energy to lose. In general, for an ion of charge z, mass number M, and energy E, the range is approximately

$$R_{z,M,E} = \frac{M}{z^2} R_{p,E/M}, \tag{7-3}$$

where $R_{p,E/M}$ is the range in the same absorber of a proton of energy E/M.

Fission fragments have $M \approx 100$, $Z \approx 45$, and initially $E \approx 100$ Mev. If the fragments were completely stripped of electrons the large value of $z^2 = Z^2$ would lead to ranges of the order of 0.14 mg cm^{-2}, roughly 1 mm in air. Actually a fission fragment probably will be stripped only of electrons with orbital velocities smaller than its own velocity and so will hold all electrons with binding energies greater than about 1 kev.[4] The fragment starts with net $z \approx 20$ and gains electrons as its velocity decreases until $z \approx 0$ at about 1 Mev (approximately 3 mm before the end of the range). Measured

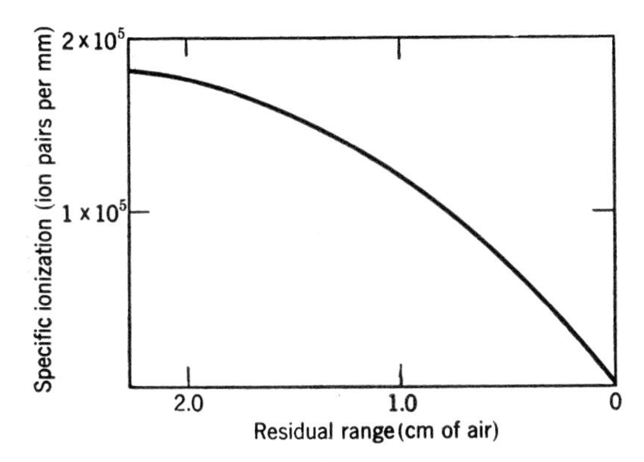

FIGURE 7-4. "Bragg curve" for a fission fragment.

fission fragment ranges in slow-neutron fission are about 1.9 to 2.9 cm in air; a curve of specific ionization versus residual range looks about as shown in figure 7-4. If particles like fission fragments but of very much higher energy were available, the curve in figure 7-4 could be extended to larger residual ranges, and, no doubt, some of the general features of the Bragg curve for α particles would be seen. The relative stopping powers of various substances are very nearly the same for fission fragments as for α particles.

B. ELECTRONS

Processes Responsible for Energy Loss. The interaction of electrons with matter is in many ways fundamentally similar to that of α particles and other ions. The processes which are responsible

[4] The kinetic energy of a bound electron (which is equal to its binding energy) with velocity equal to that of a fission fragment is in a nonrelativistic approximation the energy of the fission fragment multiplied by the ratio of the electron-to-fragment masses. For a 100-Mev fragment with mass 100, the binding energy of the corresponding electron is $100 \times 10^6 \times (0.00055/100) = 550$ ev.

for the energy loss are qualitatively the same in both cases. In fact, the average energy loss per ion pair formed is very closely the same for electrons as for α particles (35 ev for electrons in air). The primary ionization by electrons accounts for only about 20 to 30 per cent of the total ionization; the remainder is due to secondary ionization.

There are a number of differences between the interactions of the two types of particles with matter. First, for a given energy the velocity of an electron is much larger than that of an α particle (see table 7-3), and, therefore, the specific ionization is less for electrons.

TABLE 7-3

SPECIFIC IONIZATION AND VELOCITY FOR ELECTRONS OF VARIOUS ENERGIES

Velocity (in units of the velocity of light, c)	Energy (Mev)	Ion Pairs per mm of Air
0.001979	10^{-6}	0
0.006257	10^{-5}	0
0.01978	10^{-4}	
0.0240	1.46×10^{-4}	770 (maximum)
0.06248	10^{-3}	
0.1950	10^{-2}	$\sim$110
0.4127	0.05	20
0.5483	0.10	15
0.8629	0.50	6.4
0.9068	0.70	6.1
0.9411	1.0	5.9
0.9791	2.0	5.9
0.9893	3.0	6.1
0.9934	4.0	6.2
0.9957	5.0	6.4
0.9988	10	6.8
0.99969	20	7.4
0.999949	50	8.1
0.9999871	100	8.5

In table 7-3 the specific ionization in air is given for electrons of different energies. The largest specific ionization, 770 ion pairs per millimeter, occurs at 146 ev (velocity = $0.024c$), which is a much lower energy but somewhat higher velocity than corresponds to the peak in the Bragg curve for α particles. In air, ionization stops when the electron energy has been reduced to 12.5 ev (the ionization potential of oxygen molecules). On the higher-energy side of the maximum, the specific ionization reaches a flat minimum at about 1.4 Mev. The increase beyond this energy is an essentially relativistic effect: as the velocity of light is more closely approached, the Lorentz contraction of lengths enables the fast electron to ionize atoms at greater distances, even at distances of several molecular diameters.[5]

An electron may lose a large fraction of its energy in one collision; therefore, a statistical treatment of the energy-loss processes is less justified than for α particles, and straggling is much more pronounced. In the passage of an initially homogeneous beam of electrons through matter the apparent straggling is further increased by the pronounced scattering of the electrons into different directions, which makes possible widely different path lengths for electrons traversing the same thickness of absorber. Nuclear scattering is responsible for most of the large-angle deflections although energy loss is caused almost entirely by interactions with electrons.

For electrons of high energy an additional mechanism for losing energy must be taken into account: the emission of radiation (bremsstrahlung) when an electron is accelerated in the electric field of a nucleus. The ratio of energy loss by this radiation to energy loss by ionization in an element of atomic number Z is approximately equal to $EZ/800$, where E is the electron energy in millions of electron volts. Thus, in heavy materials such as lead the radiation loss becomes appreciable even at 1 Mev, whereas in light materials (air, aluminum) it is unimportant, at least for the energies available from β emitters.

Finally, the additional fact that β particles are emitted with a continuous energy spectrum makes their absorption in matter a phenomenon too complicated for theoretical analysis.

Absorption of Beta Particles. The combined effects of continuous spectrum and scattering lead—quite fortuitously—to an approximately exponential absorption law for β particles of a given maximum energy. Absorption curves, that is, curves of activity versus thickness of absorber traversed, are for this reason usually plotted on semilogarithmic paper. The nearly exponential decrease applies both to numbers and specific ionizations of β particles, although absorption curves taken with counters and ionization chambers cannot be expected to be completely identical. The exact shape of an absorption curve depends also on the shape of the β-ray spectrum and, because of scattering effects, on the geometrical arrangement of active sample, absorber, and detector. If sample and absorber are as close

[5] This has the perhaps unexpected consequence of making the physical state of the absorber of importance. For example, in liquid rather than gaseous air the dielectric polarization of the medium probably reduces the specific ionization from the values in table 7-3 by about 10 per cent at 10 Mev and about 20 per cent at 100 Mev, if W remains 35 ev per ion pair in liquid air.

as possible to the detector, the semilog absorption curve becomes most nearly a straight line; otherwise, some curvature toward the axes is generally found. When β particles belonging to two spectra of widely different maximum energies are present in a source, this is apparent from the change of slope in the absorption curve; such an absorption curve is roughly analogous to the semilog decay curve of an activity containing two different half-life periods.

If the absorption of β rays is represented by an exponential law $\mathbf{A}_d = \mathbf{A}_0 e^{-\mu d}$, where $\mathbf{A}_0$ is the measured activity without absorber and $\mathbf{A}_d$ the activity observed through absorber of thickness d, then μ is known as the absorption coefficient. The ratio of the absorption coefficient to the density ρ, known as the mass absorption coefficient, is nearly independent of the nature of the absorber. More accurately it varies about as Z/A; that is, the number of electrons per unit mass determines the mass stopping power of a substance for β particles. The thickness required to reduce the activity to one-half of its initial value is called the half-thickness $d_{½} = 0.693/\mu$; more frequently the half-thickness is expressed in grams per square centimeter, and then is equal to $0.693\rho/\mu$ and varies about as A/Z. Absorption coefficients and half-thickness values given in the literature usually refer to the initial portions of absorption curves. These values cannot be relied on as accurate measures of β-particle energies.

Determination of Beta-Particle Ranges. It is generally the purpose of absorption measurements to determine the upper energy limit of a β-ray spectrum. We should say at the outset that precision determinations of upper energy limits can be made only with electron spectrographs; yet for many purposes absorption measurements are useful.

To get a measure of the upper energy limit of a β-ray spectrum one must find the range in the absorber of the most energetic β particles. The fact that a range exists for a given β-ray spectrum means that the absorption curve cannot continue as an approximate exponential but must eventually turn downward toward $-\infty$ on a semilog plot (see figure 7-5). The ratio of range to initial half-thickness is generally between 5 and 10. In practice a β-ray absorption curve is never found to reach $-\infty$ on a semilog plot and may not even turn in that direction, because of the presence of more penetrating radiation beyond the range of the β rays. Even if neither nuclear γ radiation nor characteristic X rays are present, there is always some background of bremsstrahlung from the deceleration of the β particles in the sample itself and in the absorbers. If elements of low Z are used as absorbers, the difference in slopes between β-ray and γ- or X-ray absorption curves is particularly marked; the absorption curve then exhibits a fairly sharp break where the β-ray component turns over into the photon "tail" (see figure 7-6). For this reason β-ray absorption curves are always taken with absorbers of low atomic number; aluminum or plastic absorbers are most commonly used, and for differentiating β particles from soft X rays beryllium absorbers are particularly useful. (Beta-ray ranges expressed in milligrams per square centimeter vary only about as A/Z, whereas the absorption of electromagnetic radiation increases rapidly with Z as is discussed in section C.)

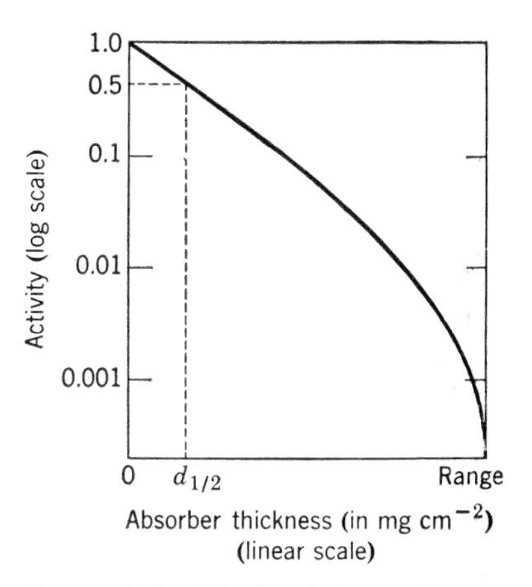

FIGURE 7-5. Idealized β-ray absorption curve (semilog plot).

The relative efficiencies of measuring instruments for β and γ rays vary with the energies of the radiations and with different instruments; most argon-filled counters and air-filled ionization chambers are about 100 times as efficient for β particles as for 1-Mev γ quanta, and the efficiency for γ rays is roughly proportional to the γ-ray energy from a few hundred kiloelectron volts to a few million electron volts. Thus a typical β-ray absorption curve for a β spectrum accompanied by γ rays will have a γ-ray "tail" with intensity of the order of 1 per cent of the initial β activity. A pure bremsstrahlung tail is usually at least an order of magnitude smaller, about 0.05 per cent or less of the initial β activity. In β^+ absorption curves there is, in addition to other electromagnetic radiation which may be present, always a background of annihilation radiation, about 1 per cent of the initial β^+ intensity in a typical detector.

The maximum range for a β-particle spectrum may be obtained from an experimental absorption curve in various ways. Visual inspection gives a rough value (usually too small) for the point at which the β activity ceases to be detectable above the γ- or X-ray background; the lower the γ- or X-ray background, the better is the visual method. Better results can sometimes be obtained by subtraction of the penetrating background radiation from the total absorption curve, which should result in a curve similar to the one in figure 7-5.

A more reliable method for the determination of β-ray ranges from absorption curves is the comparison method suggested by N. Feather. Here the absorption curve to be analyzed is compared with the absorption curve (measured under identical conditions) of a standard β emitter, usually RaE ($E_{max} = 1.17$ Mev, range = 505 mg cm^{-2} in aluminum) or better UX_2 ($E_{max} = 2.31$ Mev, range = 1105 mg cm^{-2}

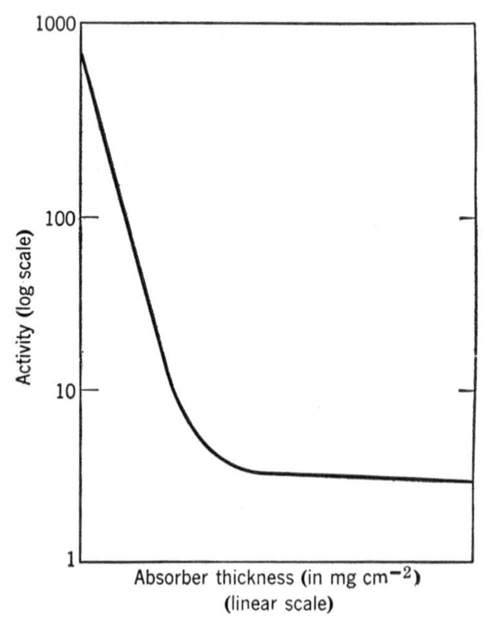

FIGURE 7-6. Typical β-ray absorption curve in aluminum (semilog plot). A γ-ray component is present.

in aluminum).[6] The net β-ray absorption curves after subtraction of all backgrounds due to electromagnetic radiation are used. If the same percentage reduction of initial activity would correspond to the same fraction of the range for each β emitter, the absorber thickness corresponding to a certain fraction (say 0.5) of the range could be readily determined for the unknown by comparison with the standard of known range. Actually this procedure gives a somewhat different apparent range for each fraction of the range at which the compari-

[6] The ranges given for the standard substances are those corresponding to the spectrographically determined E_{max} values according to the best range-energy relations (see p. 202). These, rather than the visual ranges determined for the standard substances in a particular experimental arrangement, should be used in the Feather analysis.

son is made, because of the different shapes of the absorption curves. But, if these apparent ranges are plotted against the fractions of the range at which they were determined, a smooth curve results which can be extrapolated to fraction 1.0 of the range to find the true range. This curve is called the Feather plot; one is shown in figure 7-7. If the spectra of the unknown and the standard have the same shape, the Feather plot is a straight line parallel to the abscissa. When RaE, which has an unusually large percentage of low-energy electrons in its spectrum, is used as a standard, the Feather plot often has a shape similar to that shown. The UX_2 spectrum has the allowed

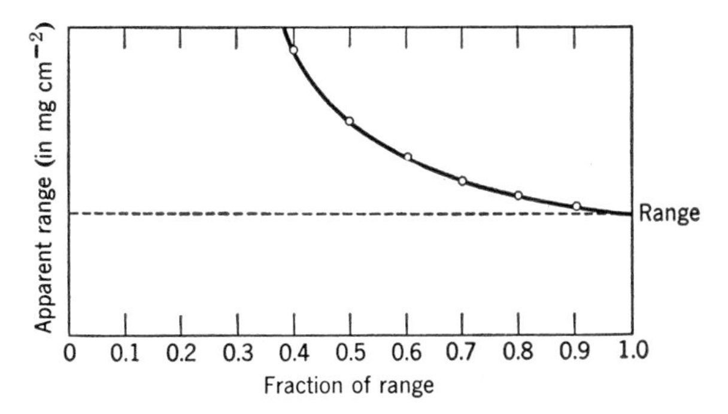

FIGURE 7-7. A typical Feather plot.

shape, as does also that of P^{32} which has been suggested as a standard. A more complicated comparison method [7] that gives better results uses as standards a number of absorption curves and takes into account the fact that the shapes of β spectra vary with the atomic number of the β emitter and with E_{max}.

When two β-spectral components are emitted from a sample it is usually very difficult to obtain by absorption measurements a reliable end point for the softer component; extrapolation of the line representing the harder component to zero absorber thickness and subtraction of this extrapolated curve from the total absorption curve is the best that can be done. In this case too the Feather method gives much better results than does visual determination.

When soft conversion electrons are emitted in addition to β particles, their presence may be revealed by the initial portion of the

[7] E. Bleuler and W. Zünti, "On the Absorption Method for the Determination of β and γ Energies," *Helv. Phys. Acta* **19**, 375 (1946). See also E. Bleuler and G. J. Goldsmith, *Experimental Nucleonics*, New York, Rinehart & Co., 1952, p. 170; and E. Segrè (Editor), *Experimental Nuclear Physics*, New York, John Wiley and Sons, 1953, Vol. I, p. 298.

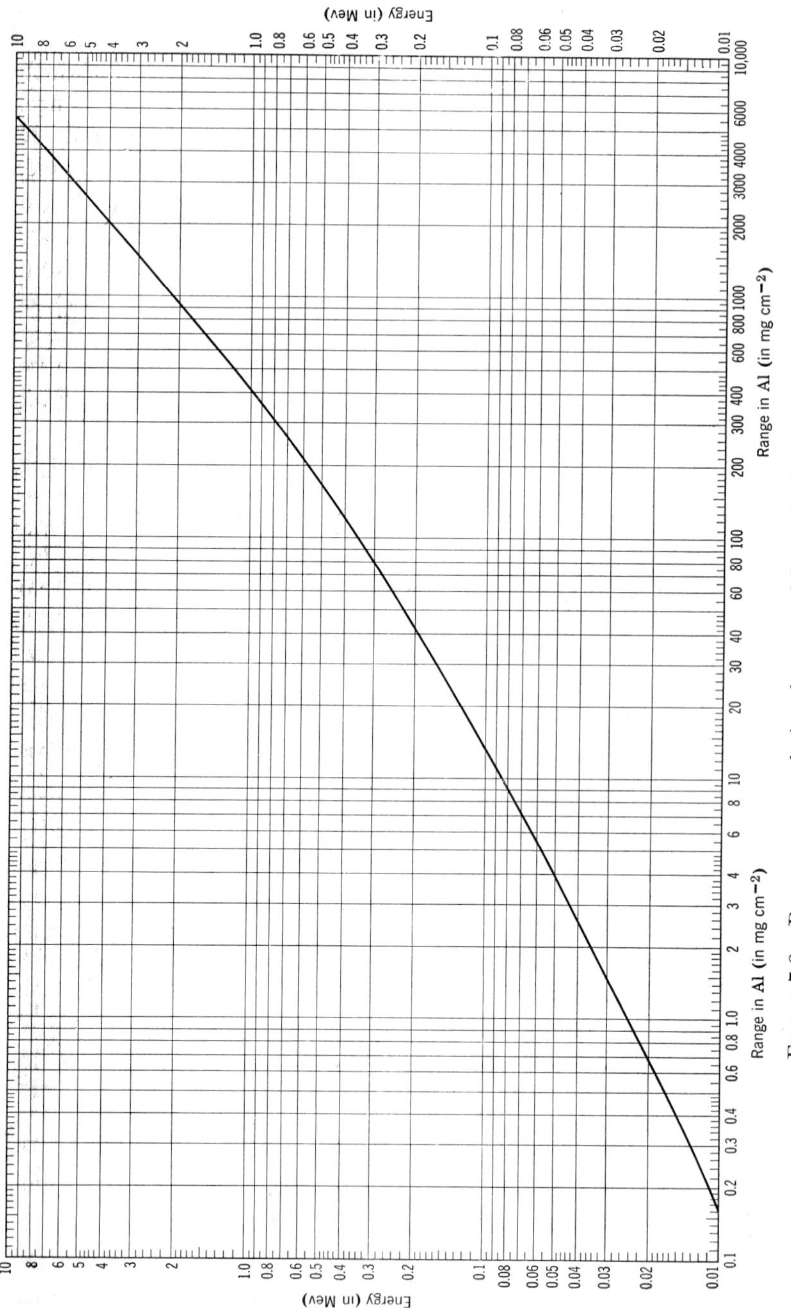

Figure 7-8. Range-energy relation for β particles and electrons in aluminum.

absorption curve. The only really good method for measuring energies of conversion electrons uses the electron spectrograph.

Range-Energy Relations. Once the range of β particles or conversion electrons is known, a range-energy relation can be used to deduce the maximum energy.[8] Many empirical relations have been proposed. One given by Feather for energies above 0.6 Mev has been most widely used: $R = 0.543E - 0.160$, where E is the maximum β energy in million electron volts and R the range in aluminum in grams per square centimeter. This relation is useful up to at least about 15 Mev. In the lower-energy region (below about 0.7 Mev) it is best to use a range-energy curve such as the one plotted in figure 7-8.

Although the same relations are commonly used for positrons, there is experimental evidence that β^+ ranges are measurably greater than β^- ranges, for the same energy. Probably this difference is no more than a few per cent.

Back-scattering. As already mentioned, scattering of electrons, both by nuclei and by electrons, is much more pronounced than scattering of heavy particles. A very significant fraction of the number of electrons striking a piece of material may be reflected as a result of single and multiple scattering processes. The reflected intensity increases with increasing thickness of reflector except that for thicknesses greater than about one-third of the range of the electrons saturation is achieved, and further increase in thickness does not add to the reflected intensity. The ratio of the measured activity of a β source with reflector to that without reflector is known as the back-scattering factor. Figure 7-9 shows measured factors for energetic β sources when mounted on thick backings of various atomic numbers, with two different geometrical arrangements: 2π geometry in which the counter was so close to the sample as to subtend half the total solid angle, and a small-aperture geometry in which the counter subtended a solid angle of only about one steradian directly over the sample. These saturation back-scattering factors increase with Z and are significantly greater for electrons than for positrons.

Saturation back-scattering factors are independent of maximum β energy above 0.6 Mev. For lower-energy β spectra the factors de-

[8] Monoenergetic electrons of a given energy and β particles of the same maximum energy should, of course, have the same ranges, and at low energies this is verified experimentally. Above 0.5 Mev, apparent β-particle ranges drop off a few per cent compared to the observed ranges of corresponding monoenergetic electrons; this is probably due to the relatively small number of electrons with energies near the upper energy limit in a β-ray spectrum.

crease rapidly with decreasing maximum energy; this variation is sufficiently pronounced below 0.3 Mev to constitute a rapid, approximate method for β-energy determination. For energetic β sources the back-scattered electrons from lead are not greatly reduced in energy; those back-scattered at large angles from low-Z materials are of low energy.

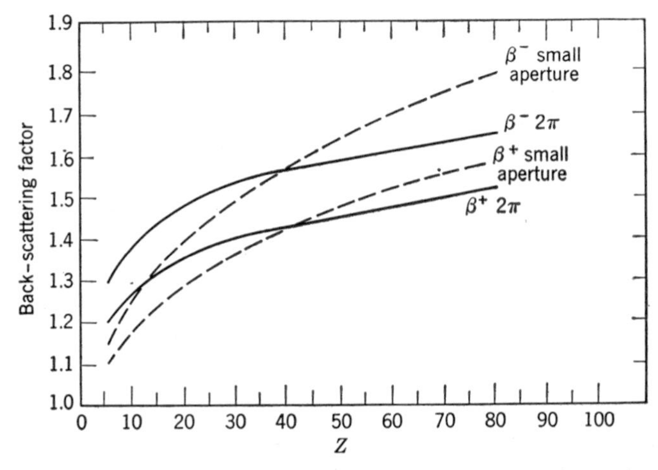

FIGURE 7-9. Saturation back-scattering factor as a function of atomic number, for two different geometries and for positrons and negatrons. These curves are applicable to β spectra of $E_{max} \geqq 0.6$ Mev. [From H. H. Seliger, *Phys. Rev.* **88**, 408 (1952).]

C. ELECTROMAGNETIC RADIATION

Processes Responsible for Energy Loss. The average specific ionization caused by a γ ray is perhaps one-tenth to one-hundredth of that caused by an electron of the same energy. The practical ranges of γ rays are therefore very much greater than those of β particles. The ionization observed for γ rays is almost entirely secondary in nature as we shall see from a discussion of the three processes by which γ rays (and X rays) lose their energy. The average energy loss per ion pair formed is the same as for β rays, namely, 35 ev in air.

At low energies the most important process is the photoelectric effect. In this process the electromagnetic quantum of energy $h\nu$ ejects a bound electron from an atom or molecule and imparts to it an energy $h\nu - b$, where b is the energy with which the electron was bound. The quantum of radiation completely disappears in this process, and momentum conservation is possible only because the remainder of the atom can receive some momentum. For any photon energy greater than the K-binding energy of the absorber, photoelectric absorption takes place primarily in the K shell, with the L shell contributing only of the order of 20 per cent, and outer shells even less. For this reason, the probability for photoelectric absorption has sharp discontinuities at energies equal to the binding energies of the K, L, etc., electrons. For photon energies well above the K-binding energy of the absorber the photoelectric absorption first falls off rapidly (about as $E_\gamma^{-7/2}$), then more slowly (eventually as E_γ^{-1}) with increasing energy. It is also approximately proportional to Z^5. The γ-ray energy at which the photoelectric contribution to the total γ-ray absorption is about 5 per cent is 0.15 Mev for aluminum, 0.4 Mev for copper, 1.2 Mev for tin, and 4.7 Mev for lead. Except in the heaviest elements photoelectric absorption is relatively unimportant for energies above 1 Mev.

The ionization produced by photoelectrons accounts largely for the ionization effect of low-energy photons. The photoelectric effect is frequently used to determine γ-ray energies. This may be accomplished by measurement of the total ionization due to the photoelectrons in a proportional or scintillation counter. In another method a thin foil of high atomic number, called a "radiator" or "converter," is placed over the γ-active sample, and the energies of the ejected photoelectrons are measured in an electron spectrograph.

Instead of giving up its entire energy to a bound electron a photon may transfer only a part of its energy to an electron, which in this case may be either bound or free; the photon is not only degraded in energy but also deflected from its original path. This process is called the Compton effect or Compton scattering. The relation between energy loss and scattering angle can be derived from the conditions for conservation of momentum and energy. The Compton scattering per electron is independent of Z, and, therefore, the scattering coefficient per atom is proportional to Z. For energies in excess of 0.5 Mev it is also approximately [9] proportional to E_γ^{-1}. Thus Compton scattering falls off much more slowly with increasing energy than photoelectric absorption, at least at moderate energies (up to 1 or 2 Mev), and even in lead it is the predominant process in the energy region from about 0.6 to 4 Mev. Photon energies can be determined from the upper energy limits of Compton electrons. For this purpose a radiator of relatively low Z, often copper, is used in the electron spectrograph, so that the Compton effect predominates over the photoelectric effect.

[9] A formula for the scattering coefficient which contains a very complicated function of E_γ was derived from relativistic quantum mechanics by O. Klein and Y. Nishina.

The third mechanism by which electromagnetic radiation can be absorbed is the pair-production process (discussed in chapter 6, page 162). Pair production cannot occur when $E_\gamma < 1.02$ Mev. Above this energy the atomic cross section for pair production first increases slowly with increasing energy, and above about 4 Mev becomes nearly proportional to $\log E_\gamma$. It is also proportional to Z^2. The energy dependence of pair production is satisfactorily predicted by a theory due to H. A. Bethe and W. Heitler. At high energies, where pair production is the predominant process, γ-ray energies can best be determined by measurements of the total energies of positron-electron pairs. Pair production is always followed by annihilation of the positron, usually with the simultaneous emission of two 0.51-Mev photons. The absorption of quanta by the pair-production process is, therefore, always complicated by the appearance of this low-energy secondary radiation.

The atomic cross sections for all three processes discussed increase with increasing Z, except for the photoelectric effect at very low energies. For this reason heavy elements, atom for atom, are much more effective absorbers for electromagnetic radiation than light elements, and lead is most commonly used as an absorber. Because photoelectric effect and Compton effect decrease and pair production increases with increasing energy, the total absorption in any one element has a minimum at some energy. For lead this minimum absorption, or maximum transparency, occurs at about 3 Mev; for copper at about 10 Mev; and for aluminum at about 22 Mev.

Determination of Photon Energies by Absorption. If only photons of the incident energy are considered, all the processes by which γ rays interact with matter lead to exponential attenuation; that is, the intensity $\mathbf{I}_d$ transmitted through a thickness d is given by $\mathbf{I}_d = \mathbf{I}_0 e^{-\mu d}$, where $\mathbf{I}_0$ is the incident intensity and μ is called the absorption coefficient. Separate absorption coefficients for photoelectric effect, Compton scattering, and pair production are sometimes quoted, and the total absorption coefficient μ is the sum of the three. The half-thickness $d_{1/2}$ is defined as the thickness which makes $\mathbf{I}_d = \frac{1}{2}\mathbf{I}_0$; $d_{1/2} = 0.693/\mu$. Absorber thicknesses are frequently given in terms of surface density (ρd, expressed in grams per square centimeter). Then $\mathbf{I}_d = \mathbf{I}_0 e^{-(\mu/\rho)\rho d}$, and μ/ρ is called the mass absorption coefficient.

Unless absorption is entirely by the photoelectric process, the condition that only photons of the incident energy be measured is not always easy to meet experimentally. It requires either a very "good" geometry (large distances between source and absorber and between absorber and detector) or a detector which responds over a narrow

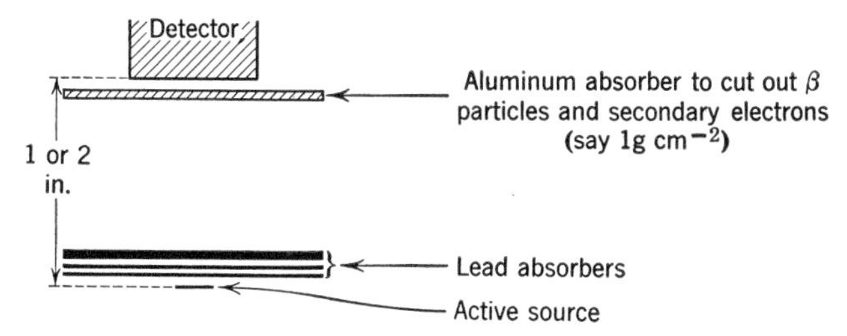

FIGURE 7-10. Suggested arrangement for γ-ray absorption measurements.

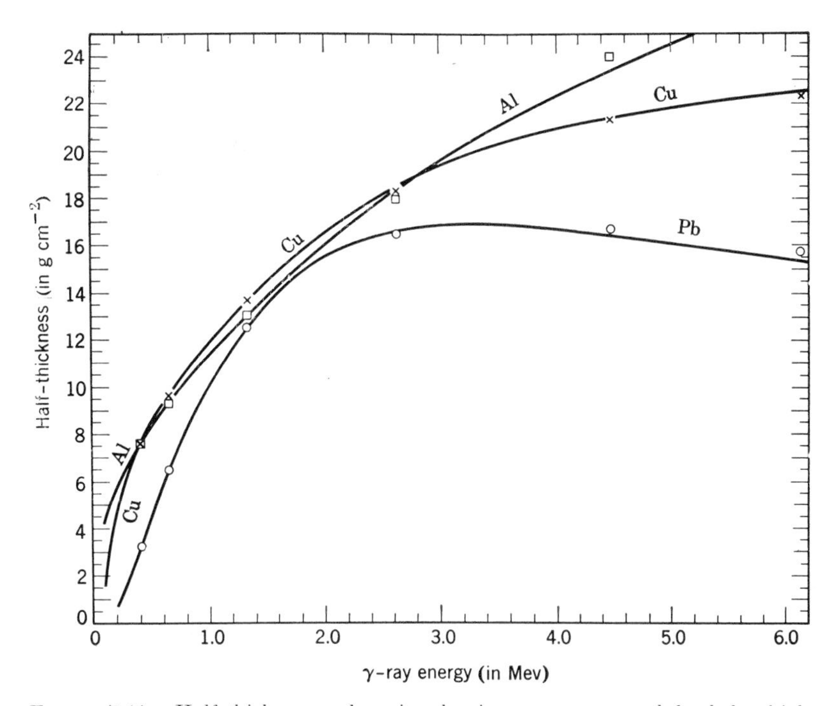

FIGURE 7-11. Half-thickness values in aluminum, copper, and lead for high-energy photons. The curves are based on the calculated absorption coefficients of C. M. Davisson and R. D. Evans, *Revs. Mod. Phys.* **24,** 79 (1952). Some experimental points (□ Al, × Cu, ○ Pb) are taken from S. A. Colgate, *Phys. Rev.* **87,** 592 (1952).

energy range only. More commonly the detector receives and records some of the degraded radiation produced in Compton and pair-production processes. This tends to cause some deviations from true exponential absorption unless the absorber is thick enough for equilibrium with the secondary radiations to be established.

The approximately exponential nature of γ-ray absorption may be used for the determination of γ-ray energies. Various thicknesses of absorber are placed between γ emitter and detector, and the measured activity is plotted versus absorber thickness (usually on semilog paper) to yield an absorption curve. For a single incident photon energy a line results which is straight over a factor of 10 or 20 in intensity if an appropriate experimental arrangement is used. When two components differing sufficiently (perhaps a factor of two) in energy are present, the absorption curve can often be resolved into two straight lines, in the same manner as a decay curve is resolved. Resolution into more than two components with any precision is generally not possible.

An adequate, simple experimental arrangement for absorption measurements is shown schematically in figure 7-10. Active source and absorbers are as far as practicable from the detector to prevent most of the scattered quanta and secondary electrons from falling on the detector. The additional absorber of low Z near the detector stops a large fraction of the secondary electrons (as well as any β particles emitted by the source which otherwise might enter the detector when little or no lead absorber is used).

The quantity most conveniently obtained from an absorption curve for electromagnetic radiation is the half-thickness, and this may be translated into photon energy. Curves of half-thickness in various absorbers versus photon energy are reproduced in figure 7-11 for energies of 0.1 to 6 Mev and in figure 7-12 for energies of about 1 to 400 kev. It should be remembered that a given half-thickness may correspond to two different energies because of the minimum in the curve of absorption versus energy. For example, a half-thickness of 15.5 g cm^{-2} in lead may correspond either to an energy of 2.0 Mev or to an energy of about 5.9 Mev. One can always eliminate this ambiguity by taking absorption curves in two different materials.

Sometimes the absorption of low-energy X rays in aluminum may simulate that of β particles. This source of confusion can be eliminated by the use of a second absorber material, because in the X-ray region the photon mass absorption coefficients vary quite rapidly with Z.

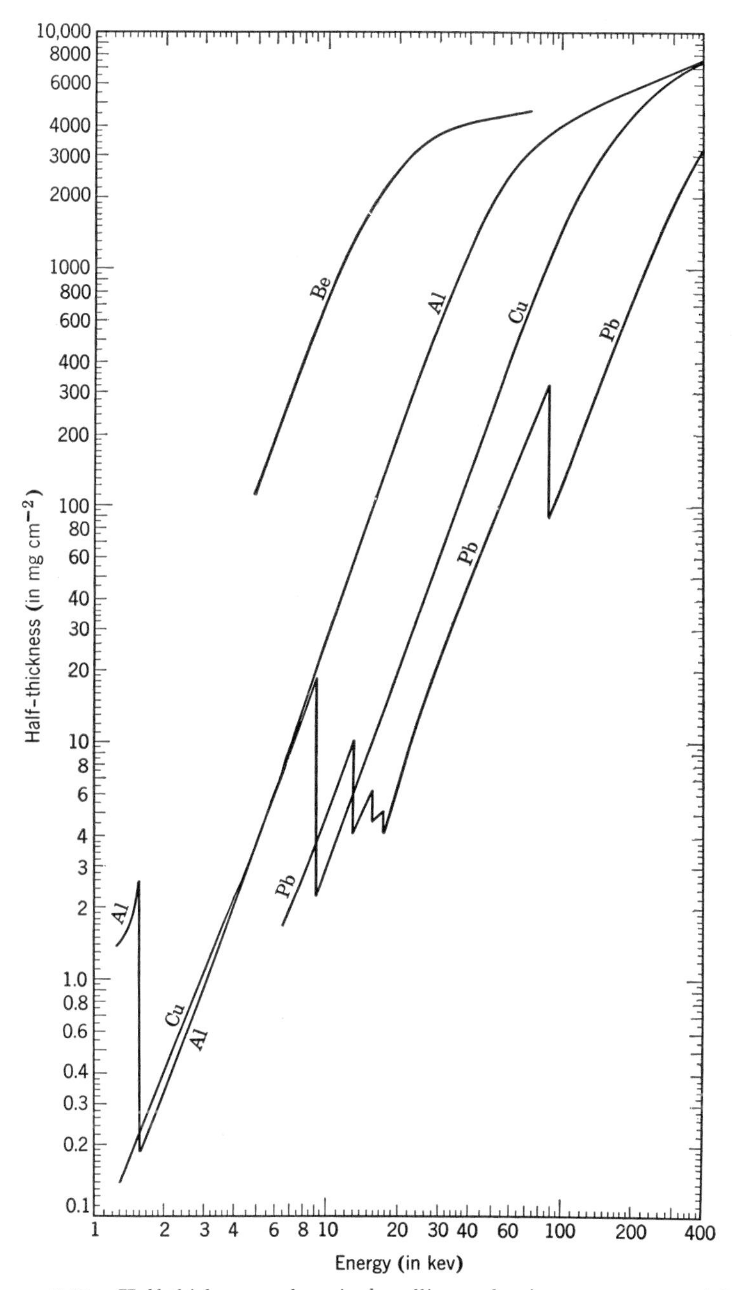

FIGURE 7-12. Half-thickness values in beryllium, aluminum, copper, and lead for low-energy photons. (Data from *Handbook of Chemistry and Physics,* 32nd ed., 1950.) The K-absorption edges of aluminum, copper, and lead as well as the three L edges of lead (corresponding to the three L subshells) are shown.

Critical Absorption of X Rays. We have already mentioned the discontinuities in absorption coefficients at photon energies corresponding to the electron binding energies. These absorption edges and their variation from element to element may be used to identify the energies of characteristic X rays. To understand this method of critical absorption we have to recall that the *emission* of an X ray from an atom is due to the transition of an electron from one of the outer shells to a vacancy in a shell farther in, say, from the L to the K shell.[10] Photoelectric *absorption* in a given electron shell, on the other hand, can occur only if the photon has enough energy to promote an electron from that shell to a vacant level (which means practically enough energy to remove the electron from the atom). It is clear from this that an element is a poor absorber for its own characteristic X rays. The K_α X rays of an element have an energy corresponding to the difference between the K and L shells and can, therefore, not lift a K electron to one of the outer vacant shells in the same element. However, the binding energy of electrons decreases with decreasing Z; therefore, the K_α emission line of an element Z has an energy rather close to but slightly greater than the K absorption edge of some element of slightly lower Z and is, therefore, strongly absorbed by that element, but not by the next higher one. These two neighboring elements will thus have very different absorption coefficients for the particular rays, and the one which absorbs more strongly is called the critical absorber for these X rays. Critical absorption can also be applied to L-emission lines, especially of heavy elements.

As an example, consider the K_α X rays of zinc ($Z = 30$) which have a wavelength of 1.43 A (energy 8.7 kev). The K absorption edges of $_{29}$Cu and $_{28}$Ni are at 1.38 A (9.0 kev) and 1.48 A (8.4 kev), respectively. Therefore, nickel is a good absorber for zinc K_α X rays, and copper is not (figure 7-13). The K_α X rays of gallium ($Z = 31$), on the other hand, are strongly absorbed both in nickel and copper because their wavelength is 1.34 A (9.3 kev), but they are not absorbed well in zinc whose K absorption edge is at 1.28 A (9.7 kev).

Both the X-ray emission lines and the absorption edges of the elements can be found in tables, and suitable elements can be chosen as absorbers to decide the origin of a set of X rays accompanying a nuclear decay process. The K_α X rays are usually the most prominent lines, but occasionally, especially with very heavy elements, the absorption of other lines (K_β and L) also must be taken into account. Absorption

[10] In X-ray terminology, X rays due to transitions from the L to the K shell are called K_α X rays ($K_{\alpha 1}$ and $K_{\alpha 2}$ corresponding to the electron originating in different sublevels of the L shell); X rays due to transitions from the M to the K shell are called K_β, etc. Similarly, there are L_α, L_β, etc., X rays.

curves are taken with each of two or three neighboring elements, and their comparison usually brackets the energy of the emission line sufficiently to determine the corresponding atomic number. It should be emphasized that it is not always necessary to use pure elements as absorbers (this would be difficult for some elements). Compounds of the desired element can be used, provided that other elements in the

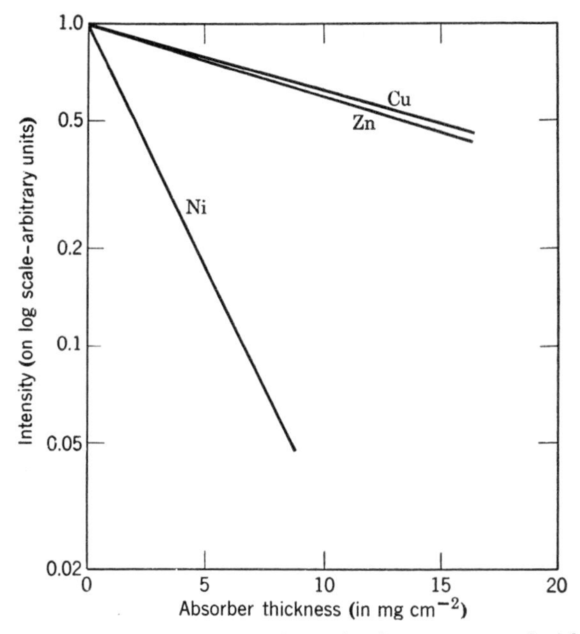

FIGURE 7-13. Absorption of zinc K_α X rays in zinc, copper, and nickel. (These absorption curves were calculated from data given in A. H. Compton and S. K. Allison, *X-rays in Theory and Experiment,* New York, D. Van Nostrand Co., 1935.)

compounds do not appreciably absorb the X rays under investigation. Light elements are very poor absorbers for energetic X rays, and oxides, hydroxides, or carbonates are, therefore, usually suitable as absorbers.

Critical absorption measurements are sometimes used to aid in the identification of a decay process. The X radiation is characteristic of the particular value of Z at the time of emission of the ray; X rays following β^- decay of a nucleus of charge Z correspond to atomic number $Z + 1$; those following β^+ or electron-capture decay correspond to atomic number $Z - 1$; those following internally converted isomeric transitions correspond to atomic number Z.

D. NEUTRONS

Because neutrons carry no charge, their interaction with electrons is exceedingly small, and primary ionization by neutrons is a completely negligible effect.[11] The interaction of neutrons with matter is confined to nuclear effects, which include elastic and inelastic scattering and nuclear reactions such as (n, γ), (n, p), (n, α), $(n, 2n)$, and fission. All these subjects have been discussed in chapter 3, and here we shall merely indicate how each of these types of interaction may be applicable to the detection and measurement of neutrons.

The recoil protons produced by fast neutrons in hydrogenous material are often used for the detection of such neutrons. About 7 protons leave a thick paraffin layer per 10^4 incident neutrons of 1 Mev energy, and for other energies the ratio of protons to neutrons is roughly proportional to neutron energy. The energy of the fastest recoil protons equals the neutron energy.

The ionization produced by protons or α particles created in n, p or n, α reactions can also be used for neutron detection. Ionization chambers or proportional counters (described in chapter 8) may be lined with boron or filled with gaseous BF_3, and the particles from the $B^{10}(n, \alpha)Li^7$ reaction may be detected. The separated isotope B^{10} is particularly effective. Fission fragments may be detected in an ionization chamber lined with fissionable material and exposed to a neutron source.

Neutron-capture reactions leading to radioactive products are frequently used for detection of neutrons by means of the induced activity. This technique is especially useful in the resonance region, where the number of neutrons of a particular energy can often be determined by the amount of resonance capture observed.

E. RADIATION CHEMISTRY

The study of the chemical effects caused by ionizing and other nuclear radiations in their passage through matter is called radiation chemistry. Although any detailed discussion of this rather large field is beyond the scope of this book, we shall mention briefly a few of its important aspects. Radiation-chemical effects are of great practical

[11] A very small cross section ($\sim 4 \times 10^{-7}$ barn) has been experimentally determined. It presumably arises from two effects: the magnetic dipole character of the neutron, and the existence of the neutron partly as a proton with a negative meson cloud around it.

significance in nuclear-reactor technology and in the interaction of radiations with biological systems.

In gases, liquids, and covalently bonded solids the chemical effects of ionizing radiations can be ascribed almost entirely to ionization, excitation, and dissociation of molecules. In gases the chemical reactions observed appear to be rather independent of the type and energy of ionizing radiation used, and the magnitude of the effects in a particular system is determined by the total energy absorbed. In condensed systems the chemical effects for a given total ionization may vary somewhat with ionization density, for example as manifested in differences between α- and β-ray effects.

Radiation Dosimetry. In the study of chemical and biological effects of radiation, a quantitative measure of radiation energy absorption (usually called the dose) is required. Most frequently the dose is inferred from a measurement of total ionization produced in a given volume of air or other material. Instruments for such measurements are discussed in chapter 8. The most frequently used unit of radiation dose is the roentgen or r unit, which is defined as "that quantity of X or γ radiation such that the associated corpuscular emission per 0.001293 g [12] of air produces, in air, ions carrying 1 esu of quantity of electricity of either sign." This means that 1 r produces 1.61×10^{12} ion pairs per gram of air, which corresponds to the absorption of 84 ergs of energy per gram of air. In water the energy absorption corresponding to 1 r is about 93 ergs per gram for all X- or γ-ray energies above about 50 kev.

Since the r unit is defined for electromagnetic radiation only, radiation effects more generally are discussed in relation to the total energy absorption. A common quantitative measure of the efficiency of a radiation-chemical effect is the number of molecules destroyed or produced for each 100 ev of energy absorbed, called the G value for the reaction.

The possible use of radiation-induced chemical reactions for the measurement of integrated radiation doses has been extensively investigated. To be suitable for this purpose the reaction should have a constant G value over a wide range of intensities and types of radiation; the extent of reaction should be proportional to dose over a wide range, and easily measurable; and the reagents employed should be convenient to prepare and store. The chemical dosimeter (or actinometer) that appears most nearly to fulfil these conditions uses the oxidation of Fe(II) in air-saturated, dilute sulfuric acid solution. The G value for this reaction has been carefully determined to be 15.5 ± 0.4.

[12] This is the weight of 1 cc of dry air at 0°C and 760 mm pressure.

Chemical dosimeters require rather sizable radiation doses to produce a measurable reaction. Since 1 r corresponds to an energy loss of 93 ergs per gram of water, we see that the energy deposited per roentgen in 1 ml of solution is about $\frac{93}{1.60 \times 10^{-12}}$ ev and therefore the number of moles of Fe(II) oxidized per milliliter is

$$\frac{93 \times 15.5 \times 10^{-2}}{1.60 \times 10^{-12} \times 6.02 \times 10^{23}} = 1.49 \times 10^{-11}.$$

Various other reactions have been suggested for use as actinometers, among them some that are accompanied by readily measurable color changes. The bleaching by radiation of very dilute solutions of dyes (such as methylene blue) in aqueous gelatin looks promising in this regard. The use of chain reactions, although very desirable because of enhanced sensitivity, is probably precluded by the lack of a linear relation between response and dose rate.

Mechanisms. Much of the work of radiation chemists has been directed toward gaining a detailed understanding of the energy absorption mechanism and of the reaction paths of the unstable intermediates (excited molecules, radicals, and ions). In general, the processes of importance in radiation chemistry include ionization, formation of excited electronic states, transfer of electronic excitation from one molecule to another, dissociation of excited vibrational states, electron capture, neutralization, and radical reactions.

It is apparent from the energy requirement for ion pair formation that only about half the energy dissipated in the passage of radiation through matter is used for ionization; the other half presumably goes into molecular excitation. Both the initial ionization and excitation may be followed by dissociation, and in either case free-radical mechanisms are believed to play an important role. For example, the radiation decomposition of water to H_2, O_2, and H_2O_2 is thought to involve H and OH radicals as intermediates. A great deal of work has been done to elucidate the reaction mechanisms in the radiation chemistry of aqueous solutions; studies of the effects of various solutes on the products of water decomposition have been particularly helpful.

As an example of the mechanism deduced for a radiation-induced reaction we consider the ferrous sulfate oxidation in air-saturated acid solution mentioned earlier. The primary reaction is thought to be the dissociation of water into radicals:

$$H_2O \rightarrow H + OH.$$

The subsequent steps are believed to be as follows:

$$(a) \qquad OH + Fe^{++} \rightarrow Fe^{+++} + OH^-,$$

$$(b) \qquad H + O_2 \rightarrow HO_2,$$

$$(c) \qquad H^+ + HO_2 + Fe^{++} \rightarrow Fe^{+++} + H_2O_2,$$

$$(d) \qquad H_2O_2 + Fe^{++} \rightarrow Fe(OH)^{++} + OH.$$

The OH radical produced in step (*d*) reacts according to (*a*). Thus, for every H_2O molecule decomposed, four Fe^{++} ions are oxidized, and this agrees with experimental observations.

Radiolysis of Organic Compounds. Most organic systems are much too complex to encourage any detailed studies of the mechanism of their radiation decomposition. However, a few generalizations may be made about the types of net reactions observed. A great variety of products can usually be found: gases such as H_2, CO, and CO_2; fragments smaller than the irradiated molecules; and polymerization products. Radiation-induced polymerization of acetylene to benzene, and of styrene to polystyrene, have been studied and found to involve chain reactions induced by free radicals. Radiation-induced changes in the mechanical properties of some polymers such as polyethylene can be traced to the formation of cross linkages between polymer chains, and such effects have found some practical applications.

One very striking general observation is that aromatic compounds are much more stable towards radiation decomposition than are aliphatic compounds. This is explained by the resonance stabilization of even the excited states of the benzene ring; as a consequence of this extra stability these excited states presumably do not dissociate readily, but may be de-activated by collisions or by emission of radiation. Aromatic compounds with aliphatic side chains (for example, ethyl benzene) exhibit about the same stability as purely aromatic substances, which indicates that excitation energy is readily transferred from the side chain to the ring before dissociation can occur. Even in mixtures this "protective" influence of benzene rings has been demonstrated; for example, the radiation decomposition of cyclohexane in benzene solution is much less than that of pure cyclohexane.

The relative stability of the first excited electronic states of aromatic molecules towards dissociation is closely connected with the fact that these states have large probabilities for de-excitation by the emission of fluorescent radiation. It is this de-excitation mechanism which accounts for the scintillations of organic compounds such as anthracene, naphthalene, stilbene, and terphenyl exposed to ionizing radiations. The fluorescence properties of these organic substances are characteristic of their molecular structure, and they scintillate in solutions as well as in the solid state.

The differences in the effects of radiation on aromatic and aliphatic compounds indicate that, even in a given compound, radiations should not be expected to affect different bonds equally. Some specificity in the attack of radiation on certain groups has indeed been established. Yet a statistical approach to the problem of the probabilities for various bond ruptures is often useful, particularly when the radiation-induced reactions of a homologous series are considered. On a statistical basis one might expect that in such a series the relative yields of the products should vary from compound to compound linearly with the relative abundances of parent groups. This is experimentally found; for example, in the radiolysis of straight-chain alkanes the ratio of H_2 to CH_4 yields varies almost linearly with the ratio of H to CH_3 groups in the molecules.

Radiation Effects in Solids. The irradiation of ionic crystals and of other insulators such as glass often results in intense coloration. This phenomenon is ascribed to absorption bands produced when electrons are trapped by lattice imperfections or impurity atoms. Various bands (designated as F, F′, V, etc., bands) are distinguished according to the type of electron-trapping center involved. Some energy levels caused by lattice defects or impurity ions are so-called luminescence centers: the electrons brought into these levels as a result of radiation effects can return to the filled (ground state) band with the emission of photons in the visible or near ultraviolet part of the spectrum. The scintillations in inorganic phosphors (thallium-activated sodium iodide, silver-activated zinc sulfide, etc.) produced by this mechanism are finding increasing use in radiation detection devices. The transparency of a phosphor to its own luminescence radiation is very important in this connection and is due to the fact that the luminescence centers lie in energy below the conduction band to which electrons can be raised by photon absorption.

In metals and semiconductors the ionization effects produced by radiation are of relatively little importance because the ionized electrons find themselves in the conduction bands, and their energy is quickly transformed into heat. In these solids the dominant effects produced by neutrons, protons, and heavier ions are due to displacement of atoms, which in other materials are quite negligible compared with the ionization effects.

Irradiation with fast neutrons or ions is found to alter many properties of solids, including thermal and electrical conductivity, hardness, other mechanical properties, and crystal lattice parameters. Many of the observed changes are similar to those induced by quite different means such as cold-working, and in most cases the original properties can be restored by appropriate heat treatment (provided, of course, that the chemical composition has not been appreciably altered by nuclear transmutations). Changes caused by nuclear transmutations are of some significance in the irradiation of semiconductors; the production of impurities by nuclear reactions, for example the formation of gallium from germanium, can be used to bring about permanent changes in the electrical properties of the semiconductor.

F. BIOLOGICALLY PERMISSIBLE DOSES

Radiation chemistry has an important application in the field of biology. The biological effects of radiation are brought about through chemical changes in the cells caused by ionizations, excitations, dissociations, and atom displacements. In determining radiation effects on living organisms, whether from external radiation or from ingested or inhaled radioactive material, one has to take into consideration not only the total dosages of ionization produced in the organism but also such factors as the density of the ionization, the dosage rate, the localization of the effect, and the rates of administration and elimination of radioactive material.

The most widely used unit of radiation dosage is the roentgen, defined on p. 213. The r is a unit of the total quantity of ionization produced by γ or X rays, and dosage rates for these radiations are therefore expressed in terms of roentgens or milliroentgens (mr) per unit time. The maximum allowable weekly dose for human beings exposed to X or γ radiation is usually taken as 0.3 r or 300 mr for total body exposure. The permissible dose on hands and forearms is 1.5 r per week at the base of the epidermis.

The r unit is not properly used for radiations other than X or γ rays and is not recommended for use with electromagnetic radiation above 3 Mev. In 1950, the International Commission on Radiological Units recommended that the dose of any ionizing radiation in relation to its biological or related effects be expressed "in terms of the quantity of energy absorbed per unit mass (ergs per gram) of irradiated material at the place of interest." A unit of dose sometimes used is the roentgen-equivalent-physical (rep), which equals 93 ergs absorbed per gram of tissue.

The same amount of energy dissipation per gram of tissue may cause different amounts of biological damage when brought about by different radiations. For example, the secondary ionization due to recoil protons from fast neutrons has been found to be about ten times as effective biologically as the same quantity of ionization due to γ rays. (The same is true for fast protons themselves in the tissues they penetrate.) Therefore the maximum allowable weekly dose for fast neutrons is $0.1 \times 0.3 \times 93 = 2.8$ ergs absorbed per gram of tissue. (This assumes that tissue is like water.) Thermal neutrons are believed to be about twice as effective biologically as γ rays for the same energy dissipation. In the case of β rays, the International Commission on Radiological Protection recommends a maximum allowable weekly exposure of the skin such that the absorption per gram of tissue (basal layer of epidermis at depth of 7 mg cm^{-2}) is equivalent to the energy absorption from 1.5 r of hard γ rays.

As an example of the practical application of some of the concepts discussed we estimate the dosage rate in roentgens per hour to be expected at a distance of 50 cm from a 100-mc Co^{60} source. Each disintegration of Co^{60} is accompanied by two γ quanta with energies 1.17 Mev and 1.33 Mev; for simplicity we use for each an average energy of 1.25 Mev. The source emits $2 \times 100 \times 3.7 \times 10^7 = 7.4 \times 10^9$ quanta per second. At a distance of 50 cm the γ flux is $7.4 \times 10^9/(4\pi \times 2500) = 2.3 \times 10^5$ photons $\text{cm}^{-2}\ \text{sec}^{-1}$ or $2.3 \times 10^5 \times 1.25 \times 10^6 = 2.9 \times 10^{11}$ ev $\text{cm}^{-2}\ \text{sec}^{-1}$. Since at an energy of 1.25 Mev the mass absorption coefficients in air and aluminum are about the same, we read the half-thickness from figure 7-11 as 12.5 g cm^{-2}. Then the fractional energy loss for the γ rays per g cm^{-2} of air is given by $\mu/\rho = 0.693/12.5 = 0.055$, and the energy lost by the γ rays in going through 1 g cm^{-2} of air is $0.055 \times 2.9 \times 10^{11} \times 3600 = 5.7 \times 10^{13}$ ev hr^{-1} or 92 erg hr^{-1}. Setting the energy absorbed per gram of air equal to this energy loss [13] we get $92/84 = 1.1$ r hr^{-1}.

Before leaving the subject of maximum allowable doses of radiation we should note that the body may receive excessive irradiations from internal as well as external sources. Many radioactive nuclides when ingested or inhaled become fixed in the body for varying lengths of time. Care must therefore be taken to avoid intake of radioactive materials. Table 7-4 lists the maximum allowable concentrations of a few nuclides in inhaled air and in ingested liquids and also the maximum permissible amounts in the body.

[13] This procedure leads to an overestimate (in the present case, by about a factor 2) of the energy absorption in air because a fraction of the energy loss occurs by Compton scattering, and some of the secondary quanta leave the local region of interest. The method used applies when the primary radiation is in equilibrium with secondaries; inside a mass of tissue this condition obtains more nearly than it does in air.

TABLE 7-4

BIOLOGICALLY PERMISSIBLE LEVELS OF RADIONUCLIDES

[From *Nucleonics* **8,** No. 2, 70 (February 1951)]

Nuclide	Maximum Permissible Level: In Body (μc)	In Air * ($\mu c/cc$)	In Liquid Media * ($\mu c/cc$)	Proportion Absorbed and Retained: Via Lungs	Via Gut
Ra^{226}	0.1	8×10^{-12}	4×10^{-8}	0.06	0.1
Pu^{239}	0.04	2×10^{-12}	1.5×10^{-6}	0.1	0.001
Po^{210}	0.005				
Sr^{89}	2.0				
$Sr^{90}(+Y^{90})$	1.0	2×10^{-10}	8×10^{-7}	0.06	0.1
I^{131}	0.3	3×10^{-9}	3×10^{-5}	0.2	0.2
Co^{60}	1		1×10^{-5}		1
P^{32}	10		2×10^{-4}		1
Na^{24}	15		8×10^{-3}		1
C^{14}		1×10^{-6} (as CO_2)			
H^3	10^4	5×10^{-5}	0.4	1	1

* Occupational exposure, 40 hours per week, 50 weeks per year, is assumed.

EXERCISES

1. Show that the maximum velocity an electron can receive in an impact with an α particle of velocity v is approximately $2v$.

2. Estimate the ranges in air of (*a*) 10-Mev H^3 ions, (*b*) doubly charged 10-Mev He^3 ions. *Answer:* (*a*) 51 cm.

3. (*a*) What thickness of aluminum foil will reduce the energy of 40-Mev He^4 ions to 32 Mev? (*b*) What energy loss will a 20-Mev deuteron beam suffer in passing through the same foil?

Answer: (*a*) 55 mg cm^{-2}; (*b*) $\Delta E \approx 2$ Mev.

4. An absorption curve of a sample emitting β and γ rays was taken, using a Lauritsen electroscope, with aluminum absorbers. The data obtained were:

Absorber Thickness (g/cm^2)	Activity (divisions/min)	Absorber Thickness (g/cm^2)	Activity (divisions/min)
0	5.8	0.700	0.11
0.070	3.5	0.800	0.10
0.130	2.2	1.00	0.10
0.200	1.3	2.00	0.092
0.300	0.60	4.00	0.080
0.400	0.28	7.00	0.065
0.500	0.12	10.00	0.053
0.600	0.11	14.00	0.040

(*a*) Find the maximum energy of the β spectrum (in million electron volts).

(*b*) Find the energy of the γ ray.

(*c*) What would be the absorption coefficient of that γ ray in lead?

5. Estimate the range of Po^{210} α particles in (*a*) air, (*b*) methane, (*c*) argon, (*d*) uranium.

6. In an attempt to measure the neutron-capture cross section of RaD (Pb^{210}) it is desired to measure the α particles of Bi^{211} in equilibrium with Pb^{211} and in the presence of a millicurie of Pb^{210}. Is this experiment feasible with the use of an aluminum absorber to cut out the β^- particles and conversion electrons of RaD? Would a lead absorber be better?

7. In a certain measuring arrangement the β rays of 13.7-day Cs^{136} are absorbed as follows (γ-ray background has been subtracted).

Absorber Thickness (mg Al/cm²)	Relative Intensity	Absorber Thickness (mg Al/cm²)	Relative Intensity
0	100	53	2.7
12	47	72	0.30
27	17	85	0.037
41	7.3		

For comparison the absorption of P^{32} β rays is measured with the same arrangement; the results are

Absorber Thickness (mg Al/cm²)	Relative Intensity	Absorber Thickness (mg Al/cm²)	Relative Intensity
0	250	530	2.30
160	100	580	0.95
245	50	620	0.45
360	20	680	0.15
420	10	725	0.05
480	5.0	780 (range)	0.0

Determine the maximum β energy of 13.7-day Cs^{136} by means of a Feather plot, using the P^{32} as a standard.

8. At 1.00 meter from 1.00 g radium (in equilibrium with its decay products and enclosed in 0.5 mm of platinum) the γ-ray dosage rate is 0.84 r per hr. What is the minimum safe working distance from a 20 mg radium source for a 40-hr week? *Answer:* 5 ft.

9. From data on X-ray spectra and X-ray absorption coefficients (in the Chemical Rubber Company Handbook, for example) locate the critical absorbers for the identification of the X rays following K capture (*a*) in A^{37}, (*b*) in Pd^{101}.

10. Estimate the linear absorption coefficient and the energy loss per centimeter of path in air (at 15°C and 760 mm pressure) for 1-Mev γ rays.

11. At a distance of 2 ft from a Cs^{137} source the dosage rate due to the γ rays from this source is found to be 127 mr per hr. The decay of Cs^{137} is accompanied by the emission of a 0.66-Mev γ ray in about 82 per cent of the disintegrations; no other γ rays are emitted. (*a*) Estimate the strength of

the Cs^{137} source in millicuries. (*b*) What thickness of lead shielding (in inches) is required around the source to reduce the dosage rate at 2 ft to 3 mr per hr? *Answer:* (*a*) 60 mc; (*b*) ~1¼ in.

12. The radiations emitted by a radioactive strontium sample were examined by aluminum absorption measurements. The following data were obtained with an argon-filled proportional counter. The decay of the sample during the course of the measurements was negligible.

Absorber Thickness (mg/cm²)	Activity (counts/min)	Absorber Thickness (mg/cm²)	Activity (counts/min)
0	32,100	200	525
10	20,900	250	445
20	13,600	300	397
40	6,050	350	368
60	2,950	400	355
80	1,610	500	342
100	1,080	700	330
120	810	1200	316
150	670	1800	300

Some check measurements with beryllium instead of aluminum absorbers gave the following results:

Absorber Thickness (mg/cm²)	Activity (counts/min)	Absorber Thickness (mg/cm²)	Activity (counts/min)
0	32,100	100	2220
10	21,000	125	2050
30	9,450	250	1940
50	4,850	400	1820
75	2,800	650	1650

Finally the following lead absorption measurements were taken, with 150 mg cm^{-2} of beryllium always covering the counter window, in addition to the lead absorbers listed.

Lead Absorber (g/cm²)	Activity (counts/min)	Lead Absorber (g/cm²)	Activity (counts/min)
0	2000	0.100	343
0.005	1110	1.20	291
0.010	680	2.50	240
0.015	490	4.30	184
0.020	405	7.00	122
0.030	350	9.90	80

What conclusions can you draw about the mode of decay of the (hypothetical) strontium isotope present in the sample and about the radiations and their energies and relative intensities?

REFERENCES

H. A. Bethe and J. Ashkin, "Passage of Radiations through Matter," *Experimental Nuclear Physics* (E. Segrè, Editor), Vol. I, pp. 166–357, New York, John Wiley & Sons, 1953.

E. Rutherford, J. Chadwick, and C. D. Ellis, *Radiations from Radioactive Substances,* Cambridge University Press, 1930.

F. Rasetti, *Elements of Nuclear Physics,* New York, Prentice-Hall, Inc., 1936.

I. Kaplan, *Nuclear Physics,* Cambridge, Mass., Addison-Wesley Publishing Co., 1955.

R. R. Williams, *Principles of Nuclear Chemistry,* New York, D. Van Nostrand Co., 1950.

S. K. Allison and S. D. Warshaw, "Passage of Heavy Particles through Matter," *Revs. Mod. Phys.* **25,** 779 (1953).

M. Rich and R. Madey, "Range-Energy Tables," University of California Report UCRL-2301 (March 1954).

J. Knipp and E. Teller, "On the Energy Loss of Heavy Ions," *Phys. Rev.* **59,** 659 (1941).

N. O. Lassen, "Total Charges of Fission Fragments in Gaseous and Solid Media," *Phys. Rev.* **79,** 1016 (1950).

E. Lisitzin, "Ueber die Ionisierungsspannungen der Elemente in verschiedenen Ionisierungszustaenden," *Societa Sci. Fennica, Commentationes Phys.-Math.* **10,** No. 4 (1940).

L. E. Glendenin, "Determination of the Energy of Beta Particles and Photons by Absorption," *Nucleonics* **2,** No. 1, 12 (January 1948).

E. Bleuler and G. J. Goldsmith, *Experimental Nucleonics,* New York, Rinehart and Co., 1952.

L. Katz and A. S. Penfold, "Range-Energy Relations for Electrons and the Determination of Beta-Ray End-Point Energies by Absorption," *Revs. Mod. Phys.* **24,** 28 (1952).

L. Yaffe and K. M. Justus, "Back-Scattering of Electrons into Geiger-Mueller Counters," *J. Chem. Soc.* Supplement No. 2, S.341 (1949).

C. M. Davisson and R. D. Evans, "Gamma-Ray Absorption Coefficients," *Revs. Mod. Phys.* **24,** 79 (1952).

R. D. Hill, E. L. Church, and J. W. Mihelich, "The Determination of Gamma-Ray Energies from Beta-Ray Spectroscopy and a Table of Critical X-Ray Absorption Energies," *Rev. Sci. Instr.* **23,** 523 (1952).

A. H. Compton and S. K. Allison, *X-Rays in Theory and Experiment,* New York, D. Van Nostrand Co., 1935.

B. T. Feld, "The Neutron," *Experimental Nuclear Physics* (E. Segrè, Editor), Vol. II, New York, John Wiley & Sons, 1953.

H. H. Barschall, L. Rosen, R. F. Taschek, and J. H. Williams, "Measurements of Fast Neutron Flux," *Revs. Mod. Phys.* **24,** 1 (1952).

M. Burton, "Radiation Chemistry," *Ann. Rev. Phys. Chem.,* Vol. 1, p. 113, Stanford, Annual Reviews Inc., 1950.

F. S. Dainton and E. Collinson, "Radiation Chemistry," *Ann. Rev. Phys. Chem.,* Vol. 2, p. 99, Stanford, Annual Reviews Inc., 1951.

G. J. Dienes, "Radiation Effects in Solids," *Ann. Rev. Nuclear Sci.,* Vol. II, p. 187, Stanford, Annual Reviews Inc., 1953.

L. D. Marinelli, "Radiation Dosimetry and Protection," *Ann. Rev. Nuclear Sci.,* Vol. III, p. 249, Stanford, Annual Reviews Inc., 1953.

H. H. Goldsmith, "Bibliography on Radiation Protection," *Nucleonics* **4,** No. 6, 62 (June 1949).

L. A. Ohlinger, "Shielding from Nuclear Radiations," *Nucleonics* **5,** No. 4, 4 (October 1949).

International Commission on Radiological Protection, "Recommendations," *Nucleonics* **8,** No. 1, 31 (January 1951).

"Safe Handling of Radioactive Isotopes," *National Bureau of Standards Handbook* **42** (1949), available from Superintendent of Documents, Washington 25, D. C. (15 cents).

"Maximum Permissible Amounts of Radioisotopes in the Human Body and Maximum Permissible Concentrations in Air and Water," *National Bureau of Standards Handbook* **52** (1953), available from Superintendent of Documents, Washington 25, D. C. (20 cents).

CHAPTER 8

RADIATION DETECTION AND MEASUREMENT

In the preceding chapter we saw that the principal interactions of the radioactive radiations with matter result in the production of ions with a reduction in energy of the radiation of about 35 ev per ion pair formed. All methods for detection of radioactivity are based on interactions of the charged particles or electromagnetic rays with matter traversed. The uncharged neutron is detected only indirectly, through recoil protons (from fast neutrons) or through nuclear transmutations or induced radioactivities (from fast or slow neutrons). Neutrinos have no charge and do not seem to interact measurably with matter to produce either ions or recoil particles, and, therefore, are not detectable by any of these methods. (It may be presumed that neutrinos should be capable of causing nuclear transmutations, but the cross section for the process is estimated from the principle of microscopic reversibility to be less than 10^{-40} cm^2; being hard to emit they must be hard to absorb. Even so, observation of this process has recently been reported.)

A. IONIZATION CURRENT MEASUREMENTS

Saturation Current. Many common radiation detectors make use of the electric conductivity of a gas resulting from the ionization produced in it. This conductivity is somewhat analogous to the electric conductivity of solutions caused by the presence of electrolyte ions. In gas conduction as produced by radiation, the ion current first increases with applied voltage (as in the electrolyte case); with increasing voltage the current eventually reaches a constant value which is a direct measure of the rate of production of charged ions in the gas volume. This constant value of the current is called the saturation current. A schematic representation of a gas volume and collecting electrodes, with potential difference V and meter to measure the ionization current I, is shown in figure 8-1, along with a plot of I versus V that might be obtained.

In the region of applied voltage below that necessary for the saturation current, recombination of positive and negative ions reduces the current collected. As the applied voltage is increased beyond the upper limit for saturation collection, the current increases again, and, finally, the gap breaks down into a glowing discharge or arc, with a very sharp rise in the current. In the measurement of gas ionization

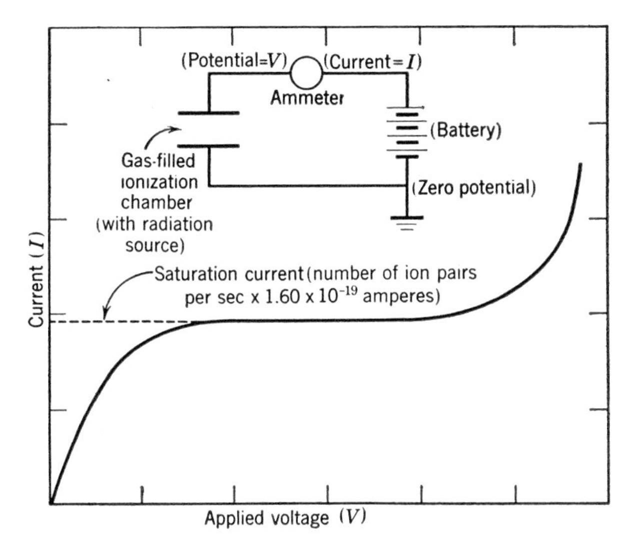

FIGURE 8-1. Ionization current.

it is obviously of some advantage to measure the saturation current: the current is easily interpreted in terms of the rate of gas ionization, and the measured current does not depend critically on the applied voltage. The range of voltage over which the saturation current is obtained depends on the geometry of the electrodes and their spacing, the nature and pressure of the gas, and the general and local density and spatial distribution of the ionization produced in the gas. In air, for many practical cases, this region may extend from $\sim 10^2$ to $\sim 10^4$ volts per cm of distance between the electrodes.

We may classify detection systems (of the ion-collection type) according to whether saturation collection is employed or whether the multiplicative collection region is used. In the multiplicative region, where V is above the maximum value for saturation collection, the additional current is due to secondary ionization processes which result from the high velocities reached by the ions (particularly electrons) moving in the high potential gradient. The use of this current amplification makes multiplicative collection methods inherently sensitive but unfortunately also inherently critical to many experimental variables.

Electroscopes. We will call the gas-filled electrode systems designed for saturation collection ionization chambers. Saturation current instruments consist of the ionization chamber, in which ions produced are collected with as little recombination and as little multiplication as possible, and of an electric system for measurement of the very small currents obtained. The essential differences between the various instruments of this sort are in the nature of the current-measuring systems. In one common and relatively inexpensive instrument, the Lauritsen-type electroscope, a sensitive quartz-fiber electrometer measures the change in voltage produced on the fiber and its support by collection of the ionization charge. An external battery or rectifier is used to provide the initial voltage V (by means of a temporary connection to the fiber support); then, the fiber position is observed through a small telescope to measure ΔV as a function of time. For a collected charge q, the resulting $\Delta V = q/\mathrm{C}$, where C is the approximately constant capacitance of the fiber and electrode system. (The order of magnitude of C may be guessed from the dimensions; the fiber and support arrangement are about 1 cm long, and C is of the order of 1 cm, which is the electrostatic unit of capacitance equal to about 10^{-12} farad or $1\mu\mu$f.) The Lauritsen electroscope is simple and rugged and can be used to detect a β activity of about 2000 disintegrations per minute (so arranged that about 50 per cent of the rays enter the ionization chamber). With the same arrangement samples up to about 1000 times this activity may be measured accurately.

Direct-Current Amplifiers. Instruments of another type use ionization chambers with electronic d-c amplifiers. The ionization current I is caused to flow through a very high resistance R, and the voltage developed, $V = \mathrm{IR}$, is applied to the control grid of a vacuum tube and measured in terms of the plate current of the tube by a galvanometer G. (See the schematic circuit in figure 8-2.) To measure the smallest currents the vacuum tube must be chosen for low inherent grid current, and several tubes are manufactured particularly for this service. High stability of the circuit is essential, and some balancing feature to reduce effects of battery voltage variations is generally employed. The circuit in figure 8-2 uses a voltage, derived from the same battery, applied to a second grid for this purpose. Another common arrangement uses two identical tubes and measures the difference in their plate currents caused by a signal applied to the control grid of one.

The ionization chamber may contain air at atmospheric pressure, which permits the use of an exceedingly thin aluminum leaf window for particles of low penetration but makes the response to penetrating radiations proportional to the barometric pressure. Sealed chambers are also used, and in special applications low-energy β emitters such as C^{14} and H^3 may be introduced as gaseous compounds directly into

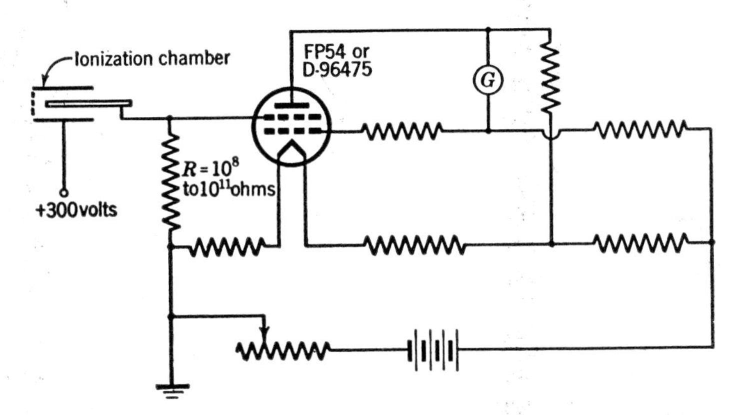

FIGURE 8-2. Ionization chamber with balanced d-c amplifier.

the chamber volume. For γ and X rays the ionization chamber may be filled to a pressure of several atmospheres with Freon (a chlorofluoromethane) or methyl bromide.

An instrument of this type with $R = 10^{11}$ ohms is sensitive to 1000 β disintegrations per minute (with the assumption that about 50 per cent of the rays enter the ionization chamber). With R switched to 10^8 ohms a sample of about 2×10^7 disintegrations per minute may be measured.

As an example we estimate the ionization current I and the voltage drop IR for an ionization chamber under these assumptions: $R = 10^{11}$ ohms; the sample is an emitter of moderately energetic β rays with 1000 disintegrations per minute; the geometry is such that 50 per cent of the β particles enter and spend an average 8-cm path length in the effective volume of an air-filled chamber. The number of ion pairs to be expected [1] is about $1000 \times 0.50 \times 80 \times 10 = 4 \times 10^5$ per min,

[1] The estimate of 10 ion pairs per mm over the 80-mm path is taken from the information on β-ray ionization in chapter 7.

or 6.7×10^3 per sec. The current I will be the corresponding charge per second:

$$I = 6.7 \times 10^3 \times 1.6 \times 10^{-19} = 1.1 \times 10^{-15} \text{ amp.}$$

$$IR = 1.1 \times 10^{-15} \times 10^{11} = 1.1 \times 10^{-4} \text{ volt.}$$

If the use of the number of ion pairs rather than the total number of ions in this calculation is not entirely clear, remember that only half of the ions—those with the proper sign of charge—are collected at either electrode.

Vibrating-Reed Electrometer. Even though special tubes and balanced circuits may be used with ionization chambers, d-c amplifiers are more susceptible to disturbance and drift and more difficult to arrange with several successive stages of amplification than those designed for amplifying alternating currents. An important development is the use of a continuously vibrating reed which, through its oscillating electrostatic capacitance to a fixed electrode, converts the IR voltage to an approximately sinusoidal alternating potential; the a-c signal is then amplified in a highly stable audio-frequency amplifier. This instrument, the vibrating-reed electrometer, is easily sensitive to 10^{-15} amp, thus to 1000 β disintegrations per minute with a typical ionization chamber, and is unusually free from troublesome zero drift and external disturbance.

Because the a-c voltage generated by the reed is affected by the amplitude of vibration, this amplifier is almost always used as a null instrument. The voltage IR developed by the ionization chamber current (with R perhaps as large as 10^{12} ohms) is applied to one side of the vibrating-reed condenser, and an accurately known d-c reference voltage from a potentiometer is applied to the other. When these two voltages are the same there is no a-c signal output. Commercial instruments find this null point electronically, and a conventional voltmeter connected to the reference voltage indicates the ionization current.

For most applications requiring high sensitivity and stability the vibrating-reed electrometer is usually the instrument of choice. The reeds must be constructed with great care, and the entire set of equipment is not inexpensive.

Linear Pulse Amplifier. An ionization chamber with directly connected a-c amplifier, as in the schematic representation of figure 8-3, will, of course, give no response to any steady ionization current. A short burst of intense ionization, such as results from the passage of an α particle through the chamber, will give a sudden change of voltage on the first grid; this grid voltage will return to normal in a time of the order of RC, where C represents the distributed capacitance of the grid and collecting-electrode system and R is the effective resistance to ground.[2] With sufficient amplification a large pulse will appear at the amplifier output terminal; the shape in time of this voltage pulse will depend on several factors, including the value of RC and the frequency-response characteristics of the amplifier. It is ordinarily desirable to have the height of the output pulse proportional to the amount of ionization produced by the particle in the

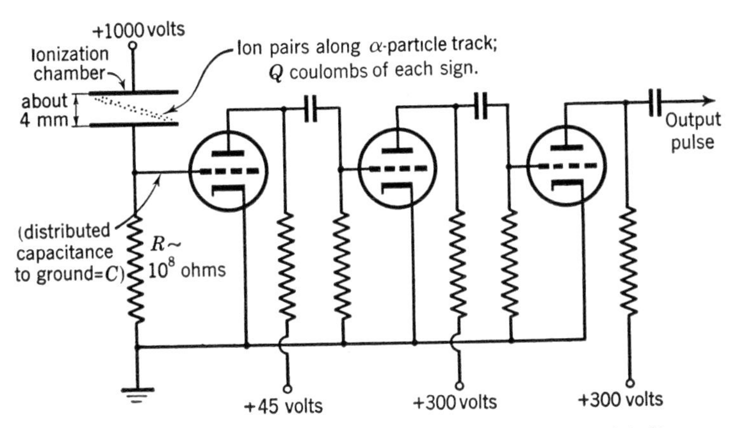

FIGURE 8-3. Schematic representation of ionization chamber with linear pulse amplifier.

chamber; thus the name linear amplifier or linear pulse amplifier is often applied to this instrument.

Since the instrument is used for counting single α particles we may estimate the voltage amplification factor (gain) needed. A fast α particle traveling 1 cm in the chamber would give in air about 25,000 ion pairs, and the collected ion charge, $q = \sim 25{,}000 \times 1.6 \times 10^{-19} = \sim 4 \times 10^{-15}$ coulomb. Guessing $C = \sim 10\ \mu\mu f$ we have then $V = q/C = \sim 4 \times 10^{-4}$ volt. If an output pulse of 100 volts is wanted (convenient for oscillographic observation and photographic recording) the required gain is $100/(4 \times 10^{-4}) = 2.5 \times 10^5$. Four amplifier stages might be used, each with gain of roughly 22.

A practical ionization chamber may have a background rate of the order of 0.1 to 1 α per min; the lower limit of sample strength easily

[2] The charge in a capacitor of capacitance C short-circuited with a high resistance R will be dissipated exponentially; the half-time for the process is given by 0.693 RC; RC is known as the time constant of the circuit and is the time required for the charge to be reduced to $1/e$ of its value.

detectable we may take as ~1 α disintegration per minute (with 50 per cent geometry). With appropriate amplifier and recording equipment the maximum usable rate is limited by the duration (~RC) of the voltage pulse, because, if the average rate of arrival of pulses is such that there is an appreciable chance of one following another within the time RC, appreciable counting error results. With R = 10^8 ohms, RC = ~10^{-3} sec, and a few thousand counts per minute would be the useful upper limit. Of course R is easily made smaller, but the full voltage q/C is achieved only if RC is long compared to the time of collection of ions in the chamber. The velocity v of ions in air under a voltage gradient E volts per centimeter is about (perhaps 1.5 times) E centimeters per second; with 1000 volts applied to a 0.4 cm chamber, v = ~4000 cm per sec, and the ion collection time is ~0.4/4000 = ~10^{-4} sec. In practice RC is usually made somewhat longer than this time; to waste much of the voltage pulse is not advisable because with higher amplifier gains much trouble would be caused by tube "noise" and by microphonic effects (sensitivity of the chamber and amplifier to vibration).

In a closed ionization chamber filled with pure argon or nitrogen the electrons formed in ionization processes do not become attached to gas molecules to form negative ions but remain principally as free electrons. The drift velocity of electrons in the field is much greater than that of ions, and they reach the collector electrode in about 10^{-6} sec. In this case not only may much higher counting rates be used, but also if the amplifier is responsive to the higher frequencies only, the microphonic disturbances are very much reduced. However, since the useful pulse corresponds to the movement in the gas of only the electrons, the pulse height may not be proportional to the total amount of ionization.

If the ionization chamber is large enough to contain the entire range of the most energetic α rays, and if the total ionization produced is collected for each pulse, then the pulse height will be an accurate measure of the α-particle energy, which is characteristic of the particular α emitter.

Linear amplifiers may be used to count fissions; because fission fragments have roughly ten times the specific ionization of α particles they are easily distinguished. Exceedingly low fission rates (of the order of 1 count per day) can be measured in the presence of high α-particle fluxes. This was important in the determination of some of the very low spontaneous-fission rates listed in chapter 6. Fission chambers are also found useful as neutron detectors.

Beta particles and γ rays do not produce enough ionization in the usual chambers to give pulses detectable above the background noise.

To some extent this limitation can be removed by the use of a more dense ionizing medium. Certain crystals, including selected diamonds, when fitted with electrodes and connected to a source of high voltage and to a fast amplifier, give pulses under the action of radioactive rays. Ionization chambers filled with liquid argon have been tested. At the present time, however, the proportional counters (to be described in section B) and the scintillation counters (section C) are much more successful for the measurement of β and γ radiations.

B. MULTIPLICATIVE ION COLLECTION

In the preceding section we discussed detection techniques utilizing saturation collection of ions in ionization chambers. Arrangements of electrodes for the multiplicative collection of ions as described in the following are found in Geiger counters and in proportional counters. Usually the currents collected in counters, even from as little as one initial ion pair, may be large enough so that no very sensitive amplifiers or extremely low-capacitance or extremely high-resistance circuits are required. To obtain multiplicative collection of the type desired we might at first think of simply increasing the voltage applied to an ordinary parallel-plate ionization chamber. This is ordinarily not practical, for several reasons which are suggested by the following discussion.

Voltage Gradients and Electrode Shapes. Figure 8-4 shows the electrostatic lines of force between parallel-plate electrodes. The

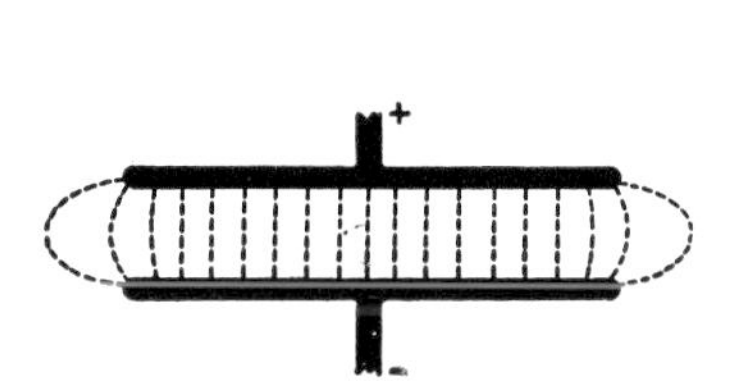

FIGURE 8-4. Electrostatic lines of force between parallel-plate electrodes.

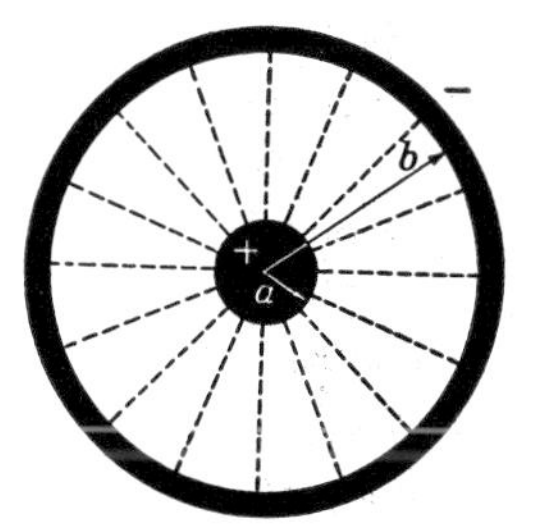

FIGURE 8-5. Electrostatic lines of force between coaxial cylindrical electrodes.

density of the lines of force is a measure of the voltage gradient (field) E in any region. The voltage gradient is the same everywhere between the plates, except for effects near the edge, and is given by the applied voltage difference ΔV divided by the plate separation. Lines of force converge on a curved electrode such as a sphere or wire or point, and indeed unless the parallel plates are perfectly smooth high local gradients will exist at surface irregularities.

In counters one electrode is usually a cylinder, the other an axial wire. Figure 8-5 shows a cross-sectional view, with the wire radius exaggerated; the lines of force are sketched in. It is readily seen that the density of these lines is inversely proportional to the radial distance r; that is, $E = k/r$. Now E is by definition dV/dr, and we may represent the voltage difference between the electrodes of radii a and b:

$$\Delta V = \int_{r=a}^{r=b} dV = \int_a^b E\,dr = \int_a^b \frac{k}{r}\,dr = k \ln\left(\frac{b}{a}\right).$$

In a practical case we might have $b = 1$ cm, $a = 4 \times 10^{-3}$ cm, $\Delta V =$ 1000 volts. Then:

$$1000 = k \ln\left(\frac{1}{4 \times 10^{-3}}\right) = 5.5k; \qquad k = 180.$$

The voltage gradients at wall and wire are

$$E_b = 180 \text{ volts cm}^{-1};$$

$$E_a = \frac{180}{4 \times 10^{-3}} = 4.5 \times 10^4 \text{ volts cm}^{-1}.$$

The field at the wire and for a small space around it is above the maximum value for saturation collection (say $\sim 10^3$ volts cm^{-1} in a practical counter gas). The voltage difference ΔV is always applied with the wall (cathode) negative with respect to the wire (anode); in this way free electrons and negative ions move to the wire.

The Geiger-Müller (G-M) Counter. If an electrode system like that just described is filled with a suitable gas such as 90 per cent argon and 10 per cent methane (total pressure 0.1 to 1 atm) and connected to a high-gain amplifier, and the pulses produced are studied as a function of the applied voltage with different types of ionizing particles, the following voltage regions are observed.

1. At relatively low voltages (of the order of 100 volts) there is no multiplication of the ionization current. The system operates as an ordinary ionization chamber, and only the pulses produced by α particles are seen and these only at very high amplification.

2. At higher voltages (of the order of 1000 volts) there is amplification (10- to 10,000-fold) of the pulse heights; α-particle pulses are

seen with moderate external amplification, and β-particle pulses appear with higher external amplification. The pulse height at fixed voltage is proportional to the amount of ionization caused by the particle. When operated in this region the device is known as a proportional counter.

3. As the voltage is increased further (still in the 1000- to 2000-volt region) the pulse heights increase, and their dependence on the initial ionization intensity disappears. This is the beginning of the Geiger counting region, where a single ion pair or the intense ioniza-

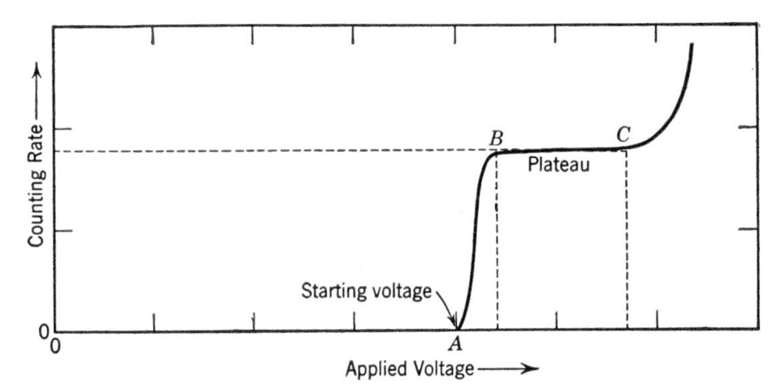

FIGURE 8-6. Plateau curve for a good Geiger-Müller counter.

tion from an α particle produces the same large pulse (perhaps about 10 volts on the counter wire and requiring little or no amplification for observation or recording).

To investigate the extent of the Geiger counting region we often arrange the counter with a fixed source of radiation and determine the counting rate produced as a function of the applied voltage. Figure 8-6 shows this curve for a good counter. The region BC in which the rate is very nearly independent of the voltage is the "plateau" region; its length may be 100 volts or more; the voltage is set in this region for counting. At voltages below B, pulses exist but are not uniform in size, and only some of them trip the recording circuits. To understand the rise in counting rate beyond C we must consider (very briefly) some of the things that happen when the Geiger counting action occurs.

(a) The negative ion of the original ion pair moves toward the wire, traveling most or all the way as a free electron and thus at high speed, and it very quickly reaches the region of pronounced multiplicative processes.

(*b*) The intense region of secondary, tertiary, etc., ions and electrons formed in the high field immediately around the wire spreads along the wire over all its effective length; spreading occurs at least partly through the photoelectric ionization of the gas by photons of high absorption coefficient (short mean path). There may also be some effect of photoelectrons from the cathode wall.

(*c*) The negative ions formed, mostly free electrons, very quickly reach the wire, and the intensely ionized region is left as a sheath of positive ions surrounding the wire. The effect of this positive charge is to reduce the voltage gradient below the value necessary for ion multiplication. All this has occurred in less than about 0.5 microsecond (0.5 μsec), and now the counting action is complete except that the counter is left insensitive and must recover before another event can be counted.

(*d*) Recovery is effected through migration of the positive gas ions away from the wire. From the approximate formula already given (p. 230) for ion mobilities, correcting for a roughly linear dependence of velocity on reciprocal pressure and taking account of the variable voltage gradient, we can estimate that migration of an ion from wire to wall will require $\sim$200 μsec at a gas pressure of about 0.1 atm, and this is about the dead time found experimentally.

(*e*) When positive ions reach the cathode secondary electrons might be emitted from the surface; this would produce a new counter discharge just about 200 μsec after the first, and quite independent of the source of radiation that the counter is intended to measure. Double, triple, and other multiple pulses with about this time spacing occur with appreciable frequency in counters operating above the upper voltage limit of the plateau.

The various recipes for counter construction contain provisions designed to repress the emission of secondary electrons from the cathode and so to insure a plateau of convenient length. The argon-methane and argon-alcohol filling mixtures seem to be effective because the positive ions are by electron transfers all converted to organic ions while moving to the cathode, and these polyatomic ions may dissipate energy by predissociation and reduce enormously the probability of secondary-electron emission. Also they may serve to quench metastable states of the argon atoms. It is significant that the organic additive is considerably consumed after 10^8 or 10^9 counts and that a polyatomic filling gas, tetramethyl lead, requires no additive. Counter filling mixtures containing small amounts of halogens as quench gas do not appear to deteriorate with use.

Geiger counter tubes in a variety of forms are commercially available. The least expensive ones cost only a few dollars. Those with a thin mica end window, about 2 to 3 mg cm^{-2} in thickness and about 2.5 cm in diameter, are more expensive.

Proportional Counters. The Geiger counter is being displaced by the proportional counter (and by the scintillation counter) for the measurement of β radiation. Operation of the counter at reduced voltage in the proportional-counting region gives smaller pulses because the lower field about the wire does not permit unlimited multiplicative processes and the discharge does not spread along the wire. Although the smaller pulses require several stages of vacuum-tube amplification, the advantages gained are quite significant. The proportional counters are generally more stable and more reproducible, the organic gas additive is not so rapidly consumed, and because there is practically no dead time during each pulse the useful range of counting rates is much greater. Most Geiger counters are not dependable at counting rates greater than about 15,000 per min; proportional counters are used at rates up to several hundred thousand per minute. Voltage plateaus of at least 100 volts are readily attainable with β-proportional counters.

Several types of proportional counters are available. Very popular are the flow-type counters, in which the argon-methane or other gas mixture flows at atmospheric pressure from a compressed-gas tank through the counter at a slow rate. This procedure avoids deterioration of the gas and minimizes the effects of gas leaks. In some of these designs the mounted sample is introduced into the counter gas volume through an air lock; others are equipped with a very thin window of aluminum or of a plastic film (such as rubber hydrochloride) with an aquadag or evaporated metal coating. Thin beryllium windows are sometimes used for very-low-energy X rays.

The proportional response of the counter can be a great advantage in several applications. If the counter tube is large enough to include all the ionization produced by a particular radiation, the pulse height (observed after linear amplification) measures the energy of the ray. Thus the proportional counter can serve as a very useful spectrometer, particularly for β rays and conversion electrons below about 0.15 Mev and for low-energy electromagnetic radiation such as X rays.

The limit of sensitivity for both G-M and proportional counters is set by the background counting rate. Even in a laboratory not contaminated by radiochemical work small amounts of activity are present as impurities in construction materials. Also the air contains an appreciable and variable amount of radon and thoron and their decay products. It has been estimated that in free air at the earth's surface most of the ionization is from these two causes, with the cosmic radiation contributing a smaller part. However, because the counter is itself closed, and enclosed in a building, it is not accessible to most of the radioactive α, β, and even γ radiation, and the cosmic-ray effect is the most significant. A counter with a diameter of 2.5 cm and length 6 cm may have a background rate of about 30 counts per minute; this may be reduced to less than 15 counts per minute by the usual lead shield of a few centimeters thickness. We may take about 10 β disintegrations per minute as a minimum sample strength easily detected by a counter (with the 50 per cent geometry estimate as before). Several techniques are sometimes employed to reduce these backgrounds, including special shielding and anticoincidence circuits which reject those counts occurring simultaneously with counts in near-by auxiliary counters (chapter 13, section B). In the case of proportional counters it is possible to obtain further reduction by the use of circuits which reject pulses of sizes that do not correspond to the radiation under measurement.

C. METHODS NOT BASED ON ION COLLECTION

Photographic Film. The historical method for the detection of radioactivity was the general blackening or fogging of photographic negatives, apparent on chemical development in the usual way. This method was soon supplanted by ionization measurements but has reappeared more recently in the "film badge" for personnel exposure control (see section E) and in the γ raying (analogous to X raying) of castings and other heavy metal parts for hidden flaws. Also, in the radioautograph technique the distribution of a radioactive tracer (preferably an α or soft-β emitter) is revealed when a thin section, perhaps of biological material, is kept in contact with a photographic plate.

Special photographic emulsions known as nuclear emulsions exposed to densely ionizing radiations such as α rays, protons, and mesons, on development show blackened grains along the path of each particle; since the range of such rays may be small, these tracks are observed under a microscope. The direction and range of each particle are indicated, and nuclear transmutations may be studied. Measurements of ranges, ionization densities, scattering, and δ-ray emission help in the identification of the ionizing particles. The number of developed grains along a track is smaller by several orders of magnitude than the number of ion pairs produced. The technique is particularly useful for the recording of very rare events, such as are of interest in cosmic-ray studies.

Cloud Chamber. A pictorial representation of the paths of ionizing particles similar to the photographic track but capable of finer detail is given by the cloud chamber (Wilson chamber). In this instrument the particle track through a gas is made visible by the condensation of water droplets on the ions produced. To accomplish this, an enclosed gas saturated with vapor (water, alcohol, and the like) is suddenly cooled by adiabatic expansion to produce supersaturation. Ordinarily a fog would be formed, but, if conditions are right and the gas is free of dust, scattered ions, and so on, the supersaturation is maintained except for local condensation along the track where the ions serve as condensation centers. The piston or diaphragm causing the expansion is operated in a cyclic way, and a small electrostatic gradient is provided to sweep out ions between expansions. There is usually an arrangement of lights, camera, and mirrors to make stereoscopic photographs of the fresh tracks at each expansion. The supersaturated vapor for cloud chamber operation can be achieved in other ways, notably by the diffusion of a saturated organic vapor into a colder region. In the diffusion cloud chamber the working volume is continuously sensitive rather than intermittently so, and the whole instrument is considerably less complicated than the conventional Wilson chamber.

The α tracks appear as straight lines of dense fog droplets, with thousands of droplets per centimeter. The β tracks are much less dense, with discrete droplets visible, several per centimeter along the path. In both cases δ rays are visible, and scattering and straggling may be studied. Electron energies may be determined from track curvature in a magnetic field, and positrons are distinguished from negative electrons by the curvature, if beginning and end of the tracks can be recognized. Cosmic-ray experts have learned to tell much about a particle's charge, mass, and energy from the relation of magnetic curvature and track density. Gamma rays in the cloud chamber produce scattered droplets and δ-ray tracks, with no obvious indication of a particular photon path; the Compton-recoil electrons and photoelectric-conversion electrons may be studied.

Advantages of photographic emulsions and of cloud chambers are combined in the more recently introduced bubble chamber. In this instrument, which promises to be one of the principal tools of high-energy physics research, the string of bubbles produced along the track of an ionizing particle in a superheated liquid is illuminated and photographed. Pentane and liquid hydrogen are among the liquids that have been successfully used in bubble chambers.

Scintillation Counting. When α particles strike a prepared fluorescent screen of zinc sulfide, discrete flashes of light may be seen by the dark-accustomed eye. The counting of α rays by this scintillation method was of great value in the early studies of radioactivity. Although it is no longer used in this way, there is a modern adaptation of scintillation counting, especially for β and γ rays. The rays produce light in an anthracene crystal or other suitable scintillator; the light can produce photoelectrons from the first, photosensitive electrode of a photomultiplier tube such as the RCA 5819 or the Du Mont 6292, and the output pulse may be recorded.

Very active experimentation in recent years has developed a variety of practical scintillators, each with particular advantages. Of the organic phosphors, anthracene gives the highest yield of photons, about 15 for each 1000 ev of energy dissipated in the crystal. Sizable anthracene crystals are commercially available. Stilbene crystals give about half as big a light yield as anthracene but are useful in coincidence experiments because the pulse has a very short decay time, of the order of 10^{-9} sec. Liquid solutions, such as *p*-terphenyl or stilbene in xylene or toluene, give good yields, short time constant, and are easily prepared in large volumes. (A liquid scintillation counter of 300-liter sensitive volume was developed for the neutrino experiment mentioned parenthetically on page 224.) Scintillators incorporated in plastics also are available. For γ-ray measurements NaI crystals (activated with about 1 per cent TlI) are most widely used. Their high density and the high Z of iodine make them especially suitable. Commercially available crystals of this phosphor, machined to specified shapes up to several inches in each dimension, can give high γ-ray counting efficiencies, close to 100 per cent for energies up to about 200 kev, perhaps 20 per cent at 1 Mev. It is somewhat inconvenient that these (expensive) crystals are hygroscopic and must be protected from moisture. The NaI (Tl) scintillator has a very high light yield (about twice that of anthracene), but its longer decay time prevents its use in very-high-speed coincidence counting. For the production of scintillations from α particles conventional ZnS phosphors are still used, in conjunction with photomultiplier tubes. The addition of boron to a ZnS phosphor permits the detection of neutrons through the α particles produced in the

$B^{10}(n, \alpha)Li^7$ reaction. A ZnS phosphor in plastic will give light pulses from the proton recoils produced by fast neutrons. Also, europium-activated LiI phosphor crystals are useful for neutron detection.

The developments in scintillators have been accompanied by improvements in the photomultiplier tubes. Modern tubes may have large, almost uniformly sensitive photocathodes (5 in. in diameter in the Du Mont K 1209), at which about 1 photoelectron results per 10 photons of the typical phosphorescence wavelength (near 4400 A). The electrons are accelerated by a potential of 100 volts or more to the first electrode (dynode) where each one produces several (n) secondary electrons; these secondary electrons are similarly accelerated to and increased n-fold at the second dynode, and so on. With 10 dynodes the charge of the original photoelectrons is multiplied n^{10} times, which may be of the order of 10^5. Thus a 0.1-Mev β ray, absorbed in an anthracene scintillator, might produce 1000 photons, giving 100 photoelectrons, and leading eventually to an output pulse of about 10^7 electrons or 1.6 $\mu\mu$coulomb. (In an output circuit of 160-$\mu\mu$f capacity, this pulse would amount to 0.01 volt, and further amplification in a conventional linear pulse amplifier would be provided.) Because the multiplication in a photomultiplier is very sensitive to the applied voltage, good high-voltage stabilization (to ± 0.1 per cent or better) must be provided for reproducible operation. For optimum performance the photomultiplier tube must be carefully shielded from magnetic fields, including the earth's field. So-called mu-metal shields are available for this purpose.

In typical scintillation counters the crystal is fixed to the photosensitive face of the multiplier tube, either directly or through a short lucite connecting section, with balsam or oil to provide good optical contact at the interface. A light-tight enclosure of aluminum foil serves also as a reflector to assist in directing light to the photocathode. For β or γ rays of more than about 50 kev very efficient light transfer may not be needed to give output pulses greater than the background of electrical "noise." However, for many applications it is important to have the pulse height accurately proportional to the energy dissipated in the crystal. This result is obtained only if light produced by rays in all parts of the crystal can reach the cathode with a uniform attenuation. The crystal should be quite transparent, and nearly total reflections at surfaces other than the photocathode should be the goal; roughening of the crystal faces and the use of a diffuse reflector such as MgO are recommended practices.

The condition of proportional response can be achieved to within about 5 per cent by good design and construction, with careful regulation of dynode voltages and other electronic variables. This proportionality is most useful if the crystal is large enough so that it can contain the entire path of the ray and so measure its total energy. For β radiation this requires a crystal with dimensions considerably larger than the range of the particles and some geometrical provisions to minimize scattering out of the crystal. For γ radiation the crystal must be large enough to contain the ranges of a good share of the photoelectrons produced in it; the resulting pulses will correspond to the total γ energy since the energy used to overcome the electron's binding energy will also contribute to the scintillation through X-ray and Auger-electron emission. In addition to this "photoelectric peak" there will appear a continuous distribution of smaller energies corresponding to Compton-recoil electrons, to the extent that the crystal is not large enough to contain the entire sequence of processes that consume the initial γ-ray energy. In practice, β- and γ-ray spectrometry based on scintillation response offers the best sensitivity but less than the best resolution, and the technique is widely used for energies from about 0.01 to 2 or 3 Mev.

Photomultiplier tubes have been used in a slightly different way for the detection and measurement of radiations in the very-high-energy range. An electron or other charged particle moving with a velocity close to that of light in a vacuum, on entering a medium of sizable index of refraction, finds itself moving faster than electromagnetic waves. The result is something like a shock wave of visible and ultraviolet radiation (the Cerenkov radiation) which can be detected by a photomultiplier tube. The intensity of light is much less than could be produced by the same ray in a scintillation crystal.

Other Methods. A few other detection methods not based on ion collection find occasional applications. The heating effect of the radiations can be measured with precision for very active preparations to the extent that the radiations are stopped in the calorimeter; with α emitters this condition is readily met. Charged-particle radiations constitute an electric current, quite apart from any interactions with gaseous or other absorbers. For α and β sources in the millicurie range this current is easily measurable with a good electrometer (1 mc of β particles = 5.92 $\mu\mu$amp) provided that secondary electron currents are suppressed by a suitable bias voltage. The use of chemical changes produced by radiations as a measure of radiation dosage has already been mentioned in chapter 7, section E.

D. AUXILIARY INSTRUMENTATION

Scalers and Recorders. The pulses produced by the various types of counters and pulse-ionization chambers, after suitable amplification, may be recorded or measured in a variety of ways. A cathode-ray oscilloscope on which individual pulses may be displayed is almost indispensable if the behavior of counters and associated electronic equipment is to be checked, but is of course not very useful for ordinary counting-rate measurements. At low counting rates (perhaps up to 10 per sec) pulses may be used directly to actuate a mechanical recorder. Almost universally, however, the mechanical register is preceded by a scaling circuit which reduces the rate electronically by some factor, usually a power of 2 or, more conveniently, a power of 10. Most of these circuits employ multivibrator [3] scaling pairs, each pair reducing the rate by a factor of 2. The scaled impulses are recorded mechanically, with electric power supplied by a suitable output circuit. Many types of scaling circuits are commercially available. Scaling factors of 64, 100, 256, and 1000 are popular, and many instruments have provisions for selection among several possible scaling factors. A commercial circuit may or may not include an amplifier, the mechanical register, and the stabilized high-voltage supply (perhaps 1500 or 3000 volts maximum, with 0.1 per cent stability for a 10-volt change in line voltage). Depending upon the accessories included, the price might be somewhere between 200 and 700 dollars.

The particular choice of circuit depends on the counter used. For G-M tubes no amplifier is required, high scaling factors (>100) are usually not needed (because of the dead-time limitation on counting rates), and good voltage stabilization is relatively unimportant. For scintillation counters, excellent voltage regulation is desirable, and, for both scintillation and proportional counting, stable, nonoverloading amplifiers are wanted, with gains somewhere between 10^2 and

[3] In this application both tubes of the basic multivibrator pair (square-waveform oscillator) are biased to prevent oscillation; each incoming pulse triggers the pair through a half-cycle; completion of each cycle provides an output pulse to trigger the next pair. One of the most dependable circuits is that employing direct rather than capacitor coupling, devised by W. A. Higinbotham. A scale factor of 10 may be obtained by modification of a scale of 16. A more recent development is the glow-transfer tube which provides a scale of 10 in a single gas-filled tube by means of a glow discharge that is moved to 10 different positions by 10 successive pulses. These tubes are limited to slower repetition rates than are the vacuum-tube scalers.

10^5. The amplifiers need not be linear unless the counters are used for pulse height analysis.

There are some modifications of the basic circuit arrangements useful with counting instruments. In one design the time required for a fixed number of input pulses is automatically measured; this unit has no mechanical register, but rather a very high scaling factor, and the first output pulse turns off the counter and stops an electric timer. In other variations of the same principle the time for each output pulse is printed by a triggered time clock, or the output pulses are recorded by a galvanometer on paper tape moving at a constant known speed; these modifications are particularly useful for determinations of decay curves. Refinements such as automatic changing of samples after a certain time or after a certain number of counts are available in some commercial instruments. In the counting-rate meter the pulses are integrated electrically, and their average rate of arrival (averaged over a suitably long time interval) is indicated directly by a meter deflection.

Pulse Height Analysis. Whenever the output pulse from a counter or ionization chamber is proportional to the energy dissipation in the detector, the measurement of pulse heights may be a useful tool for energy determinations. Some pulse height selection is used even in the simplest scalers in the form of a "discriminator," which allows only pulses above a certain minimum size to be recorded. If a calibrated, adjustable discriminator is provided, counting rates may be measured as a function of discriminator setting; the resulting curve is called an integral bias curve. The derivative of this curve (a differential bias curve) gives the distribution of pulse heights.

Pulse height distributions may be obtained more directly and much more accurately with a single-channel analyzer. In this instrument there are two discriminators, and usually an anticoincidence arrangement is used to pass only pulses of such a height that they fall between the two discriminator settings. The two discriminators may be separately controlled or, more frequently, they may be moved up and down the voltage scale together with a constant "channel" or "window" width between them. The usual pulse height range of a single-channel analyzer is 0 to 50 volts or 0 to 100 volts. Different parts of a pulse height spectrum may be brought into this range by the choice of suitable amplifier gains. Channel widths of 1 to 5 volts are often used. High stability is required in the discriminators, the amplifier, and the high-voltage supply.

A typical pulse height spectrum obtained with a NaI scintillation counter and single-channel analyzer is shown in figure 8-7. The γ-ray source used is Cs^{137} with the single γ-ray energy 0.662 Mev. The full-energy peak is due to photoelectric absorption and to those

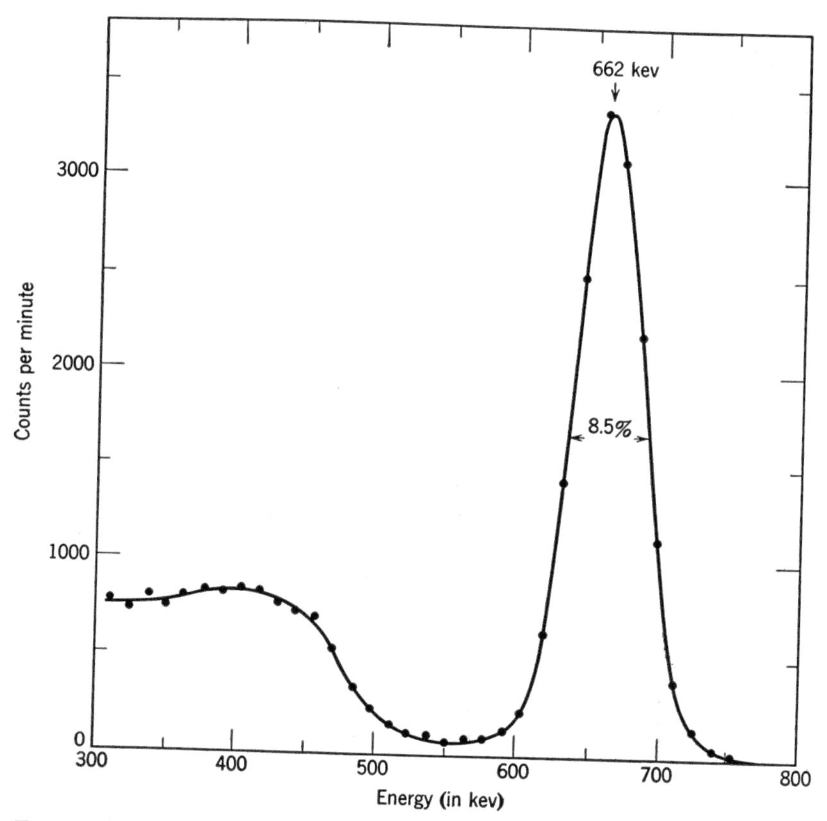

FIGURE 8-7. Pulse height spectrum obtained with a NaI(Tl) scintillation counter for a Cs^{137} source. The broad peak at the left is the Compton distribution; at the right is the photopeak due to absorption of the full energy (662 kev) of the γ ray in the crystal. The width of the photopeak at half maximum is 56.5 kev or 8.5 per cent of 662 kev. (Courtesy J. P. Welker.)

Compton processes followed by absorption of the scattered photon in the crystal. The broad Compton distribution with its spectrum of lower pulse heights is also seen. The pulse height scale is usually calibrated by use of one or more radiations of known energy.

A variety of multichannel analyzers have been developed. Perhaps 10 to 50 equally spaced discriminator voltages may be used, the pulse from each channel being fed into an appropriate output circuit and register. Multichannel analyzers are obviously advantageous for the study of short-lived radioactivities because they allow simultaneous measurement of a large number of points on a pulse height spectrum. These instruments, in conjunction with ionization chambers, have been especially successful in the study of α-particle spectra.

Excellent single-channel pulse height analyzers are commercially available at a cost of a few hundred dollars. A complete set-up including high-voltage supply with 0.01 per cent regulation, amplifier, analyzer, and scaler can be assembled from commercially available units for close to 2000 dollars. Some multichannel instruments can be purchased commercially but are much more expensive.

Photographic methods of pulse height analysis can compare with multichannel analyzers in speed and have the advantage of lower cost. In the most successful of these, the gray-wedge analyzer, the amplified pulses are electronically extended in time and displayed on an oscilloscope screen so that each pulse appears as a horizontal line across the screen, the distance from the baseline being the pulse height. The screen is then photographed through a gray wedge which is transparent at the left and becomes more and more opaque towards the right. The greater the number of pulses at a given height, the farther to the right will there be enough light intensity to blacken the film. The photograph will thus show the pulse height distribution with the energy axis vertical and a quantity related to intensity on the horizontal scale.

Coincidence Techniques. Studies of the time relations between various radiations emitted from one nucleus may be made by means of coincidence techniques and are very useful in decay scheme studies.

Whether a β ray goes to the ground state of the product nucleus or is followed by γ emission can be established by a coincidence experiment in which the sample is placed between a β and a γ counter and time-coincident pulses in the two counters are recorded. Similarly, with appropriately chosen detectors, and possibly with the aid of absorbers or pulse height discrimination to make detection more selective, one may study γ-γ, α-γ, X-γ, β-e^-, e^--γ, etc., coincidences. Coincidence measurements with pulse height analysis at one or both detectors offer a particularly powerful tool for detailed decay scheme studies. The gray-wedge technique has proved to be especially useful in coincidence analyzers.

In most coincidence measurements rather strong samples are used. This is because the number of coincidence counts recorded is proportional to the product of the solid angles subtended by the two counters at the sample, and frequently the sample-to-counter distances have to be rather large (inches) to minimize scattered radiation from one counter entering the other. Since the coincidence rates are often quite low, background rates are a problem. Apart from a very small true coincidence background (for example, due to a cosmic ray striking both detectors) there is always a certain chance or accidental background that comes about because sometimes two rays not originating from the same nucleus happen to arrive at the two counters within the resolving time of the coincidence circuit. If the single counting rates in the two counters are $\mathbf{R}_1$ and $\mathbf{R}_2$ per second and if the coincidence resolving time (the time within which the two counters have to be tripped for a coincidence to be recorded) is τ second, then the accidental coincidence rate is $2\mathbf{R}_1\mathbf{R}_2\tau$ per second. To reduce the chance rate it is desirable to make the resolving time as short as possible. Coincidence resolving times of 10^{-6} to 10^{-8} sec are common, and for delayed-coincidence measurements of very short half-lives resolving times of less than 10^{-9} sec have been achieved. To be used with coincidence circuits, the detectors must have pulse-rise times not much longer than the coincidence resolving time, and for this reason G-M tubes are not very useful for fast coincidence work. Scintillation counters are most commonly used.

Spectrographs and Spectrometers. In addition to the scintillation- and proportional-counter spectrometers there are a variety of devices for energy measurements on α, β, γ, and X rays, and conversion electrons. We can make only the briefest mention of these. In the 180° magnetic spectrograph (or spectrometer), use is made of the fact that identical charged particles emerging from a point source with equal momenta but at slightly divergent angles (say within 20°) are brought to an approximate focus after traveling about 180° in a plane perpendicular to a uniform magnetic field (figure 8-8). If a constant magnetic field is used, electrons or α particles of different momenta are detected in different positions either on a photographic film or by a movable counter. Instruments of this type are particularly useful for line spectra such as conversion-electron or α spectra. For the continuous β spectra it is more practical to leave the detector (G-M, proportional, or scintillation counter) fixed and vary the field to bring β particles of different energies into focus at the detector. By slight shaping of the magnetic field greatly improved focusing has been achieved in 180° spectrometers, and much precision work in β-ray spectrometry has been done with such instruments.

Another type of β-ray spectrometer is the lens spectrometer. Here the source and the detector are located on the axis of an axially symmetric magnetic field. It is a property of such a system that all electrons emitted with a large spread of angles but with a given momentum will, after traveling along spiral paths, be focused at some other point on the axis. Very high geometric efficiencies (several per cent of 4π) and good momentum resolution ($\sim$1 per cent) can be attained, although in the latter respect the 180° instruments are superior.

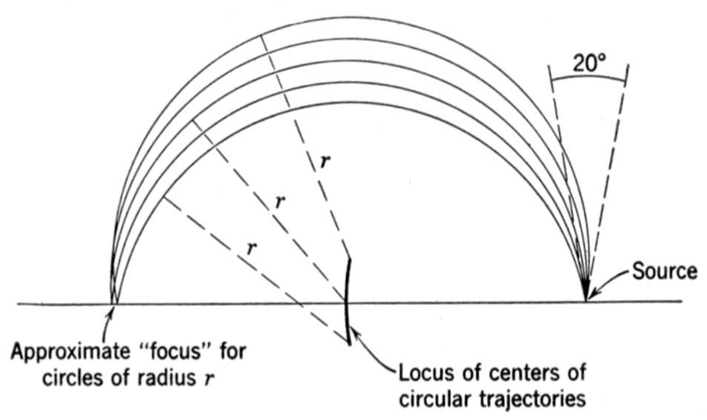

FIGURE 8-8. Principle of 180° focusing. The magnetic field is perpendicular to the plane of the paper. The angular divergence of the trajectories shown is 20° at the source.

In all electron spectrometers source preparation is a problem because sources must be extremely thin (often <0.1 mg cm^{-2}) and mounted on equally thin backings to minimize self-absorption and back-scattering. Also the counters used must have very thin windows.

Electron spectrometers are used not only for conversion-electron and β-ray measurements but also for γ-ray spectra. The energies of photoelectrons ejected from a radiator are measured in this case. For certain detailed studies of complex decay schemes two lens-type spectrometers have been used end-to-end; coincidences between two electron lines or between one electron line and a β spectrum can thus be studied. More common are coincidence arrangements with one scintillation counter and one electron spectrograph as the detectors.

An instrument for the precision measurement of X rays and low-energy γ rays is the curved-crystal spectrograph. This is analogous to an optical spectrograph of the grating type, with the atomic planes of a bent crystal replacing the ruled lines of the curved grating. The detector may be a photographic plate, or a counter in the curved-crystal spectrometer.

E. HEALTH PHYSICS INSTRUMENTS

By the term health physics instruments we refer to detection and measuring instruments designed for the monitoring of personnel radiation exposures, and for the surveying of laboratories, equipment, clothing, hands, and the like, for biologically harmful radioactive contaminations. Very many types of such instruments are in use. Those which are generally available commercially may be divided into a few categories, and are all derived from the instrumentation principles already discussed in this chapter.

Pocket Ion Chambers. Perhaps the most widely used radiation monitor is the pocket ionization chamber. This is an ordinary ionization chamber in most respects, made small enough to be worn clipped in the pocket like a fountain pen. The charging potential is applied through a temporary connection, and at the end of the day or end of exposure the residual charge is read on an electrometer. A pocket ionization chamber with a built-in electrometer and scale is more convenient, but also more expensive. This style of chamber is initially charged on an external device and then may be read directly at any time without auxiliary apparatus and without effect on the indication.

These pocket meters are calibrated in roentgen units, with full scale corresponding most commonly to 0.1 or 0.2 r, so that they easily detect general radiation dosage below tolerance levels. They may not give a measure of local exposure (say, of the hands, while other parts of the body are shielded by a lead screen) and, of course, are not sensitive to soft radiations that do not penetrate the chamber wall.

Film Badges. Personnel in almost every large nuclear or radiochemical project routinely wear badge-type holders containing photographic film. These give a permanent record of general body exposure to radiation integrated over a longer period of time—usually one week. Development, calibration, and dosage evaluation for the badges can be obtained on a subscription basis. Film holders can be worn on the wrist or even arranged as finger rings, thus serving as more accurate monitors of hand exposure. Because thermal-neutron flux is not well indicated on ordinary films, special boron-loaded films are also available on a routine basis. Very-high-energy radiations (from synchrocyclotrons, proton synchrotrons, etc.) may be monitored with nuclear emulsions; track counting must then be resorted to.

Portable Counters and Direct-Current Amplifiers. More sensitive detection instruments are used to determine the rate at which exposure is being received in a given radiation field. These may be larger ionization chambers with compact d-c amplifiers operated from self-contained batteries, so that a readily portable survey meter weighing perhaps 3 pounds is achieved. Models of this type ordinarily have several calibrated scale ranges, from about 0 to 20 mr per hr to about 0 to 3000 mr per hr, or have a logarithmic response which compresses a wide range into a single scale. Battery-operated portable Geiger counter sets of about the same size and weight are available and can be used for the same purpose. They are usually arranged as counting-rate meters, with full-scale readings calibrated at about 0.2 to 20 mr per hr. Although the counter type of meter is much more sensitive than the ionization chamber, the latter is usually sensitive enough and may be expected to give a response more nearly proportional to the biological effects of the radiation. Both types are ordinarily provided with a movable shield to permit a distinction between hard and soft radiations. These two types of instruments are also useful for surveying the laboratory and its apparatus for radioactive contamination. The G-M counter instrument with its higher sensitivity, especially when used with earphones so that each count may be heard, is more convenient in rapid surveys for small amounts of activity but in its usual form is not useful for very soft β rays such as those from C^{14}. The ionization chamber instrument is more easily fitted with a window thin enough for this purpose (not more than a few milligrams per square centimeter), and some available models have very thin windows (or simply open screens) that will pass even α particles. The most sensitive γ-ray monitor is the more recently introduced portable scintillation counter.

Other Procedures. A number of other more specialized instruments have been devised. Geiger counters and atmospheric-pressure proportional counters may be arranged particularly to detect β and α contaminations on the hands. The monitoring of air-borne contamination requires special instruments, and may be particularly important in laboratories handling long-lived α activities. One method for air-borne dusts is to filter a large volume of the air and to assay the activity left on the filter paper with a standard counter or linear-amplifier instrument. (The radon decay products ordinarily present in air can be detected in this way.) A very simple and widely applicable semiquantitative method of contamination monitoring which requires no special instrumentation is worth mentioning here; this is the so-called swipe method. A small piece of clean filter paper of a standard size is wiped over a roughly uniform path length on the suspected desk top, floor, wall, laboratory ware, or almost anywhere, and then measured for α, β, or γ activity on a standard instrument. Even air-borne contamination may be checked in a rough way by swipe samples of accumulated dust from an electric-light fixture or some such place which is exposed only to contamination from the air.

EXERCISES

1. Estimate roughly the voltage (IR) applied to the grid of a d-c amplifier tube; use these assumptions: $R = 10^{11}$ ohms; the sample emits 1-Mev γ rays at the rate of 10^6 per min; the geometry is such that 30 per cent of the γ's spend an average 8-cm path length in the ionization chamber, which is filled with CF_2Cl_2 at 2 atm total pressure.

2. A β particle of 2 Mev enters a G-M counter and spends a 1.0-cm path length in the gas, which is $Pb(CH_3)_4$ at a pressure of 1.0 cm. What is the (average) number of ion pairs that should be expected to result from ionization in the gas? *Answer:* 6.

3. Calculate the time required for a positive ion to move from the wire to the wall of a Geiger counter; take 0.005 in. for the wire diameter, 1⅛ in. for the cathode diameter, 1000 volts as the applied voltage, 10 cm as the gas pressure, and 1.5 cm per sec for the mobility of the ion at 1 volt per cm gradient and at 76 cm pressure. *Answer:* 490 μs.

4. A Lauritsen electroscope is to be used for work with Cl^{38}. Its fiber system has a capacity of 0.3 esu. Its chamber has a diameter of 5 cm. In order to get a sufficiently accurate reading, its discharge rate must be at least 0.10 volt per min (corresponding to about 0.1 division per min). Making appropriate assumptions, estimate the minimum sample strength that should be used.

5. What type of instrument would you use for each of the following: (*a*) Detection of 0.1 μc of P^{32}? (*b*) Detection of 10^{-3} μc of H^3? (*c*) Detection of 10^{-5} μc of At^{211}? (*d*) Following the decay of a sample of Cu^{64} (initially 3×10^5 disintegrations per second) over a period of 8 days? (*e*) Determining the relative amounts of Co^{57} and Co^{60} in a sample (without decay measurements over a long period of time)? State briefly the reason for each choice.

6. An anthracene crystal and a 10-stage photomultiplier tube are to be used as a scintillation spectrometer for β rays. It is desired that a 10-kev β particle incident on the scintillator produce a 2-millivolt pulse in the photomultiplier output circuit, which has a capacity of 120 $\mu\mu$f. What average electron multiplication per stage is required in the photomultiplier? Assume a light collection efficiency of unity and a photocathode efficiency (number of photoelectrons emitted per incident photon) of 0.1. *Answer:* 3.3

7. A certain nuclide decays predominantly by emission of β^- particles of 1.25 Mev maximum energy to a 25-sec isomeric state which in turn decays to the product ground state by emission of 0.45-Mev γ rays. A rare β^- branch (0.1 per cent abundance, 0.81 Mev maximum energy) leads to a state which decays by γ emission to the 25-sec isomeric level. To establish this branch by a β-γ coincidence measurement with scintillation detectors, a true coincidence rate at least three times the accidental coincidence rate is desired. The sample strength is chosen as 1000 disintegrations per second to make background effects in the counters negligible. Assume equal counting efficiency of the β counter for the two β groups. What coincidence resolving time is required? *Answer:* 0.17μs.

REFERENCES

H. H. Staub, "Detection Methods," *Experimental Nuclear Physics,* Vol. I (E. Segrè, Editor), New York, John Wiley & Sons, 1953.

E. Bleuler and G. J. Goldsmith, *Experimental Nucleonics,* New York, Rinehart, 1952.

G. B. Cook and J. F. Duncan, *Modern Radiochemical Practice,* Oxford, Clarendon Press, 1952.

D. H. Wilkinson, *Ionization Chambers and Counters,* Cambridge University Press, 1950.

S. C. Curran and J. D. Craggs, *Counting Tubes,* New York, Academic Press, 1949.

W. H. Jordan, "Detection of Nuclear Particles," *Ann. Rev. Nuclear Sci.,* Vol. I, p. 207, Stanford, Annual Reviews Inc., 1952.

B. B. Rossi and H. H. Staub, *Ionization Chambers and Counters,* National Nuclear Energy Series, Div. V, Vol. 2, New York, McGraw-Hill Book Co., 1949.

S. A. Korff, *Electron and Nuclear Counters,* New York, D. Van Nostrand Co., 1946.

L. B. Loeb, *Fundamental Processes of Electrical Discharge in Gases,* New York, John Wiley & Sons, 1939.

J. D. Cobine, *Gaseous Conductors,* New York, McGraw-Hill Book Co., 1941.

H. Yagoda, *Radioactive Measurements with Nuclear Emulsions,* New York, John Wiley & Sons, 1949.

A. Beiser, "Nuclear Emulsion Technique," *Revs. Mod. Phys.* **24,** 273 (1952).

M. Snowden, "The Diffusion Cloud Chamber," *Progress in Nuclear Physics,* Vol. 3 (O. R. Frisch, Editor), London, Pergamon Press, 1953.

D. A. Glaser, "The Bubble Chamber," *Scientific American* **192,** No. 2, 46 (February 1955).

S. C. Curran, *Luminescence and the Scintillation Counter,* London, Butterworth's Scientific Publications, 1953.

G. A. Morton, "The Scintillation Counter," *Advances in Electronics,* Vol. 4, New York, Academic Press, 1952.

R. K. Swank, B. R. Linden, F. B. Harrison, G. Cowper, A. Kantz, R. Hofstadter, C. L. Cowan, Jr., F. Reines, H. W. Koch, and R. S. Foote, "Scintillation Counting Today," *Nucleonics* **12,** No. 3, 13 (March 1954).

R. K. Swank, "Nuclear Particle Detection (Characteristics of Scintillators)," *Ann. Rev. Nuclear Sci.,* Vol. IV, p. 111, Stanford, Annual Reviews Inc., 1954.

J. V. Jelley, "Cerenkov Radiation," *Progress in Nuclear Physics,* Vol. 3 (O. R. Frisch, Editor), London, Pergamon Press, 1953.

D. West, "Energy Measurements with Proportional Counters," *Progress in Nuclear Physics,* Vol. 3 (O. R. Frisch, Editor), London, Pergamon Press, 1953.

A. Van Rennes, "Pulse-Amplitude Analysis in Nuclear Research," *Nucleonics* **10,** No. 7, 20 (July 1952); No. 8, 22 (August 1952); No. 9, 32 (September 1952) and No. 10, 50 (October 1952).

W. Bernstein, R. L. Chase, and A. W. Schardt, "Gray Wedge Pulse-Height Analysis," *Rev. Sci. Instr.* **24,** 437 (1953).

W. C. Elmore and M. Sands, *Electronics: Experimental Techniques,* National Nuclear Energy Series, Div. V, Vol. 1, New York, McGraw-Hill Book Co., 1949.

R. W. Hayward, "Beta-Ray Spectrometers," *Advances in Electronics,* Vol. 5, New York, Academic Press, 1953.

J. W. M. Du Mond, "A High Resolving Power, Curved-Crystal Focusing Spectrometer for Short Wave-Length X-Rays and Gamma Rays," *Rev. Sci. Instr.* **18,** 626 (1947).

CHAPTER 9

STATISTICAL CONSIDERATIONS IN RADIOACTIVITY MEASUREMENTS

A. RANDOM PHENOMENA

The occurrence of nuclear disintegrations is a random phenomenon subject to established methods of statistical analysis. We therefore discuss in this chapter the application of these methods and the nature of the statistical laws. First consider the set of data actually obtained with a Geiger counter measuring a "steady" source, as given in table 9-1. The number of counts recorded per minute (the counting rate) is clearly not uniform. Which minute gave the most accurate result? The best thing we can do is to compute the arithmetic mean (the average value) and consider this to represent the proper counting rate.

TABLE 9-1

Minute	Counts	Δ_i	Δ_i^2
1	89	−10	100
2	120	+21	441
3	94	−5	25
4	110	+11	121
5	105	+6	36
6	108	+9	81
7	85	−14	196
8	83	−16	256
9	101	+2	4
10	95	−4	16
Totals	990	0	1276

Average Value. If the determinations, minute by minute, are denoted by $x_1, x_2, \ldots x_i$ for the first, second, . . . ith minute, then the arithmetic mean value $\bar{x}$ is, by definition,

$$\bar{x} = \frac{1}{N_0} \sum_{i=1}^{i=N_0} x_i,$$

where N_0 is the number of values of x to be averaged. For the counting rates in the table $\bar{x} = 990/10 = 99.0$.

Standard Deviation. After the experiment which gave these data we might have repeated the measurements and so obtained another average rate. The best figure would then have been the average of all the results. Knowing merely the average value we do not know anything about the statistical dependability of the data from which the average was computed, that is, the degree of agreement between the individual results. We want to define a quantitative measure of the closeness of agreement. Consider for a moment the deviation Δ_i of each number x_i, defined as the difference between x_i and $\bar{x}$: $\Delta_i = x_i - \bar{x}$. These deviations are tabulated in the third column of the table. The average value of Δ_i cannot be taken as a measure of internal agreement because it is just zero:

$$\frac{1}{N_0}\sum_{i=1}^{i=N_0} \Delta_i = \frac{1}{N_0}\sum_{1}^{N_0} x_i - \frac{1}{N_0}\sum_{1}^{N_0} \bar{x} = \bar{x} - \bar{x} = 0.$$

The average of the squares of the individual deviations, called the variance or dispersion and denoted by σ_x^2, gives a useful measure of the degree of agreement among the results.

$$\sigma_x^2 = \frac{1}{N_0}\sum_{1}^{N_0} \Delta_i^2 = \frac{1}{N_0}\Sigma(x_i - \bar{x})^2.$$

The standard deviation σ_x, which is just the square root of the dispersion, is commonly used. For the data of table 9-1 we compute $\sigma_x^2 = 1276/10 = 127.6$; $\sigma_x = 11.3$. A useful relation that may be derived is $\sigma_x^2 = \overline{x^2} - \bar{x}^2$; that is, the variance is given by the difference between the average of the squares of the x values and the square of the average value.

B. PROBABILITY AND THE COMPOUNDING OF PROBABILITIES

The ideas and definitions just presented may be applied, with varying degrees of usefulness, to any set of data, whether or not strictly random phenomena are involved. Before proceeding further, we must consider very carefully the concept of probability. As illustrations we will investigate the answers to questions such as:

(*a*) What is the probability that a card drawn from a deck be an ace?

(*b*) If a coin is flipped twice, what is the probability of it falling "heads up" both times?

(*c*) Given a sample of a radioactive material what is the probability that exactly 100 disintegrations occur during the next minute?

We shall define probability in this way: Given a set of N_0 objects (or events, or results, etc.) containing n_1 objects of the first kind, n_2 objects of the second kind, and n_i objects of the ith kind; the probability p_i that an object specified only as belonging to the set is of the ith kind is given by $p_i = n_i/N_0$. By applying this definition we find that the probability that one card drawn from a full deck be an ace is just $4/52$.

We may now rewrite the definition of the average value $\bar{x}$ of a set of quantities x_i, taking into account the possibility that any particular value may appear several, say n_i, times. Then

$$\bar{x} = \frac{1}{N_0} \Sigma n_i x_i = \Sigma p_i x_i.$$

This may be generalized, and the expression for the average value of any function of x is

$$\overline{f(x)} = \Sigma p_i f(x_i). \tag{9-1}$$

In experimental measurements we may make a large number K of observations and find the ith result k_i times. Now the ratio k_i/K is not the probability p_i of the ith result as we have defined it, but for our purposes we assume that k_i/K approaches arbitrarily closely to p_i as K becomes very large:

$$\lim_{K \to \infty} \frac{k_i}{K} = p_i.$$

This assumption is not subject to mathematical proof, because a limit may not be evaluated for a series with no law of sequence of terms.

Addition Theorem. We turn now to the compounding of several probabilities, and consider first the addition theorem. Given a set of N_0 objects (or events, or results, etc.) containing n_i objects of the kind a_i, and given that the kinds $a_1, a_2, \ldots a_i$ have no members in common; then the probability that one of the N_0 objects belongs to a combined group $a_1 + a_2 + \cdots a_j$ is just $\sum_{i=1}^{i=j} p_i$. Thus for two mutually exclusive events with probabilities p_1 and p_2 the probability of one or the other occurring is just $p_1 + p_2$. When one card is drawn from a full deck the chance of its being either a five or a ten is $4/52 + 4/52 = 2/13$. (When one draws one card while already holding, say, four cards none of which is a five or ten, the probability then of getting either a five or a ten is slightly greater, $4/48 + 4/48 = 1/6$, provided that there is available no information as to the identity of other cards that may already have been withdrawn.) When a coin is tossed the probability of either "heads" or "tails" is $1/2 + 1/2 = 1$.

Multiplication Theorem. Another type of compounding of probabilities is described by the multiplication theorem. If the probability of an event i is p_i, and if after i has happened the probability of another event j is p_j, then the probability that first i happens and then j happens is $p_i \times p_j$. If a coin is tossed twice the probability of getting "heads" twice is $1/2 \times 1/2 = 1/4$. If two cards are drawn from an initially full deck the probability of two aces is $4/52 \times 3/51$. The probability of four aces in four cards drawn is $4/52 \times 3/51 \times 2/50 \times 1/49$. (The probability of drawing five aces in five cards is $4/52 \times 3/51 \times 2/50 \times 1/49 \times 0/48 = 0$.)

Binomial Distribution. The binomial distribution law treats one fairly general case of compounding of probabilities. Given a very large set of objects in which the probability of occurrence of an object of a particular kind w is p; then, if n objects are withdrawn from the set, the probability $W(r)$ that exactly r of the objects are of the kind w is given by

$$W(r) = \frac{n!}{(n-r)!r!} p^r(1-p)^{n-r}. \tag{9-2}$$

To see how this combination of terms actually represents the probability in question, think for a moment of just r of the n objects. That the first of these is of the kind w has the probability p; that the first and second are of the kind w has the probability p^2, etc., and the probability that all r objects are of the kind w is p^r. But, if exactly r of the n objects are to be of this kind, the remaining $n - r$ objects must be of some other kind; this probability is $(1 - p)^{n-r}$. Thus we see that, for a particular choice of r objects out of the n objects, the probability of exactly r of kind w is $p^r(1 - p)^{n-r}$; this particular choice is not the only one. The first of the r objects might be chosen (from the n objects) in n different ways; the second in $n - 1$ ways; the third in $n - 2$ ways, and the rth in $n - r + 1$ ways. The product of these terms, $n(n - 1)(n - 2) \cdots (n - r + 1)$, is $\frac{n!}{(n-r)!}$, and this coefficient must be used to multiply the probability just found. But this coefficient is actually too large in that it not only gives the total number of possible arrangements of the objects in the way required but also includes the number of arrangements which differ only in the order of selection of the r objects. So we must divide by the number of permutations of r objects which is $r!$. Thus, the final coefficient is

$n!/(n-r)!r!$, which is that in equation 9-2. The law (equation 9-2) is known as the binomial distribution law because this coefficient is just the coefficient of the x^r term in the binomial expansion of $(1+x)^n$.

C. RADIOACTIVITY AS A STATISTICAL PHENOMENON

Binomial Distribution for Radioactive Disintegrations. We may apply the binomial distribution law to find the probability $W(m)$ of obtaining just m disintegrations in time t from N_0 original radioactive atoms. We think of N_0 as the number n of objects chosen for observation (in our derivation of the binomial law) and we think of m as the number r that are to have a certain property (namely, that of disintegrating in time t), so that for this case the binomial law becomes

$$W(m) = \frac{N_0!}{(N_0 - m)!m!} p^m (1-p)^{N_0 - m}.$$

Now the probability of an atom not decaying in time t, $1 - p$ in the equation above, is given [1] by the ratio of the number N that survive the time interval t to the initial number N_0,

$$\frac{N}{N_0} = e^{-\lambda t};$$

and p is then $1 - e^{-\lambda t}$. We now have

$$W(m) = \frac{N_0!}{(N_0 - m)!m!} (1 - e^{-\lambda t})^m (e^{-\lambda t})^{N_0 - m}. \tag{9-3}$$

Time Intervals between Disintegrations. Since the time of Schweidler's derivation of the exponential decay law from probability considerations (p. 6) a number of experiments have been made to test the applicability of these statistical laws to the phenomena of radioactivity. As an example of the positive evidence obtained we consider the distribution of time intervals between disintegrations. The probability of this time interval having a value between t and $t + dt$, which we write as $P(t)\,dt$, is given by the product of the probability of no disintegration between 0 and t and the probability of a disintegration between t and $t + dt$. The first of these two probabilities is given by equation 9-3 with $m = 0$:

$$W(0) = \frac{N_0!}{N_0!0!} (1 - e^{-\lambda t})^0 (e^{-\lambda t})^{N_0} = e^{-N_0 \lambda t}.$$

[1] See chapter 1, p. 6.

(Notice that $0! = 1$.) The probability of one of the N_0 atoms disintegrating in the time dt is clearly $N_0\lambda\, dt$. (See chapter 1, page 6, or obtain this result as $W(1)$ from equation 9-3 with $m = 1$, t replaced by dt, and all terms in $(dt)^2$ and higher powers of dt neglected.) Then

$$P(t)\, dt = N_0\lambda e^{-N_0\lambda t}\, dt.$$

Experiments designed to test this result usually measure a large number s of time intervals between disintegrations and classify them into intervals differing by the short but finite length Δt; then the probability for intervals between t and $t + \Delta t$ should be $N_0\lambda e^{-N_0\lambda t}\, \Delta t$, and the number of measured intervals between t and $t + \Delta t$ should be $sN_0\lambda e^{-N_0\lambda t}\, \Delta t$. For example, Feather has found experimentally that the logarithm of the number of intervals between t and $t + \Delta t$ is proportional to t, as required by this formula.

Average Disintegration Rate. Another application of the binomial law to radioactive disintegrations may be seen if we calculate the expected average value for a set of numbers obeying the binomial distribution law. We will for the moment revert to the notation of equation 9-2 and for further convenience will represent $1 - p$ by q:

$$W(r) = \frac{n!}{(n-r)!r!}\, p^r q^{n-r}.$$

The average value to be expected for r is obtained from equation 9-1:

$$\bar{r} = \sum_{r=0}^{r=n} W(r)r = \sum_{r=0}^{r=n} r \frac{n!}{(n-r)!r!}\, p^r q^{n-r}.$$

To evaluate this awkward-appearing summation consider the binomial expansion of $(px + q)^n$:

$$(px + q)^n = \sum_{r=0}^{r=n} \frac{n!}{(n-r)!r!}\, p^r x^r q^{n-r} = \sum_{r=0}^{r=n} x^r W(r).$$

Differentiating with respect to x, we obtain

$$np(px + q)^{n-1} = \sum_{r=0}^{r=n} r x^{r-1} W(r). \tag{9-4}$$

Now letting $x = 1$ and using $q = 1 - p$, we have the desired expression:

$$np = \sum_{r=0}^{r=n} rW(r) = \bar{r}.$$

This result should not be surprising; it means that the average number $\bar{r}$ of the n objects which are of the kind w is just n times the probability for any given one of the objects to be of the kind w.

The foregoing result may be interpreted for radioactive disintegration if n is set equal to N_0 and $p = 1 - e^{-\lambda t}$, as before. Then the expected average number M of atoms disintegrating in the time t is $M = N_0(1 - e^{-\lambda t})$. For small values of λt, that is, for times of observation short compared to the half-life, we may use the approximation $e^{-\lambda t} = 1 - \lambda t$, and then $M = N_0\lambda t$. The disintegration rate $\mathbf{R}$ to be expected is $\mathbf{R} = M/t = N_0\lambda$. (This corresponds to the familiar equation $-\dfrac{dN}{dt} = \lambda N$.)

Expected Standard Deviation. A more interesting question is: What may we expect for the standard deviation σ_r for this expected average value $\bar{r}$ (or M)? If we differentiate equation 9-4 again with respect to x, we get

$$n(n-1)p^2(px+q)^{n-2} = \sum_{r=0}^{r=n} r(r-1)x^{r-2}W(r).$$

Again letting $x = 1$ and using $p + q = 1$, we have

$$n(n-1)p^2 = \sum_{r=0}^{r=n} r(r-1)W(r) = \sum_{r=0}^{r=n} r^2W(r) - \sum_{r=0}^{r=n} rW(r);$$

$$n(n-1)p^2 = \overline{r^2} - \bar{r}.$$

Recall that the variance σ_r^2 is given by

$$\sigma_r^2 = \overline{r^2} - \bar{r}^2.$$

Now, combining, we have

$$\sigma_r^2 = n(n-1)p^2 + \bar{r} - \bar{r}^2,$$

and with $\bar{r} = np$:

$$\sigma_r^2 = n^2p^2 - np^2 + np - n^2p^2 = np(1-p) = npq;$$

$$\sigma_r = \sqrt{npq}.$$

For the case of radioactive disintegration this becomes

$$\sigma = \sqrt{N_0(1 - e^{-\lambda t})e^{-\lambda t}} = \sqrt{Me^{-\lambda t}}.$$

In counting practice λt is usually small; that is, the observation time t is short compared to the half-life, and when this is so $\sigma = \sqrt{M}$.

If a reasonably large number m of counts has been obtained that number m may be used in the place of M for the purpose of evaluating σ. Thus if 100 counts are recorded in 1 min the expected standard deviation is $\sigma \approx \sqrt{100} = 10$, and the counting rate might be written 100 ± 10 counts per min. If 1000 counts are recorded in 10 min the standard deviation of this number is $\sigma = \sqrt{1000} = 32$; the counting rate is $\dfrac{1000 \pm 32}{10} = 100 \pm 3.2$ counts per min. Thus we see that for a given counting rate **R** the σ for the rate is inversely proportional to the square root of the time of measurement:

$$\mathbf{R} = \frac{m}{t};$$

$$\sigma_{\mathbf{R}} = \frac{\sqrt{m}}{t} = \frac{\sqrt{\mathbf{R}t}}{t} = \sqrt{\frac{\mathbf{R}}{t}}. \tag{9-5}$$

What is the result in an experiment in which the counting time is long compared to the half-life? As $\lambda t \to \infty$, $e^{-\lambda t} \to 0$, and in this limit $\sigma = \sqrt{Me^{-\lambda t}} = 0$. The explanation is clear; if we start with N_0 atoms and wait for all to disintegrate, then the number of disintegrations is exactly N_0. However, in actual practice we observe not the number of disintegrations but that number times a coefficient c which denotes the probability of a disintegration resulting in an observed count. Taking this into account, we see that in this limiting case the proper representation of $\sigma = \sqrt{npq}$ is $\sigma = \sqrt{N_0c(1 - c)}$. If $c \ll 1$, then $\sigma = \sqrt{N_0c} = \sqrt{\text{number of counts}}$ as before. When $\lambda t \sim 1$ and c is neither unity nor very small, a more exact analysis based on $\sigma = \sqrt{npq}$ should be made, with the result that $\sigma = \sqrt{Mc(1 - c + ce^{-\lambda t})}$.

The introduction of the detection coefficient c in the preceding paragraph may raise the question as to why it is not necessary to take account of this coefficient in the more familiar case with λt small, where we have written $\sigma = \sqrt{m}$. If we do consider c in this case, we have for the probability of one atom producing a count in time t, $p = (1 - e^{-\lambda t})c$; and $q = 1 - p = 1 - c + ce^{-\lambda t}$. Then,

$$\sigma = \sqrt{N_0(1 - e^{-\lambda t})c(1 - c + ce^{-\lambda t})},$$

and for λt small and the same approximations as before:

$$\sigma = \sqrt{N_0\lambda tc} = \sqrt{Mc} = \sqrt{\text{number of counts recorded.}}$$

This is just the conclusion we had reached without bothering about the detection efficiency. However, it should be emphasized that actual counts and not scaled counts from a scaling circuit must be used in these equations.

D. POISSON AND GAUSSIAN DISTRIBUTIONS

Poisson Distribution. The binomial distribution law may be put into a more convenient approximate form if we impose the restrictions $\lambda t \ll 1$, $N_0 \gg 1$, $m \ll N_0$, that is, if we consider a large number of active atoms observed for a time short compared to their half-life. It is also necessary to make use of these mathematical approximations:

(1) $$e^{\lambda t} = 1 + \lambda t, \quad \text{neglecting subsequent terms.}$$

(2) $$x! = \sqrt{2\pi x}\, x^x e^{-x} \quad \text{(Stirling's approximation).}$$

(3) $$\left(1 - \frac{m}{N_0}\right)^{N_0} = \lim_{N_0 \to \infty} \left(1 - \frac{m}{N_0}\right)^{N_0} = e^{-m}, \quad \text{since } N_0 \gg 1.$$

With these restrictions and approximations and with $M = N_0\lambda t$, equation 9-3 may in a straightforward way be put into the form known as the Poisson distribution:

$$W(m) = \frac{M^m e^{-M}}{m!}.$$

In words, the probability of obtaining the particular number of counts m is $M^m e^{-M}/m!$, where M is the average to be expected. This approximation is very good even for N_0 as small as 100 and λt as large as 0.01. Two features of this distribution might be noticed in particular. The probability of obtaining $m = M - 1$ is equal to the probability of obtaining $m = M$, or $W(M) = W(M - 1)$. For large M the distribution is very nearly symmetrical about $m = M$ if values of m very far from M be excluded.

Gaussian Distribution. A further approximation of the distribution law may be made for large m (say >100) and for $|M - m| \ll M$. With these additional restrictions and with the approximate expansion,

$$\ln\left(1 + \frac{M - m}{m}\right) = \frac{M - m}{m} - \frac{(M - m)^2}{2m^2},$$

neglecting subsequent terms, we may modify the Poisson distribution to obtain the Gaussian distribution:

$$W(m) = \frac{1}{\sqrt{2\pi M}} e^{-(M-m)^2/2M}.$$

It will be noticed that this distribution is symmetrical about $m = M$. For both the Poisson and Gaussian distributions we may derive $\sigma = \sqrt{M}$, or, for large m, $\sigma = \sqrt{m}$.

E. EXPERIMENTAL APPLICATIONS

Addition and Subtraction of Counting Rates. An important practical consideration is the addition and subtraction of counting results or counting rates. The Poisson distribution expression is suitable for the treatment of these cases, but the derivations are too tedious to be included here. The very significant results are these:

1. The sum of two Poisson distributions is itself a Poisson distribution. Hence, the variance σ_s^2 and standard deviation σ_s of a sum are given by $\sigma_s^2 = \sigma_1^2 + \sigma_2^2 + \cdots$ and $\sigma_s = \sqrt{\sigma_1^2 + \sigma_2^2 + \cdots}$.
2. The difference of two Poisson distributions is not a Poisson distribution; the variance σ_d^2 and standard deviation σ_d of the difference are given by $\sigma_d^2 = \sigma_1^2 + \sigma_2^2$ and $\sigma_d = \sqrt{\sigma_1^2 + \sigma_2^2}$.

As an example suppose that the background counting rate of a counter is measured, and 600 counts are recorded in 15 min. Then with a sample in place the total counting rate is measured, and 1000 counts are recorded in 10 min. We wish to know the net counting rate due to the sample and the standard deviation of this net rate. First the background rate $\mathbf{R}_b$ is

$$\mathbf{R}_b = \frac{600 \pm \sqrt{600}}{15} = \frac{600 \pm 24}{15} = 40 \pm 1.6 \text{ counts per min.}$$

The total rate $\mathbf{R}_t$ is

$$\mathbf{R}_t = \frac{1000 \pm \sqrt{1000}}{10} = \frac{1000 \pm 32}{10} = 100 \pm 3.2 \text{ counts per min.}$$

The net rate $\mathbf{R}_n = 100 - 40 = 60$ counts per min, and its standard deviation is $\sigma_n = \sqrt{1.6^2 + 3.2^2} = 3.6$; and $\mathbf{R}_n = 60 \pm 3.6$ counts per min.

Ratios and Products of Counting Rates. In many types of experiments the ratio of two counting rates is wanted. What is the standard deviation of this ratio $Q = \mathbf{R}_1/\mathbf{R}_2$, if the two standard deviations σ_1 and σ_2 are known? It may be shown by straightforward algebraic operations that for small deviations the ratio σ_Q^*/Q is given by

$$\frac{\sigma_Q^*}{Q} = \pm \frac{\sigma_1}{\mathbf{R}_1} \pm \frac{\sigma_2}{\mathbf{R}_2},$$

where for the moment we mean by σ_Q^* the particular deviation in Q resulting from possible combinations of the deviations σ_1 and σ_2 in $\mathbf{R}_1$ and $\mathbf{R}_2$. To obtain instead the standard deviation σ_Q we must assume that the two fractional deviations of the rates are not simply additive but on the average combine to give a root-mean-square deviation:

$$\frac{\sigma_Q}{Q} = \sqrt{\left(\frac{\sigma_1}{\mathbf{R}_1}\right)^2 + \left(\frac{\sigma_2}{\mathbf{R}_2}\right)^2}.$$

This is the formula to be used for evaluation of the standard deviation σ_Q of the ratio Q of two quantities. A similar expression is applicable for the product P of two or more rates:

$$\frac{\sigma_P}{P} = \sqrt{\left(\frac{\sigma_1}{\mathbf{R}_1}\right)^2 + \left(\frac{\sigma_2}{\mathbf{R}_2}\right)^2 + \cdots}.$$

More generally, if two measured quantities x and y have standard deviations σ_x and σ_y, the standard deviation σ_f of a function $f(x, y)$ is

$$\sigma_f = \sqrt{\left(\frac{\partial f}{\partial x}\right)^2 \sigma_x^2 + \left(\frac{\partial f}{\partial y}\right)^2 \sigma_y^2},$$ provided that all deviations are small.

This may be shown as follows. Let the mean values of the quantities x and y and of the function $f(x, y)$ be $\bar{x}$, $\bar{y}$, and $\bar{f}$, and consider an individual set of values $\bar{x} + \Delta_i x$, $\bar{y} + \Delta_j y$. Then the value of the function f may be written

$$\bar{f} + \Delta_{ij} f = f(\bar{x} + \Delta_i x,\ \bar{y} + \Delta_j y), \quad \text{and}$$

$$\Delta_{ij} f = \left(\frac{\partial f}{\partial x}\right) \Delta_i x + \left(\frac{\partial f}{\partial y}\right) \Delta_j y.$$

By definition

$$\sigma_f^2 = \overline{(\Delta_{ij} f)^2} = \sum_i \sum_j \left[\left(\frac{\partial f}{\partial x}\right)^2 (\Delta_i x)^2 + 2\left(\frac{\partial f}{\partial x}\right)\left(\frac{\partial f}{\partial y}\right) \Delta_i x\, \Delta_j y + \left(\frac{\partial f}{\partial y}\right)^2 (\Delta_j y)^2\right] p_i p_j,$$

where p_i and p_j are the probabilities of particular deviations $\Delta_i x$ and $\Delta_j y$. The sum of the cross products contains equal positive and negative terms and will therefore be zero. Then

$$\sigma_f^2 = \left(\frac{\partial f}{\partial x}\right)^2 \sum_i (\Delta_i x)^2 + \left(\frac{\partial f}{\partial y}\right)^2 \sum_j (\Delta_j y)^2 = \left(\frac{\partial f}{\partial x}\right)^2 \sigma_x^2 + \left(\frac{\partial f}{\partial y}\right)^2 \sigma_y^2.$$

Gaussian Error Curve. Knowledge of the distribution law permits a quantitative evaluation of the probability of a given deviation of a measured result m from the proper average M to be expected. The Gaussian distribution is convenient for this purpose. With the absolute error $|M - m| = \epsilon$, and with the assumption that the integral numbers are so large that the distribution may be treated as continuous, the probability $W(\epsilon)\,d\epsilon$ of an error between ϵ and $\epsilon + d\epsilon$ is given by

$$W(\epsilon)\,d\epsilon = \frac{2}{\sqrt{2\pi M}}\,e^{-\epsilon^2/2M}\,d\epsilon.$$

The factor 2 arises from the existence of positive and negative errors with equal probability within the limits of validity of this approximation. Recalling that $\sigma = \sqrt{M}$, we have

$$W(\epsilon)\,d\epsilon = \frac{1}{\sigma}\sqrt{\frac{2}{\pi}}\,e^{-\epsilon^2/2\sigma^2}\,d\epsilon.$$

The probability of an error greater than $k\sigma$ is obtained by integration from $\epsilon = k\sigma$ to $\epsilon = \infty$. Numerical values of this integral as a function of k may be found in handbooks. For example, we have taken for table 9-2 some representative values from the table, "Probability of Occurrence of Deviations" in the Chemical Rubber Publishing Company's *Handbook of Chemistry and Physics.*

TABLE 9-2

k	0	0.674	1	2	3	4
Probability of $\epsilon > k\sigma$	1.00	0.50	0.32	0.046	0.0027	0.00006

Notice that errors greater than 0.674σ and errors smaller than 0.674σ are equally probable; 0.674σ is called the "probable error," and is sometimes given rather than the standard deviation when counting data are reported. In plots of experimental curves it can be very convenient to indicate the probable error of each point (by a mark of the proper length); then on the average the smooth curve drawn should be expected to pass through about as many "points" as it misses.

Comparison with Experiment. We now return to a consideration of the typical counting data in table 9-1. We have already found from the deviations between the ten measurements $\sigma = \sqrt{\frac{1}{N_0} \Sigma(x_i - \bar{x})^2} =$ 11.3. If the counting rate measured there represents a random phenomenon, as we expect it should, we may evaluate the expected σ for the result in any minute as the square root of the number of counts. For a typical minute, the ninth, we find $\sigma = \sqrt{101} = 10$, and for other minutes other values not much different. Because these agree reasonably with the 11.3 there is evidence for the random nature of the observed counting rate. This test should occasionally be made on the data from a counting instrument.

In addition to estimating σ for any minute's counting in table 9-1, we may now estimate the σ for the average of the ten observations (which we could not do directly from the definition of σ). The average counting rate with its standard deviation is $\bar{x} = \frac{990 \pm \sqrt{990}}{10} =$ 99.0 $\pm$ 3.1 counts per min. This means that the probability that the true average is between 95.9 and 102.1 is, from table 9-2, just 1 − 0.32 = 0.68. Actually, when the counting data given in table 9-1 were obtained the average rate was measured much more accurately in a 100-min count, and the result was $\frac{10{,}042 \pm \sqrt{10{,}042}}{100} = 100.4 \pm 1.0$ counts per min.

Case of Very Few Counts. A question sometimes met in counting experiments is what can be done with results which show very few total counts (not net counts), or even no counts at all. A treatment of this problem given by R. W. Dodson is based on the assumption that all sample strengths are a priori equally probable. It can then be shown that observations may be fitted by a Poisson distribution with a true average number of counts M not equal to the measured value m, but rather to $m + 1$. (This is clearly related to one of the features already pointed out for the Poisson distribution.) The most probable value of M turns out to be equal to m; the standard deviation $\sigma = \sqrt{m + 1}$. Thus if the observed count is $m = 0$, we take for the answer $M = 1 \pm 1$; if the observed $m = 1$, we take $M = 2 \pm 1.4$; etc.

Counter Efficiencies. As another application of the methods of this chapter to counting techniques we may estimate the efficiency of a Geiger counter for rays of a given ionizing power, with the assumptions that any ray which produces at least one ion pair in the counter gas is counted and that effects at the counter walls are negligible. Knowledge of the nature of the radiation and the information given in chapter 7 permit an estimate of the average number of ion pairs a to be expected within the path length of the radiation in the counter filling gas. The problem then is to find the probability that a ray pass through the counter leaving no ion pairs and thus not be counted. We think of the path of the ray in the counter as divided into n segments of equal length; if n is very large, each segment will be so small that we may neglect the possibility of having two ion pairs in any segment. Then just a of the n segments will contain ion pairs, and by definition the probability of having an ion pair in a given segment is $p = a/n$. Now by equation 9-2 for the binomial distribution we have the probability for no ion pairs in n segments; that is, for $r = 0$:

$$W(0) = \frac{n!}{n!0!} p^0(1 - p)^n = (1 - p)^n = \left(1 - \frac{a}{n}\right)^n.$$

Since the probability [2] is evaluated correctly only as n becomes very large,

$$W(0) = \lim_{n\to\infty} \left(1 - \frac{a}{n}\right)^n = e^{-a}.$$

The probability of counting the ray, which is the efficiency to be determined, is then $1 - W(0) = 1 - e^{-a}$. As a particular example consider a fast β particle with the relatively low specific ionization of 5 ion pairs per millimeter in air and a path length of 10 mm in a counter gas which is almost pure argon at 7.6 cm pressure. We estimate a from these assumptions, correcting for the relative densities of air and the argon:

$$a = 5 \times 10 \times \frac{7.6}{76} \times \frac{40}{29} = 7.$$

The corresponding estimated counter efficiency is $1 - e^{-7} = 99.9$ per cent. It should not be expected that an efficiency calculated in this way is very precise. Wall effects may be important, and the assumption of random distribution of ion pairs along the β-ray path is not entirely consistent with the mechanism of energy loss by ionization presented in chapter 7.

Coincidence Correction. If a counter has a recovery time (or dead time or resolving time) τ after each recorded count during which it is completely insensitive, the total insensitive time per unit time is

[2] We might have evaluated this probability more easily from the Poisson distribution expression: $W(0) = a^0e^{-a}/0! = e^{-a}$.

$\mathbf{R}\tau$, where $\mathbf{R}$ is the observed counting rate. If $\mathbf{R}^*$ is the rate that would be recorded if there were no coincidence losses, the number of lost counts per unit time is $\mathbf{R}^* - \mathbf{R}$, and is given by the product of the rate $\mathbf{R}^*$ and the fraction of insensitive time $\mathbf{R}\tau$:

$$\mathbf{R}^* - \mathbf{R} = \mathbf{R}^*\mathbf{R}\tau,$$

$$\mathbf{R}^* = \frac{\mathbf{R}}{1 - \mathbf{R}\tau}. \qquad (9\text{-}6)$$

A number of variants of this formula are also in use. One expression (the Schiff formula) is $\mathbf{R}^* = \mathbf{R}e^{\mathbf{R}^*\tau}$; this is derived from a calculation of the probability $W(0)$ of having had no event during the time τ immediately preceding any event. An event, whether recorded or not, is here considered to prevent the recording of a second event occurring within the time τ[3]. Another approximate expression is derived from the first two terms in the binomial expansion of $(1 - \mathbf{R}\tau)^{-1}$ appearing in equation 9-6:

$$\mathbf{R}^* = \mathbf{R}(1 + \mathbf{R}\tau) = \mathbf{R} + \mathbf{R}^2\tau.$$

This form is especially convenient for the interpretation of an experiment designed to measure τ by measuring the rates $\mathbf{R}_1$ and $\mathbf{R}_2$ produced by two separate sources and the rate $\mathbf{R}_t$ produced by the two sources together, each of these rates including the background effect $\mathbf{R}_b$. Obviously,

$$\mathbf{R}_1^* + \mathbf{R}_2^* = \mathbf{R}_t^* + \mathbf{R}_b,$$

where we have neglected the coincidence loss in the measurement of the low background rate. Replacing by $\mathbf{R}_1^* = \mathbf{R}_1 + \mathbf{R}_1^2\tau$, etc., and rearranging we have

$$\tau = \frac{\mathbf{R}_1 + \mathbf{R}_2 - \mathbf{R}_t - \mathbf{R}_b}{\mathbf{R}_t^2 - \mathbf{R}_1^2 - \mathbf{R}_2^2}.$$

Integrating Measuring Instruments. For measurements with counting instruments we have seen the convenience of the simple expression $\sigma = \sqrt{\text{number of counts}}$. In the counting-rate meter, where a steady meter deflection is observed, what value may be assigned to the standard deviation? In this instrument a combination of resistance R and capacitance C effectively averages the rate of arrival of

[3] It may be noticed that the Schiff formula might be expected to correspond more closely to the conditions of coincidence loss in a mechanical register, where a new pulse within a dead time could initiate a new dead-time period although it would not be recorded. There exists also the opportunity for coincidence losses in the electric circuits.

pulses over an interval of the order of magnitude of the time constant RC; a quantitative analysis shows that the effective interval is 2RC. Representing the counting rate in counts per minute by $\mathbf{R}_1$ we obtain the standard deviation of this rate from equation 9-5, where $t =$ 2RC/60 min for R in ohms and C in farads:

$$\sigma_{\text{rate}} = \sqrt{\frac{\mathbf{R}_1}{t}} = \sqrt{\frac{30\mathbf{R}_1}{\text{RC}}}.$$

For an instrument consisting of an ionization chamber with a d-c amplifier the same expression may be used, provided that the activity can be evaluated approximately as a rate of arrival of ionizing particles and the value of the longest time constant is known (ordinarily that of the collecting electrode and first grid circuit unless a very slow galvanometer is employed). If necessary the time constant may be approximated as the time for a deflection to be reduced to $1/e$ of its value after removal of an active sample.

In a rate-of-drift-measuring method, as in the d-c amplifier with infinite grid resistance or in the Lauritsen electroscope, the number m of ionizing particles arriving during the time of measurement is estimated, and the standard deviation of the activity $\mathbf{A}$ is given by $\sigma = \mathbf{A}\frac{\sqrt{m}}{m} = \frac{\mathbf{A}}{\sqrt{m}}$. These considerations are not easily applied to γ-ray measurements in ionization chambers, but the statistical uncertainties would be at least as great as indicated by these formulas.

Statistics of Pulse Height Distributions. When a monoenergetic source of radiation is measured with a proportional or scintillation counter spectrometer, the observed pulse heights have a Gaussian distribution around the most probable value. The energy resolution of such an instrument is usually expressed in terms of the full width at half maximum of the pulse height distribution curve, stated as a fraction or percentage of the most probable pulse height H. The pulse height $h_{1/2}$ at the half maximum of the distribution curve may be obtained from the ratio of probabilities $W(h_{1/2})/W(H) = e^{-(H-h_{1/2})^2/2H} = 0.5$. Then $(H - h_{1/2})^2/2H = \ln 2$, and the full width at half maximum is

$$\frac{2|H - h_{1/2}|}{H} = 2\sqrt{2 \ln 2}\,\sqrt{H}/H = 2.36\sqrt{H}/H = 2.36\sigma_h/H,$$

where σ_h is the standard deviation of the pulse height distribution.

In a proportional counter the spread in pulse heights for monoenergetic rays absorbed in the counter volume arises from statistical fluctuations in the number of ion pairs formed and statistical fluctuations in the gas amplification factor. The pulse height is proportional to the product of the gas amplification and the number of ion pairs, and therefore the fractional standard deviation of the pulse height equals the square root of the sum of the squares of the fractional standard deviations of these two quantities. As an example consider the pulse height spectrum produced by the absorption of manganese K X rays in a proportional counter filled with 90 per cent argon and 10 per cent methane and operating with a gas gain of 1000. From table 7-1 the energy per ion pair is about 27 ev, and therefore the number of ion pairs formed by a 5.95-kev X ray is $5950/27 = 220 \pm \sqrt{220}$. If the numbers of ions collected per initial ion pair have a Poisson distribution, the fractional standard deviation in the gas gain is $\sqrt{1000}/1000$. Thus $\sigma_h/H = \sqrt{220/220^2 + 1000/1000^2} = \sqrt{0.00455 + 0.00100} = 0.0745$, and the full width at half maximum is $2.36 \times 0.0745 = 0.176$ or 17.6 per cent. If the gas gain is made sufficiently large, the fluctuations in the number of ion pairs determine the resolution, and in this case the resolution of a given counter is seen to be inversely proportional to the square root of the energy of the ionizing radiation absorbed.

In a scintillation counter the statistical fluctuations in output pulse heights arise from several sources. The conversion of energy of ionizing radiation into photons in the scintillator, the electron emission at the photocathode, and the electron multiplication at each dynode are all subject to statistical variations. Although the photocathode emission has been shown to have somewhat larger fluctuations than correspond to the Poisson law, the observed pulse height distributions are for most practical purposes in sufficiently close agreement with those calculated on the assumption of Poisson distributions for all the statistical processes involved. With this assumption the standard deviation of a pulse height distribution for a single energy of ionizing radiation absorbed in the phosphor turns out to be approximately $\sigma_h = H\sqrt{\bar{n}/E\bar{q}\bar{f}\bar{p}(\bar{n} - 1)}$, where H is the most probable pulse height for an incident energy E kev, $\bar{q}$ is the mean value of the phosphor efficiency (number of light quanta emitted per 1000 ev of incident energy), $\bar{f}$ is the mean value of the light collection efficiency at the photocathode, $\bar{p}$ is the mean value of the photocathode efficiency (number of photoelectrons arriving at the first dynode for each photon incident on the photocathode), and $\bar{n}$ is the average electron multiplication per dynode.

In practice $\bar{f}$ can be made almost unity, $\bar{p}$ is of the order of 0.1, $\bar{n}$ is usually about 3 to 5, and $\bar{q}$ is approximately 30 for NaI (Tl), 15 for anthracene, and 7 for stilbene and for the best liquid scintillators. As an example we estimate the resolution attainable for the 662-kev photopeak of the Cs^{137} γ rays with a sodium iodide scintillation counter. Taking $\bar{f}\bar{p} = 0.1$ and $\bar{n} = 4$, we get $\sigma_h/H = \sqrt{\dfrac{4}{662 \times 30 \times 0.1 \times 3}} =$ 0.026. The corresponding full width at half maximum is 2.36 σ_h/H = 0.061 or 6.1 per cent, which is indeed not far from the best resolution obtained experimentally. (See the experimental pulse height distribution with 8.5 per cent width at half maximum shown in figure 8-7.)

EXERCISES

1. Derive the relation given on p. 253: $\sigma_x^2 = \overline{x^2} - \bar{x}^2$.

2. Mr. Jones' automobile license carries a six-digit number. What is the probability that it has (*a*) exactly one 4, (*b*) at least one 4? Make the assumption that the numbers 0 to 9 inclusive are equally probable for each of the six digits. *Answer:* (*b*) 0.46856.

3. Given an atom of a radioactive substance with decay constant λ, what is:

(*a*) The probability of it decaying between 0 and dt?

(*b*) The probability of it decaying between 0 and t?

4. The following numbers were obtained in the measurement of a physical quantity x:

Set 1: 90,110,100.
Set 2: 99,101,100.

What is the average value obtained in each set? In which set would you consider the measurements more reliable? What is the standard deviation for each set?

5. A given proportional counter has a measured background rate of 900 counts in 30 min. With a sample of a long-lived activity in place, the total measured rate was 1100 counts in 20 min. What is the net sample counting rate and its standard deviation? *Answer:* 25.0 ± 1.9 counts per min.

6. Denote by $\mathbf{R}_t$ and $\mathbf{R}_b$ the total and background counting rates for a long-lived sample, and calculate the optimum division of available counting time between sample and background for minimum σ on the net counting rate.

Answer: $\dfrac{t_t}{t_b} = \sqrt{\dfrac{\mathbf{R}_t}{\mathbf{R}_b}}$.

7. Refer to exercise 2, chapter 8. What would be the detection efficiency for that counter and that β ray?

8. (*a*) Sample A, sample B, and background alone were each counted for 10 min; the observed total rates were 110, 205, and 44 counts per min, respectively. Find the ratio of the activity of sample A to that of sample B and the standard deviation of this ratio. (*b*) Sample C was counted on the same counter for 2 min, and the observed total rate was 155 counts per min. Find the ratio, and its standard deviation, of the activity of C to that of A.

Answer: (*a*) 0.41 ± 0.027.

9. What is the probability of a penny turning heads up *at least* once in n throws?

10. Use the data given in exercise 5-1 to find the half-lives by the method of least squares rather than by graphical solution. Assume that there is no error in the measured time intervals and that all the measured counting rates have standard deviations of ± 1 per cent.

11. The scintillation spectrometer of exercise 6, chapter 8, is to be used for the measurement of 120-kev conversion electrons. What will be the full width at half maximum of the pulse height distribution?

12. Would the same spectrometer (preceding exercise) completely resolve (that is, give a dip between the pulse height peaks of) two conversion-electron groups of 44 and 52 kev, present in the abundance ratio 2:1? Would a proportional-counter spectrometer be better for this application?

REFERENCES

T. C. Fry, *Probability and Its Engineering Uses,* New York, D. Van Nostrand Co., 1928.

R. A. Fisher, *Statistical Methods for Research Workers,* London, Oliver and Boyd, 1936.

L. J. Rainwater and C. S. Wu, "Applications of Probability Theory to Nuclear Particle Detection," *Nucleonics* **1,** No. 2, 60 (October 1947) and **2,** No. 1, 42 (January 1948).

L. J. Schiff and R. D. Evans, "Statistical Analysis of the Counting Rate Meter," *Rev. Sci. Instr.* **7,** 456 (1936).

N. Feather, "On the Distribution in Time of the Scintillations Produced by the α Particles from a Weak Source," *Phys. Rev.* **35,** 705 (1930).

R. Peierls, "Statistical Error in Counting Experiments," *Proc. Roy. Soc.,* Series A **149,** 467 (1935).

F. Seitz and D. W. Mueller, "On the Statistics of Luminescent Counter Systems," *Phys. Rev.* **78,** 605 (1950).

S. C. Curran, *Luminescence and the Scintillation Counter,* London, Butterworth's Scientific Publications, 1953.

CHAPTER 10

TECHNIQUES FOR THE STUDY OF RADIONUCLIDES

A. SOME GENERAL PRACTICES

The principal types of instruments used for detection and measurement of radiations from radioactive substances have been discussed in chapter 8. Here we wish to review some of the techniques employed in the course of measurements of this kind. The choice of instruments and techniques will be determined in large part by the kinds of information desired. In a simple tracer application, employing one active isotope of favorable properties and available with ample activity and known purity, a single instrument (counter, electrometer, or electroscope) is likely to be sufficient, and measuring techniques may offer no problems. The opposite extreme would be a large radiochemical laboratory devoted to the detailed study of the radiation characteristics of a variety of radionuclides, to the identification of new radioactive species, and to quantitative investigations of nuclear reactions produced in nuclear chain reactors and accelerators. Here a large number and wide variety of instruments, including highly specialized types, must be available, and the associated techniques and manipulations will be complex and ingenious. Most radiochemical laboratories represent intermediate situations. Even where tracer work only is carried out, a number of tracers are likely to be in use, calling for different choices of detectors and sample handling procedures. Frequently the desired radioactivity must be isolated and identified and checked for purity with regard to contamination by other radioactive substances. The typical laboratory may have thin-window proportional (or G-M) counters for most β counting, sodium iodide scintillation counters for γ counting, and perhaps a gas-flow proportional counter arranged for introduction of α or soft-β emitters into the counter.

It is very convenient to have a standard arrangement for holding standard-size samples in various positions, the same arrangement being used for as many of the instruments as possible. A typical sample-holder arrangement, that used in the Chemistry Department of Brookhaven National Laboratory, is shown in figure 10-1. This standard arrangement is fitted to all instruments (G-M, proportional,

FIGURE 10-1. Gas-flow proportional counter with lucite stand and lead shield. The bubbler tube at the upper left is used to indicate the rate of gas flow. A sample is in place under the counter window on the top sample shelf. An aluminum card for sample mounting (*right*) and a thin aluminum absorber mounted in a frame (*left*) are shown in front of the counter assembly. (Courtesy A. Weinstein and Brookhaven National Laboratory.)

and scintillation counters) which are used to measure externally placed solid samples. The entire stand is made of lucite to minimize scattering of β and γ rays, and a lucite shelf (either solid or with a central hole) may be placed in any of the milled slots to hold samples at various distances from the detector. The samples themselves are mounted on cardboard or aluminum cards 2.5 in. by 3 in. by $\frac{1}{32}$ in. These sample cards slide broadwise into the lucite stand on top of one of the shelves. The back wall of the stand serves as a stop determining the position. The machining of the stands is sufficiently precise and the clearance between cards and stand sufficiently small to allow placement of samples reproducible within a few thousandths of an inch. For ease of handling each card has a tab along one of its 3-in. edges.

Absorbers may be placed directly on top of the sample or on a frame-like shelf in a slot nearer the detector. Absorbers are cut to the same 2.5- by 3-in. size as the sample cards. Sets of aluminum absorbers are the most useful. They should be available in an assortment of thicknesses so that absorption curves may include points from about a milligram per square centimeter up to several grams per square centimeter. Our thicker absorbers are cut from thick aluminum stock, with a small tab left on one of the long sides which is marked with the thickness in milligrams per square centimeter. The thinnest absorbers are compounded of thin aluminum foils, held in rectangular 2.5- by 3-in. aluminum frames, again provided with tabs. A set of lead absorbers is more convenient for the determination of γ-ray absorption curves, but it need not include very thin pieces. A few beryllium, paraffin, or polyethylene absorbers of the same shape are useful because of their very small absorption coefficients for all but the softest electromagnetic radiations.

All the measuring instruments should be checked occasionally—preferably daily—with standard samples; it is best if a standard is chosen to have radiations similar to those of the activity to be measured. Background rates should be measured at least daily. To reduce backgrounds due to cosmic rays and strong samples in the laboratory, most counters including their stands are enclosed in lead shields 1 to 1½ in. thick. Voltage plateaus, particularly for G-M counters, should be checked occasionally. An intercalibration of all the instruments for activities of interest can be useful but ordinarily should be depended on only for semiquantitative results. A knowledge of at least the relative geometry factors for samples placed on various shelves is often useful.

Each instrument must have its response to samples of different strengths determined; outside the linear-response region it should be used cautiously, with calibrated corrections. This calibration can be made in several ways: (1) with samples of different activity carefully prepared from aliquot portions of an active solution; (2) by comparison of the decay curve of a very pure short-lived activity of known half-life with the exponential decay to be expected; and (3) by measurements of the separate and combined effects of samples located in reproducible assigned positions (see chapter 9, page 266). With counters the failure of linearity at high counting rates is attributed to coincidence losses; the correction is known as a coincidence correction.[1] Ordinarily the necessity for corrections amounting to more than a few per cent should be avoided.

B. PROBLEMS IN SAMPLE PREPARATION

Many points of experimental technique arise in the preparation of samples for activity measurements. Most of these have to do with the attainment of a suitable and reproducible geometrical arrangement and with the scattering and absorption of radiations in the sample and in its support. The difficulties encountered in sample preparation are greatest when absolute disintegration rates or energies are wanted, are less when samples of different radiation characteristics are compared, and are least when the relative strengths of several samples of the same kind, or of the same sample at several times, are to be determined. Fortunately the last-mentioned problem is probably the one most often met in radiochemical work. However, even here adequate reproducibility may sometimes be troublesome to achieve.

Choice of Counting Arrangement. Careful consideration must be given to the chemical and physical form in which samples are to be measured. The radiations emitted by the substance and the available measuring equipment are among the determining factors. Alpha emitters are usually counted in the form of thin deposits preferably prepared by electrodeposition or by distillation and placed inside a counter or ionization chamber. Nuclides that emit primarily soft radiations (low-energy β rays, X rays, conversion electrons, or Auger electrons) may be counted very efficiently if they can be prepared in the form of a gas suitable as a component of a counter-filling mixture. For example, C^{14}-labeled compounds may be burned to CO_2, which is then introduced into a proportional counter along with an appropriate amount of argon, methane, or argon-methane mixture; essentially 100 per cent counting efficiency and good counter

[1] If the dead time of the counter tube is known to be much larger than the time constants of any of the other components the coincidence correction for any counting rate can be calculated from the dead time; see chapter 9, page 265. The following is a convenient method for the determination of G-M tube dead time. By adjustment of the counter voltage the minimum pulse height necessary to trip the counter circuit is measured on an oscilloscope. Then a strong source is used, the counter is operated on the plateau, and, with the pulses triggering the oscilloscope sweep, the time required after each pulse for the pulse heights to come back up to the previously determined minimum height is observed on the oscilloscope.

behavior can be obtained over a fair range of CO_2 partial pressures (0.5 to 5 mm of mercury). This technique requires the use of a good gas-handling and purification system.

Beta-active nuclides are most commonly prepared in the form of thin solid samples and counted with thin-window counters. However, lack of reproducibility of absorption and self-absorption effects can be troublesome in this technique. Therefore, if a sample emits both β and γ rays, the possible advantages of γ counting should be considered. Absorption effects are generally much smaller for γ rays than for β rays, and therefore variations in the thicknesses of samples and counter walls are usually negligible when γ rays are counted. Particularly where scintillation counters with their high efficiency for γ-ray detection are available, γ counting will often be the method of choice. Samples may be counted as solids or in solutions which are placed under the counter in standard liquid cells. Even with G-M or proportional counters γ counting may be preferable to β counting, especially in experiments where specific activity rather than total activity is a limiting factor; in γ counting a much larger sample can be used effectively.

Much of the work of nuclear chemists almost inevitably involves measurement of β particles from solid samples. The following paragraphs therefore deal more specifically with problems encountered when solid samples are used for β counting.

Back-scattering. The phenomenon of back-scattering of electrons has been described on page 203. To achieve reproducibility in the measurement of β activities it is clearly necessary to mount samples in such a way that the back-scattering from the mount is either negligible or constant from sample to sample. For determinations of relative counting rates it is probably best to mount all samples on thick supports of low Z (plastic or aluminum) and to count them in the same geometry, preferably at no more than 20 per cent of the total solid angle. For accurate comparisons of different β emitters it will still be necessary to take into account the difference between β^- and β^+ scattering and the dependence of back-scattering on energy for low-energy spectra. For work of the highest precision, samples should be mounted on essentially weightless plastic films (<0.1 mg cm^{-2}).[2]

[2] Such films of polystyrene, Formvar, Zapon lacquer, nylon, or the like are readily prepared. The plastic is dissolved in a suitable solvent, a drop of the solution is allowed to spread on a clean water surface, the solvent evaporates, and the resulting film is lifted off the water by means of a metal frame or wire loop.

Because the back-scattered electrons are degraded in energy, an absorption curve for a given β emitter has a somewhat steeper initial slope when the sample is mounted on a thick backing than when it is deposited on a thin film. The end point is, of course, unaffected.

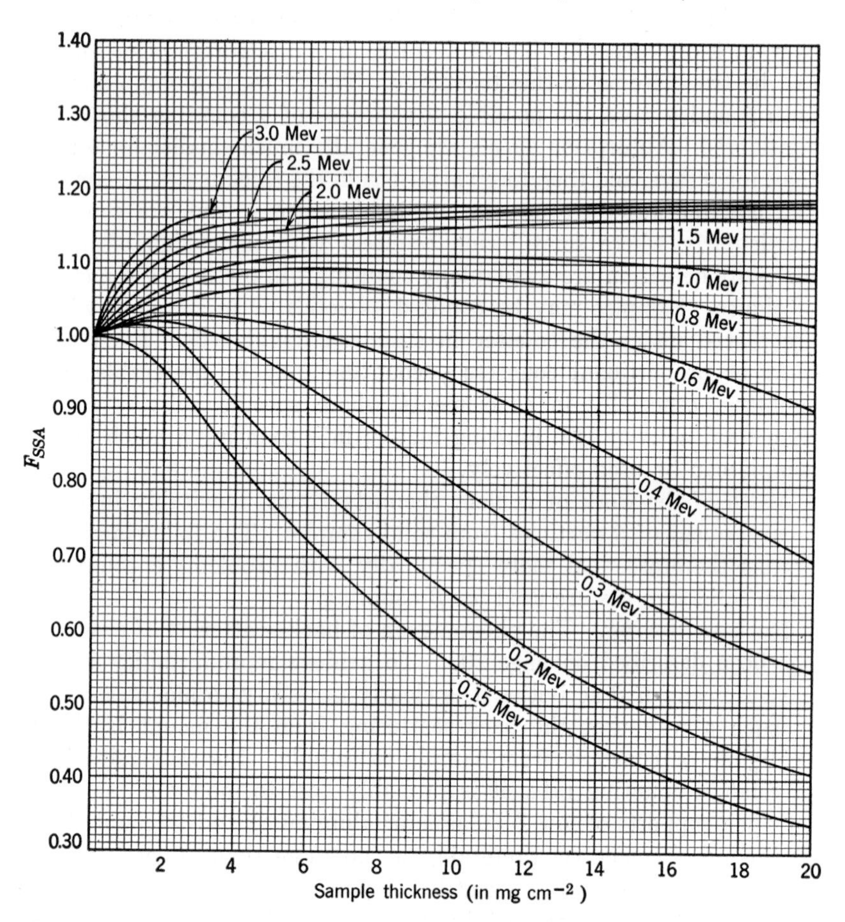

FIGURE 10-2. Self-absorption and self-scattering effect in NaCl for β spectra of various maximum energies. The observed counting rate is to be divided by the factor F_{SSA} to correct for self-scattering and self-absorption. [From W. E. Nervik and P. C. Stevenson, *Nucleonics* **10,** No. 3, 18 (March 1952).]

Self-absorption and Self-scattering. Whenever the β activities of samples of finite thickness are measured, consideration should be given to the effect of absorption and scattering of electrons in the samples themselves. To make corrections for these effects negligible, sample thicknesses should be no more than about one per cent of the range of the electrons. When thicker samples must be used it is advisable either to standardize the thickness at a fixed value or to prepare an empirical calibration curve for different thicknesses; in

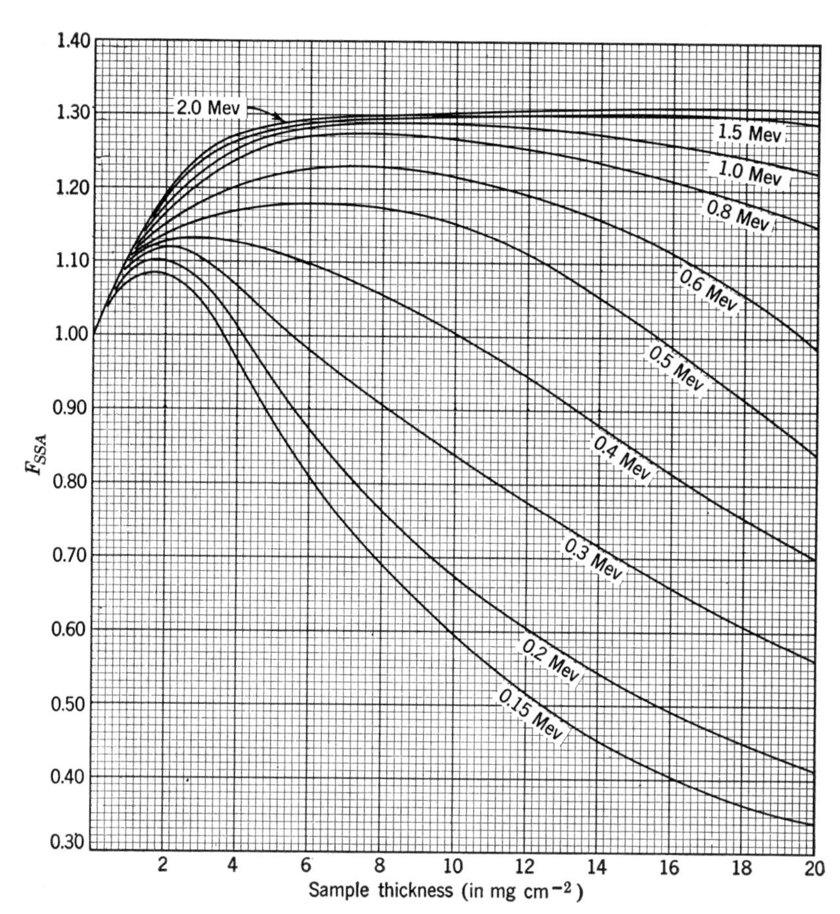

FIGURE 10-3. Self-absorption and self-scattering effect in $Pb(NO_3)_2$ for β spectra of various maximum energies. The observed counting rate is to be divided by the factor F_{SSA} to correct for self-scattering and self-absorption. [From W. E. Nervik and P. C. Stevenson, *Nucleonics* **10**, No. 3, 18 (March 1952).]

either case careful attention must be given to a reproducible mechanical form for the sample, and reproducibility should be tested by experiment.

If a uniformly radioactive material is used to make sources of various thicknesses but equal areas, the measured activities will not be found proportional to the sample thickness; that is, the measured specific activities will not be constant. Figures 10-2 and 10-3 show such results for two sample materials and for several maximum β energies. The ordinate in each figure is the self-scattering and self-absorption factor F_{SSA}, the factor by which the observed specific activity must be divided to obtain the specific activity of an infinitely thin sample. The somewhat surprising initial increase is due to the scattering of electrons by the material of the sample out of the sample plane and into the counter. (The magnitude of this self-scattering effect depends upon the geometry and disappears when the detector completely surrounds the sample.) At greater thicknesses, when self-absorption predominates over self-scattering, the factor is approximately proportional to $(1 - e^{-\mu x})/\mu x$, where μ is the ordinary absorption coefficient for the β particles in the sample material and x is the sample thickness.

It may be noted that the curves of figures 10-2 and 10-3 were determined for a typical end-window counter arrangement, mica window 3.5 mg cm^{-2}, and window-to-sample distances from 2 to 7 cm (geometry factors 0.03 to 0.2). The samples were on thick stainless-steel backings, and after correction by F_{SSA} a separate backscattering correction would have to be applied. The factor F_{SSA} would no doubt be somewhat different for other mounts.

When thicker and thicker samples are prepared from an active material, say, for example, $BaCO_3$ containing C^{14}, the measured counting rate at first increases because of the greater total activity in the sample and then approaches a constant value. This "saturation value" is clearly not a measure of the total activity of the sample, but rather is related to the activity of the amount of sample material in an upper layer no thicker than the particle range R, and is thus a measure of the specific activity of the sample material. This fact is sometimes used to advantage in the measurement of the low-energy tracers; no correction for self-absorption is applied, and it is only necessary to measure the activities of thick samples of the same uniform area and the same chemical composition. Indeed in many tracer experiments the specific activity is more directly significant than the total activity. The minimum sample thickness required for this type of measurement is clearly not more than the range R, and for most practical purposes $0.75R$ is adequate because of the very small relative contribution of the lowest layers and the additional absorption due to the counter window.

Useful Sample-Mounting Techniques. If thin samples are to be used, so that the self-absorption correction is small, it is usually necessary to arrange that they be spread uniformly over the sample-mounting area. If a solution is merely evaporated to dryness in a very shallow cup [3] the deposit left will probably show very obvious lack of uniformity; most of the residue will ordinarily be found near the edge. If the active substance is first precipitated and the slurry evaporated, preferably with stirring, a much improved deposit usually results. In another procedure the slurry is added and dried a little at a time. It is sometimes helpful to place a circular piece of cigarette paper, slightly smaller than the dish or disk, on the flat surface; the solution or slurry is allowed to spread over the paper and then to dry; when dry this type of paper weighs about 1 mg cm^{-2}.

Other methods of preparing samples are sometimes more convenient, especially if the bulk of the deposit or the volume of solution or suspension is large. Filtration on a small Büchner or Gooch filter can give reasonably uniform and very nearly quantitative deposits of precipitates on the filter paper. If the precipitate and filter are washed finally with alcohol [4] the bits of precipitate creeping up the sides of the filter are likely to be washed down; also the paper is then more easily dried, either with or without an ether wash. A glass chimney held tightly against the paper in a Büchner funnel with perforated surface ground flat will help to confine the precipitate to a definite area. A particularly convenient arrangement for sample preparation by filtration is shown in figure 10-4. The filter paper is supported on a sintered glass disk with a fire-polished rim, which is clamped between the thickened and ground ends of two glass tubes; the top tube serves as the area-defining chimney, the bottom tube is fitted into a rubber stopper on a filter flask.

Sedimentation of a precipitate followed by decantation or evaporation can be used to give uniform deposits. Special cells with demountable bottoms are employed for this purpose so that the sample

[3] Some workers use shallow flat-bottom porcelain ashing dishes. Very shallow cups stamped from a suitably inert metal foil are better for some purposes. Actually cups are not necessary since a flat disk such as a microscope cover glass with a smooth (and possibly greased) edge will hold water. The evaporations are conveniently carried out under an ordinary infrared lamp.

[4] The use of alcohol (presumably to lower surface tension) has other applications in the manipulation of samples. For example, when a precipitate is centrifuged down in a semimicro cone some is almost always trapped in the liquid surface (meniscus); addition of a few drops of alcohol on top of the solution followed by another centrifugation will usually bring down most of this precipitate. In the mounting of slurries as described previously a few drops of alcohol as a wash will often clean the residual slurry from the transfer micropipet (a glass tube drawn down to have a long tip less than 1 mm in diameter and fitted with a rubber bulb, like an "eye dropper").

may be removed on its mounting for measurement. Sedimentation cells of this type fitted into laboratory centrifuge cups may be used to give harder deposits in very much less time.

Samples prepared in any of these ways should be thoroughly dry before measurement, otherwise the self-absorption and self-scattering will change with time as water evaporates. Samples may be

Figure 10-4. Convenient set-up for preparation of counting samples by filtration. The separate components are shown next to the assembled apparatus. (Courtesy Brookhaven National Laboratory.)

found subject to loss of precipitate through powdering when dry; this can be especially troublesome if the active dust should contaminate a measuring instrument. To avoid this effect a few drops of a solution of zapon lacquer in alcohol or of Duco cement in acetone may be used to wet the sample when it is first dried; the concentration of the lacquer or cement in the solution should be so small that only about 0.1 mg cm^{-2} of its dry residue will be left on the sample.

Dry powders may be compacted into disks with a piston-and-cylinder arrangement, or simply pressed smoothly into shallow depressions cut in aluminum or other suitable sample-mounting cards. These techniques cannot be recommended for the preparation of very thin samples for measurements of soft radiations. If the radiation is penetrating, solutions of active materials may be counted directly in a thin-walled glass jacket slipped over a tubular counter, or better in an outer jacket built as a part of a glass counter tube. A dipping counter is arranged to permit immersion of the whole counter (except an end for electric connections) in the solution to be measured. Radiations from relatively thick layers of solutions may be counted reproducibly only if the solution densities are comparable, and if the relative composition of the solutions in terms of elements of various atomic numbers is kept approximately constant, especially for γ-ray measurements (see chapter 7, section C).

If the radioactive element is a metal like copper excellent samples for measurement may be prepared by electrodeposition. Other types of ions may often be deposited by different electrode reactions under suitable conditions. For example, lead may be deposited on an anode as PbO_2 from alkali plumbite solutions. Insoluble hydroxides may be deposited from neutral solutions on cathodes because of the liberation of hydroxide ions there: $H_2O + e^- = \frac{1}{2}H_2 + OH^-$. Insoluble ferrocyanides may form on a cathode from the reduction of some metal ferricyanide solutions. A metal fluoride may be precipitated in adherent form if the metal can be oxidized or reduced at an electrode from a fluoride-soluble to a fluoride-insoluble state; for example, UF_4 may be deposited in this way and then ignited in air to U_3O_8.

When quantitative deposition is not essential, thin uniform samples may sometimes be prepared very satisfactorily by volatilization. Volatile elements such as polonium, astatine, and francium have been transferred by flaming from a metal holder to a counting disk placed above it. In a more refined version of the procedure, the distillations are carried out in a vacuum system. Particularly in the preparation of carrier-free deposits distillation techniques are very useful. For example, after isolation by wet chemistry of a Be^7 sample from a proton-bombarded lithium target, the final weightless ($<2\ \mu g$) Be^7 samples were obtained by evaporation onto a disk from a tungsten ribbon at 1500°C. Thin standard boron films are sometimes wanted. These can be prepared by the decomposition of B_2H_6 on hot tungsten at about 900°C under carefully controlled conditions.

Some specialized sample-spreading techniques have been developed to a high state of the art for the preparation of standard foils, for example, of uranium. In one of these a wetting agent, tetraethylene glycol (TEG), is used to improve spreading on evaporation. In this procedure a platinum foil of the right dimension is prepared with a Zapon lacquer border, then a few microliters of TEG per square centimeter are applied, and the uranium as chloride in dilute hydrochloric acid solution is added. Evaporation is carried out under an infrared lamp, with some rotation of the foil to insure mixing. Finally, the plate is ignited to red heat for a few minutes to convert the deposit to an adherent highly colored layer of U_3O_8. This is rubbed gently with lens paper and then may be weighed to establish the uranium content. This procedure is suitable for the preparation of uranium foils of the order of 0.1 mg cm^{-2} and with larger amounts of TEG can be used up to about 1 mg cm^{-2}. Another technique uses uranyl nitrate dissolved in alcohol (about 50 mg per ml), with about 1 per cent of Zapon lacquer added; this mixture is painted on the platinum or aluminum foil with a brush; each coat is dried, ignited to U_3O_8, and rubbed with lens paper. Thick foils, weighable for uranium content, may be built up by this method. Other elements with alcohol-soluble salts give satisfactory plates with the same technique.

Incidentally, polyethylene glycols have been found useful in sample preparation. These waxy water-soluble materials are sold under the name of Carbowax. Like TEG they serve as effective wetting and spreading agents, but unlike TEG they remain after evaporation and serve as binder for the sample. Excellent foils of LiF have been prepared by sedimentation and evaporation of water-alcohol solutions in the presence of polyethylene glycol.

C. DECAY SCHEME STUDIES

A great deal of work by nuclear chemists and physicists has been directed toward the collection of data on decay schemes (disintegration schemes) of radioactive nuclides. A complete decay scheme includes all the modes of decay of the nuclide, their abundances, the energies of the radiations, the sequence in which the radiations are emitted, and the measurable half-lives of any intermediate states. Where possible, spin and parity assignments of the various energy levels involved are included in the decay scheme. Elucidation of decay schemes usually requires very careful and specialized measurements of the radiations, and particularly if spins and parities are wanted, information is desirable on the shapes of β spectra and on angular correlations of various radiations. Some illustrative examples of decay schemes are shown in figures 10-5, 10-6, and 10-8; these will be discussed individually in some detail in subsequent paragraphs.

The amount of detail known about any given decay scheme depends very strongly on the refinements in instrumentation and technique used in its investigation. Frequently, when a previously well-studied decay scheme is reinvestigated with instruments of improved resolution or sensitivity, new features such as branch decays of low abundance are discovered; it now appears that, except among the lightest nuclei, there are indeed few decay schemes that are truly simple (for example, consisting of a single β transition to a ground or first excited state).

The starting point of a decay scheme investigation depends, of course, on the information already available about the nuclide under study. If one deals with a newly discovered nuclide, the half-life is usually established first.[5] The nature of the radiations may be identified by measurements with different detectors—α counters, thin-window β counters, γ scintillation counters—and by some absorption measurements. Electron capture may be discovered by identification of the characteristic X rays emitted.

It is occasionally necessary to distinguish between β^- and β^+ particles. In the electron spectrograph this distinction is made easily according to the polarity of the magnetic field.[6] Without such an instrument a crude determination may be made to distinguish a predominantly positron from a predominantly negatron emitter. If the sample and detector are separated by a few inches and shielded from each other, a magnetic field from an electromagnet or sizable permanent magnet [7] may be arranged to bend particles of one sign around the shield toward the detector. Another method for the identification of positrons is based on the detection of the annihilation radiation (two γ rays of 0.51 Mev for each positron annihilated at the end of its range). Crudely this may be done by a comparison of counting rates in a γ counter with and without a beryllium or plastic backing behind the sample. A substantial increase in the detector response with addition of the backing would indicate positrons stopping in the backing material and giving rise there to annihilation radiation. A much more sensitive method for detection of annihilation radiation is based on the fact that the two γ quanta are emitted

[5] Even when the decay scheme of a nuclide of well-known half-life is under investigation, the nuclide may not be available free from other radioactive isotopes. In that case measurements may have to be made as a function of time to sort out those radiations associated with the nuclide of interest.

[6] In a magnetic lens spectrometer electrons of either sign are focused unless special spiral baffles are incorporated which allow electrons of only one sign to reach the detector for a given polarity of the field.

[7] A field of 1000 to 2000 gauss over a volume of about 1 cubic inch is convenient and readily available with a permanent magnet such as the ones designed for radar magnetrons.

in opposite directions. If a positron emitter and sufficient material to absorb some or all of the positrons are placed between two γ counters, measurements of γ-γ coincidences with the counters placed at 180° and at a slightly different angle will give different coincidence rates, even if other coincidences due to nuclear γ rays are recorded also.

The determination of the energy spectra of the radiations emitted involves the use of the various types of spectrometers and spectrographs mentioned in chapter 8. The choice of instrument may depend on the information desired, on the resolution needed, on the source strength and specific activity available, and on the half-life. Source thickness and uniformity requirements also differ widely for different types of measurement. For γ-ray measurements they are least exacting. If only the end point of a rather high-energy β spectrum is wanted, a source thickness of 1 mg cm^{-2} may be quite satisfactory. But if one desires to resolve the Kurie plot of a β spectrum into several components or to determine accurately the shape of a β spectrum, extremely thin sources (say 0.01 mg cm^{-2}) uniformly deposited on equally thin supports may be required.

Questions about the sequence in which various radiations are emitted and about the existence of alternative decay paths are usually answered by coincidence measurements. As was already indicated in chapter 8, the more selectively each of the two detectors used in a coincidence study records one particular radiation, the more readily even very complex decay schemes may be disentangled. Since increased selectivity is almost always accompanied by decreased detection efficiency, some compromise usually needs to be made in practice. Coincidence techniques are often very helpful in energy determinations also. For example, a low-intensity, low-energy β branch in the presence of an intense high-energy component may well escape detection in a β-spectrographic measurement. If, however, the high-energy β spectrum is not coincident with γ rays, while the low-energy branch is, then a β spectrum taken in coincidence with γ rays will show the low-energy component only, and precise measurement of its end point and spectrum shape thus becomes possible. With a β spectrometer and a scintillation spectrometer in coincidence, the β spectrum coincident with each of several γ radiations may be observed.

The following examples may serve to illustrate the techniques of decay scheme studies.

Gold-198. This nuclide, of 2.69 days half-life, was for a long time thought to have a very simple disintegration scheme, decaying by the emission of a single β^- group of allowed spectrum shape and upper energy limit 0.96 Mev to the lowest excited state of Hg^{198} at 0.412 Mev above the ground state. This scheme was verified by numerous spectrometer and coincidence measurements.[8] The nuclide has in fact been frequently used as a standard source for the calibration of spectrometers and coincidence circuits. The energy of the γ rays has been determined with great precision in a crystal spectrometer and is given as 0.411770 ± 0.000036 Mev. The internal conversion coefficients have been measured in magnetic spectrometers by comparison of the areas under the conversion electron peaks with the area under the entire β spectrum. The best values appear to be 0.031 for the K-conversion coefficient, 3.1 for the K/L conversion ratio, and 3.3 for the L/M ratio. These data are consistent with an $E2$ assignment for the 412-kev transition. Since the ground state of even-even Hg^{198} is presumably $0+$, it thus appears likely that the 412-kev level is $2+$, in accord with the general rule for first excited states of even-even nuclei. Since the shape of the 0.963-Mev β^- spectrum of Au^{198} corresponds to an allowed or (nonunique) first forbidden transition, the spin change for this transition must be 0 or 1. The log ft value, from equation 6-2, is 7.7, indicating most likely a first forbidden transition and therefore odd $(-)$ parity for Au^{198}. A $1-$ assignment for Au^{198} is presumably excluded because it would make the β transition to the Hg^{198} ground state of the same order as that to the 412-kev state; this ground-state transition, however, is certainly not prominent and must therefore have a much higher log ft value than the observed 963-kev β transition. The likely spin and parity designation for Au^{198} is therefore $2-$ or $3-$.

Since Pt^{198} is stable, Au^{198} might be expected to decay by β^+ emission or electron capture in addition to β^- emission. However, searches for annihilation radiation by means of 180° coincidences, for platinum K X rays with a scintillation counter, and for platinum Auger electrons with a lens spectrometer have been negative; therefore upper limits have been set at 0.2 per cent of all disintegrations for K-electron capture and 0.003 per cent for positron emission.

With scintillation counters two additional γ rays of low abundance were found in Au^{198} decay in 1950. Their energies have now been

[8] When reactor-produced Au^{198} sources became available there was some confusion about the decay scheme because several workers found additional lower-energy γ rays in such sources. Subsequently the relative intensity of these γ rays was found to depend on the neutron flux in which the gold had been irradiated, and they turned out to be associated with 3.15-day Au^{199} formed with very large cross section by neutron capture in Au^{198}.

determined as 0.676 Mev and 1.089 Mev; their intensities relative to the 0.412-Mev γ ray are 8.2×10^{-3} and 1.6×10^{-3} respectively. A γ-γ coincidence measurement with variable bias on one of the scintillation counters showed that the 0.676-Mev γ ray is in coincidence with the 0.412-Mev radiation, and that the 1.089-Mev γ is

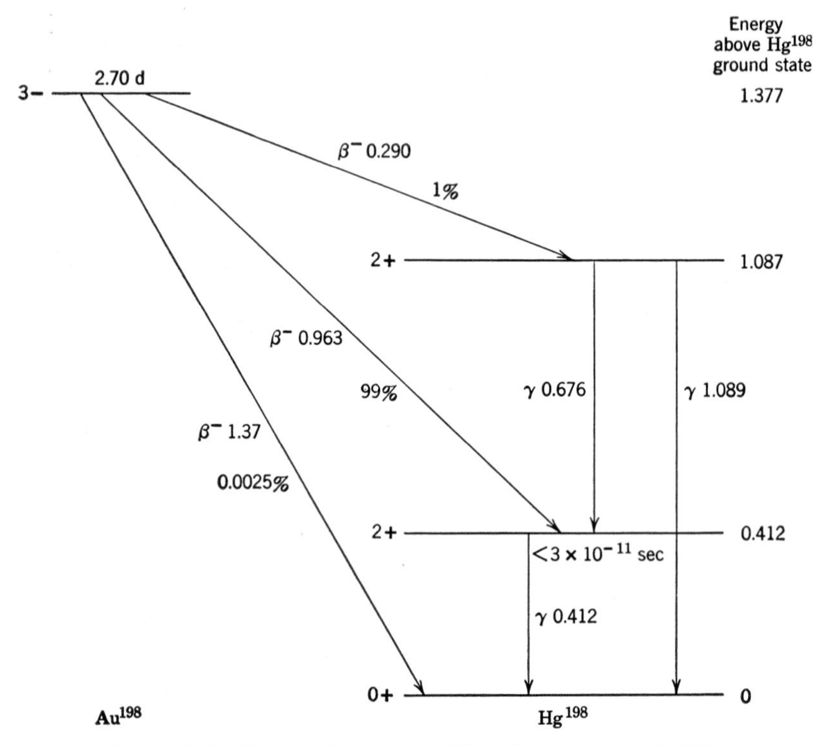

FIGURE 10-5. Decay scheme of Au^{198}. All energies are in Mev.

not in coincidence with any other γ radiation. Quite clearly the second excited state of Hg^{198} is at 1.089 Mev, and transitions from this state occur both to the 0.412-Mev level and to the ground state. Measured internal conversion coefficients for the K shell and K/L conversion ratios indicate that the 0.676-Mev transition ($\alpha_K = 0.022$, $K/L = 5.7$) is $M1$ and that the 1.089-Mev transition ($\alpha_K = 0.005$ and $K/L = 6.3$) is $E2$. (More detailed information comes from a γ-γ angular-correlation experiment, which showed the 0.676-Mev transition to be a mixture of 60 per cent $E2$ and 40 per cent $M1$.) The ground, first excited, and second excited states of Hg^{198} are therefore 0+, 2+, and 2+.

Coincidence experiments with a lens spectrometer and a NaI scintillation spectrometer as the two detectors showed the 0.676-Mev γ ray to be in coincidence not only with the conversion electrons of the 0.412-Mev γ ray, but also with a β^- spectrum of upper limit 0.290 ± 0.015 Mev which has the allowed shape and an intensity about 1 per cent that of the main β spectrum. A third β^- transition, with an intensity 2.5×10^{-5} of the main spectrum and an upper limit of 1.37 Mev, was found in a magnetic-spectrometer study of a strong source and evidently represents the ground-state transition. The spectrum shape identifies this transition as $\Delta I = 3$,yes; thus the spin and parity assignment of Au^{198} becomes 3−. The log ft value of 12.8 for the ground-state transition (computed from equation 6-2) corroborates the assignment.

Finally we mention that various attempts to measure the half-life of the 0.412-Mev excited state by delayed coincidences have yielded negative results, the best determination setting an upper limit of about 3×10^{-11} sec. The decay scheme deduced from all these data [9] is shown in figure 10-5.

Iodine-125.[10] An iodine isotope of about 60 days half-life produced by deuteron bombardment of tellurium has been assigned to mass number 125. Its decay proceeds entirely by electron capture to Te^{125}. The low-lying levels of Te^{125} (including an isomeric level of 58 days half-life at 145 kev above the ground state) and the transitions between them were already well characterized when an investigation of the I^{125} decay scheme was undertaken, and this information is included in figure 10-6 without further discussion.

To check whether any I^{125} electron capture transitions go to the 145-kev level, tellurium and iodine carriers first were added to an aged I^{125} sample and then separated. The thoroughly purified tellurium fraction was found to be inactive, and from this experiment an upper limit of 5×10^{-4} can be set for the fraction of I^{125} decays that go to the 58-day Te^{125m} isomer.

When the radiations from I^{125} were allowed to enter a krypton-filled proportional counter through a beryllium window, the pulse height spectrum observed with a single-channel pulse height analyzer

[9] Some of the pertinent data and references to other work on Au^{198} may be found in the following papers: P. E. Cavanagh, *Phys. Rev.* **82,** 791 (1951); A. R. Brosi, B. H. Ketelle, H. Zeldes, and E. Fairstein, *Phys. Rev.* **84,** 586 (1951); C. D. Broyles, D. A. Thomas, and S. K. Haynes, *Phys. Rev.* **89,** 715 (1953); L. G. Elliott, M. A. Preston, and J. L. Wolfson, *Can. J. Phys.* **32,** 153 (1954).

[10] G. Friedlander and W. C. Orr, *Phys. Rev.* **84,** 484 (1951); E. der Mateosian, *Phys. Rev.* **92,** 938 (1953).

showed the presence of 35-kev γ rays as well as tellurium K X rays. In another experiment, a sodium iodide crystal containing I^{125} was grown from a melt and used as a scintillation detector; in this case every transition to the 35-kev level gives rise to a pulse height that corresponds to the sum of 35 kev and the (K or L) X-ray energy, whereas a transition to the ground state gives a pulse height corre-

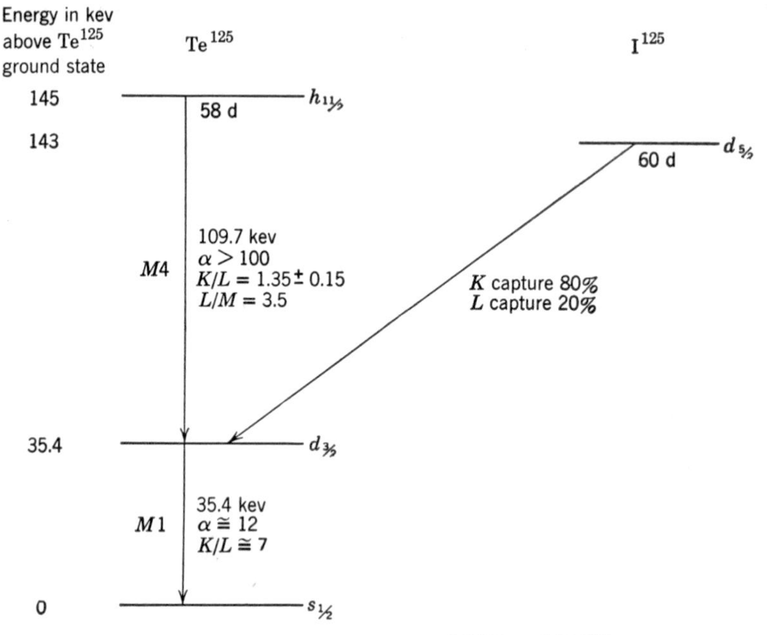

FIGURE 10-6. Decay scheme of I^{125} and Te^{125m}.

sponding to the X-ray energy only. No ground-state transitions were found, and it thus appears that all I^{125} decays go to the 35.4-kev level of Te^{125}. This result is consistent with a $d_{5/2}$ assignment for I^{125} and an allowed transition to the $d_{3/2}$ 35.4-kev level of Te^{125}; the unobserved transition to the $s_{1/2}$ ground state is then second forbidden.[11]

The ratio of K-electron to L-electron capture may be evaluated from the pulse height spectrum observed with the I^{125}-containing NaI scintillation crystal. The areas under the two peaks—one cor-

[11] According to shell structure, the ground state of I^{125} might be expected to be either $d_{5/2}$ or $g_{7/2}$. A $g_{7/2}$ assignment would make the transition to the 35.4-kev level of Te^{125} second-forbidden and that to the 145-kev isomeric level first-forbidden and thus appears to be ruled out by the experimental data. The $d_{5/2}$ assignment is also supported by the measured spin of 5/2 for I^{127}.

responding to the sum of 35 kev and tellurium K X rays, the other to the sum of 35 kev and tellurium L X rays—were compared, and an L-capture to K-capture ratio of 0.23 ± 0.03 was deduced. By an equation given in chapter 6, p. 166, this ratio leads to a value of 103 kev for the transition energy of the electron-capture decay to the 35.4-kev level. The corresponding log ft value (from equation 6-4) is 4.5, corroborating the conclusion that the transition is allowed.[12] The I^{125} decay scheme is shown in figure 10.6.

Lead-204m_2.[13] An interesting case of isomerism occurs in the even-even nuclide Pb^{204}. A 68-min isomer decaying with the emission of γ rays of about 1 Mev has been known for some time. It is formed in the electron-capture decay of Bi^{204}, but not in the β^- decay of Tl^{204}. An investigation of the electron spectrum of the lead isomer with a lens spectrometer showed K- and L-conversion lines of two γ rays, of energies 374 kev and 905 kev (figure 10-7). The K/L conversion ratios for the two γ rays, obtained directly from the areas under the conversion peaks, are about 2.1 and 1.5, respectively. From figure 6-1 these K/L ratios suggest an $E2$ assignment for the 374-kev transition and an $E5$ assignment for the 905-kev transition. Very approximate values of 0.05 and 0.1, respectively, for the total internal conversion coefficients of the 374-kev and 905-kev transitions were indicated by absorption curves of the electrons and γ rays taken with a G-M counter; these values also are compatible with the $E2$ and $E5$ assignments (see table 6-3). According to equation 6-1, the 68-min half-life is compatible with a 905-kev $E5$ transition, but not with an $E2$ transition of 374 kev. Thus the 905-kev step is believed to precede the 374-kev transition and so to determine the half-life of the isomer.

Delayed coincidences between the two γ rays were found with scintillation counters as detectors. By variation of the delay time the half-life of the second transition was determined to be 3×10^{-7} sec. By delayed-coincidence measurements with lead absorbers between the sample and one of the detectors, the 905-kev γ ray was shown to precede the delayed 374-kev transition. More recently a third γ ray of 890 kev has been reported; it had been missed in the

[12] More rigorous calculations lead to a decay energy of 108 kev and a log ft value of 4.8.

[13] A. W. Sunyar, D. Alburger, G. Friedlander, M. Goldhaber, and G. Scharff-Goldhaber, *Phys. Rev.* **79,** 181 (1950); H. Frauenfelder, J. S. Lawson, Jr., W. Jentschke, and G. DePasquali, *Phys. Rev.* **92,** 1241 (1953); V. E. Krohn and S. Raboy, *Phys. Rev.* **97,** 1017 (1955); E. der Mateosian and A. Smith, *Phys. Rev.* **88,** 1186 (1952).

earlier measurements because its energy is so close to that of the 905-kev γ ray and because careful relative intensity determinations were not made. This 890-kev γ ray is found to be in prompt coincidence with the 374-kev γ ray and delayed with a 3×10^{-7}-sec half-life relative to the 905-kev transition. The order of emission of the 374-kev and 890-kev γ rays has not been directly established; but strong indirect evidence favors the decay scheme shown in figure

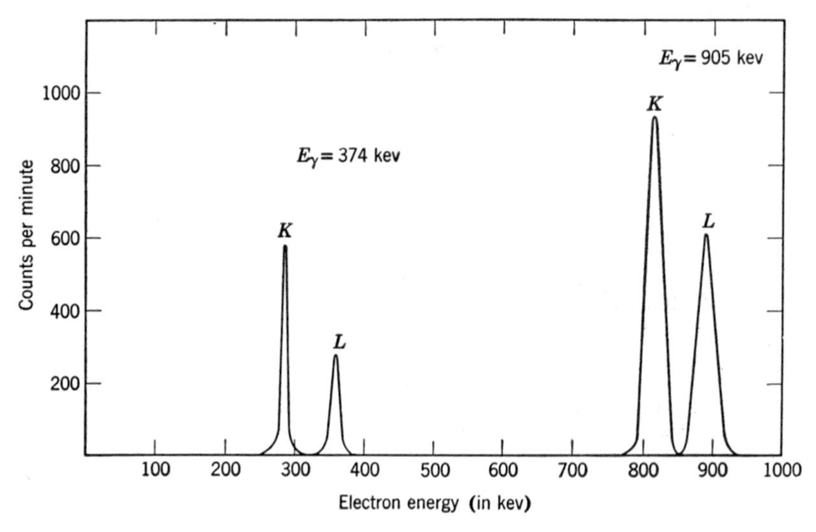

FIGURE 10-7. Spectrum of internal conversion electrons from Pb^{204m_2}, measured with a lens spectrometer. (Courtesy D. E. Alburger.)

10-8, with the 374-kev transition preceding the 890-kev γ ray. The 3×10^{-7}-sec half-life is almost exactly what one calculates from equation 6-1 for a 374-kev transition with $\Delta I = 2$, whereas a transition of 890 kev does not give a good fit for any ΔI. Furthermore the absence of γ rays in the Tl^{204} β^- decay ($<10^{-4}$ γ quanta per disintegration) speaks against a first excited state of Pb^{204} at 374 kev above ground. Since the shape of the Tl^{204} β spectrum labels the 765-kev β transition to the Pb^{204} ground state as unique first-forbidden ($\Delta I = 2$,yes), Tl^{204} must be $2-$, and a β transition to a $2+$ first excited state of Pb^{204} would be first-forbidden. However, the experimental upper limit of γ-ray abundance in Tl^{204} sets a lower limit of about 13 (computed from equation 6-2) for the log ft value of a β transition to a 374-kev level, and this would be very abnormally high for a first-forbidden transition. Similarly the absence of observable 374-kev γ rays or of α-energy fine structure in the α

decay of Po^{208} would be very difficult to reconcile with the regular trends of partial α half-lives with α-disintegration energy (figure 6-7) if the first excited state of Pb^{204} were at 374 kev. The spin and parity assignments for the excited states of Pb^{204} shown in figure 10-8

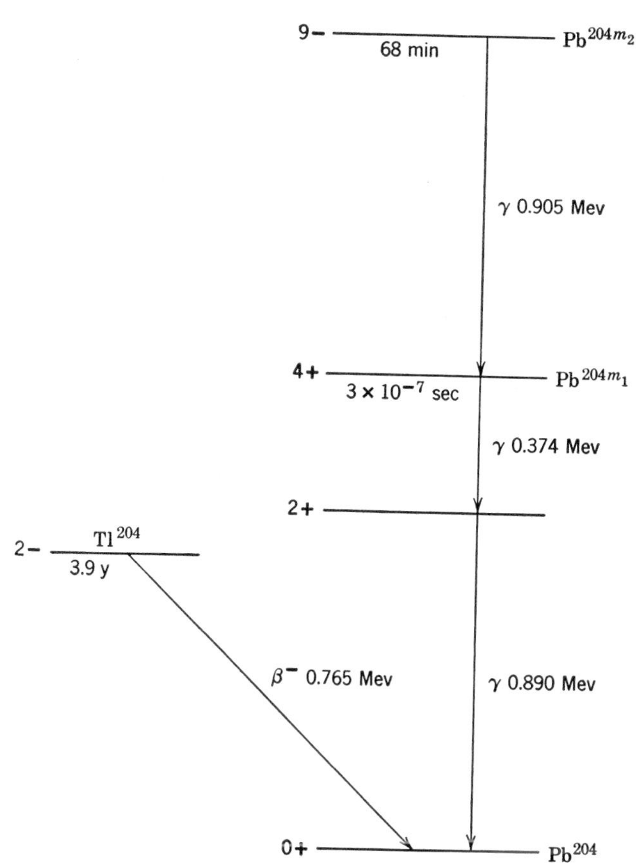

FIGURE 10-8. Probable decay scheme of Pb^{204} isomers. The β− decay of Tl^{204} is also shown.

are the only ones consistent with all the existing data on conversion coefficients and angular correlations.(13)

D. ABSOLUTE DISINTEGRATION RATES

Alpha-Disintegration Rates. The determination of absolute disintegration rates for α emitters requires: (1) a detector of known efficiency, usually an ionization chamber with linear amplifier adjusted to count 100 per cent of the particles crossing the chamber; (2) a sample of known weight spread so uniformly thin that corrections for α particles stopped in the sample are small; (3) a known geometrical factor, usually about 50 per cent, including the correction for back-scattering of α rays from the sample support (which may amount to several per cent). With reasonable care values reliable to about 10 per cent can readily be obtained, and with great care the errors may be reduced to about 1 per cent. The calorimetric method mentioned in chapter 5, section E, for the measurement of absolute α-disintegration rates is capable of at least comparable accuracy. It requires a larger sample activity but makes no demands on the sample's geometrical arrangement, thinness, and the like. It does require a knowledge of the α-particle energy; this is conveniently obtained from the range, or better from magnetic-spectrometer measurements.

"Low-Geometry" Counting. Counting of β particles with a known solid angle and known detector efficiency is probably the most widely used, though by no means the most accurate, method for the absolute determination of β-disintegration rates. Proportional or G-M counters are generally used as detectors because they count individual β particles of all energies with practically 100 per cent efficiency. Gas-flow proportional counters with very thin windows ($\leqq 1$ mg cm^{-2}) are particularly useful for the purpose. With the sample placed near the window, the geometrical factor is extremely difficult to evaluate accurately, because it depends very sensitively on the sample-to-window distance and on the exact extent of the sensitive volume inside the counter (which may vary somewhat with the energy of the radiations). Also, the window absorption correction is relatively large, because many of the rays go through the window at very oblique angles. For these reasons it is preferable to use a "low-geometry" arrangement, with the sample placed several centimeters from the counter window and with a shield and aperture to define a cone of rays directed toward the sensitive region of the counter. The solid angle is then readily calculated. A disadvantage of this arrangement is that absorption and scattering of the electrons in the air between sample and counter may require a sizable correction not readily evaluated. This difficulty is avoided if the space between sample and counter is evacuated or filled with helium. The self-absorption and back-scattering effects discussed in section B must be evaluated. To obtain results of the highest accuracy, these corrections should probably be minimized by the use of very thin samples mounted on very thin backings, usually plastic films of thicknesses in the range of 0.01 to 0.1 mg cm^{-2}.

The method of low-geometry counting is well suited to the determination of absolute X-ray emission rates, for example from samples decaying by electron capture. Particularly for X rays in the region from about 4 to 40 kev, absorption in the air and in beryllium windows can be made almost negligible, and counter dimensions and filling gases (argon or krypton with hydrocarbon admixture) can readily be chosen such that almost all the X rays entering the counter are recorded. With a proportional counter and pulse height analyzer it is then possible to measure the desired X-ray counting rate even in the presence of other radiations. To convert an absolute X-ray emission rate into an electron-capture rate, the fluorescence yield must be known.

4π Counting. For the determination of absolute disintegration rates there are obvious advantages to the use of 4π geometry, particularly if the counting efficiency is 100 per cent. Under these conditions every disintegration gives rise to one count regardless of the decay scheme (provided that there is included no state with lifetime comparable to or greater than the resolving time of the equipment). The observed counting rate then equals the disintegration rate.

A number of arrangements for 4π counting have been used. The introduction of a β-active sample in gaseous form inside a counter (usually a proportional counter) provides almost a 4π geometry; the end effects and wall effects can be made small and can be evaluated by experiments with different counters in which the ratio of sensitive to insensitive volume is deliberately varied. Gas counting is particularly useful for soft-β emitters (such as H^3, C^{14}, S^{35}, Ni^{63}) and for low-Z electron-capture nuclides (such as A^{37}); in the latter case even the very soft Auger electrons may be counted quantitatively. In an analogous technique the sample may be dissolved in a liquid scintillator. For any but the lowest-energy β emitters and for emitters of electromagnetic radiation of less than about 200 kev, every disintegration may again be counted. To minimize losses by edge effects it is necessary to use scintillator dimensions large compared with the range of the radiations.

With solid samples, 4π counting requires the use of extremely thin deposits on very thin supports. In the usual 4π counter such a sample is mounted in the central hole of a thin metal partition between two identical G-M or proportional counters connected in parallel. One type of 4π counter is shown in figure 10-9. The supporting film should be made conducting, for example by sputtering with a very thin layer of metal, to avoid distortion of the electric field in the counters.

Even with the thinnest practical sample support the absorption of soft β rays in this film may not be negligible. Fortunately this

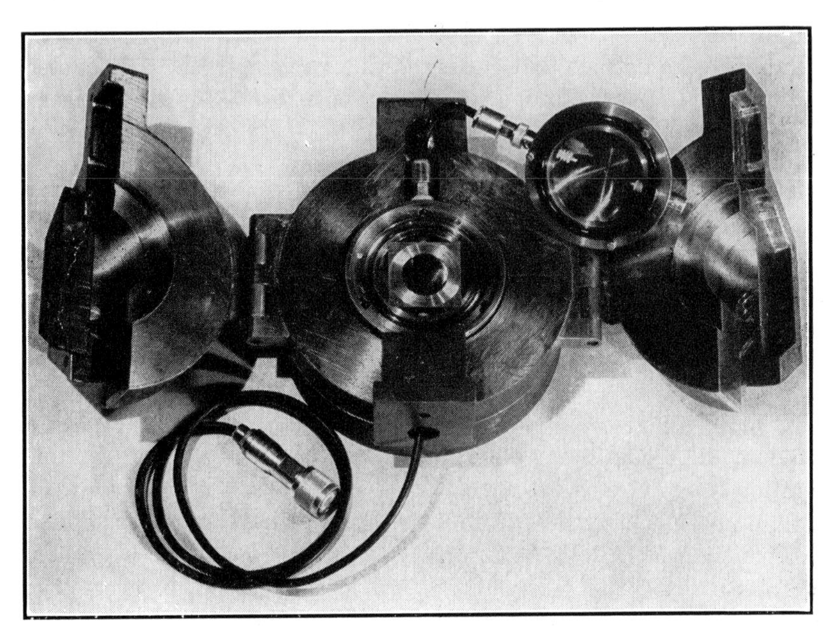

FIGURE 10-9. A 4π counter and its lead shield. A sample holder with thin plastic film for sample support is in place. The two halves are put together by a simple bayonet lock. The gas flow system is not visible. (Courtesy Brookhaven National Laboratory.)

absorption loss can be evaluated experimentally. Assume that the sample is mounted in the top half of the counter and the fraction of the radiation emitted towards the lower hemisphere which is absorbed in the sample support is f. Neglecting back-scattering by the thin film, we may write for the total counting rate (top and bottom connected in parallel)

$$\mathbf{R}_{12} = \frac{\mathbf{R}_0}{2} + \frac{\mathbf{R}_0}{2}(1 - f) = \mathbf{R}_0\left(1 - \frac{f}{2}\right),$$

where $\mathbf{R}_0$ is the disintegration rate. If the top half alone is connected, the counting rate is

$$\mathbf{R}_1 = \frac{\mathbf{R}_0}{2}[1 + (1 - f)B],$$

where B is the fraction back-scattered into one half of the chamber by the other half. The counting rate in the bottom half alone is

$$\mathbf{R}_2 = \frac{\mathbf{R}_0}{2}(1 - f + B).$$

Combination of the three relations to eliminate B and $\mathbf{R}_0$ gives

$$f = \frac{\mathbf{R}_1 - \mathbf{R}_2}{\mathbf{R}_{12} - \mathbf{R}_2}.$$

Thus the absorption loss in the film may be found from the three measured counting rates. Even for a film of only 0.04 mg cm^{-2} thickness, f is about 0.05 for Co^{60} β rays ($E_{max} = 0.30$ Mev).

Coincidence Method. For nuclides with relatively simple decay schemes, the absolute disintegration rates may be determined by coincidence measurements. The method is easily understood for the simple case in which the emission of one γ quantum follows each β decay and the spectrum is simple. Consider two counters arranged to count β rays and γ rays, respectively, with measured counting rates $\mathbf{R}_\beta$ and $\mathbf{R}_\gamma$, and with β-γ coincidences also measured with rate $\mathbf{R}_{\beta\gamma}$; then $\mathbf{R}_\beta = \mathbf{R}_0 c_\beta$, $\mathbf{R}_\gamma = \mathbf{R}_0 c_\gamma$, where the coefficients c_β and c_γ may be thought of as defined by these equations and include all effects of solid angles, counting efficiencies and absorption corrections, and $\mathbf{R}_{\beta\gamma} = \mathbf{R}_0 c_\beta c_\gamma$. Now $\mathbf{R}_\beta \mathbf{R}_\gamma / \mathbf{R}_{\beta\gamma} = \mathbf{R}_0$, and the absolute disintegration rate is given very simply in terms of this ratio of three measured counting rates. The contribution of γ rays to the counting rate in the β counter (and thereby to coincidence counts) must be measured in a separate experiment with an absorber which prevents the β rays from entering the β counter; this is essentially a background which must be subtracted from $\mathbf{R}_\beta$ (and from $\mathbf{R}_{\beta\gamma}$).

If the β spectrum is complex, the ratio $\mathbf{R}_\beta \mathbf{R}_\gamma / \mathbf{R}_{\beta\gamma}$ will give the correct disintegration rate only if the β-counter window is sufficiently thin, and that counter does not discriminate appreciably against any component group of the spectrum. Other sources of error must also be considered. It is possible, although not likely, that strong angular correlation between the directions of emission of coincident β and γ rays might exist; this effect could be detected through variation of the angle between the two counters. A small source of error of somewhat uncertain magnitude results from detection in the γ counter of bremsstrahlung produced by β particles stopping in the absorber used to shield the γ counter from β rays. This effect will increase $\mathbf{R}_\gamma$ without a corresponding increase in $\mathbf{R}_{\beta\gamma}$ because the particular β particles giving rise to this bremsstrahlung have little chance of being counted in the β counter. A more appreciable error of the same sort would be expected for any sample emitting positrons because of the annihilation radiation. This is minimized if the absorber is placed near the sample rather than near the γ counter. Any delayed γ rays which trip the γ counter too late to be recorded in coincidence would of course lead to too large values of $\mathbf{R}_0$.

Care must be exercised in the application of the coincidence technique to more complex decay schemes. For example, it is interesting to note that for a nuclide which decays by both β^+ emission and electron capture, but always to the same excited state of the product nuclide, the measurement of β-γ coincidences yields the total disintegration rate, not just the rate of β^+ emission.

Calibrated Detector. When a standardized source of a radionuclide is available, any detector may be calibrated in terms of this standard. This calibration will be correct for other samples of the same nuclide provided that they are mounted in precisely the same way. Calibration for one β emitter may also be quite satisfactory for other β emitters if geometrical effects (including scattering) and counter efficiency are relatively insensitive to the differences in β spectra.

A β emitter in secular equilibrium with an α activity provides a satisfactory standard, because the α-disintegration rate usually may be measured with good precision. The rather energetic β particles from UX_2 in secular equilibrium with U_I, or possibly in transient equilibrium with freshly isolated UX_1, are often used as standard, with a thin absorber to exclude U_I α particles and soft UX_1 (and UY) β particles. (Absorption of UX_2 β rays in this absorber and the counter window is corrected for by extrapolation of a measured absorption curve back to zero absorber.[14]) The calibration of such

[14] For such an extrapolation to zero absorber the relative positions of sample, absorber, and sensitive region of the counter are very important. If the sample is placed at some distance, say 2 or 3 cm, from the counter, the measured counting rate with an absorber directly above the sample will be appreciably (perhaps as much as 10 or 15 per cent) higher than with the same absorber placed directly under the window. In fact, the addition of a thin absorber near the sample may cause an increase in the counting rate. This effect results from the scattering of β particles into the counter by the absorbers and is clearly related to the "self-scattering" effect discussed earlier (on pp. 276 ff.). When a straight-line extrapolation to zero absorber thickness is wanted, the absorbers should be placed close to the counter window.

a standard could be made by α-particle counting, but since the disintegration constant for U_I is already known it is necessary only to weigh the uranium. The National Bureau of Standards supplies (among other radioactivity standards including P^{32}, Co^{60}, and I^{131}) carefully standardized RaD-plus-RaE samples; the RaD β particles and RaF α particles may be absorbed in a 0.001-in. aluminum foil, and the medium-energy RaE β particles used as a standard for calibration. As supplied, these preparations are deposited electrolytically (in PbO_2) on palladium-clad silver disks, and considerable back-scattering is to be expected. Identical blank disks are available so that the activity to be measured may be mounted on the same type of surface.

E. MASS ASSIGNMENTS

The identification of new radioactive species in terms of their mass numbers and atomic numbers has historically been one of the chief problems of the nuclear chemist. Most of the nuclides near the region of stability have by now been identified, and the emphasis has recently shifted to those nuclides so far removed in A or Z from the region of stability that they can be produced only by very-high-energy or very-heavy-ion bombardments or by very intense neutron fluxes. In this section we review some of the techniques developed for the assignment of mass numbers. We assume that the atomic number of a nuclide can be determined by chemical analysis (see chapter 4, section D). This is, of course, not true for very short-lived species (say <1 sec), but in these cases the assignment can often be made indirectly by identification of a longer-lived radioactive precursor or descendant.

Cross Bombardments. The only case in which the mass number of a reaction product is practically uniquely determined in a single bombardment is the slow-neutron activation of a single nuclear species. For example, the slow-neutron bombardment of arsenic (with the single stable species As^{75}) produces a 26.8-hr β-emitting arsenic isotope which is, therefore, readily assigned to As^{76}.

One can frequently make a mass assignment by investigating whether or not the radioactive species being studied is formed in a number of different types of bombardments; this is called the method of cross bombardments. For this purpose target elements as well as projectiles may be varied. In each bombardment the possible products are limited by the stable isotopes of the target element and by the types of reactions possible with the projectile and energy used. As an illustration consider some radioactive isotopes of strontium;

figure 10-10 displays the stable nuclides in the region of strontium. Slow-neutron activation of strontium produces strontium isotopes with 2.7-hr and 54-day half-lives; either or both of these activities might be assigned to any of the isotopes Sr^{85}, Sr^{87}, Sr^{88}, Sr^{89}, since they are produced by neutron capture from the stable strontium isotopes. The fact that the same two activities are produced by fast neutrons (say 15 Mev) in zirconium, presumably by n, α reactions, eliminates Sr^{85}. The fast-neutron bombardment of yttrium (say with 10- or 15-Mev neutrons) produces only the 54-day strontium, presumably by n, p reaction, and this activity is therefore assigned

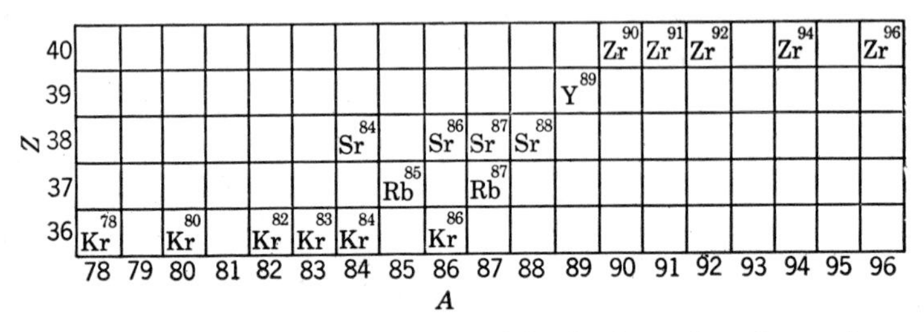

FIGURE 10-10. Naturally occurring nuclides in the region of strontium.

to Sr^{89}. The 2.7-hr activity is then to be assigned to an isomeric state of Sr^{87} or Sr^{88}. The fact that 2.7-hr strontium is also produced by proton bombardment of rubidium by p, n reaction leads to its assignment to Sr^{87m}.

In the interpretation of the results of cross bombardments the relative abundances of isotopes in the target elements often have to be considered. For example, failure to observe a certain reaction product may simply be due to low abundance of the isotope from which that product could have been made.

Use of Isotope Separations. In many cases the mass number of a radioactive species is uncertain because it is not known from which isotope of the target element the activity has been produced. The bombardment of separated isotopes, or of isotopic mixtures sufficiently enriched in some isotope, is, therefore, of great advantage. Enrichment or impoverishment of an isotope by a factor of two or even less may be sufficient for this purpose; by comparing the yield of the activity of interest from samples of normal and altered isotopic composition we can deduce the origin of the activity. For a long time the assignment of the 37-min chlorine activity produced by slow neutrons or by deuterons in chlorine (stable isotopes Cl^{35} and Cl^{37}) was uncertain and could not be readily determined by cross bombardments; but when it was shown that this activity was not produced by slow-neutron bombardment of a sample of almost pure

Cl^{35} the 37-min period could be assigned to Cl^{38} rather than Cl^{36}. Electromagnetically enriched stable isotopes of over forty elements have in recent years become available in milligram to gram quantities through the United States Atomic Energy Commission. Many of these have been successfully used in mass-assignment studies.

Isotope separation can be used in an even more direct way for the identification of radioactive species: the reaction products themselves may be subjected to an isotope separation process. The mass numbers of many radionuclides have been unambiguously established by mass-spectrographic identification; the technique has been successfully applied for half-lives as short as one hour, and in special cases (rare-gas fission products) even half-lives down to 10 sec. In some of these mass-assignment studies the technique is something like the following. The material containing the active isotope of interest is sent through an ordinary mass-spectrograph, and the ions are collected on a photographic plate. After development that plate is placed face to face with another unexposed plate called the transfer plate; the β particles from a radioactive isotope deposited along a narrow line on the first plate will blacken the transfer plate, and from the position of the exposed line on the transfer plate the mass number of the active isotope can be deduced. By exposing successive transfer plates to the first plate at various times and in each case finding the exposure time necessary to get the same degree of blackening, one can obtain a rough check on the half-life of the activity. To establish the half-life more accurately the area of the original plate on which the activity is located can be counted over a period of time. Mass spectrometers for mass identification of radioactive species should have high collection efficiencies. Often mass-separated samples can be used to great advantage in decay scheme studies.

Excitation Functions. An excitation function for the production of the nuclide under study may help very much to determine the type of reaction involved, through comparison with similar excitation functions for known reactions. This technique becomes a particularly valuable extension of the cross-bombardment method at higher bombarding energies. For example, in the unraveling of the exceedingly complex conversion-electron spectra of the mercury isotopes formed in high-energy proton bombardments of gold, the excitation functions were of great value. The various electron lines, with characteristic energies and half-lives, were found to fall into three groups produced with maximum yields by protons of about 54, 63, and 72 Mev, respectively, and with corresponding thresholds at about 35, 45, and 55 Mev. On this basis the reactions producing these activities could be identified as $p, 5n$; $p, 6n$; and $p, 7n$ reactions, respectively, and the activities themselves (including not only mercury isotopes, but also their gold and platinum descendants) therefore are assigned to mass numbers 193, 192, and 191.

If a complete excitation function is not available, even a knowledge of the energy of the bombarding particle in a single experiment, together with an approximate yield of the product, can be of value for the mass assignment. For example, if a certain activity of element $Z + 1$ is produced in good yield in the bombardment of element Z with 5-Mev deuterons, the reaction can hardly be anything but a d, n reaction; if the deuteron energy had been 20 Mev, a $d, 2n$ reaction or perhaps a $d, 3n$ reaction might more likely have been responsible. Referring again to figure 10-10, we see that the 2.7-hr strontium cannot be expected to result from the bombardment of rubidium with 5-Mev deuterons if it is Sr^{87}, but it could be formed in such a bombardment if it were Sr^{88}.

In the case of neutron-induced reactions the difference between the activities produced with and without cadmium shielding is often taken as an approximate measure of the thermal-neutron effect. This may almost always be ascribed to n, γ reactions. However, it should be noted that a cadmium shield does not completely eliminate n, γ reactions because they may occur with appreciable cross sections at energies above the cadmium resonance.

Beam Contamination and Secondary Reactions. In connection with the subject of cross bombardments it should be noted that extraneous bombarding particles or secondary particles produced by bombardment of the targets may sometimes give rise to nuclear reactions to an extent which can interfere with the recognition of the primary-reaction products. For example, α-particle beams in cyclotrons are commonly contaminated with small amounts of deuterons (from residual deuterium in the ion source); because deuteron cross sections are often much higher than α-particle cross sections the deuteron-produced activities may actually exceed in intensity those from α particles.

The neutrons produced in the bombardment of targets with charged particles or γ rays usually give rise to nuclear reactions in the target material. The products of these reactions may be confused with those that are found or expected to be produced by the primary bombarding particle. For example, in the deuteron bombardment of a thick sodium target to make Na^{24} by the d, p reaction, the Na^{24} activity is found at depths beyond the range of the deuterons, because it can be produced there by n, γ reaction.

In high-energy spallation reactions each primary interaction may give rise to a number of secondary particles—neutrons, protons, deuterons, helium ions, and even heavier fragments (see chapter 3, section F)—which often are themselves energetic enough to produce further nuclear reactions. This is evidenced, for example, by the formation of products of atomic numbers $Z + 2$ to $Z + 4$ from a target element Z in very-high-energy proton bombardments. These secondary effects can usually be minimized by the use of targets which are thin compared to the ranges of the secondary particles.

Radiation Characteristics and Genetic Relationships. Half-life and atomic number are frequently not sufficient to characterize a radioactive species. It happens rather often that two isotopes of the same element have not very different half-lives. Then the isotopes can usually be distinguished by the types and energies of the radiations they emit. We may use again our example of the strontium isotopes (figure 10-10); an investigation of the radiations emitted by the slow-neutron-bombarded strontium sample after the 2.7-hr period has decayed reveals, in addition to the 1.5-Mev β^- particles of the 54-day Sr^{89}, some γ rays and characteristic rubidium X rays. On closer examination these last two radiations are found to follow a 65-day half-life. The 54-day and 65-day periods could certainly not be resolved in a gross decay curve of the neutron-bombarded sample. The presence of rubidium X rays shows that the 65-day isotope decays to rubidium by β^+ emission or K capture; no positrons are observed, and the process must be an electron capture. From the evidence the assignment is probably to Sr^{85} or Sr^{87}; the latter is ruled out by the fact that the 65-day species is not formed by n, α reaction from Zr^{90}. Proton bombardment of rubidium produces the 65-day period (but not the 54-day Sr^{89}) as well as the 2.7-hr Sr^{87m} already discussed, and in addition a 70-min strontium which also fails to appear in the fast-neutron bombardment of zirconium.

Using these four strontium activities as examples we shall illustrate how a study of the mode of decay of an isotope helps in its assignment. The fact that the 54-day isotope emits β^- particles rules out its assignment to any mass number less than 89: a strontium nucleus of mass 88 or less would by β^- decay move away from rather than toward the stability region. A study of the radiations from the 70-min and 2.7-hr activities reveals that both emit strontium X rays, indicating that these periods are associated with isomeric transitions. The electron-capture decay of the 65-day isotope eliminates its assignment to any mass number greater than 87. From the facts listed in this and in the previous paragraph the 65-day and 70-min periods can both be assigned to Sr^{85}; the 70-min period is associated with an isomeric transition to the lower state, which in turn decays by electron capture with a 65-day half-life to Rb^{85}.

On the basis of the systematics of α and β decay and of isomeric transitions (see chapter 2, section E, and chapter 6) it is often possible to correlate not only modes of decay but also half-lives and decay energies with the mass assignments of isotopes. Semiquantitative predictions of β-decay energies on the basis of binding-energy formulas like equation 2-5 are often very useful in this connection (although account may have to be taken of shell effects). For the identification of new nuclides in the transuranium region the predictions of α systematics have been particularly helpful.

If the product of a radioactive decay is itself radioactive, the genetic relationship may be investigated by studies of the growth and decay curves of fractions chemically separated at successive times. An understanding of genetic relationships helps in the assignment of the activities. This is particularly important in the fission product decay chains on the neutron-excess side of stability and in the decay chains of neutron-deficient nuclides produced in very-high-energy reactions. Nuclides far removed from stability are most commonly identified by determinations of genetic relationships with already characterized descendants near the stability valley. For example, the fission product chain of mass 89 was identified with that mass number because its last active member was shown to be the 54-day Sr^{89} already discussed. The decay chain containing 275-day cerium was assigned the mass number 144 by mass-spectrographic determination of the mass of that long-lived cerium.

Target Material and Effect of Impurities. When the product of a particular nuclear reaction is to be studied, it is important that the target not contain other elements from which the same product might result. As an obvious example, in a study of the production of 34-hr bromine (Br^{82}) by neutron bombardment of rubidium we would not wish to use rubidium bromide as a target. For the same reason impurities of neighboring elements, such as iridium impurity in an osmium target, may lead to misinterpretation of results. In general, it is advisable to use free elements as targets; however, sometimes the bombardment of a compound is indicated, for example, if the element is too reactive, or in a physical state unsuitable for bombardment, or if the dissolving of the element would make a slow step in the subsequent chemical separation procedure.

The presence of some impurities in a target is in most cases unavoidable. If the impurities are known, the chemical separation procedure can be designed to separate the products of interest from the products likely to result from the bombardment of the impurities. The purity requirements for the target material may become very exacting if a reaction of low cross section is studied, for then the expected product yield is small, and care must be taken that comparable amounts of the same species are not produced from an impurity by a much more probable reaction. For example, the formation of Mg^{23} from Al^{27} by γ, $p3n$ reaction could be studied only with aluminum very free of magnesium, because the $Mg^{24}(\gamma, n)Mg^{23}$ reaction has a much larger cross section.

EXERCISES

1. The γ-ray activities of two portions of a solution of Co^{60} were found under identical conditions to be: 350 counts per min for a 0.10-cc portion, and 9900 counts per min for a 3.00-cc portion.

(*a*) What would you expect for the counting rate of a 2.00-cc portion?

(*b*) What is the approximate dead time of the Geiger counter? Assume all other resolving times are negligibly small. Neglect self-absorption effects.

Answer: (*b*) 3.5×10^{-4} s.

2. A certain activity chemically proved to be associated with technetium (element 43) is produced in the bombardment of molybdenum with 12-Mev deuterons and in the bombardment of ruthenium with 12-Mev deuterons, but not in the bombardment of ruthenium with fast (up to 15 Mev) neutrons. To what isotope of technetium should the activity be assigned? What mode of decay would you expect?

3. Element Z has a single stable nuclide of mass number A. In the bombardment of element Z with 28-Mev deuterons the following activities chemically identified with element $Z + 1$ were found:

A moderately strong 3-hr positron emitter.

A strong 2.6-day activity emitting mostly γ and X rays.

A weak 30-min positron emitter.

The last activity was not produced when the deuteron energy was lowered to 20 Mev.

Critical-absorption measurements showed the X rays of the 2.6-day activity to be those of element Z. An 11-day isotope of element Z was shown to grow from the 2.6-day activity, whereas the 3-hr activity decayed to a 50-min X-ray emitter chemically identified with element Z. The X rays from this latter activity were characteristic of element Z.

One-million-electron-volt neutrons produced in a target of element Z the 50-min X-ray emitter, in addition to a 14-hr β^--emitting isotope of Z which had also been identified in the deuteron-bombarded Z samples. With 15-Mev neutrons the 11-day isotope of Z was also produced.

Make mass assignments for the various radioactive isotopes of elements Z and $Z + 1$, and indicate the most likely mode of decay for each. The stable nuclides of $Z + 1$ have mass numbers $A + 1$, $A + 2$, and $A + 3$; those of $Z - 1$ have mass numbers $A - 3$, $A - 2$, and $A - 1$.

4. A sample of Mn^{52} (6.0 d), contained in a 7.3-mg precipitate of MnO_2 uniformly distributed over a circular area of 1.5 cm^2 on a thick aluminum disk, is placed at a distance of 4.2 cm from the end window of a proportional counter. The counter is filled to one atmosphere with helium-methane mixture, has a plastic window 1.0 mg cm^{-2} thick and a cathode of 1¼ in. inner diameter. A counting rate of 6540 counts per min is observed. A 3.0 mg cm^{-2} aluminum absorber placed over the counter window reduces the counting rate to 5890 counts per min, a 5.5 mg cm^{-2} aluminum absorber to 5500 counts per min, a 300 mg cm^{-2} aluminum absorber to 150 counts per min. Estimate as well as you can the absolute strength of the sample in microcuries.

5. The radiations emitted by a certain radioactive species were studied in a β-ray spectrometer. The β^- spectrum was resolved into two components of 0.61 ± 0.01 Mev and 1.438 ± 0.007 Mev maximum energies. The higher-energy component was about four times as abundant as the lower-energy one. When γ rays were allowed to strike a thin silver radiator placed in the source position of the spectrometer, the following five photoelectron energies were measured:

Energy in Mev	Intensity
0.216 ± 0.002	Strong
0.237 ± 0.002	Weak
0.801 ± 0.003	Weak
0.823 ± 0.003	Very weak
1.046 ± 0.005	Very weak

The K and L binding energies in silver are 25 and 4 kev, respectively. Draw a plausible decay scheme for the radioactive species under investigation.

6. The nuclide Z^A decays by β^- emission, largely to the first excited state of $(Z+1)^A$; a small β^- branch (0.9 Mev maximum energy) goes directly to the ground state of $(Z+1)^A$. The decay of $(Z+2)^A$ proceeds entirely by K-electron capture to the first excited state. One sample of each of these two radionuclides is used in the following coincidence measurements with an anthracene (C_1) and a NaI (C_2) scintillation detector. The samples are placed in a standard position between the two counters, and a 0.5 g cm^{-2} copper absorber, sufficient to absorb the Z^A β particles and the K X rays of $(Z+1)$, is placed between the sample and C_2 during all the measurements. The following data are obtained:

Sample	Delay between C_1 and C_2	0.5 g cm^{-2} Cu between C_1 and sample	Counts per min in C_1	Counts per min in C_2	Coincidence counts per min
Z^A	0	No	188,600	125,100	2928
Z^A	2 μs	No	188,300	125,600	237
Z^A	0	Yes	2,753	125,800	3.5
$(Z+2)^A$	0	No	40,930	55,340	655
$(Z+2)^A$	2 μs	No	41,070	55,090	23
$(Z+2)^A$	0	Yes	1,216	55,510	0.7

(*a*) What is the disintegration rate of the $(Z+2)^A$ sample? (*b*) What fraction of the Z^A decays go to the $(Z+1)^A$ ground state directly? (*c*) What is the disintegration rate of the Z^A sample? (*d*) What is the coincidence resolving time of the circuit used? (*e*) If the *K* X rays of $(Z+1)$ and the β particles emitted by Z^A are counted with the same efficiency in C_1, what is the *K*-fluorescence yield of $(Z+1)$? Assume the two β^- groups of Z^A to be counted in C_1 with equal efficiency. Sample decay during the course of the measurements may be neglected.

Answers: (*b*) 0.088; (*c*) 8.63×10^6 min^{-1}; (*d*) 0.3 μs.

7. In an investigation of the decay scheme of 2.3-min Ag^{108} the β^- spectrum was measured in an anthracene scintillation spectrometer and found to have an upper energy limit of 1.77 ± 0.06 Mev and a simple, allowed shape within the accuracy of the measurements. Measurements with a proportional counter and pulse height analyzer showed that Ag^{108} emits Pd *K* X rays and that the ratio of the number of these X rays to the number of β particles emitted is 0.013 ± 0.001. The gamma spectrum obtained with a NaI scintillation spectrometer showed weak gamma rays of 435, 510, and 616 kev with relative intensities 1.0, 0.27, and 0.27. In a β-γ coincidence experiment, 616-kev γ rays were found to be in coincidence with β rays; however, these coincidences could be eliminated with an aluminum absorber of 480 mg cm^{-2} placed between sample and β counter. Gamma-gamma coincidences were found between 435-kev and 602-kev γ rays, and between 510-kev and 510-kev γ rays, the latter, however, only when the two counters were 180° apart with respect to the sample. The spectrum of γ rays in coincidence with X rays showed 435-kev and 602-kev γ rays in the intensity ratio 1.0:0.79. The 602-kev peak in these coincidence spectra was definitely at a lower energy than the 616-kev peak found in the singles spectrum. Additional experiments proved that 85 per cent of all the electron capture transitions lead to the Pd^{108} ground state. Derive as much information as you can about the Ag^{108} decay scheme, including the intensities of the various β and γ transitions, and as many of the log *ft* values as possible. Discuss spin and parity assignments.

Most of the information in this exercise is based on a paper by M. L. Perlman, W. Bernstein, and R. B. Schwartz, *Phys. Rev.* **92,** 1236 (1953).

REFERENCES

G. B. Cook and J. F. Duncan, *Modern Radiochemical Practice,* Oxford, Clarendon Press, 1952.

W. J. Whitehouse and J. L. Putman, *Radioactive Isotopes. An Introduction to Their Preparation, Measurement and Use,* Oxford, Clarendon Press, 1953.

E. Bleuler and G. J. Goldsmith, *Experimental Nucleonics,* New York, Rinehart & Co., 1952.

G. K. Schweitzer and I. B. Whitney, *Radioactive Tracer Techniques,* New York, D. Van Nostrand Co., 1949.

M. D. Kamen, *Radioactive Tracers in Biology, an Introduction to Tracer Methodology,* 2nd ed., New York, Academic Press, 1951.

W. F. Libby, "Measurement of Radioactive Tracers," *Anal. Chem.* **19,** 2 (1947).

T. P. Kohman, "Measurement Techniques of Applied Radiochemistry," *Anal Chem.* **21,** 352 (1949).

L. Yaffe and K. M. Justus, "Back-Scattering of Electrons into Geiger-Mueller Counters," *J. Chem. Soc.,* Supplement No. 2, S. 341 (1949).

W. E. Nervik and P. C. Stevenson, "Self-Scattering and Self-Absorption of Betas by Moderately Thick Samples," *Nucleonics* **10,** No. 3, 18 (March 1952).

R. W. Dodson, A. C. Graves, L. Helmholz, D. L. Hufford, R. M. Potter, and J. G. Povelites, "Preparation of Foils," *Miscellaneous Physical and Chemical Techniques of the Los Alamos Project,* National Nuclear Energy Series Div. V, Vol. 3, New York, McGraw-Hill Book Co., 1952.

M. Deutsch, "Critical Survey of Techniques of Beta- and Gamma-Spectroscopy," *Physica* **18,** 1037 (1952).

C. S. Cook, "Experimental Techniques in Beta-Ray Spectroscopy," *Nucleonics* **11,** No. 12, 28 (December 1953) and **12,** No. 2, 43 (February 1954).

A. Hedgran and D. Lind, "Precision Measurements of Nuclear Gamma Radiation by Techniques of Beta-Spectroscopy," *Arkiv Fysik* **5,** 1, 29, and 177 (1952).

D. West, "Energy Measurements with Proportional Counters," *Progress in Nuclear Physics,* Vol. 3 (O. R. Frisch, Editor), London, Pergamon Press, 1953.

A. C. G. Mitchell, "The Use of Coincidence Counting Methods in Determining Nuclear Disintegration Schemes," *Revs. Mod. Phys.* **20,** 296 (1948).

M. L. Perlman and J. P. Welker, "Disintegration of I^{126}," *Phys. Rev.* **95,** 133 (1954).

H. Slätis, S. J. Du Toit, and K. Siegbahn, "The Disintegration of In^{116}," *Arkiv Fysik* **2,** 321 (1951).

G. G. Manov, "Standardization of Radioactive Sources," *Ann. Rev. Nuclear Sci.,* Vol. IV, p. 51, Stanford, Annual Reviews Inc., 1954.

H. H. Seliger and A. Schwebel, "Standardization of Beta-Emitting Nuclides," *Nucleonics* **12,** No. 7, 54 (July 1954).

R. G. Baker and L. Katz, "Absolute Beta Counting of Thick Planar Samples," *Nucleonics* **11,** No. 2, 14 (February 1953).

B. P. Burtt, "Absolute Beta Counting," *Nucleonics* **5,** No. 2, 28 (August 1949).

G. I. Gleason, J. D. Taylor, and D. L. Tabern, "Absolute Beta Counting at Defined Geometries," *Nucleonics* **8,** No. 5, 12 (May 1951).

J. C. Lee and M. L. Pool, "Radioactive Tin 121, 123, 125" (enriched isotope bombardments), *Phys. Rev.* **76,** 606 (1949).

R. J. Hayden, "Mass Spectrographic Mass Assignment of Radioactive Isotopes," *Phys. Rev.* **74,** 650 (1948).

O. Kofoed-Hansen and K. O. Nielsen, "Measurements on Shortlived Radioactive Krypton Isotopes from Fission after Isotopic Separation," *Kgl. Danske Videnskab. Selskab, Mat.-fys. Medd.* **26,** No. 7 (1951).

"Isotopes, Catalog and Price List," Oak Ridge National Laboratory, P. O. Box P, Oak Ridge, Tennessee (Price $1.00).

L. P. Gillon, K. Gopalakrishnan, A. de Shalit, and J. W. Mihelich, "Nuclear Spectroscopy of Neutron-Deficient Hg Isotopes," *Phys. Rev.* **93,** 124 (1954).

G. Wilkinson and H. G. Hicks, "Radioactive Isotopes of Lutetium and Hafnium," *Phys. Rev.* **81,** 540 (1951).

G. T. Seaborg, J. J. Livingood, and J. W. Kennedy, "Radioactive Isotopes of Tellurium," *Phys. Rev.* **57,** 363 (1940).

A. Turkevich and N. Sugarman, "Gallium, Germanium, and Arsenic Nuclides Produced in the Bombardment of Copper with 2.2-Bev Protons" (secondary reactions), *Phys. Rev.* **94,** 728 (1954).

CHAPTER 11

TRACERS IN CHEMICAL APPLICATIONS

A. THE TRACER METHOD; DIFFUSION STUDIES

Isotopic Tracers. Most of the ordinary chemical elements are composed of mixtures of isotopes, and each mixture remains essentially invariant in composition through the course of physical, chemical, and biological processes. That this is so is shown by the constant isotopic ratios found for elements from widely scattered sources [(1)] and by the fact that atomic weights reliable to many significant figures may be determined by chemical means. It is true that isotopic fractionation may be appreciable for the lightest elements where the percentage mass difference between isotopes is greatest, and this effect must always be considered in the use of hydrogen tracer isotopes. However, apart from H^3 (tritium) there is no practical radioactive tracer lighter than Be^7, which differs in mass from stable Be^9 by only about 25 per cent, and the next heavier tracer is in carbon where already the specific isotope effect may be neglected in most tracer work of ordinary precision. (More reference to the magnitude of isotope effects will be made in section B.)

The fact that a given nuclide may be radioactive does not in any way affect its chemical (or biological) properties; at least this is true for each atom until its nucleus actually undergoes the spontaneous radioactive change. Because the tracer-isotope atoms are detected by their radioactivity, they behave normally up to the moment of detection; after that moment they are not detected, and their fate is of no consequence. Of course, if the resulting atoms after the nuclear transformation are themselves radioactive and capable of a further nuclear change, the detection method must be arranged to give a response which measures the proper (in this case

[1] Some exceptions to the constancy of isotopic ratios were mentioned in chapter 2, section D.

the first) radioactive species only. For example, if RaE (Bi^{210}) is used as a tracer for bismuth, the α particles from its daughter Po^{210} should not be allowed to enter the detection instrument but should be absorbed by a suitable absorber or by the counter wall. As a tracer for thorium, UX_1 is suitable in spite of the fact that most of the detectable radiation will be from its daughter UX_2; the reason is that the short half-life, 1.18 min, of UX_2 insures that it will be in transient equilibrium with the UX_1 by the time the sample is mounted and ready for counting, so that the total activity will be proportional to the UX_1 content. Many multiple decays are found in the fission-product activities. If Ba^{140} ($t_{1/2} = 12.8$ days) is to be used as a tracer for barium, the isolated samples either should be freed chemically of the daughter La^{140} ($t_{1/2} = 40$ hr) or should be kept before counting for a week or two until the transient equilibrium is achieved. The isomeric-transition activities present interesting cases; if the 4.4-hr Br^{80m} is chosen as a tracer for bromine the 18-min lower isomeric state of Br^{80} will always be present, and, because of chemical effects accompanying the isomeric transition (section E), the two isomers may be present in different chemical forms. However, one may use the 4.4-hr Br^{80m} with confidence, provided only that one measures isolated samples for the 4.4-hr period by analysis of the decay curves or simply by holding the prepared samples for a time long compared to 18 min before counting. These special cases do not arise in the use of the great majority of popular tracer isotopes. Another source of interference with the tracer principle is a possible chemical (or biological) effect produced by the ionizing rays; this radiation chemistry effect is not often encountered at the usual tracer activity levels and may always be checked by experiments with a much higher or lower level of radioactivity.

A definite limitation of the radioactive tracer method is the absence of known active isotopes of suitable half-life for a few elements, especially oxygen and nitrogen. There are radioactive oxygen isotopes, O^{14}, O^{15}, and O^{19}, but these have half-lives of 77 sec, 118 sec, and 29 sec, respectively. The 7-sec N^{16} and 4-sec N^{17} are useless as tracers, but some applications of the 10-min N^{13} β^+ activity have been made. Also, helium, lithium, and boron do not have periods longer than 1 sec. The use of separated stable isotopes as tracers is a very valuable technique, and availability of the necessary concentrated isotopes is increasing. Enriched O^{18} and N^{15} are essential for many interesting and important purposes, and C^{13} offers significant advantages for some carbon tracer experiments. Deuterium has found many applications as a hydrogen tracer, and the use of tritium (H^3) is not entirely equivalent because its properties are even more different from those of protium (H^1).

Stable isotope tracers are most commonly assayed by mass spectrometers. (For the lightest elements, especially hydrogen, isotopic composition can be determined by measurement of physical properties such as density or thermal conductivity, and for a number of separated isotopes assays could be made by measurement of a nuclear property, as in the nuclear resonance absorption mentioned on page 40.) Samples for introduction into a mass spectrometer are ordinarily put into gaseous form. Carbon-13 is commonly analyzed in CO_2. The same gas is often used for O^{18} measurements, and, since CO_2 and H_2O reach isotopic equilibrium by exchange in a day or so, a convenient analysis for O^{18} in H_2O is provided. It is interesting that the most precise determinations of the radioactive C^{14} have been made by mass spectrometry on samples of high specific activity.

The uses of isotopic tracers may be classified into two groups: (1) applications in which the tracer is necessary in principle, and (2) applications in which a tracer not necessary in principle may be a great practical convenience. Those applications which depend uniquely on the tracer principle—although the tracers may be either radioactive or separated stable isotopes—may be illustrated by studies of self-diffusion of an element or other substance into itself; no other investigative technique can give information on such matters. On the other hand, the studies on coprecipitation which have been made with radioactive tracers might have been done, at least at the higher concentrations, by careful application of conventional chemical methods, or perhaps by spectroscopic or other means of analysis. In some of the more involved applications, particularly in biology, both of these aspects of tracer usefulness appear together.

Self-diffusion. To illustrate the unique tracer method we will discuss first studies that have been made of self-diffusion. By the use of sensitive spectroscopic analyses the rates of diffusion of various metals (including gold, silver, bismuth, thallium, and tin) in solid lead at elevated temperatures have been investigated, but the first attempt (by G. Hevesy and his collaborators) to observe the diffusion of radioactive lead into ordinary lead failed, showing that the diffusion rate must be at least one hundred times smaller than that for gold in lead (which is the fastest of those just named, the others showing decreasing rates in the order listed). The method first used was a rather gross mechanical one, and the workers evolved a much more sensitive method based on the short range of the α particles from ThC in transient equilibrium with ThB. The lead containing ThB isotopic tracer was pressed into contact with a thin foil of inactive lead which was chosen just thick enough to stop all the α rays, and then as diffusion progressed an α activity appeared and increased as measured through this foil. The diffusion coefficient **D** is obtained through a suitable integration of Fick's diffusion law, $\frac{\partial c}{\partial t} = \mathbf{D} \frac{\partial^2 c}{\partial x^2}$, where c is concentration of the diffusing tracer, t is time, and x is the coordinate along which the diffusion is measured; some typical values for **D** were 0.6×10^{-6} cm^2 per day at 260°C, 2.5×10^{-6} at 300°C, and 47×10^{-6} at 320°C. A similar but even more sensitive technique than the α-range method was based on the very much shorter ranges (a few millionths of a centimeter in lead) of the nuclei recoiling from α emission, with the radioactivity of the resulting ThC″ as an indicator of the emergence of recoil nuclei from the very thin lead foils. At 200°C the diffusion of lead in lead is about ten times slower than that of tin in lead, and roughly 10^5 times slower than that of gold in lead.

The diffusion of bismuth in bismuth has been studied with ThC as tracer; an interesting result is that the diffusion parallel to the c axis of the crystal is very different in magnitude ($\sim 10^5$ times slower at 250°C) and in temperature dependence from that perpendicular to the c axis. Self-diffusion of gold was studied by H. A. C. McKay; he induced activity principally on one surface only of a thin gold disk by an ingenious activation with resonance neutrons, for which the capture cross section in gold is so great that few neutrons could penetrate far below the exposed surface. Self-diffusion of copper has been studied by several investigators, with the use of copper disks either activated on one surface by deuteron irradiation or plated on one side with active copper. Self-diffusions of zinc and of silver have been measured from electroplated surfaces. Diffusion of some ions in crystals has been investigated, for example, of Pb^{++} in $PbCl_2$ and in PbI_2.

The rates of diffusion of ions through aqueous salt solutions of uniform composition may be determined with radioactive tracers, and this information may be of special significance since each rate is a property of the particular ion in that system, whereas salt-diffusion rates under a concentration gradient as ordinarily observed must necessarily depend on the diffusion tendencies of ions of both charges. Determinations of the self-diffusion coefficients for a number of ions in solutions of their salts have been made chiefly by two techniques. One of these is the diaphragm cell method, in which the solution with tracer is separated by a porous diaphragm from a chemically identical solution without added tracer. The conditions are so arranged that each of the two solutions is kept homogeneous (by stirring if necessary); the diaphragm, usually fritted glass, prevents convective mixing between the two. Transport of tracer across the barrier is measured, and the rate is proportional to the diffusion coefficient. The cell constant may be determined by calibration either with a known self-diffusion rate or with the conventional concentration-gradient diffusion of a well-studied salt such as KCl.

The other technique generally used for aqueous self-diffusion studies is the open-ended-capillary method. Here a capillary tube about 0.06 cm in diameter and a few centimeters long is filled with the traced solution and immersed open end up in an essentially infinite volume of an untraced salt solution of the same concentration. The small bore of the capillary tube prevents serious convective mixing from residual thermal gradients and minor mechanical vibration. As demonstrated by comparisons between tubes of different lengths, end effects associated with the capillary mouth are made negligible by adjustment of the stirring rate in the large bath. The use of 2 per cent deuterium oxide as solvent in the capillary has been shown to eliminate the danger of convection caused by accidental small differences in salt concentration. (Differences in composition, particularly pH differences, can lead to serious errors from junction potential effects.) When conditions are such that tracer is lost from the capillary by diffusion only, the fraction of the original tracer remaining in the capillary after time t (corrected for any radioactive decay) is approximately $\frac{\pi^2 Dt}{4l^2 \ln (8/\pi^2)}$, where D is the self-diffusion coefficient, l is the length of the capillary, and the approximation is quite accurate for $Dt/l^2 > 0.2$. This result, as well as the more general expression valid for any value of Dt/l^2, may be derived by appropriate integrations of Fick's diffusion equation.

Self-diffusion coefficients have been obtained for a number of common ions, especially alkali metal and halide ions, in solutions over wide concentration ranges. Unfortunately the two experimental methods have so far given results which sometimes differ in details. The coefficients for smaller, "hydrated" cations such as Na^+ and K^+ exhibit a maximum in the vicinity of one mole per liter. The larger, "unhydrated" ions such as Rb^+, Cs^+, and I^- in their solutions show a more regular behavior; indeed for these ions the product of the self-diffusion coefficient and viscosity of the solution is a linear function of concentration at least up to concentrations well above one molar. The slopes of such plots have been related to certain Debye-Hückel parameters.

Other Migration Problems. Radioactive tracers are useful in the study of numerous migration problems other than self-diffusion, particularly where movements of very small amounts of material are involved. In most such applications the tracer is serving only as a very sensitive and relatively convenient analytical tool. Erosion and corrosion of surfaces may be measured with great sensitivity if the surface to be tested can be made intensely radioactive. Transfer of very minute amounts of bearing-surface materials during friction has been studied in this way. Radioactive gases or vapors may be detected in small concentrations, and leakage, flow, and diffusion rates of gases may therefore be studied by the tracer method.

B. ISOTOPIC AND EXCHANGE REACTIONS

Qualitative Observations. In a very early exchange experiment in 1920 Hevesy demonstrated by the use of ThB (Pb^{212}) the rapid interchange of lead atoms between $Pb(NO_3)_2$ and $PbCl_2$ in water solution. The experiment was performed by the addition of an active $Pb(NO_3)_2$ solution to an inactive $PbCl_2$ solution and by the subsequent crystallization of $PbCl_2$ from the mixture. The result is not at all surprising because the well-known process of ionization for these salts leads to chemically identical lead ions, Pb^{++}. Very many exchange systems have been examined since that time, and for the majority of cases where exchange is rapid at ordinary temperature there are known reversible reactions which would lead to interchange. For the other observed exchanges there either exist such reversible reactions, which are possibly unknown, or the exchange occurs by a simple collision mechanism (which may amount to about the same thing).

It was soon shown when artificially radioactive isotopes became available that aqueous Cl^- and Cl_2, Br^- and Br_2, and I^- and I_2 exchanged at room temperature so quickly that the rates could not be measured by ordinary methods. These exchanges are interpreted as occurring through the reactions illustrated by $I^- + I_2 \rightleftharpoons I_3^-$. It has been found that Br_2 and HBr, either in the gas phase or in solution in dry carbon tetrachloride, exchange rapidly at room temperature, probably through reversible formation of a complex HBr_3, although the life of this intermediate may be very short and thus its concentration very low. Also I_2 and SbI_3 in dry pentane exchange within 20 min at 37°C, very possibly through SbI_5. Rapid exchanges at room temperature in carbon tetrachloride are found between Br_2 and $AsBr_3$ and between Br_2 and $SnBr_4$; we may imagine that these proceed through intermediates like $AsBr_5$ and $SnBr_2$, or bromides of other oxidation states. In aqueous solution $PtBr_4^{=}$ or $PtBr_6^{=}$ rapidly exchanges all bromine atoms with Br^- ion; the four iodine atoms in $HgI_4^{=}$ exchange with I^- ion.

In dilute-acid solution at room temperature there is no rapid exchange of halogen atoms between Cl_2 and ClO_3^- or ClO_4^-, Br_2 and BrO_3^-, I_2 and IO_3^-, ClO_3^- and ClO_4^-, IO_3^- and IO_4^-; however, some of these do exchange at measurable rates. No exchange was found in alkaline solution between Cl^- and ClO_4^-, Br^- and BrO_3^-, I^- and IO_3^-.

Interesting exchange studies have been made with the tracer S^{35}. Sulfur and sulfide ions exchange in polysulfide solution. Even at 100°C $S^{=}$ and $SO_4^{=}$, $SO_3^{=}$ and $SO_4^{=}$, H_2SO_3 and HSO_4^- do not exchange appreciably. If active sulfur is reacted with inactive $SO_3^{=}$ to form $S_2O_3^{=}$, and then the sulfur removed with acid, the H_2SO_3 is regenerated inactive; therefore, the two sulfur atoms in thiosulfate are not equivalent. The ions $S_2O_3^{=}$ and $SO_3^{=}$ exchange only very slowly at room temperature, but exchange one sulfur fairly rapidly at 100°C. (Notice that this result can be found only by labeling the proper sulfur atom, the one attached directly to the oxygen atoms.) Sulfide ion and $S_2O_3^{=}$ slowly exchange (probably only one sulfur) at 100°C. Sulfur does not exchange with CS_2 at 100°C; SO_2 and SO_3 do not exchange appreciably even at 280°C. Radioactive carbon has been used to show that CO and CO_2 do not exchange in 1 hr at 200°C.

The exchange reactions of various manganese compounds have been surveyed. The following do not exchange readily: MnO_4^- and Mn^{++}, MnO_4^- and $Mn(C_2O_4)_3^{\equiv}$, MnO_4^- and MnO_2, Mn^{++} and MnO_2. Rapid exchanges at room temperature were found for the pairs Mn^{++} and $Mn(C_2O_4)_3^{\equiv}$, and MnO_4^- and $MnO_4^{=}$.

Phosphoric and phosphorous acids, H_3PO_4 and $H_2(HPO_3)$, and also phosphoric and hypophosphorous acids, H_3PO_4 and $H(H_2PO_2)$, do not exchange phosphorus atoms even at 100°C, although the first of these exchanges might be expected to proceed (at some unknown rate) through the formation of hypophosphoric acid, $H_4P_2O_6$. Arsenate and arsenite ions, and H_3AsO_4 and $HAsO_2$ do not exchange appreciably even at 100°C.

The availability of appreciably enriched stable isotope O^{18} has led to a number of observations on exchanges between oxygen-containing ions and water. In neutral or alkaline solution perchlorate, chlorate, nitrate, sulfate, and phosphate do not exchange appreciably with water; in acid solutions the exchange reactions are faster. The hypothesis that these exchanges proceed through reversible formation of the acid anhydride has been advanced and receives support from the observation that the weaker acids such as H_2SO_3 and HIO_3 exchange more readily with water. Moreover, the sulfate-water exchange is catalyzed by hydrogen ion quantitatively as if the reaction proceeded through undissociated H_2SO_4 molecules. Exchange between water of hydration and solvent water also may be studied with O^{18}. For most ions, including Al^{+++}, Fe^{+++}, Ga^{+++}, Th^{++++}, and Co^{++}, this exchange is too rapid to have been observed. But for Cr^{+++}, actually $Cr(H_2O)_6{}^{+++}$, the exchange is about half complete in 40 hr.

Some metal surfaces exchange rather well with the corresponding metal ions in solution, as observed in the case of silver, zinc, and lead. With silver the exchange reaches to a depth of 10 to 100 atomic layers in about 1 hr at room temperature. In part these effects may be due to local electrolysis caused by imperfections in the metal surface. Precipitates such as AgBr exchange rather effectively with component ions such as Br^- when freshly formed, but only much more slowly when aged. An exchange of over 100 per cent completion is simulated in some cases; that is, initially inactive crystals may reach a higher specific activity than that of the final halide solution, because the inner and outer parts of grown crystals may not be in equilibrium.

Alkyl halides of all types ordinarily do not exchange readily at room temperature with either free halogens or halide ions. However, the nature of the solvent (particularly ethyl alcohol, acetone, and amyl alcohol in some reported experiments) can exert a marked influence in producing exchange in these systems. In the solvents named, I^- exchanges with ethyl, *n*-propyl, isopropyl, and methylene iodides and iodoform in about 15 min or less at 100°C. Most remarkably, in these solvents I^- and CH_3I are reported to exchange in 1 min at room temperature; the exchange of CH_3I with I_2 is much less rapid. Iodide ion exchanges rapidly with iodoacetic acid, but rapidly only at elevated temperatures with β-iodopropionic acid. The phenyl halides (including *p*-nitro and *p*-amino derivatives) exchange less readily than the alkyl halides. Halogen exchanges with alkyl halides have been produced photochemically. On the other hand, gaseous HBr and C_2H_5Br did not exchange photochemically but did exchange thermally at 300°C.

The behavior of aluminum bromide in exchange reactions is remarkable, paralleling its extraordinary character as a catalyst. It exchanges bromine atoms readily at room temperature with many alkyl bromides, with benzyl bromide, and with many aliphatic polybromides; it exchanges also, but more slowly, with aryl bromides. Aluminum iodide appears to behave in a similar way. Because these aluminum halides also exchange readily with gaseous halogen or hydrogen halide, a convenient synthesis of labeled organic halides is provided. Obviously the presence of aluminum bromide will catalyze an exchange between two organic bromides.

Knowledge of the occurrence or nonoccurrence of rapid exchange has been used in the study of bond character. It is obvious that exchange data give information on the degree of stability of particular bonds, but the relation of this information to the bond type and to other aspects of bond character is still under investigation.

Quantitative Exchange Law. Consider a schematic exchange-producing reaction,

$$AX + BX^0 = AX^0 + BX,$$

where X^0 represents a radioactive atom of X. The radioactive decay of this species will be neglected; in practice if the decay is appreciable, correction of all measured activities to some common time must be used to avoid error from this condition. The rate of the reaction between AX and BX in the dynamic equilibrium we call $\mathbf{R}$, in units of moles liter^{-1} second^{-1}; notice that $\mathbf{R}$ is quite independent of the concentration and even of the existence of the active tracer X^0. We indicate mole-per-liter concentrations as follows: $(AX) + (AX^0) = a$, $(BX) + (BX^0) = b$, $(AX^0) = x$, $(BX^0) = y$, and $x + y = z$. The rate of increase $\left(\frac{dx}{dt}\right)$ of (AX^0) is given by the rate of its formation minus the rate of its destruction. The rate of formation of AX^0 is given by $\mathbf{R}$ times the factor y/b, which is the fraction of reactions that occur with an active molecule BX^0, and times the factor $(a - x)/a$, which is the fraction of reactions with the molecule AX initially inactive. The rate of destruction of AX^0 is given by $\mathbf{R}$ times the factor x/a, which is the fraction of reactions in the reverse direction that occur with an active molecule AX^0, and times the factor $(b - y)/b$, which is the fraction of reverse reactions with the molecule BX initially inactive. The differential equation is then

$$\frac{dx}{dt} = \mathbf{R}\frac{y}{b}\frac{(a-x)}{a} - \mathbf{R}\frac{x}{a}\frac{(b-y)}{b} = \frac{\mathbf{R}}{ab}(ay - bx)$$

$$= \frac{\mathbf{R}}{ab}(az - ax - bx) = -\frac{a+b}{ab}\mathbf{R}x + \frac{z}{b}\mathbf{R}.$$

The solution of this first-order linear equation is found by standard methods:

$$x = Ce^{-\frac{a+b}{ab}\mathbf{R}t} + \frac{a}{a+b}z.$$

After a very long time, that is, at $t = \infty$, let $x = x_\infty$ and $y = y_\infty$. Substituting these values in the previous solution, we have then

$$x_\infty = \frac{a}{a+b} z,$$

and, since $y_\infty = z - x_\infty$,

$$y_\infty = \frac{b}{a+b} z.$$

These two relations constitute an algebraic expression for the reasonable and well-known rule that when exchange is complete the specific activity (activity per mole or per gram of X) is the same in both fractions. At that time the specific activity of AX is $\frac{x_\infty}{a} = \frac{z}{a+b}$, and the specific activity of BX is $\frac{y_\infty}{b} = \frac{z}{a+b}$.

The solution may now be rewritten:

$$x = Ce^{-\frac{a+b}{ab}\mathbf{R}t} + x_\infty.$$

If at $t = 0$ we have $x = 0$, that is, if AX is inactive at the start, we find the constant $C = -x_\infty$, and some useful (final) forms may be obtained:

$$1 - \frac{x}{x_\infty} = e^{-\frac{a+b}{ab}\mathbf{R}t},$$

$$2.303 \log \left(1 - \frac{x}{x_\infty}\right) = -\frac{a+b}{ab}\mathbf{R}t; \qquad (11\text{-}1)$$

and, by differentiation with respect to t,

$$\mathbf{R} = -2.303 \frac{ab}{a+b} \frac{d}{dt} \log \left(1 - \frac{x}{x_\infty}\right).$$

The last result shows that $\mathbf{R}$ may be evaluated from the slope of a plot of log $[1 - (x/x_\infty)]$ vs. t. Probably the most convenient procedure is to plot $[1 - (x/x_\infty)]$ on semilog paper against t, read off the half-time $T_{1/2}$ at which the fraction exchanged, x/x_∞, is ½, and find $\mathbf{R}$ from an equation derived immediately from equation (11-1):

$$\mathbf{R} = \frac{ab}{a+b} \cdot \frac{0.69315}{T_{1/2}}.$$

It is important to notice that if a or b or both should be varied the variation in half-time for the exchange would not directly reflect the variation in $\mathbf{R}$, because of the factor $ab/(a + b)$.

For a number of practical exchange studies the simple formulas AX and BX may not represent the reacting molecules; for example, AX_2 or BX_n might be involved. So long as the several atoms of X are entirely equivalent (or at least indistinguishable in exchange experiments) in each of these molecules, the equations just derived may be applied without modification, provided only that we redefine all the concentrations in gram atoms of X per liter rather than moles of AX or AX_2, etc., per liter. This is equivalent to considering (for this purpose only) one molecule of AX_2 as replaceable by two molecules of $A_{1/2}X$, etc., in the derivation. If in a molecule like AX_2 the two X atoms are not equivalent, and if they exchange through two different reactions with rates $\mathbf{R}_1$ and $\mathbf{R}_2$, it may be seen that the resulting semilog plot will be not a straight line but a complex curve. The differential equations for the exchanges to the several positions may be set up and solved simultaneously, so that the curve may, at least in principle, be resolved to give values for the several $\mathbf{R}$'s; however, this becomes very difficult for more than about two rates. A simplification may be made if $a \ll b$, with the several nonequivalent positions in the molecule AX_n; here the value of y is very nearly a constant, and in this limit the complex semilog curve is resolvable in the same way as a radioactive decay curve into straight lines measuring $\mathbf{R}_1$, $\mathbf{R}_2$, etc. No example of a complex homogeneous exchange curve has been reported except the limiting case with $\mathbf{R}_1$ measurable, but $\mathbf{R}_2 = 0$ within experimental accuracy (like the sulfur exchange between $S_2O_3^{=}$ and $SO_3^{=}$). In this limiting case no unusual feature appears if x_∞ is used in an experimental sense, although after a much longer time x_∞ may be expected to reach a higher value.

Reaction Kinetics and Mechanisms. Radioactive tracers are finding an important place in the investigations of reaction kinetics and mechanisms. We will discuss several examples to illustrate the kinds of information in this field that can be obtained with tracers but hardly in any other way. Consider the reversible reaction:

$$HAsO_2 + I_3^- + 2H_2O \rightleftharpoons H_3AsO_4 + 3I^- + 2H^+.$$

The familiar theory of dynamic equilibrium takes $K = k_f/k_r$, where K is the equilibrium constant and k_f and k_r are the specific rate constants of the forward and reverse reactions. Ordinarily K may be measured only at equilibrium and k_f or k_r far from equilibrium. Using radioactive arsenic to measure the rate of exchange between arsenious and arsenic acids induced by an iodine catalyst in accordance with the foregoing equilibrium reaction, J. N. Wilson and R. G. Dickinson were able to find the rate law and specific rate constant at equilibrium. For the reverse direction as written they found $\mathbf{R} = k_r\,(H_3AsO_4)(H^+)(I^-)$, with $k_r = 0.057$ liter^2 mole^{-2} min^{-1}, which is in satisfactory agreement with the information from ordinary rate studies made far from equilibrium, $\mathbf{R} = 0.071\,(H_3AsO_4)(H^+)(I^-)$.

A theory of the Walden inversion calls for inversion at each substitution by the schematic mechanism:

$$I^- \rightarrow \begin{matrix} R_1 & & \\ & \diagdown & \\ & & C\text{—}I \\ & \diagup & | \\ R_2 & & R_3 \end{matrix} = \begin{matrix} & & R_1 \\ & \diagup & \\ I\text{—}C & & \\ | & \diagdown & \\ R_3 & & R_2 \end{matrix} + I^-.$$

As shown here the substitution is by a like group, and if the initial molecules are optically active the final product will be the racemic mixture. It has been shown that for *sec*-octyl iodide (or for α-phenyl ethyl bromide) the rate of exchange with radioactive iodide ion (or bromide ion) is identical with the rate of racemization, which is a verification of the mechanism.

A different type of racemization is that of chromioxalate ion, $Cr(C_2O_4)_3^{\equiv}$, which may be optically active through different linkings of the six octahedral bonds of the chromium with the carbon-oxygen chains. This racemization in aqueous solution is fairly rapid and apparently first order; it had been proposed that the mechanism involved an ionization as the rate-determining step:

$$Cr(C_2O_4)_3^{\equiv} = Cr(C_2O_4)_2^- + C_2O_4^=.$$

Another theory favored an intramolecular rearrangement instead. The racemization has been allowed to proceed in a solution containing radioactive $C_2O_4^=$. The activity did not enter the chromium complex compound; therefore, the ionization mechanism is disproved, and the intramolecular rearrangement hypothesis supported.

Some of the applications of tracers to reaction mechanism studies are essentially qualitative. For example, when HClO traced with Cl^{38} oxidizes ClO_2^-, the product Cl^- contains the tracer, and the product ClO_3^- is inactive. Also when Cl^- is oxidized by ClO_3^- the product Cl_2 is formed from the Cl^-, and the product ClO_2 is formed from the ClO_3^-. When traced I^- reduces IO_4^- to IO_3^-, the tracer appears only in the I_2 product. Clearly any reaction intermediates containing the reactants in these reactions must be unsymmetrical in that the two halogen atoms of initially different oxidation state are distinguished. This information at least rules out some of the conceivable reaction paths.

Another example may be taken from the many studies of organic reaction mechanisms made with radioactive carbon. Today almost all such studies use C^{14}, which is a very convenient long-lived tracer discovered in 1940 by S. Ruben and M. D. Kamen. But because so little C^{14} was then available those workers used the 20-min C^{11} to study the oxidation by alkaline permanganate of propionate to the products carbonate and oxalate (1 mole of each from 1 mole of propionate). It might have been a plausible guess that the $CO_3^=$ is formed from the carboxyl group; however, with the carboxyl carbon labeled they found that only about 25 per cent of the $CO_3^=$ was from that part of the molecule. In acid solution in the oxidation of propionic acid by dichromate they found that all the CO_2 did originate from the —COOH, demonstrating different mechanisms in the two instances. The oxidation of fumaric acid,[2] HOOC*CHCHC*OOH, by acid permanganate has been investigated; the product HCOOH (1 mole per mole of fumaric acid) is formed always from one of the secondary carbon atoms, and the CO_2 (3 moles per mole of fumaric acid) is from the carboxyl carbons and the other secondary carbon.

J. Halperin and H. Taube and other workers have used the stable isotope O^{18} as a tracer of oxygen atom transfers in oxidation reactions. When ClO_3^- is reduced to Cl^- by $SO_3^=$, approximately 2.3 of the three oxygen atoms in ClO_3^- are found in the product $SO_4^=$. Corresponding numbers are 1.5 for ClO_2^- and 0.36 for ClO^- as oxidizing agents. The interpretation is that the reduction occurs in steps $ClO_3^- \rightarrow ClO_2^- \rightarrow ClO^- \rightarrow Cl^-$, and that the reaction is an oxygen atom transfer from the halogen ion to the sulfite at least in the first two steps. (The reduction of ClO^- may also be predominantly by atom transfer but with a competing exchange of O^{18} between hypochlorite and water.) These studies show also that when sulfite is oxidized by BrO_3^-, by O_2, by MnO_2, and by MnO_4^- there is a trans-

[2] By common usage these asterisks indicate labeled positions (the two carboxyl carbons in this case) in the molecules; of course, because the active tracers are almost always very highly diluted with ordinary atoms it is very improbable for any given molecule actually to contain two radioactive atoms. Thus the asterisk denotes not a radioactive atom, but an atom taken at random from a sample containing some active atoms; in other words, the position marked with the asterisk will in some of the molecules be labeled with a radioactive atom. Notice that on page 315 we avoided the asterisk and chose a different superscript because there we wished to indicate an actual radioactive atom.

fer of 2, 2, 1, and 0.2 atoms of oxygen, respectively, per formula unit of the oxidizing agent. The most striking result is that labeled H_2O_2 transfers both oxygen atoms to one sulfite, giving a sulfate ion which contains two labeled oxygens. Incidentally, the O_2 evolved in the decomposition of H_2O_2 solutions under a wide variety of conditions is derived from the peroxide only.

Electron Transfer Reactions. In many oxidation-reduction reactions the net change appears to be a transfer of one or more electrons, for example, the oxidation of ferrous ion by ceric ion,

$$Fe^{++} + Ce^{++++} = Fe^{+++} + Ce^{+++}.$$

Some such reactions, including this one, are quite fast; others are much slower. An early observation was that the reactions generally are not fast unless the number of electrons lost by a mole of the reducing agent is the same as the number gained by a mole of the oxidizing agent. However, many reactions which meet this condition are slow, and the reasons are not known. Of course, two ions of like charge may so repel one another that close collisions are unlikely, but experiments would indicate that this factor is only a small part of the whole explanation.

Isotopic tracers make possible the study of a relatively simple class of electron transfer reactions, the exchange reactions between different oxidation states of the same element. For example, radioactive iron has been used by several investigators to study the rate of oxidation of ferrous ion by ferric ion,

$$Fe^{*++} + Fe^{+++} = Fe^{*+++} + Fe^{++}.$$

Such a reaction of course follows the quantitative exchange law already derived, and the rate is measured by the rate at which the tracer becomes randomly mixed between the two oxidation states. If the exchange is carried out in 6 *f* HCl the ferric iron is readily separated from the ferrous iron by ether extraction, but the rate is too rapid for measurement. In this system chloride complexes such as $FeCl_3$ are surely present, and the exchange observed may proceed through such species. In perchloric acid the exchange rate is fast, but measurable in dilute solutions at 0°C. When fluoride ion is added, so that species such as FeF^{++}, FeF_2^{+}, and FeF_3 are present, the variation of the rate with F^- concentration can be used to show that the reaction proceeds through all of these forms, and that the exchange rate is fastest with FeF^{++}.

Fast electron transfer exchange has been observed between $Fe(CN)_6^{====}$ and $Fe(CN)_6^{\equiv}$, Ce^{+++} and Ce^{++++}, Mn^{++} and $Mn(C_2O_4)_3^{\equiv}$, $MnO_4^{=}$

and MnO_4^-, Hg^{++} and Hg_2^{++}, NpO_2^+ and NpO_2^{++}, Co^{++} and Co^{+++}, ClO_2^- and ClO_2, Ag^+ and Ag^{++}, between the tris-(2,2′bipyridyl) complexes of Os(II) and Os(III), and between the tris-(5,6-dimethyl-1,10-phenanthroline) complexes of Fe(II) and Fe(III). In several of these cases the rate could not be followed quantitatively, because the exchange is too fast either in the solution or at some stage in the separation process. (If the rate can be measured a correction can be made for any exchange induced during separation.) Exchange half-times as short as 1 sec at 0°C have been established in a few instances. The availability of high specific activities has sometimes made it possible to go to sufficiently low concentrations of reactants to bring exchange rates from an inaccessible into a measurable range. Very much slower exchanges have been reported between Eu^{++} and Eu^{+++}, Sn (II) and Sn(IV) in HCl solutions, Pb(II) and Pb(IV) in glacial $HC_2H_3O_2$, Sb(III) and Sb(V) in HCl, $Co(NH_3)_6^{++}$ and $Co(NH_3)_6^{+++}$, and between Co(II) and Co(III) tris-ethylenediamine complexes.

Many of these exchange reactions have been the subject of detailed kinetic studies, including the determination of effects of reactant concentrations, *p*H, complexing agents, and temperature on the rates. For example, the moderately slow exchange ($T_{1/2} \backsim 1$ day) between thallous and thallic ions is faster with a hydrolyzed species $Tl(OH)^{++}$ and also with chloride and nitrate complexes than with uncomplexed Tl^{+++}. (The effect with chloride is not simple, but an optimum chloride concentration produces strong catalysis.) The hypothesis has arisen that the reaction intermediate in many of these electron transfer reactions contains the two reactants joined together through bonding to a common group such as chloride or hydroxyl. The decomposition of this intermediate may effect a transfer of the Cl or OH; transfer of the neutral atom or radical constitutes oxidation:

$$Fe^{*++} + FeCl^{++} = (Fe^{*}ClFe)^{++++} = Fe^{*}Cl^{++} + Fe^{++}.$$

Rates of Isotopic Reactions. Although we often ignore quantitative differences in the rates of reactions of molecules containing different isotopes, these differences usually are measurable, especially for isotopes of the light elements. For example, A. Cahill and Taube found that several cationic reducing agents, Fe^{++}, Sn^{++}, Cr^{++}, and Cu^+, at 25°C reacted about 6 per cent slower with $H_2O^{16}O^{18}$ than with ordinary $H_2O_2^{16}$. Although these fractionation effects can sometimes be inconvenient in tracer studies, it is much more important that they can be turned into a new and useful tool for the investigation of reaction mechanisms. The fractionation factor for a pair of isotopic molecules at a given temperature is characteristic of the particular process and may serve to identify that process in a complex reaction. The uniform fractionation factor for the H_2O_2 reductions just quoted led to the belief that in each case the process is a two-electron transfer from a single Fe^{++}, Sn^{++}, etc. One other cationic agent, Ti^{+++}, reduces H_2O_2 with a corresponding isotopic fractionation effect of less than 1 per cent. The same authors concluded that a different process—a one-electron transfer step—was operative in this case.

Fractionation effects would be a more powerful investigative method if a complete quantitative theory of isotopic reaction rates were available. Quantum-mechanical calculations of the equilibrium distribution of isotopes in chemical reactions seem to be entirely satisfactory. These considerations have been combined with statistical rate theory, particularly by J. Bigeleisen, but a difficulty arises immediately because quantum-mechanical data on the transition states are lacking. The maximum possible relative retardation of the reaction rate for the heavier isotope corresponds to vanishingly small binding of the isotopic atoms in the transition state, and upper limits to fractionation factors have been computed on this basis. Various approximations to the transition state for actual reactions are in the process of being tested. Because the effects are quite small, for example about 1 to 10 per cent for carbon isotopes, sufficiently accurate measurements are not always realized; but without doubt the theoretical results are somewhere near the truth.

Intramolecular isotopic reactions, with both isotopes present initially in the same molecule, are a special case most easily treated theoretically. For example, the decarboxylation of malonic acid containing a $—C^{13}OOH$ group may occur in either of two ways:

$$CH_2(C^{13}OOH)(C^{12}OOH) \xrightarrow{a} C^{12}O_2 + CH_3C^{13}OOH$$

$$CH_2(C^{13}OOH)(C^{12}OOH) \xrightarrow{b} C^{13}O_2 + CH_3C^{12}OOH$$

Theory predicts that the difference between the two rate constants a and b is largely caused by the different entropies of activation rather than by differences in activation energies. A calculation of just the entropy effect gives for the ratio a/b a value of 1.020. The temperature dependence due to a difference in the activation energies is difficult to calculate, but should be small. The best experimental results give a value of 1.029 for the ratio, independent of temperature within the experimental error. Another feature of the theoretical results, also independent of specific properties of the transition state, is that, for small isotope effects expressed in per cent, the magnitude of the effect is proportional to the differences in isotopic masses. For example, any C^{14} effect should be very closely twice the corresponding C^{13} effect, both compared to ordinary C^{12}. Although some earlier experiments gave ratios of C^{14} to C^{13} effects in excess of two, the best experimental data on decarboxylation reactions now appear to agree substantially with the theoretical prediction.

It may be noted that isotope fractionation measurements often can be carried out with ordinary materials, without a requirement for enriched isotopic samples. However, very precise isotope ratio determinations are essential, even when highly enriched materials are used.

C. ANALYTICAL APPLICATIONS

Test of Separations. Radioactive tracers can be very conveniently used to follow the progress and test the completeness of chemical separation procedures. If one component of a mixture is radioactive, frequently it can be followed satisfactorily through successive operations if beakers containing filtrates, funnels with precipitates, and so on, are merely held near a counter or ionization chamber. We have seen good chemical isolations made by these methods in the almost complete absence of knowledge of specific chemical properties. The crude qualitative procedure may be refined as far as desired, and valuable tests of analytical separation methods have been made with tracers. As the first of a few examples we consider a procedure that has been used for the determination of gold-platinum-iridium compositions. The three elements in solution are precipitated by reduction with hot alkaline sodium formate; the residue after ignition is treated with aqua regia to dissolve gold and platinum but leave iridium; the resulting solution on treatment with hydrogen peroxide gives the gold as a precipitate of the metal, and the platinum is finally precipitated from the filtrate with sodium formate. By simple gravimetric studies on known compositions the iridium fraction was found to be too heavy, the gold fraction too heavy, and the platinum fraction too light. With radioactive tracer it was shown that the gold fraction actually contained only 97 per cent of the original gold, but with more than enough platinum to mask this; the remainder of the gold was mostly in the platinum fraction.

The coprecipitation of cobalt with SnS_2 has been investigated in relation to various experimental conditions, with active cobalt as a tracer. The amount of coprecipitation was smaller at higher hydrogen-ion concentrations; the cobalt contamination could be made negligible provided that acrolein was present as a flocculating agent. Radioactive beryllium has been used to find that aluminum precipitated by 8-hydroxyquinoline carries some beryllium at *p*H values greater than 6; below *p*H 6 the coprecipitation is absent. The carrying down of tellurium by antimony oxide precipitated from boiling concentrated nitric acid has been studied with tracers. Also a number of solvent extraction procedures have been tested in this way for interference effects.

The solubility of quite insoluble precipitates may be judged by the use of radioactivity. This has been done in the precipitation of tin as $Sn_3[Fe(CN)_6]_2$. The approach to equilibrium between solid phase and solution can be followed very conveniently by repeated measurements of the activity of the supernatant solution. A somewhat analogous tracer method is applicable to the determination of small vapor pressures.

Analysis by Isotope Dilution. It may frequently occur that quantitative analysis for a component of a mixture is wanted where no quantitative isolation procedure is known. Particularly for complex organic mixtures it may be possible to isolate from the unknown the desired compound with satisfactory purity but only in low and uncertain yield. In such a case the analysis may be made by the technique of isotope dilution. To the unknown mixture is added a known weight of the compound to be determined containing a known amount (activity) of radioactively tagged molecules. Then the specific activity of that pure compound isolated from the mixture is determined and compared with that of the added material; the extent of dilution of the tracer shows the amount of inactive compound present in the original unknown. (You may think of the tracer as serving to measure the chemical yield of the isolation procedure. Obviously exchange reactions which would reduce the specific activity of the compound must be absent.) To date this powerful method has found uses principally in biochemistry and biology. Recently M. Inghram has described isotope dilution analyses using mass-spectrometric assay which give accuracies of a few per cent in the parts-per-billion to parts-per-trillion range for some elements.

Analysis by Activation. Throughout most of the tracer work discussed radioactive isotopes are assayed by measurement of their activities. This is actually an analytical procedure, but we have not emphasized that aspect because the samples are subject to analysis only if the tracer was provided earlier in the experiment. Of course, the naturally radioactive elements, including uranium, thorium, radium, potassium, and rubidium, may be assayed by radioactive measurement; a very practical although not very sensitive procedure for potassium assay by means of its radioactivity has been reported.

A somewhat different technique can be useful, in which an unknown sample is subjected to activation by neutrons for appropriately chosen lengths of time, and chemical elements are identified and assayed by measurement of characteristic radionuclides formed. In general the irradiation must be followed by chemical isolation of the desired radionuclides, carried out in the usual manner after the addition of appropriate carriers. Standardization is provided by irradiation, along with the unknown sample, of a standard sample containing a known amount of the element to be analyzed. It is sometimes desirable to use a standard of similar composition to the unknown, or else to use sufficiently small samples, to avoid errors due to strong neutron absorption by other constituents.

The specificity of activation analysis is usually excellent since the purity of the radionuclide measured may be checked by half-life and energy determinations. Sensitivity depends on the flux of bombarding particles, the cross section of the reaction involved, the isotopic abundance of the isotope giving rise to the reaction, the half-life of the nuclide measured, and the detection efficiency of the measuring equipment. With a neutron flux of 10^{12} cm^{-2} sec^{-1}, sensitivities for most elements are in the range of 10^{-16} to 10^{-11} g. Thus analysis by neutron activation is practical for impurities present in parts per million or even parts per billion. Activation analyses carried out with the Oak Ridge graphite reactor are available for over sixty elements through the U. S. Atomic Energy Commission. The samples submitted for analysis may be in a variety of forms, including for example alloys, minerals, petroleum products, ceramics, pharmaceuticals, and biological materials.

Although slow-neutron irradiation is by far the most widely used technique in activation analysis, some applications of charged-particle activation have also been reported. By deuteron irradiation very small impurities of gallium in iron, of copper in nickel, and of iron in cobalt oxide have been found. A simple quantitative method for the determination of carbon in steels by means of the reaction $C^{12}(d, n)N^{13}$ has been described.

Radiometric Analysis. Analytical procedures by tracer methods for elements which are not themselves radioactive have been introduced and given the name radiometric analysis. For example, silver ion may be determined by the precipitation of AgI with radioactive iodide ion. One report describes the collection by adsorption on $Fe(OH)_3$ of very small amounts of AgI formed, so that as little as 10 ppm of silver could be detected.

D. CHEMICAL PHENOMENA AT TRACER CONCENTRATIONS

Limits of Detection. The working region of concentrations in ordinary chemical studies is limited by the sensitivity of available analytical methods. The lower detection limits for different substances vary widely. Gravimetric procedures rarely are useful for concentrations as low as one part per million (1 ppm). Except for the newer techniques of activation analysis and isotope dilution with mass spectrometry, spectroscopic elementary analysis in favorable cases offers about the best sensitivity, and detection of a number of elements at 0.01 ppm and less may be practical. It is true that some compounds of very pronounced odor may be noticed at much lower concentrations; for example, at 0.01 ppm in air the odor of mercaptan is very strong, and it may be recognized at 0.00001 ppm. The number of mercaptan molecules sufficient for recognition in this way is estimated to be about 3×10^{10}, corresponding to 2×10^{-12} g in about 100 ml of air. Other detection methods, especially biological assays, may approach and exceed even this sensitivity. But for the most part these methods have not offered practical means for extending knowledge of chemical behavior to such extremely low concentrations. The property of radioactivity does offer a rather convenient analytical method for concentrations so low and even much lower. As few as several thousand radioactive molecules may be detected, even when contained in sizable samples. The practical working limits are fixed by the half-life and by the nature of the radiation. A polonium solution at 10^{-12} mole per liter has an easily detectable activity of 35 disintegrations per second per milliliter. The shorter-lived La^{140} (40-hr half-life) may be studied in 10^{-14} molar solution. A new concentration region is opened for study by the technique of radioactive tracers.

Radiocolloids. It was observed many years ago that radioactive elements in some solutions where they existed at extremely low concentrations showed unusual physical properties in that they behaved more like colloids than true solutes. That the active atoms or molecules were clustered together in these solutions was shown in suitable cases by photographic registration of the spotty distribution of disintegration α rays. The size of the colloidal particles has been estimated from observed sedimentation rates on centrifugation, and it has been established that in some cases the phenomenon is one of adsorption of many of the active solute molecules or ions on particles of dust, silica, or the like, inevitably present even in "pure" water. The general adsorption phenomena are discussed in the following paragraphs. It should be remembered that effects of this sort, including adsorptions on container surfaces, filter paper, and so on, may be quite important in work at these very low "tracer" concentrations. The same effects, no doubt, occur in work at ordinary concentrations, but then the amount of material involved represents such a small fraction of the total amount that these effects are not noticed.

Coprecipitation and Adsorption. Many of the manipulations of ordinary chemistry and also of radiochemistry require precipitation reactions. How are substances at tracer concentrations to be separated by precipitation, when often the concentration is too small to exceed the solubility-product condition, and when the amount of precipitate even if formed would be quite imperceptible? Of course, if the radioactivity is isotopic with an element available in quantity, more of the element may be added in a suitable chemical form as a carrier, and then the chemical problems become ordinary ones. If necessary or if desirable, nonisotopic carriers may be tried. Microscopic amounts of radium in solution are brought down with barium in the precipitation of $BaSO_4$. Strontium ions have been carried by calcium salts, iodide ions by chloride precipitates, and so on. In some cases precipitates carry down active substances where the chemical similarities are not so obvious; for example, tracer lead (ThB) is well carried by ammonium dichromate crystals, and many active bodies are carried by $Fe(OH)_3$ precipitates. On the basis of a number of such observations K. Fajans in 1913 formulated this principle: the lower the solubility of the compound formed by the radioelement (as cation) with the anion of the precipitate, the greater the amount of radioelement carried with the precipitate. As an illustration, bismuth tracer is carried by $BaCO_3$ and $Fe(OH)_3$ but not by $BaSO_4$ or $PbSO_4$ from acid solutions. Lead tracer may be carried by all these, but is carried less well by AgCl, and is not carried by a nitron nitrate precipitate. Exceptions to this rule are not uncommon; ThB (a lead isotope) is not precipitated with HgI_2 or with cupric fumarate although both PbI_2 and lead fumarate are rather insoluble. The occurrence of carrying not predicted by this rule is widely observed even on the macroscale in analytical chemistry; for example, KNO_3 is appreciably coprecipitated with $BaSO_4$. Clearly factors in addition to that expressed in the Fajans rule are important in these phenomena.

It should be noticed that precipitates previously formed in the absence of tracer may take up a tracer when added in suspension to the tracer solution. This is the method of preformed precipitates. This procedure and an intermediate case between it and ordinary coprecipitation find convenient uses in radiochemical separations. For example, consider the carrying of radioactive yttrium by lanthanum fluoride; after a single precipitation of LaF_3 with excess HF a small fraction of the yttrium activity may remain in solution. Now, when more lanthanum is added to excess, a new precipitate of LaF_3 forms immediately, probably before the La^{+++} and Y^{+++} ions are well mixed. This precipitate may carry yttrium with it, but probably not so well as the first precipitate, or the third precipitate which may now be formed by addition of excess HF.

Hahn's Classification. O. Hahn in 1926 proposed a classification of carrying phenomena, distinguishing cases of true coprecipitation from cases of surface adsorption. The four principal types of carrying which he described are (1) isomorphous replacement, (2) surface adsorption, (3) anomalous mixed crystals, and (4) internal adsorption. In discussing these we will give most emphasis to the first two; the others are not so well understood.

1. *Isomorphous Replacement.* If the carrying ion and the ion carried form with the precipitating ion isomorphous crystalline compounds, coprecipitation of this type is to be expected. The radioelement is distributed throughout the precipitate crystals as may be shown by a radioautograph technique, and the mechanism is simply one of replacement at normal ion sites in the crystal lattice. This true coprecipitation is not much affected by conditions during precipitation such as acidity, order of addition of reagents, rate of crystallization, and temperature; and repeated washing of the precipitate cannot remove the coprecipitated substance. The precipitation of radium with barium salts is an example of this class of carrying.

2. *Surface Adsorption.* Freshly formed precipitate crystals with large surface areas may be capable of adsorbing radioelements effectively. For this type of carrying the Fajans rule is significant, but also another important factor is the surface charge on the precipitate relative to the ionic charge of the tracer substance. Because important adsorption occurs only when these charges are of opposite sign, experimental factors affecting the surface charge of the precipitate strongly influence the carrying, and this type is recognized by sensi-

tivity to such factors as acidity, order of addition of reagents, and physical state of subdivision of the precipitate. In many instances an appreciable part of the adsorbed activity may be washed off, or displaced by another ion of similar charge. The carrying of ThB (a lead isotope) at tracer concentrations by $CaSO_4$ or AgBr, and of Ra by Ag_2CrO_4 are examples. Table 11-1 shows the importance of excess

TABLE 11-1

CARRYING OF ThB BY $CaSO_4$

Excess Ca^{++} (%)	Excess $SO_4^{=}$ (%)	ThB Carried (%)
600		1.7
10		5.2
	5	88
	900	98

of the anion, necessary to produce a negative surface charge on the precipitate crystals, for the carrying of cations.

3. *Anomalous Mixed Crystals.* A type of carrying which at least superficially closely resembles isomorphous replacement is observed in a number of cases where true isomorphism is unexpected and even unlikely. An example is the carrying, in a manner hardly affected by precipitate surface charges, of RaB or RaD (lead isotopes) by $BaCl_2 \cdot 2H_2O$; these crystals are monoclinic, but $PbCl_2$ in macroscopic amounts crystallizes in the rhombic system. The capacity of barium chloride for lead ions has been found to be limited to about 0.1 mol per cent lead in the crystals.

4. *Internal Adsorption.* There are some cases of carrying that do not fit into any of the three types already discussed and are characterized by a spotty distribution of tracer within the precipitate crystals as shown by radioautographs. These cases may not be very numerous and seem to be associated with very poor carrying. For example, although lead tracer is carried in an anomalous mixed crystal by barium chloride, it is carried only very slightly by barium bromide; the small fraction of ThB that is carried is distributed in spots and patches scattered through the barium bromide crystals.

In addition to these four types Hahn considers the mechanical inclusion in precipitate crystal masses of radiocolloids that might exist in the solution, and inclusion of portions of the mother liquor itself.

Doerner-Hoskins and Berthelot-Nernst Distributions. For true coprecipitation of the isomorphous-replacement type, and apparently also of the anomalous-mixed-crystal type, the progress of crystal separation and the detailed distribution of the active tracer within the precipitate crystals may tend to approach either of two limiting laws. For the assumption that the precipitate crystals grow progressively, with equilibrium conditions maintained between the solution and the crystallizing layer, and with both re-solution and solid-diffusion effects negligible, a quantitative treatment is easily made. Let x and y be the amounts of the two substances X and Y precipitated before a given instant, and let a and b be the total amounts of X and Y; then

$$\frac{dx}{dy} = \lambda \frac{a - x}{b - y},$$

where λ is a constant characteristic of the system. In words, the ratio of X to Y in the forming surface layer is proportional to the ratio of the respective concentrations still remaining in the solution. On integration,

$$\log \frac{a}{a - x} = \lambda \log \frac{b}{b - y};$$

this is the logarithmic distribution law derived by H. A. Doerner and W. M. Hoskins. There is evidence that it is closely approached in many actual coprecipitations; it is found especially for precipitations produced by gradual evaporation with care to avoid any supersaturation, and for precipitations from supersaturated solutions that are vigorously stirred and quickly separated (filtered).

If for any reason the entire crystal rather than just the surface layer is brought into equilibrium with the solution, the differential equation just given should be replaced by a similar nondifferential expression:

$$\frac{x}{y} = D \frac{a - x}{b - y}.$$

Here the ratio of X to Y in the crystals is proportional to the ratio of X to Y left in solution; this is the Berthelot-Nernst homogeneous distribution law applicable to partition of a solute between liquid phases. Coprecipitations made from strongly supersaturated solutions and coprecipitations in which a finely divided precipitate is left standing in contact with the solution are likely to approach this distribution law. In the first case failure to maintain equilibrium between the growing crystals, the immediately surrounding solution, and the bulk of the solution seems to be involved; in the other re-solution and recrystallization probably play an important role.

Other Chemical Properties. Studies in the tracer concentration region have been made of partition between solvents, volatility, electrochemistry, and behavior in ion-exchange columns. To a large extent these have been in connection with the separation of carrier-free radioactivities and from this point of view have been discussed in chapter 4, section D. Here we make a few additional remarks on the implications of these experiments with regard to the chemical properties involved. In the partition of active solutes between two immiscible liquid phases, any deviation from the Berthelot-Nernst distribution law, if it is not due to a gross change in the composition or ionic strength, may be attributed to the existence of the solute in different states of aggregation in the two phases. For example, in an ether extraction, if the solute is a monomer in water and a dimer in ether, the distribution coefficient (concentration in ether divided by concentration in water) must change in direct proportion to the aqueous concentration. In the same way, all chemical equilibria are affected by dilution. On extreme dilution a molecule such as I_2 must eventually become unstable with respect to monomeric forms,

$$I_2 = 2I, \quad \text{or}$$

$$I_2 + H_2O = H^+ + I^- + HIO, \text{ etc.}$$

Oxidation-reduction potentials involving monomeric and dimeric, etc., forms must change on dilution, with possibly surprising results at tracer concentrations.

The electrochemical deposition potentials of some tracers have been measured for the extremely low concentrations; the cathode potential (measured with respect to a suitable auxiliary reference electrode) necessary for the deposition of the tracer is interpreted as analogous to the decomposition potential. These data, and also simple displacement experiments, give means of locating the trace substance in the electromotive series and permit approximate evaluation of the standard electrode potential, provided that proper account is taken of the large shifts in emf caused by the extremely low ion concentrations.

Tracer ions in a solution between electrodes move in a direction determined by their charge, and the rough average sign of charge is revealed by observation of the net average transport of the tracer. In simple cases some information on the magnitude of the charge can be obtained by a careful quantitative study.

E. HOT-ATOM CHEMISTRY

Szilard-Chalmers Process. In 1934 L. Szilard and T. A. Chalmers showed that after the neutron irradiation of ethyl iodide most of the iodine activity formed could be extracted from the ethyl iodide with water; they used a small amount of iodine carrier, reduced it to I^-, and finally precipitated AgI. Evidently the iodine-carbon bond was broken when an I^{127} nucleus was transformed by neutron capture to I^{128}. This type of process has since been used to concentrate the products of a number of n, γ reactions, and of some γ, n; $n, 2n$; and d, p reactions. It is referred to as the Szilard-Chalmers process. Three conditions have to be fulfilled to make a Szilard-Chalmers separation possible. The radioactive atom in the process of its formation must be broken loose from its molecule; it must neither recombine with the molecular fragment from which it separated, nor rapidly interchange with inactive atoms in other target molecules; and a chemical method for the separation of the target compound from the radioactive material in its new chemical form must be available.

Most chemical bond energies are in the range of 1 to 5 ev (20,000 to 100,000 cal per mole). In any nuclear reaction involving heavy particles either entering or leaving the nucleus with energies in excess of 10 or 100 kev the kinetic energy imparted to the residual nucleus far exceeds the magnitude of bond energies.[3] In thermal-neutron capture, where the Szilard-Chalmers method has its most important applications, the incident neutron does not impart nearly enough energy to the nucleus to cause any bond rupture. But neutron capture is almost always followed by γ-ray emission, and the nucleus receives some recoil energy in this process. A γ ray of energy E_γ has a momentum $p_\gamma = E_\gamma/c$. To conserve momentum the recoiling atom must have an identical momentum, and, therefore, the recoil energy $E_r = p_\gamma{}^2/2M = E_\gamma{}^2/2Mc^2$, where M is the mass of the atom. For M in atomic mass units and the energies in millions of electron volts we have

$$E_r = \frac{E_\gamma{}^2}{1862\,M}. \tag{11-2}$$

Table 11-2 shows values of E_r for a few values of E_γ and M. Neutron capture usually excites a nucleus to about 6 or 8 Mev, and a large

[3] For reactions other than n, γ, particularly for d, p reactions, the Szilard-Chalmers technique is less useful because the energy dissipated by the incident radiation in the target is so great that many inactive molecules are also disrupted.

TABLE 11-2

RECOIL ENERGIES IN ELECTRON VOLTS IMPARTED TO NUCLEI BY GAMMA RAYS OF VARIOUS ENERGIES

M	E_γ = 2 Mev	E_γ = 4 Mev	E_γ = 6 Mev
20	107	430	967
50	43	172	387
100	21	86	193
150	14	57	129
200	11	43	97

fraction of this excitation energy is dissipated by the emission of one or more γ rays. Unless all the successive γ rays emitted in a given capture process have low energies (say below 1 or 2 Mev), which is a relatively rare occurrence, the recoiling nucleus receives more than sufficient energy for the rupture of one or more bonds. Of course, it is not the entire recoil energy but something more like its component in the direction of a bond that should be compared with the bond energy; furthermore, the momenta of several γ rays emitted in cascade and in different directions may partially cancel each other. There is no evidence that two capture γ rays in cascade are preferentially emitted in opposite directions, and momentum cancelation is, therefore, hardly expected to reduce the probability of bond rupture by a very large factor. In most n, γ processes the probability of rupture is certainly very high.

The second condition for the operation of the Szilard-Chalmers method requires at least that *thermal* exchange be slow between the radioactive atoms in their new chemical state and the inactive atoms in the target compound. The energetic recoil atoms may undergo exchange more readily than atoms of ordinary thermal energies. These exchange reactions and other reactions of the high-energy recoil atoms, called "hot atoms," determine to a large extent the separation efficiencies obtainable in Szilard-Chalmers processes. Hot-atom reactions are considered further after a discussion of some examples of Szilard-Chalmers separations.

The largest amount of work in the field of Szilard-Chalmers separations has been done on halogen compounds. Many different organic halides (including CCl_4, $C_2H_4Cl_2$, C_2H_5Br, $C_2H_2Br_2$, C_6H_5Br, CH_3I) have been irradiated, and the products of neutron capture reactions (Cl^{38}, Br^{80}, Br^{82}, I^{128}) removed by various techniques. Extraction with water, either with or without added halogen or halide carrier, results in rather efficient separations. Yields are often improved, especially in the case of iodine, by extraction with an aqueous solution of a reducing agent such as HSO_3^-. Nearly complete extraction of activity has been reported in some cases when carrier was present. In the absence of carrier, yields of 50 per cent and large concentration factors have been found. In an interesting study, the yields of extractable iodine in d, p; $n, 2n$; γ, n; and n, γ activations of ethyl iodide were shown to be the same when other conditions were kept the same. Similar results were found with methyl iodide. This demonstrates that the chemical effects which determine the eventual fate of the active atom are rather independent of the initial recoil energy. Methods which have been used for the removal of the active halogen from irradiated organic halides include adsorption on activated charcoal (with 30 or 40 per cent yields of halogen without added carrier) and collection on charged plates (with up to 70 per cent yields of halogen without added carrier).

Szilard-Chalmers separations of halogens with 70 to 100 per cent yields have been obtained in neutron irradiations of solid or dissolved chlorates, bromates, iodates, perchlorates, and periodates; from these the active halogen can be removed as silver halide after addition of halide ion carrier. Szilard-Chalmers separations based on differences in oxidation state before and after the neutron capture have been successful for a number of other elements. About half the P^{32} activity formed in neutron irradiation of phosphates (solid or in solution) is found in +3 phosphorus. Most of the Mn^{56} activity can be removed from neutron-irradiated neutral or acid permanganate solutions in the form of MnO_2. Tellurium and selenium activities can be concentrated through the separation of tellurite or selenite carrier from irradiated tellurate or selenate solution by reduction of the lower oxidation state to the element with SO_2 (reduction of the +6 state proceeds much more slowly than of the +4 state). Similarly a Szilard-Chalmers separation for arsenic has been reported by the addition of arsenite carrier to irradiated arsenate solution and precipitation of As_2S_3. Reduction to the metal has been found to occur in the neutron capture of gold in various compounds. Whether or not an active element can be successfully isolated in a different oxidation state from the bombarded compound depends not only on the relative stabilities of the two oxidation states but also on the speed of exchange between them under the conditions of the experiment.

Collection of charged fragments on electrodes has been used successfully for a number of Szilard-Chalmers separations. Arsenic activity has been separated by this method from arsine gas with yields up to 34 per cent. Deposition occurs on both positive and negative electrodes in this case.

The bombardment of metal-organic compounds and complex salts is often useful for Szilard-Chalmers separations if the free metal ion does not exchange with the compound, and if the two are separable. Some of the compounds which have been used successfully are cacodylic acid, $(CH_3)_2AsOOH$, from which As^{76} can be separated as silver arsenite in 95 per cent yield; copper salicylaldehyde *o*-phenylene diamine, from which as much as 97 per cent of the Cu^{64} activity can be removed as Cu^{++} ion; uranyl benzoylacetonate, $UO_2(C_6H_5COCHCOCH_3)_2$, from which U^{239} activity has been extracted in about 10 per cent yield. It has been suggested that metal ion complexes which exist in optically active forms and do not racemize rapidly may be generally suitable for Szilard-Chalmers processes because the metal ion in such a complex is not expected to exchange rapidly with free metal ion in solution. Some complexes of this type have been used successfully, for example, the triethylenediamine nitrates of iridium, platinum, rhodium, and cobalt, $Ir(NH_2CH_2CH_2NH_2)_3(NO_3)_3$, etc.

Chemistry of Recoil Atoms. The highly excited recoil atoms resulting from neutron-capture reactions have been shown to undergo various types of chemical reactions. One of these is recombination with the fragment from which the "hot" atom had broken away. Insofar as it occurs, such recombination increases the retention of the activity, retention being defined as the fraction of the active atoms not separable from the target compound. By means of retention studies recombination reactions have been shown to be more probable in the liquid than in the gas phase, and often more probable in the solid than in the liquid phase. For example, in liquid ethyl bromide the retention of bromine activity was found to be 75 per cent, and in ethyl bromide vapor (390 mm partial pressure with 370 mm of air) only 4.5 per cent. Retention has been shown to decrease markedly when the target substance is diluted. For example, the retention of bromine activity is about 60 per cent in solid carbon tetrabromide, about 28 per cent in an alcohol solution containing 1.15 mol per cent CBr_4, and 0 ± 2 per cent in an alcohol solution containing 0.064 mol per cent CBr_4. These results have been interpreted as indicating that retention cannot be caused entirely by recombination of fragments (in a so-called reaction cage) but is at least in part brought about through replacement by recoil atoms of isotopic atoms in other molecules of the target substance.

It has been shown that in reacting with a molecule a "hot" atom may replace another atom or group. For example, after the slow-neutron irradiation of CH_3I, 11 per cent of the I^{128} activity was found in the form of CH_2I_2; furthermore, this result was shown to be temperature-independent between $-195°C$ and $15°C$, which proves that the substitution is not an ordinary thermal reaction. The formation of labeled CH_2Br_2 in the irradiation of $CH_2BrCOOH$, of labeled CH_3I and C_2H_5I in the irradiation of iodine dissolved in ethyl alcohol, and of labeled C_6H_5Br in the irradiation of aniline hydrobromide shows that the excited halogen atoms can replace such groups as $-COOH$, $-OH$, $-CH_2OH$, $-NH_2$, and probably many others. The yield of active atoms in one of these substitution products is usually less than about 10 per cent. Reactions of this type may be used to synthesize labeled compounds of high specific activity. The formation of C^{14}-labeled compounds in high specific activity by slow-neutron irradiation of nitrogenous materials has been demonstrated. For example, the formation of labeled anthracene in the neutron irradiation of acridine has been reported. The interpretation is that a small fraction of the "hot" C^{14} atoms formed by $N^{14}(n, p)$ reactions end up, after losing most of their kinetic energy in other collisions, by replacing nitrogen atoms in acridine to form anthracene.

Some hot-atom reactions have been studied in inorganic systems. The retention of activity in permanganate, phosphate, and arsenate in thermal-neutron irradiations has been determined under varying conditions of pH and concentration. The results have been interpreted by W. F. Libby on the basis of competition between hydration reactions and oxidation-reduction reactions for the hot atoms. For permanganate, for example, Libby found the retention to be practically independent of permanganate concentration in neutral and alkaline solution and concluded from this that the manganese in the primary recoil fragment is in the +7 oxidation state (MnO_3^+, MnO_2^{+++}, MnO^{+++++}, or $Mn^{+++++++}$). These species are then considered to undergo either hydration reactions, such as $MnO_3^+ + 2OH^- = MnO_4^- + H_2O$, or reduction by water, such as $4MnO_3^+ + 2H_2O = 4MnO_2 + 3O_2 + 4H^+$. At $pH \geq 12$ the retention is nearly 100 per cent, presumably because the hydration reactions strongly predominate. Below pH 12 the retention falls rapidly with decreasing pH and reaches a constant value of about 7 per cent for pH values between 8 and 2. According to Libby's interpretation the reduction by water is faster than hydration in neutral and acid solutions. At still higher acid concentrations the retention again rises slightly, perhaps because exchange reactions between the active MnO_3^+ and inactive MnO_4^- can then compete with reduction by water; in support of this Libby showed that in acid solutions the retention increases with permanganate concentration. It is interesting to note that in arsenate bombardments the retention is nearly 100 per cent over a wide pH range; here the hydration reactions apparently far outweigh the oxidation-reduction reactions with water. The phosphate experiments showed retentions of about 50 per cent under all conditions tried, which might possibly be taken to indicate that only about 50 per cent of the primary recoil fragments contain phosphorus in the +5 state. More recently extensive studies have been made of hot-atom reactions in solid potassium bromate, potassium chloriridate, triphenyl arsine, a number of iodates, and a series of compounds of trivalent and hexavalent chromium, both as solids and in solution.

Chemical Effects of Radioactive Decay. "Hot" atoms may result not only from nuclear reactions but also from radioactive decay processes. The chemistry of hot atoms formed as a result of β-decay processes has been studied in a number of cases. For example, reactions such as

$$TeO_3^{=} \rightarrow IO_3^{-} + \beta^{-} \quad \text{and} \quad MnO_4^{-} \rightarrow CrO_4^{=} + \beta^{+}$$

can occur in addition to molecular disruption leading to other forms. Of course, for these studies the nucleus resulting from the β decay must itself be radioactive if its fate is to be investigated.

In solutions hot-atom reactions are so complex that it is difficult to obtain quantitative information on the primary bond ruptures accompanying decay processes. This difficulty was avoided by R. Wolfgang, R. C. Anderson, and R. W. Dodson in a gas phase study of the chemical effects of C^{14} decay in ethane. High-specific-activity C^{14} was used to synthesize ethane, so that an appreciable fraction of the molecules were doubly labeled. Decay of one C^{14} in a doubly labeled ethane molecule should lead to C^{14}-labeled methylamine if the C-C bond remains intact or rather becomes a C-N bond. The experiment showed that indeed about 50 per cent of the bonds remained unbroken, and other possible explanations for the labeled methylamine were carefully eliminated. The result is in agreement with approximate quantum-mechanical calculations by M. Wolfsberg.

The chemistry of recoil atoms following isomeric transitions has been studied more than the hot-atom chemistry of other radioactive decay processes. It is perhaps not immediately clear why isomeric transitions may lead to bond rupture. The γ-ray energies in isomeric transitions are much lower than in neutron-capture processes, often below 100 kev and rarely above 500 kev. According to equation 11-2, a 100-kev γ ray would give a nucleus of mass 100 a recoil energy of only about 0.05 ev, which is not nearly enough to break a chemical bond. Although internal-conversion electron emission gives rise to roughly ten times greater recoil energy than γ emission at the same energy,[4] even this is not sufficient for bond rupture in most cases. However, the vacancy left in an inner electron shell by the internal conversion leads to electronic rearrangements and emission of Auger electrons. The atom is, therefore, in a highly excited state (and positively charged), and molecular dissociation may take place if the atom is bound in a molecule.[5]

Separations of nuclear isomers analogous to Szilard-Chalmers separations have been performed in a number of cases where the isomeric transition proceeds largely by conversion-electron emission. The 18-min Br^{80} has been separated from its parent, the 4.4-hr Br^{80m}, by a number of different methods analogous to the Szilard-Chalmers methods used for bromine. The lower states of Te^{121} (17 days), Te^{127} (9.3 hr), Te^{129} (72 min), and Te^{131} (25 min) have been separated as tellurite in good yield from tellurate solutions containing the corresponding upper isomeric states. Isomer separations are sometimes useful for the assignment of isomer activities and for the elucidation of genetic relationships. That the possibility of obtaining isomer separations depends on internal conversion was shown in experiments using the gaseous compounds $Te(C_2H_5)_2$ containing 115-day Te^{127m} and 33-day Te^{129m}, and $Zn(C_2H_5)_2$ containing the 13.8-hr isomer Zn^{69m}. The lower isomeric states of the tellurium isomers could be separated on the walls of the vessels or on charged plates, but under identical conditions no separation of the zinc isomers was obtained; the isomeric transition in Zn^{69} proceeds by an unconverted 435-kev γ ray, whereas the tellurium transitions have energies of only about 100 kev but are almost completely converted.

F. ARTIFICIALLY PRODUCED ELEMENTS

More than half a century ago the methods of chemistry conventional at that time had already reached a limit in the search for new and missing elements; discoveries since that time have depended on the introduction of new physical methods. Through studies of optical spectra the elements rubidium, cesium, indium, helium, and gallium

[4] In nonrelativistic approximation an atom of mass M receives a recoil energy $E_r = E_e(m/M)$ from a conversion electron of energy E_e.

[5] An experimental measurement of the charges of Xe^{131} atoms following isomeric transition of Xe^{131m} shows that on the average 8.5 electrons are lost. Similar measurements give +3.4 for the average charge of Cl^{37} atoms following electron capture in A^{37}. In both isomeric transitions and electron captures the high charges are believed to result largely from Auger processes. In $\beta-$ decay, atomic charges in the neighborhood of +1 have been reported.

were found. The first evidence for hafnium and rhenium came from X-ray spectra. Early investigations of the natural radioelements revealed the existence (often in extremely small amounts) of polonium (number 84), radon (86), radium (88), actinium (89), and protactinium (91), and more recently the missing element number 87 has been found in the same way. Through studies of nuclear reactions and artificially induced radioactivities the elements 43, 61, and 85 have been identified, and elements 93, 94, 95, 96, 97, 98, 99, and 100 have been added to the periodic chart. In this section we shall discuss briefly the discoveries of the last twelve elements mentioned.

Technetium. In 1925 W. Noddack, I. Tacke, and O. Berg found the new element rhenium through its X-ray spectrum, and reported that in sulfide concentrates of several ores they observed a faint X-ray line also that corresponded to the lighter homolog of rhenium, the missing element 43; they proposed for it the name masurium, symbol Ma. The element could not be concentrated, and the work has not been verified.

C. Perrier and E. Segrè working in Italy isolated and studied radioactive isotopes of element 43 from an old molybdenum deflector plate of the Berkeley 37-in. cyclotron. These were long-lived electron-capture activities, produced through d, n reactions by the deuteron beam. Perrier and Segrè gave this element the name technetium, symbol Tc, derived from the Greek word meaning "artificial."

It now appears quite unlikely that the element technetium exists in nature in stable form, since all mass numbers from 94 to 102 are occupied by stable isotopes of one or both of the neighboring elements molybdenum and ruthenium. However, recent spectroscopic evidence indicates the existence of technetium in certain types of stars (and probably in the sun). Since formation of technetium near the surfaces of these stars is considered most unlikely and diffusion from the interior is believed to be exceedingly slow, the isotope or isotopes of technetium responsible for the stellar spectral lines must be very long-lived, probably with a half-life of at least 10^8 years. It is then possible that long-lived radioactive technetium in very small abundance exists naturally on the earth, and a number of searches in various ores for such naturally occurring technetium have been undertaken. According to nuclear systematics Tc^{97} and Tc^{98} are the likely candidates. One of the most promising techniques in the search for traces of technetium, particularly Tc^{98}, is activation analysis; neutron irradiation followed by isolation and identification of 6-hr Tc^{99m} would constitute good evidence for Tc^{98}, provided that the absence of molybdenum in the sample is established since Tc^{99m} can also be formed by neutron capture in Mo^{98} followed by β^- decay of Mo^{99}.

In their early studies, Perrier and Segrè compared the chemical behavior of technetium tracer with that of several carrier substances which might be guessed to be chemically similar, particularly manganese and rhenium, because technetium falls between these in subgroup VII of the periodic table. They found the stability of the +7 oxidation state to be greater than for manganese and less than for rhenium, as expected. Technetium was carried by a precipitate of Re_2S_7 on addition of H_2S to HCl solutions up to 6 normal; the technetium seemed to concentrate somewhat in the solution on partial precipitation, which suggests a greater solubility for Tc_2S_7, although this evidence taken alone is subject to other interpretations. Precipitates of MnO_2 and $Mn(OH)_2$ did not carry technetium unless strong reducing agents were present. $KReO_4$ and $CsReO_4$ did carry the tracer, and the insolubility of the technetium compound seemed to be less than that of the perrhenate for the potassium salts and greater for the cesium salts. Nitron perrhenate was found to carry technetium quantitatively. The technetium tracer volatilized completely in air at about 300°C, probably as an oxide; technetium chloride formed from Tc_2S_7 plus Cl_2 volatilized at 100°C. Technetium may be separated from molybdenum by precipitation of the latter with 8-hydroxyquinoline. It may be separated from ruthenium by volatility of technetium chloride or by distillation of RuO_4 from perchloric acid solution. It may be freed of rhenium by volatilization of the rhenium at about 180°C in dry hydrogen chloride, by fractional crystallization of $KReO_4$, or by precipitation of Re_2S_7 from 10 *N* HCl. It may be volatilized from niobium in oxygen at a high temperature.

At this time sixteen activities have been established for technetium isotopes. Perhaps most interesting is the lower isomeric state of Tc^{99}; it has a half-life of about 2×10^5 years and may be produced in quantity in a chain reactor. It is currently priced at $35 per milligram. Its chemical properties have now been investigated at macroconcentrations and found to agree well with the indications given by the tracer experiments. Chemically the new element is similar to rhenium. Its oxidation potentials in acid solution are given by J. W. Cobble, W. T. Smith, Jr., and G. E. Boyd:

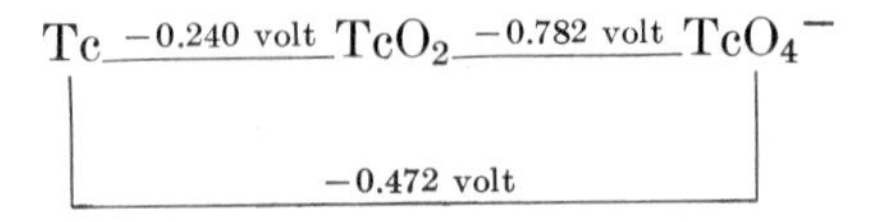

Pertechnetate ion TcO_4^- is slightly colored, appearing yellow or pink according to concentration, and crystals of $HTcO_4$ are dark red. A light yellow oxide Tc_2O_7 is formed by ignition of technetium in oxygen. The sulfide Tc_2S_7 precipitated from 4 *f* H_2SO_4 is dark brown and highly insoluble. Technetium metal has been prepared and found by X-ray diffraction to be in the hexagonal close-packed arrangement, isomorphous with rhenium, with density 11.49 g cm^{-3}.

Promethium. In 1926 several groups of researchers reported evidence based on optical and X-ray spectral lines for the existence of element 61 in various minerals and rare-earth concentrates. The names of these workers included J. A. Harris, B. S. Hopkins, and L. F. Yntema; L. Rolla and L. Fernandes; and J. M. Cork, C. James, and H. C. Fogg. Names for the element proposed in this period were illinium, Il, by Hopkins, and florentium by Rolla. If the element actually exists in nature in stable form and is detectable by methods then used, it is rather surprising that higher concentrations have not been prepared. Arguments similar to those stated in the case of technetium (β-stable isotopes of Nd and Sm at all mass numbers from 142 to 150) make it very unlikely that a stable isotope of element 61 exists. About 1941 and shortly thereafter workers at Ohio State University, including H. B. Law, M. L. Pool, J. D. Kurbatov, and L. L. Quill, and later C. S. Wu and Segrè in Berkeley obtained from cyclotron bombardments several activities which were attributed to isotopes of the missing element; however, the certainty of this interpretation was not positively established. Pool and Quill proposed for the element the name cyclonium, symbol Cy. The fission of uranium produces several radioactive isotopes of element 61, and these have been investigated and definitely characterized by workers at Oak Ridge, including C. D. Coryell, J. A. Marinsky, and L. E. Glendenin. They were able to concentrate the tracer activities by the ion-exchange resin adsorption and elution technique. Their discovery is responsible for the name of the element, promethium, symbol Pm. Many milligrams of Pm^{147}, a β emitter of 2.6 years half-life, have been isolated, and visible amounts of pink promethium salts have been exhibited. An even longer-lived isotope, 30-year Pm^{145}, has been reported.

Astatine. Isotopes of element 85 have been claimed and fairly well identified by their radiations as very short-lived branch products in the radium and thorium series, formed from RaA and ThA by β decay in a very small fraction of the disintegrations (the normal mode is α decay for both). F. Allison claimed in 1931 that this element had been observed as a natural substance by the magneto-optic technique. However, the first quite definite demonstration of element 85 was given by D. R. Corson, K. R. Mackenzie, and Segrè; they produced a radioactive isotope 85^{211} by the $\alpha, 2n$ reaction on Bi^{209}, using 30-Mev helium ions from the then newly completed 60-in. cyclotron in Berkeley. The half-life is 7.5 hr, and the decay is 40 per cent by α emission and 60 per cent by electron capture. Corson, Mackenzie, and Segrè proposed the name astatine, symbol At, derived from the Greek word meaning "unstable." About 20 astatine isotopes are now known, but the longest half-life found is that of At^{210}, 8.3 hr. Recently At^{219}, of 0.9 min half-life, has been chemically identified as a very rare branch product in the actinium series.

Astatine is the halogen just heavier than iodine, and its chemical properties make a very interesting study. Because of the short half-life macroscopic quantities may not be accumulated, but tracer studies by G. L. Johnson, R. F. Leininger, and Segrè have given information which we may summarize. The element is separated from bismuth, from which it is formed, and from simultaneously produced radioactive polonium by its volatility from molten bismuth in vacuum. The free element is quite volatile, particularly from a glass surface, even at room temperature. It has a rather specific affinity for metallic silver surfaces even at 325°C. The free element exists in aqueous solution (presumably as At_2 or possibly At) and usually is partly lost on evaporation of acidic solutions. The free element is readily extracted from water solutions into benzene or carbon tetrachloride very much like iodine. It may not be extracted from alkaline solution, again like iodine.

Astatine may be reduced by SO_2 or by zinc, but not by ferrous ion, almost certainly to the -1 oxidation state. This ion is precipitated with AgI or TlI from acidic or basic solutions. Cold concentrated nitric acid seems to oxidize elemental astatine only slowly. It is oxidized by bromine, and to some extent by ferric ion, to some positive oxidation state (possibly AtO^-). This state is shown by migration experiments to be an anion; it can hardly be AtO_3^- since it is not carried by a precipitate of $AgIO_3$. With HClO or hot $S_2O_8^=$ as oxidizing agent a different anion results; this is carried by $AgIO_3$ and may be AtO_3^-.

Francium. In 1914 F. Paneth observed some α-particle emission from $_{89}Ac^{227}$, which decays mostly by β emission to RdAc. In 1939 M. Perey observed the daughter produced in the 1 per cent α branch and called the isotope of element 87 so produced AcK. This body decays by β emission (to AcX); the half-life is 21 min. Mlle. Perey has proposed the name francium, symbol Fr, for the new element. Its chemical properties appear to be as expected from its position in the periodic table in group I below cesium. It is carried by $CsClO_4$ or Cs_2PtCl_6 and also by the analogous rubidium salts. Although the corresponding sodium and potassium salts apparently crystallize in the same crystal systems (rhombic for the perchlorates and cubic for the chloroplatinates), these do not carry francium effectively, presumably because of the great differences in ionic radii. Another isotope of francium may be formed in a rare α-particle branching of $MsTh_2$ (Ac^{228}), but this product has not been observed. A number of francium isotopes have been produced artificially, but Fr^{223} (AcK) remains the longest-lived isotope known.

Transuranium Elements. When Fermi and his group in Rome first exposed uranium to slow neutrons they observed a number of activities, and in the following few years many more active species were found to be produced; most of these were at that time assigned to transuranium elements. The assignments were made because the substances were transformed by successive β^- emissions which led to higher Z values, and because they could be shown by chemical tests to be different from all the known elements in the neighborhood of uranium in the periodic chart. This situation was resolved in the discovery by Hahn and F. Strassman that these activities could be identified with known elements much lighter than uranium and that, therefore, the neutrons produce fission of the uranium nuclei. Further investigation of the fission process and products led to the proof by E. M. McMillan and P. Abelson that one of the activities, the one with 2.3 days half-life, could not be a product of fission and was actually the daughter of the 23-min β-particle-emitting U^{239} which resulted from $U^{238}(n,\gamma)U^{239}$. Also, they devised a procedure for separating chemically the element 93 tracer from all known elements through an oxidation-reduction cycle, with bromate as the oxidizing agent in acid solution, and with a rare-earth fluoride precipitate as carrier for the reduced state. They gave the name neptunium, symbol Np, to the new element, taking the name from Neptune, the planet next beyond Uranus in the solar system.

At the present time eleven isotopes of neptunium are known, with half-lives of a few minutes to 2.20×10^6 years (for α-active Np^{237}). Both Np^{239} discovered by McMillan and Abelson and Np^{238} from $\alpha,p3n$ or $d,2n$ reactions on U^{238} emit β particles and lead to known isotopes of element 94, very naturally named plutonium after Pluto (a planet beyond Neptune), with symbol Pu. These isotopes, Pu^{238}

and Pu^{239}, are moderately long-lived α emitters first studied by McMillan, Seaborg, Segrè, Wahl, and Kennedy; Pu^{239} is distinguished for its practical usefulness in slow- and fast-neutron fission. Another isotope, Pu^{241}, decays with a half-life of about 13 years by β^- emission to produce Am^{241}, an isotope of the element 95, named americium with symbol Am. This americium isotope has a half-life of 470 years and emits α particles. By an n, γ reaction Am^{241} is converted to Am^{242m}, a β-emitting 16-hr isotope; this decays to the isotope of curium, Cm^{242}. This last substance emits α particles and has a half-life of 162 days; it is formed also by the reaction $Pu^{239}(\alpha, n)Cm^{242}$. Many other isotopes have been prepared and are listed in appendix G. The longest-lived isotopes of plutonium, americium, and curium (Pu^{242}, 5×10^5y; Pu^{244}, $> 10^7$y; Am^{243}, 8.8×10^3y; Cm^{245}, 1.2×10^4y; Cm^{246}, 4×10^3y) have mass numbers so much larger than uranium that they are very difficult to prepare in quantity.

The chemical properties of these transuranium elements—neptunium, plutonium, americium, and curium—have been studied first at tracer concentrations and later by ultramicrochemical techniques. At the present time Pu^{239} exists in quantity, Np^{237} has been isolated to the extent of hundreds of milligrams, Am^{241} has been isolated on a microscale, and a very small amount of Cm^{242} has been isolated. Much of the work has been done in Seaborg's laboratory, at the University of Chicago Metallurgical Project and at the University of California Radiation Laboratory; the elements americium and curium were discovered by Seaborg, R. A. James, L. O. Morgan, and A. Ghiorso.

Four transcurium elements have been discovered but so far have been produced only in tracer amounts. In 1949 and 1950 S. G. Thompson, K. Street, Ghiorso, and Seaborg carried out helium-ion bombardments of very small amounts of Am^{241} and Cm^{242} in the Berkeley 60-in. cyclotron. By $\alpha, 2n$ reactions isotopes of elements 97 and 98 were produced. These elements were named berkelium, Bk, and californium, Cf. In 1954 reports [6] appeared announcing the production of element 99, both by reaction of accelerated

[6] Delays in publication due to national security regulations at this moment make the history of this subject obscure. The groups that have reported so far are G. R. Choppin, Ghiorso, B. G. Harvey, G. B. Rossi, and Thompson (Berkeley); H. Diamond, P. R. Fields, A. M. Friedman, J. R. Huizenga, L. B. Magnusson, J. F. Mech, G. Pyle, P. A. Sellers, C. M. Stevens, and M. H. Studier (Argonne Laboratory); and more recently H. Atterling, W. Forsling, L. W. Holm, L. Melander, and B. Astrom (Stockholm).

$(N^{14})^{++++++}$ ions with U^{238} and by many successive neutron captures and β decays with Pu^{239} as starting material. The latter method has also yielded two isotopes of element 100, and a third has been reported as a result of oxygen-ion bombardment of uranium. To date five isotopes of element 99 and three isotopes of element 100 have been assigned to mass numbers from 246 to 255; of these 99^{253} is a 19-day α emitter, and 100^{254} is a 3.3-hr α emitter with about one spontaneous fission per 1500 α disintegrations. The production of 100^{254} from Pu^{239} requires 15 successive neutron capture reactions and was carried out in the intense neutron flux of the Materials Testing Reactor at Arco, Idaho. The only information available on the chemical properties of elements 99 and 100 concerns their elution from ion-exchange columns.

Actinide Series. The transuranium elements (at least through californium) and uranium and thorium all have similar precipitation properties when in the same oxidation state; they differ principally in the ease of formation and in the existence of the various oxidation states. Seaborg has advanced the hypothesis, and with considerable evidence, that a new rare-earth series begins with actinium (number 89), with the $5f$ electron orbitals being filled in subsequent elements. This would be analogous to the lanthanide rare-earth series beginning with lanthanum (number 57), with the $4f$ orbitals filling in the next fourteen elements. Some of the evidence for this actinide series may be seen in these facts: (1) actinium is chemically similar to lanthanum; (2) thorium is similar to cerium in the +4 state; (3) the ease of removal of more than three electrons decreases from uranium to curium. (Approximate oxidation potentials for uranium, neptunium, plutonium, and americium are given in table 11-3.) There is additional evidence for the second rare-earth series from spectroscopic and crystal-structure data, from magnetic susceptibilities, and from ion-exchange elution sequences.

It does seem evident that this new series differs from the familiar rare-earth series in that the resemblance of successive elements is less than for the lanthanide series. The lanthanide earths are for the most part separable only by multiple fractionation processes, or better by adsorption and elution from ion-exchange resins. The elements from 89 to 95 are separable by oxidation-reduction processes, but the separation of 95, 96, 97, 98, 99, and 100 is best done with an ion-exchange column. On the actinide hypothesis, curium, by analogy to gadolinium, is expected to resist oxidation or reduction in the +3 state, because the $5f^7$ and $4f^7$ structures, with one electron in each of the

TABLE 11-3

OXIDATION POTENTIALS (IN VOLTS) OF URANIUM, NEPTUNIUM, PLUTONIUM, AND AMERICIUM IONS

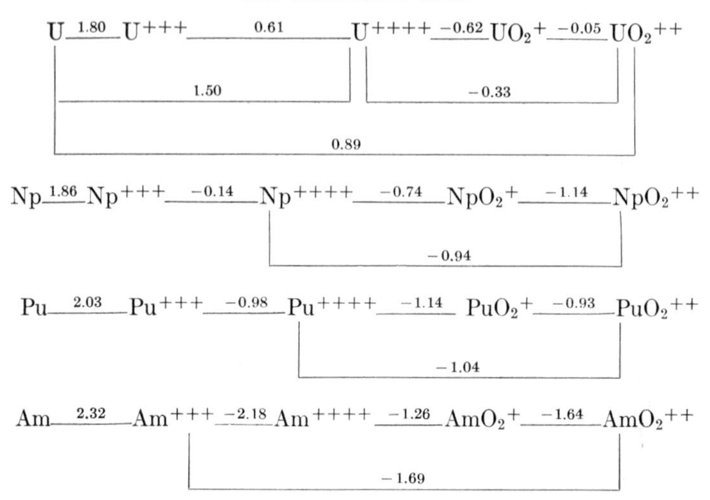

seven f orbitals, are particularly stable. Actually no state of curium other than $+3$ has been observed in solution. Americium, by analogy to europium, should be reducible to a $+2$ state. Berkelium, with the configuration $5f^8$, might be oxidized by powerful oxidizing agents from the ordinary Bk^{+++} to Bk^{++++}; the potential of this couple is about -1.6 volts. Actually, it is on the basis of these analogies between the actinides and the lanthanides that the names for 95, 96, and 97 were suggested: curium for Pierre and Marie Curie, americium for the Americas, and berkelium, of course, for Berkeley.

Some of the difficulties in work with substances like Cm^{242} may be mentioned here, difficulties in addition to those naturally associated with work on the ultramicrochemical scale. The heavy short-lived α emitters are extremely dangerous as radioactive poisons, and amounts of the order of a few micrograms taken into the body may produce harmful effects. Also, the high level of α radiation in concentrated samples can be expected to have some effect on chemical reactions; notice that a Cm^{242} preparation glows in the dark. In fact the rate of energy release is so great that if cooling effects are neglected it may be estimated that a 0.1 molar Cm^{242} solution would begin to boil in about 15 sec and reach dryness in about 2 min. The more recently discovered longer-lived isotopes will make it possible to minimize these difficulties.

EXERCISES

1. Would you expect almost complete exchange, and by what mechanism, in 1 hr at room temperature, between the members of each of the following pairs?

(*a*) Hg^{++}, very finely divided Hg (*b*) $Cr^*O_4^=$, CrO_2^-
(*c*) $Cr^*O_4^=$, $Cr_2O_7^=$ (*d*) CH_3I^*, C_6H_5I
(*e*) $Hg^*(CH_3)_2$, $Hg(C_2H_5)_2$ (*f*) H_2O^*, H_2SeO_3

2. Refer to the information on fumaric acid oxidation on page 319. The authors of that report (M. B. Allen and S. Ruben) in the experiment measured the specific activities of the original fumaric acid, the CO_2 evolved, and the formic acid remaining. If the C^{11} activity of the original acid had been 20,000 counts min^{-1} mg^{-1} of carbon at 6:00 P.M., what would they have found for the specific activity of the CO_2 if measured at 7:22 P.M., and of the HCOOH if measured at 8:30 P.M.? What must have been the activity per milligram of carbon of the KC*N used to synthesize the fumaric acid from ethylene dichloride, corrected to 6:00 P.M.?

Answer to last part: 40,000 counts min^{-1} mg^{-1}.

3. Approximately what fraction of a gram of copper may be detected by the tracer method if the tracer copper (Cu^{64}) has been prepared by irradiation of copper with 14-Mev deuterons? See appendix E.

Answer: We estimate $\sim 10^{-12}$ g for a thick copper target, less for a thin one.

4. A mixture is to be assayed for penicillin. You add 10.0 mg of penicillin of specific activity 0.405 μc mg^{-1} (possibly prepared by biosynthesis). From this mixture you are able to isolate only 0.35 mg of pure crystalline penicillin, and you determine its specific activity to be 0.035 μc mg^{-1}. What was the penicillin content of the original sample?

5. The exchange between I_2^* and IO_3^- has been studied under these conditions: $(I_2) = 0.00050$ mole per liter (formal), $(HIO_3) = 0.00100$ formal, $(HClO_4) = 1.00$ formal, at 50°C. At specified times samples were taken and measured for total (I_2 plus IO_3^-) radioactivity by γ counting. These counting rates corrected to the time $t = 0$ on the basis of the 8.0-day half-life of I^{131} are given below in the column "Corrected total activity." The I_2 fractions were removed by extraction with CCl_4 and the residual (IO_3^-) radioactivity measured and corrected in the same way; these rates are in the column "Corrected IO_3^- activity."

Time (hours)	Corrected total activity	Corrected IO_3^- activity
0.9	1680	9.9 ± 3.0
19.1	1672	107 ± 4.1
47.3	1620	246 ± 6.6
92.8	1653	438 ± 9.4
169.2	1683	610 ± 13
"∞"	1640	819 ± 9.8

Find the half-time $T_{1/2}$ for the exchange and the rate **R** of the exchange reaction. *Answer:* $T_{1/2} = 90.6$ hr; $\mathbf{R} = 3.83 \times 10^{-6}$ mole $liter^{-1}$ hr^{-1}.

6. The experiment described in exercise 5 was repeated but with this difference, $(I_2) = 0.00100$ formal. The results are tabulated as before.

Time (hours)	Corrected total activity	Corrected IO_3^- activity
0.9	1717	7.6 ± 2.7
19.1	1483	70.1 ± 3.6
47.3	1548	178 ± 5.2
92.8	1612	305 ± 7.3
169.2	1587	413 ± 9.8
"∞"	1592	534 ± 5.7

For these conditions find $T_{1/2}$ and **R**. What is the apparent order of the exchange reaction with respect to I_2? *Note:* Do not be surprised if the order is not an integer; according to O. E. Myers and Kennedy, *J. Am. Chem. Soc.* **72,** 897 (1950), the order is consistent with this rate law for the exchange-producing reaction: $\mathbf{R} = k(I^-)(H^+)^3(IO_3^-)^2$.

7. Estimate the sensitivity of the neutron activation method for the detection of (*a*) arsenic, (*b*) dysprosium with a thermal-neutron flux of 1×10^{11} cm^{-2} sec^{-1}.

8. Calculate the electrode potentials corresponding to these half-reactions at the specified concentrations:

(*a*) $Ag = Ag^+ + e^-$, with $(Ag^+) = 10^{-13}$ molar;
(*b*) $Al = Al^{+++} + 3e^-$, with $(Al^{+++}) = 10^{-15}$ molar;
(*c*) $2Hg = Hg_2^{++} + 2e^-$, with $(Hg_2^{++}) = 10^{-8}$ molar.
(*d*) Would the shift in emf in (*c*) continue to be proportional to the logarithm of the concentration of mercury ions in solution as that concentration was indefinitely reduced? *Answer:* (*a*) -0.031 v.

9. In analytical chemistry Fe^{+++} is used as an oxidizing agent to convert I^- to I_2. Would Fe^{+++} be suitable to oxidize a solution of (pure) I^{128}, concentration 0.004 μc ml^{-1}?

10. What is the recoil energy imparted to a Te^{129} atom by the emission of a 74-kev conversion electron? (Use the relativistic expression for the electron energy.) *Answer:* 0.34 ev.

11. What is the electrode potential for $Cu = Cu^{++} + 2e^-$ at a Cu^{++} concentration equal to exactly zero? What do you suppose would be the result if a pure copper electrode were immersed in absolutely pure water?

12. In an experiment on the crystallization of mixed radium-barium chlorides from supersaturated solutions the following data were obtained:

Percentage of radium remaining in solution	Percentage of barium remaining in solution
87.41	97.48
60.30	89.21
59.01	88.45
54.72	86.58
47.61	83.53
43.15	80.24

Do these fractional crystallizations obey the Doerner-Hoskins or the Berthelot-Nernst equations? Find λ or D.

13. Take the partition coefficient for the distribution of astatine between carbon tetrachloride and water as 100 at 10^{-10} molar for the nonaqueous phase. Furthermore, assume that the substance in carbon tetrachloride has the molecular formula At_2. What might you expect for this partition coefficient at 10^{-11} molar (nonaqueous phase) if the zero state in water at these concentrations is predominantly (*a*) At_2, (*b*) At, (*c*) $At^- + HAtO$, (*d*) $At_3^- + HAtO$, (*e*) $3\ At^- + AtO_2^-$? *Answer:* (*b*) 32.

14. In an experiment (by T. C. Hoering) bromate ion synthesized to contain 1.13 per cent O^{18} in its oxygen was reacted with excess sulfurous acid in ordinary water. The product sulfate was isolated, and its oxygen was found to contain 0.314 per cent O^{18}. What average number of the three oxygen atoms in BrO_3^- appeared in the $SO_4^=$? *Answer:* 1.4.

15. Suggest hopeful easily prepared compounds for use in Szilard-Chalmers processes of (*a*) iron, (*b*) mercury, (*c*) technetium.

REFERENCES

A. C. Wahl and N. A. Bonner (Editors), *Radioactivity Applied to Chemistry,* New York, John Wiley & Sons, 1951.

W. J. Whitehouse and J. L. Putman, *Radioactive Isotopes. An Introduction to Their Preparation, Measurement and Use,* Oxford, Clarendon Press, 1953.

R. R. Williams, *Principles of Nuclear Chemistry,* New York, D. Van Nostrand Co., 1950.

O. Hahn, *Applied Radiochemistry,* Ithaca, Cornell University Press, 1936.

M. D. Kamen, *Radioactive Tracers in Biology, an Introduction to Tracer Methodology,* 2nd ed., New York, Academic Press, 1951.

W. E. Siri, *Isotopic Tracers and Nuclear Radiations,* New York, McGraw-Hill Book Co., 1949.

G. T. Seaborg, "Artificial Radioactivity," *Chem. Revs.* **27,** 199 (1940).

M. Calvin, C. Heidelberger, J. C. Reid, B. M. Tolbert, and P. F. Yankwich, *Isotopic Carbon,* New York, John Wiley & Sons, 1949.

R. R. Edwards, "Isotopic Tracers in Chemical Systems," *Ann. Rev. Nuclear Sci.,* Vol. I, p. 301, Stanford, Annual Reviews Inc., 1952.

J. Bigeleisen, "Isotopes," *Ann. Rev. Nuclear Sci.,* Vol. II, p. 221, Stanford, Annual Reviews Inc., 1953.

G. A. Ropp and O. K. Neville, "A Review of the Uses of Isotopic Carbon in Organic Chemical Research," *Nucleonics* **9,** No. 2, 22 (August 1951).

J. H. Wang, "Self-Diffusion and Structure of Liquid Water," *J. Am. Chem. Soc.* **73,** 510 and 4181 (1951).

J. M. Nielsen, A. W. Adamson, and J. W. Cobble, "The Self-Diffusion Coefficients of the Ions in Aqueous Sodium Chloride and Sodium Sulfate at 25°," *J. Am. Chem. Soc.* **74,** 446 (1952).

J. T. Burwell, Jr., "Radioactive Tracers in Friction Studies," *Nucleonics* **1,** No. 4, 38 (December 1947).

J. P. Hunt and H. Taube, "The Exchange of Water between Aqueous Chromic Ion and Solvent," *J. Chem. Phys.* **18,** 757 (1950).

J. Halperin and H. Taube, "The Transfer of Oxygen Atoms in Oxidation-Reduction Reactions, III and IV," *J. Am. Chem. Soc.* **74,** 375 and 380 (1952).

H. Taube, "Rates and Mechanisms of Substitution in Inorganic Complexes in Solution," *Chem. Revs.* **50,** 69 (1952).

J. Hudis and A. C. Wahl, "The Kinetics of the Exchange Reactions between Iron (II) Ion and the Fluoride Complexes of Iron (III)," *J. Am. Chem. Soc.* **75,** 4153 (1953).

R. W. Dodson, "Salt and Acid Effects on the Thallous-Thallic Exchange Reaction," *J. Am. Chem. Soc.* **75,** 1795 (1953).

J. Bigeleisen, "The Validity of the Use of Tracers to Follow Chemical Reactions," *Science* **110,** 14 (1949).

P. E. Yankwich, "Isotope Effects in Chemical Reactions," *Ann. Rev. Nuclear Sci.,* Vol. III, p. 235, Stanford, Annual Reviews Inc., 1953.

"Symposium on Nucleonics and Analytical Chemistry," *Anal. Chem.* **21,** 318–368 (1949).

M. Inghram, "Stable Isotope Dilution as an Analytical Tool," *Ann. Rev. Nuclear Sci.,* Vol. IV, p. 81, Stanford, Annual Reviews Inc., 1954.

J. E. Hudgens, Jr., "Analytical Applications of Radiochemical Techniques," *Anal. Chem.* **24,** 1704 (1952).

M. L. Salutsky, J. G. Stites, Jr., and A. W. Martin, "Fractionation of Barium-Radium Mixtures as Chromates," *Anal. Chem.* **25,** 1677 and 1938 (1953).

M. Kahn and A. C. Wahl, "Some Observations of the Chemical Behavior of Iodine at Low Concentrations," *J. Chem. Phys.* **21,** 1185 (1953).

H. A. C. McKay, "The Szilard-Chalmers Process," *Progress in Nuclear Physics,* Vol. I (O. R. Frisch, Editor), London, Pergamon Press, 1950.

R. H. Schuler, "Chemical Effects of (d, p), $(n, 2n)$, and (γ, n) Activation of Iodine," *J. Chem. Phys.* **22,** 2026 (1954).

J. E. Willard, "Chemical Effects of Nuclear Transformations," *Ann. Rev. Nuclear Sci.,* Vol. III, p. 193, Stanford, Annual Reviews Inc., 1953.

A. G. Schrodt and W. F. Libby, "Direct Production of Radioactive Aliphatic Hydrocarbons by Pile Irradiation," *J. Am. Chem. Soc.* **76,** 3100 (1954).

A. P. Wolf and R. C. Anderson, "Radioactive Anthracene-C^{14} and Acridine-C^{14} from the Neutron Irradiation of Acridine," *J. Am. Chem. Soc.* **77,** 1608 (1955).

G. Harbottle, "Szilard-Chalmers Reaction in Crystalline Compounds of Chromium," *J. Chem. Phys.* **22,** 1083 (1954).

L. M. Fishman and G. Harbottle, "Szilard-Chalmers Reaction in Aqueous Solutions of Tri- and Hexavalent Chromium," *J. Chem. Phys.* **22,** 1088 (1954).

M. L. Perlman and J. A. Miskel, "Average Charge on the Daughter Atoms Produced in the Decay of A^{37} and Xe^{131m}," *Phys. Rev.* **91,** 899 (1953).

C. Perrier and E. Segrè, "Some Chemical Properties of Element 43," *J. Chem Phys.* **5,** 715 (1937), and **7,** 155 (1939).

J. A. Marinsky, L. E. Glendenin, and C. D. Coryell, "The Chemical Identification of Radioisotopes of Neodymium and of Element 61," *J. Am. Chem. Soc.* **69,** 2781 (1947).

G. L. Johnson, R. F. Leininger, and E. Segrè, "Chemical Properties of Astatine," *J. Chem. Phys.* **17,** 1 (1949).

M. Perey, "Propriétés chimiques de l'élément 87: Actinium K," *J. chim. phys.* **43,** 262 (1946).

G. T. Seaborg and J. J. Katz (Editors), *The Actinide Elements,* National Nuclear Energy Series, Div. IV, Vol. 14A, New York, McGraw-Hill Book Co., 1954.

G. T. Seaborg, "The Transuranium Elements; Present Status" (Nobel Lecture), University of California Radiation Laboratory Report UCRL-1724 (1951).

S. G. Thompson, B. B. Cunningham, and G. T. Seaborg, "Chemical Properties of Berkelium," *J. Am. Chem. Soc.* **72,** 2798 (1950).

K. Street, Jr., S. G. Thompson, and G. T. Seaborg, "Chemical Properties of Californium," *J. Am. Chem. Soc.* **72,** 4832 (1950).

Papers on Elements 99 and 100 in *Phys. Rev.* **93,** 257, 908, 1129, 1428, 1433 (1954); **94,** 209, 1080, 1083 (1954); and **95,** 581, 585 (1954).

Announcement of Element 101 in *Chem. Eng. News* **33,** 1956 (1955).

CHAPTER 12

NUCLEAR ENERGY

A. NUCLEAR REACTORS

Speculation about the possible use of nuclear processes for the large-scale production of power dates back to the early years of radioactivity. Only with the discovery of fission did such applications become a real possibility. The unique feature of the fission reaction which makes it suitable as a practical energy source is the emission of several neutrons in each neutron-induced fission; this makes a chain reaction possible.

Chain Reaction. The condition for the maintenance of a chain reaction is that on the average at least one neutron created in a fission process cause another fission. This condition is usually expressed in terms of a multiplication factor k, defined as the ratio of the number of fissions produced by a particular generation of neutrons to the number of fissions giving rise to that generation of neutrons. If $k < 1$ no self-sustaining chain reaction is possible; if $k = 1$ a chain reaction is maintained at a steady state; if $k > 1$ the number of neutrons and therefore the number of fissions increases with each generation, and a divergent chain reaction results. An assembly of fissionable material is said to be critical if $k = 1$ and supercritical if $k > 1$.

Since one neutron per fission is required to propagate the chain reaction, the number of neutrons increases by the fraction $k - 1$ in each generation. Thus the rate of change of the number of neutrons in a chain reacting system is

$$\frac{dN}{dt} = \frac{N(k-1)}{\tau},$$

where τ is the average time between successive neutron generations. By integration we find that at time t the number of neutrons is

$$N = N_0 e^{(k-1)t/\tau}, \qquad (12\text{-}1)$$

where N_0 is the number of neutrons at $t = 0$. If τ is very short (as it is when no moderator is used and fission takes place with fast neutrons) and if k is suddenly made to exceed unity by an appreciable amount, the chain reaction can proceed explosively as in a fission bomb.

In a nuclear reactor k is kept equal to unity for steady operation. However, a reactor must be designed in such a way that k can be made slightly larger than one (say 1.01 or 1.02) to allow the neutron flux and therefore the power to be brought up to a desired level. Control of the reactor, for example by the motion of neutron-absorbing control rods, is possible only if τ is not too short. Assume that $\tau = 10^{-3}$ sec (approximately the life expectancy of a thermal neutron) and $k = 1.001$. Then, according to equation 12-1, $N = N_0 e^t$, where t is in seconds, and the neutron level will increase by a factor e every second or by a factor of about 20,000 in 10 sec. This is too rapid an increase for safe and convenient control. Fortunately the fact that in thermal-neutron uranium fission some neutrons (about 0.75 per cent of the total) are delayed with half-lives between 0.05 sec and 56 sec makes the average time τ between neutron generations about 0.1 sec. Then, with $k = 1.001$, the e-folding time or "period" of the system is about 100 sec, and ample time is available for control.

Critical Size. The multiplication factor in a medium of infinite extent, denoted by k_∞, is given by the product of the number ν of neutrons emitted per fission and the fraction of the neutrons that produce another fission. The latter fraction is the ratio of the total fission cross section ($\sigma_f N_f$, where N_f is the number of fissionable nuclei per cubic centimeter) to the total absorption cross section. In a reactor of finite extent the multiplication factor k is a fraction of k_∞, determined by the loss of neutrons by leakage through the surface; the smaller the reactor, the greater is its ratio of surface to volume and therefore the greater is this loss.

Quantitative estimates of neutron losses from a reactor surface are very complicated but are quite essential to any estimate of critical size. As a rough approximation for thermal reactors the fractional loss of neutrons is proportional to the sum $L_S^2 + L^2$, where L_S and L are the average (crow-flight) distances traveled in the moderating medium by a fission neutron before reaching thermal energy (L_S) and after reaching thermal energy (L). For a spherical reactor of radius R the approximate relation is $k_\infty - k = \pi^2 R^{-2}(L_S^2 + L^2)$. The critical radius R_c is that radius for which $k = 1$. Thus

$$R_c = \pi(L_S^2 + L^2)^{1/2}(k_\infty - 1)^{-1/2}. \tag{12-2}$$

The slowing-down length L_S may be known from measurements on various moderators, and generally is not appreciably altered by the addition of fuel to the moderator. The diffusion length L will be smaller than that for the pure moderator (L_0), and is given by $L^2 = xL_0^2$, where x is the total moderator absorption cross section, $\sigma_m N_m$, divided by the total absorption cross section for the medium, $\sum_i \sigma_i N_i$. Table 12-1 gives L_S, L_0, $\sigma_m N_m$, and the density for some popular moderators.

TABLE 12-1

PROPERTIES OF MODERATORS

	L_S (cm)	L_0 (cm)	$\sigma_m N_m$ (cm^{-1})	Density ($g\ cm^{-3}$)
H_2O	5.7	2.88	0.017	1.00
D_2O	11.0	100	0.000080	1.1
Be	9.9	23.6	0.0013	1.84
C	18.7	50.2	0.00036	1.62

In most reactors x, which is the fraction of neutrons absorbed by the moderator, is kept rather small for reasons of neutron economy. Therefore, a crude equation which neglects L, namely, $R_c = \pi L_S (k_\infty - 1)^{-1/2}$, gives the right order of magnitude of the critical size for practical thermal reactors. For the same reason reactors often have k_∞ not much less than η (see page 73). As an illustration, we may estimate the critical radius for a solution of U^{235} in ordinary water:

$$R_c \cong \frac{\pi L_S}{(k_\infty - 1)^{1/2}} \cong \frac{\pi \times 5.7}{(2.1 - 1)^{1/2}} = 17 \text{ cm}.$$

Here we assumed that the concentration of the solution was great enough to insure that neutron reaction with U^{235} was much more probable than capture by hydrogen. The ratio of the two cross sections is $687/0.328 = 2100$, so that this condition is met if the concentration of U^{235} is a few tenths of a mole per liter.

In many reactors the fissionable material is not dissolved in the moderator but is separated from it in a heterogeneous arrangement. All the reactors which have been constructed with ordinary uranium as the fuel have the uranium in lumps or rods arranged in a lattice which is embedded in graphite or heavy water. The reason is that much of the loss of neutrons is due to several strong absorption resonances in U^{238} between 6 and 200 ev. In a homogeneous mixture of uranium and moderator the probability that a neutron during the slowing-down process is absorbed by $U^{238}(n, \gamma)$ reaction in the resonance region is quite large. If, however, the uranium is arranged in aggregates, a much greater fraction of the neutrons will be slowed down in the moderator to energies below the resonance region before encountering uranium nuclei. The optimum lattice spacing is approximately L_S for the moderator. Without the advantage of this ingenious device, normal uranium-graphite assemblies would have k_∞ slightly less than unity; even with it k_∞ cannot be greater than η, which is 1.3. For normal uranium-graphite reactors k_∞ is commonly about 1.07, and the critical radius must be about $R_c = \pi \times 18.7 \times (0.07)^{-1/2} = 220$ cm. For a cube-shaped assembly the length of an edge is approximately $\sqrt{3}\, R_c$, or about 13 ft.

In all practical reactors the core is surrounded by a neutron reflector which reduces neutron loss. This makes the necessary size of the reactor core slightly smaller, but operating in the other direction are effects of impurities, provisions for cooling and for control, and overdesign. Another important effect of the reflector in power reactors is the increase in neutron flux in the outer parts of the core; because the power level is likely to be limited by the temperature rise at the center this makes the outer parts contribute a better share to the over-all power output. In addition, the fuel lattice may be altered near the center to flatten the neutron- and power-flux distributions.

Types of Reactors. Reactors may be classified in a variety of different ways. We may consider the fuel used and distinguish among reactors using natural uranium, uranium enriched in U^{235}, Pu^{239}, or U^{233}. Or reactors may be grouped according to the neutron energy used to produce fission (fast, partially moderated or intermediate energy, or thermal), or according to the moderator (water, heavy water, graphite, beryllium) or the coolant (air, water, liquid metal). Often reactors are classified according to whether fuel and moderator are homogeneously mixed or arranged in a heterogeneous manner. In terms of purpose, reactors may be designed primarily to produce fissionable material (Pu^{239} or U^{233}), or to provide excess neutrons for the production of other nuclides (such as H^3), or to produce useful power, or to serve as research tools, or for a combination of these purposes. Table 12-2 is a catalog of the essential characteristics of a number of reactors now in operation. We shall devote a few paragraphs to several particular reactors, each representative of a different general type.

Oak Ridge Graphite Reactor. Built in 1943 and called the X-10 reactor, this was the world's first reactor operating at an appreciable power level. Because it is a natural uranium-graphite reactor it is

TABLE 12-2

PROPERTIES OF REACTORS

Reactor	Fuel	Moderator	Coolant	Power (kw)	Neutron Flux (cm^{-2} sec^{-1})	Special Features
BEPO, Harwell	U	Graphite	Air	4,000	1×10^{12}	
Brookhaven	U	Graphite	Air	28,000	5×10^{12}	
CP5, Argonne	U^{235}	D_2O		1,000	3×10^{13}	
EBR, Arco	U^{235}	None	Na-K alloy	~1,000	10^{14}	Breeds Pu^{239} in a U blanket
Fast Reactor, Los Alamos	Pu	None	Hg	10	5×10^{12}	A Pu-fueled, fast reactor (no longer in operation)
Hanford	U	Graphite	H_2O	High		Used for production of Pu^{239}
HYPO, Los Alamos	$U^{235}O_2(NO_3)_2$	H_2O	H_2O	6	3×10^{11}	Homogeneous
JEEP, Kjeller	U	D_2O	D_2O	100	3×10^{11}	
MTR, Arco	U^{235}	H_2O	H_2O	30,000	5×10^{14}	A "materials testing reactor"
NRX, Chalk River	U	D_2O	H_2O	10,000	6×10^{13}	
X-10, Oak Ridge	U	Graphite	Air	3,800	2×10^{12}	Used for isotope production
Raleigh	$U^{235}O_2SO_4$	H_2O	H_2O	10	5×10^{11}	Homogeneous
Saclay, France	U	D_2O	N_2	1,500	6×10^{12}	
Savannah River	U	D_2O		High		Can produce H^3 by $Li^6(n, \alpha)$
STR, Arco						Prototype "submarine thermal reactor"
ZOE, Chatillon	UO_2	D_2O	D_2O	10		

a large one. Its core is a 24-ft cube of graphite blocks, provided with 1248 fuel channels each 1.75 in. square located in an 8-in. rectangular lattice. The fuel is 35 tons of uranium metal in the form of cylindrical slugs 1.1 in. in diameter, 4 in. long, and jacketed in aluminum for protection from oxidation. Because the fuel elements are round pegs in square holes, clear spaces are provided through which the coolant air is blown. At 3800 kw, with 100,000 cu ft of air per min passing through the core channels, the metal slugs are kept below 245°C; the average graphite temperature is 130°C.

The fuel loading does not extend quite to the outer surfaces of the graphite, and the outer part of pure graphite serves as a neutron reflector. A concrete shield 7 ft thick surrounds the entire core, with a space left between for air passage. The fuel channels extend through the shield at one end, so that old slugs may be pushed out and new fuel inserted (figure 12-1). Of course, these openings in the shield are ordinarily kept plugged to reduce the leakage of dangerous radiations. Some of the channels serve for irradiations of other materials and for various experiments. There are also special channels for similar purposes and for the control rods. A reactor of

FIGURE 12-1. Charging face of the Brookhaven National Laboratory's uranium-graphite reactor (similar to the X-10 reactor at Oak Ridge). The uranium rods are inserted from this face. (Courtesy Brookhaven National Laboratory.)

this size is quite expensive. In round numbers, the value of the 620 tons of very pure graphite is about $2,000,000, and the value of the uranium is probably about $2,000,000. In addition, the costs of the building and of the air-handling system have been estimated at about $1,000,000 each.

Provided that all the aluminum jackets on the thousands of fuel slugs are intact the exhausted cooling air should be free of fission product contamination. Rupture of a slug jacket could cause contamination of the exhaust air with fission products and necessitate the removal of the slug. At all times the cooling air will be made radioactive by passage through the reactor, chiefly by the reaction $A^{40}(n, \gamma)$ to produce β-emitting A^{41} of 109 min half-life. This thermal reaction cross section is approximately 0.5 barn, and from the dimensions given we estimate that roughly 500 cu ft of air (containing ~160 g argon) are exposed to the average thermal neutron flux, which is about 5×10^{11} cm^{-2} sec^{-1}. On this basis the activity of the A^{41} in secular equilibrium is about $(160/40) \times 6 \times 10^{23} \times 0.5 \times 10^{-24} \times 5 \times 10^{11} = 6 \times 10^{11}$ disintegrations sec^{-1} or about 16 curies. Because of its radioactivity the air is discharged through a tall stack.

The reactor was originally built as a pilot plant for the plutonium-producing reactors at Hanford. Plutonium is produced by the neutron capture occurring in U^{238}:

$$_{92}U^{238} \xrightarrow{n,\,\gamma} {}_{92}U^{239} \xrightarrow{\beta^-} {}_{93}Np^{239} \xrightarrow{\beta^-} {}_{94}Pu^{239}.$$

As we have seen from the neutron material balance, very roughly one such capture occurs per fission of U^{235}. The total energy released for each fission (exclusive of neutrino energies) is 190 Mev so that the rate of fission at 3800 kw is about 10^{17} sec^{-1}. Thus Pu^{239} is produced at the rate of about 10^{22} atoms day^{-1} or 4 g per day. In recent years the reactor has been operated primarily as a source of radioactive isotopes for distribution through the United States Atomic Energy Commission. Some of these isotopes are fission products, extracted from discharged fuel slugs. Others are produced by n, γ reaction on appropriate targets, for example, Na^{24} from Na_2CO_3, and I^{131} from tellurium metal by $Te^{130}(n, \gamma)Te^{131} \xrightarrow{\beta^-} I^{131}$. A few are produced in special reactions, particularly C^{14} from $N^{14}(n, p)$, P^{32} from $S^{32}(n, p)$, and H^3 from $Li^6(n, \alpha)$.

Uranium-Heavy Water Reactors. The core of the experimental reactor at Kjeller, Norway, is a cylindrical tank 2 meters in diameter filled with 7 tons of D_2O. This volume of heavy water is expensive; the value is almost $2,000,000. But because of the very small thermal-neutron absorption cross section and the fairly small neutron-slowing-down length (L_S) for D_2O, the reactor is much smaller than a uranium-graphite reactor and requires much less uranium. The fuel charge in this reactor is 2.5 tons of uranium metal (value about $200,000) in the form of 1-in. diameter slugs in 76 aluminum tubes

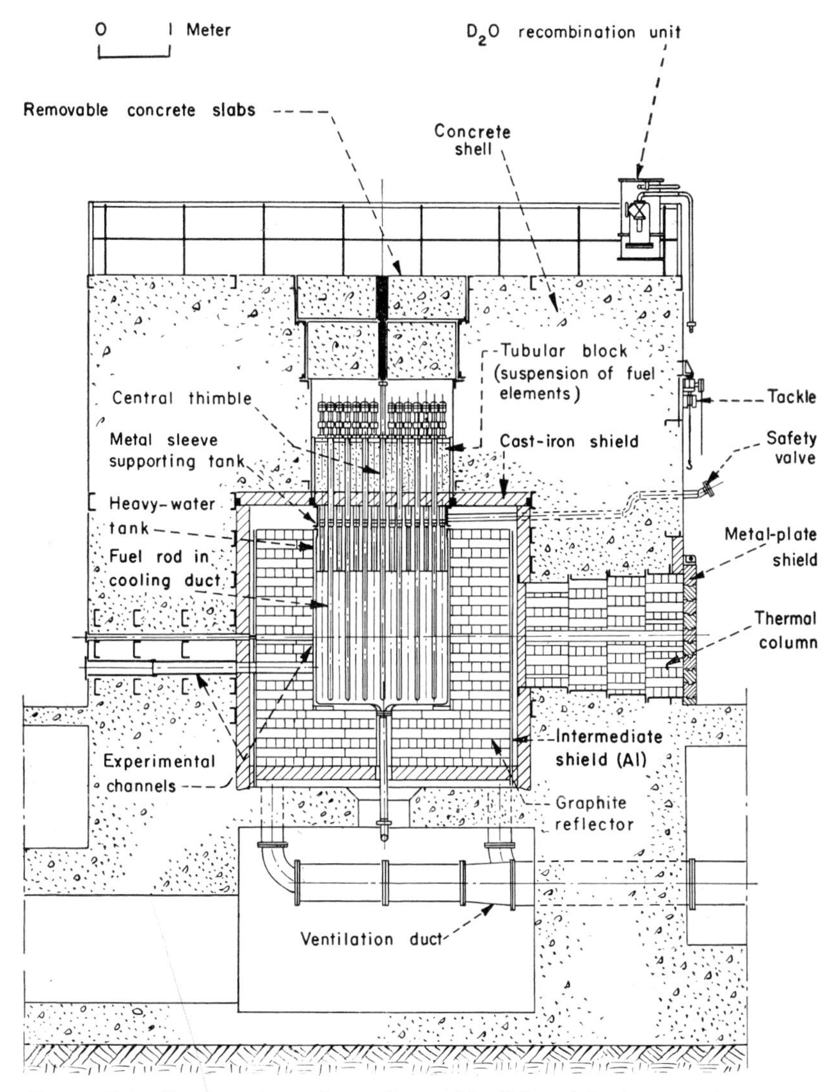

FIGURE 12-2. Construction and experimental facilities of the heavy-water reactor at Saclay, France. [Reproduced from L. Kowarski, *Nucleonics* **12,** No. 8, 9 (1954), by permission of the McGraw-Hill Publishing Co.]

arranged in a rectangular lattice. A graphite reflector about 3 ft thick surrounds the core. Control of the reactor is by insertion of cadmium plates into the space between core and reflector. (In an emergency the heavy water moderator could be drained from the core.) A concrete radiation shield at least 2 meters thick gives biological protection.

Cooling is provided by forced circulation of the heavy water through an external heat exchanger. This permits operation at 100 kw, giving a central neutron flux of more than 3×10^{11} cm^{-2} sec^{-1}. Several experimental holes into the core are used for experimental purposes and for isotope production.

The French uranium-heavy water reactor at Saclay (figure 12-2) is similar in size to the Kjeller reactor. A significant difference is that each fuel rod is cooled by a flow of nitrogen gas under 10 atm pressure through a surrounding annular space. The operational power level is about 1500 kw, and the maximum neutron flux is about 6×10^{12} cm^{-2} sec^{-1}. This reactor was designed primarily as an experiment and for radioisotope production.

Water Boiler at Raleigh. With fissionable material in concentrated form, for example Pu^{239} or concentrated isotope U^{235}, quite small critical assemblies are possible. The high neutron yield per neutron captured permits the use of H_2O as a moderator in spite of its appreciable neutron-capture cross section. If such an assembly were made without provision for cooling, the increasing nuclear reaction would heat the water until k were reduced to unity, probably by boiling with attendant moderator density reduction. A low-power reactor consisting of a solution of U^{235} in water is commonly known as a "water boiler," although the temperature is usually kept below about 80°C. Typical of such reactors is one built for research purposes on the campus of North Carolina State College. Its core is a 14-liter cylindrical stainless-steel vessel almost filled with a solution of uranyl sulfate in water. The uranium (loaned by the United States Atomic Energy Commission) is 860 g of 93 per cent U^{235}. For economy in fuel inventory the core is surrounded by about 20 in. of graphite reflector. A shield of about 5 ft of concrete immediately surrounds the reflector; the concrete is of special composition with high density and some boron content. Experimental holes through shield and reflector are available. Cooling is provided by circulation of water through stainless steel coils inside the core. Operation is at 10 kw, and the maximum thermal neutron flux is about 5×10^{11} cm^{-2} sec^{-1}.

Control of the reactor, apart from adjustment of the volume and concentration of the uranyl sulfate solution, is by two rods containing boron carbide which are lowered into, or raised from, channels in the core. Both rods are attached only through electromagnets to their worm gear drives, so that any power failure will drop the rods into place. The reactor automatically adjusts itself to steady operation, with a proper control setting, because the temperature coefficient of reactivity is negative, k being reduced by about 0.0002 per degree Centigrade on account of the expansion of the solution.

The intense radiation produces decomposition of the water in the core so that the solution continuously evolves hydrogen and oxygen. To avoid the danger of a gas explosion these may be continuously removed and reacted on a catalyst. Provision must be made for the escape of gaseous fission products. At Raleigh these are stored in holding tanks until much of the radioactivity, particularly Xe^{133}, has decayed and then are discharged with air dilution from a tall stack. Nonvolatile fission products accumulate in the core. The emerging cooling water is slightly radioactive, containing O^{19} and some activities induced in impurities, but this is not troublesome at low power.

Materials Testing Reactor. For the purpose of testing the behavior of various materials at high radiation levels the United States Atomic Energy Commission has had constructed at its Reactor Proving Station near Arco, Idaho, a reactor which provides the record high thermal-neutron flux of 5×10^{14} cm^{-2} sec^{-1}. This reactor, designated MTR, uses enriched U^{235} as fuel and H_2O as moderator and coolant. The fuel elements are metal plates supported vertically in a lattice which is 40 by 70 cm and 60 cm high. A reflector of beryllium metal surrounds the fuel lattice and is contained in an aluminum and stainless steel tank 55 in. in diameter and about 30 ft deep. The tank is filled with water, and access to the reactor core for replacement of fuel elements, etc., is through the 20 ft of water, which is an adequate biological shield during shut-down. For cooling, water flows by gravity downward through the tank between the fuel elements and through holes in the beryllium reflector at the rate of 20,000 gal per min. The operating power level is 30,000 kw. Outside the tank is a secondary reflector of graphite about 4 ft thick, the inner part of which is made of loosely packed graphite spheres 1 in. in diameter. The construction is such that these spheres are free to expand upward without exerting undue stress on the tank wall or the solid graphite. Since the pebbles are exposed to a higher neutron flux than is the rest of the graphite, any radiation damage will affect these first. They can be replaced when necessary. The solid graphite is provided with holes for air cooling. Outside the reflector is a thermal shield consisting of two 4-in. thicknesses of steel, also air cooled. Outside this a 9-ft shield of special concrete reduces the radiation level during operation to less than 1 mr hr^{-1}. Many experimental holes penetrate the shields and reflectors. Some reach the maximum neutron flux of 5×10^{14} thermal and 1×10^{14} fast neutrons cm^{-2} sec^{-1}, which is in the beryllium reflector at the surface of the fuel lattice. Of course, these holes may not be opened during operation.

Reactor control is provided by two cadmium-loaded regulating rods (one is a spare) in the beryllium reflector. Automatic control circuits drive the rod in or out to maintain steady operation. To insure that no accidental rod withdrawal could make the reactor critical with regard to prompt neutrons only, each regulating rod controls no more than 0.5 per cent in k, which is less than the delayed-neutron contribution. Further control of reactivity is provided by up to eight shim safety rods in the fuel lattice. These rods contain cadmium, and as the cadmium section is withdrawn a U^{235} fuel section is brought up into the lattice. Safety circuits prevent too rapid removal of these shim rods, and if any minor malfunction or irregularity occurs rods are automatically re-inserted until the power level is reduced. One of the electronic circuits measures the reactor period (or time rate of change of reactivity); if the period for any reason becomes shorter than one second a complete "scram" results, with all shim rods dropped by their magnetic clutches.

One reason why a wide range of reactivity control is needed in a high-flux reactor is the effect known as xenon poisoning. One of the fission products is Xe^{135}, a radioactive isotope of 9.2 hr half-life and with the astonishing thermal-neutron absorption cross section 3.5×10^6 barns. In steady-state operation the presence of this poison reduces k by about 0.04. On shut-down after steady operation the concentration of Xe^{135} increases, because it is still being formed by decay of its parent, 6.7-hr I^{135}, and is no longer being consumed by n, γ reaction. After a few minutes' shut-down the reactor cannot be started up again. After about 10 hr the poisoning is a maximum, amounting to a reduction of about 0.3 in k. Thereafter the poison decays away, and the reactor can be made critical again after about 2 days.

Breeding. Any reactor fueled with ordinary uranium makes new fissionable material as it burns up its U^{235}. When reactors (such as the X-10 reactor) make Pu^{239} at a rate that is not much less than the rate at which U^{235} is consumed, they are known as converters. This conversion can be very useful in extending the supply of fissionable fuel, especially if the yield of new fuel can actually exceed the consumption, in which case the process is called breeding. A breeder reactor must use its neutrons very economically since only 2.5 neutrons are produced per U^{235} fission and 3.0 neutrons per Pu^{239} fission. For thermal reactors, because of the competition between n, γ reactions and fission, only approximately 2.1 neutrons are released for each neutron absorbed in either U^{235} or Pu^{239}. After subtracting the one neutron needed to keep the chain alive, we see that in thermal reactors not more than approximately 1.1 neutron per U^{235} or Pu^{239} atom consumed can be used to produce new fissionable material. Better neutron economy can be achieved in a fast-neutron reactor, where the neutron yield per neutron absorbed in either fuel is probably greater and there is no moderator to absorb additional neutrons.

A reactor to test the possibility of breeding, the Experimental Breeder Reactor (EBR), was put into operation at the Arco station by the Argonne National Laboratory in December 1951. The core containing the U^{235} is "about the size of a football." It is surrounded by a "blanket" of uranium metal which is almost entirely U^{238}. The coolant is a liquid alloy of sodium and potassium flowing through blanket and core. Because the Na-K alloy becomes highly radioactive, it is cooled in a shielded heat exchanger by a second Na-K system, which in turn gives useful steam in a suitable boiler. In 1953 the A.E.C. announced that the EBR was "changing non-fissionable uranium into fissionable plutonium at a rate at least equal to the rate at which U^{235} is being consumed." If the EBR were fueled with Pu^{239}, for example that produced in its own blanket, it should have a breeding ratio substantially greater than unity.

If the blanket should be loaded with thorium instead of U^{238}, a different breeding reaction would occur:

$$\mathrm{Th}^{232} \xrightarrow{n,\gamma} \mathrm{Th}^{233} \xrightarrow{\beta^-} \mathrm{Pa}^{233} \xrightarrow{\beta^-} \mathrm{U}^{233}.$$

The product U^{233} is a long-lived, fissionable isotope similar to U^{235}. The starting materials Th^{232} and U^{238} are said to be "fertile" materials. In principle, successful breeding can enlarge the supply of nuclear fuel from only U^{235} to the total available uranium and thorium. However, the fuel materials will have to be chemically processed to separate fission products several times in each breeding cycle, and in the final analysis the efficiency of the chemical processing will determine the practicality of breeder reactors.

Nuclear Power. There is no question but that nuclear reactors will be used as power sources. Already a nuclear-powered submarine, the *Nautilus,* driven by a thermal-neutron reactor with pressurized water as a coolant, has been tested at sea. Also a Submarine Intermediate Reactor (SIR) is being readied for similar service. Reactors in the form of packaged power plants can and very likely will be used to supply power at special installations where ordinary fuels are not easily available, for example, at Arctic stations. A question remains as to whether or not nuclear reactors can compete economically with coal-burning steam plants at central power stations. The present rough estimates are that without breeding, uranium may well be more costly than coal per kilowatt-hour generated, but that with breeding, fuel costs alone may be considerably cheaper for uranium than for coal. But especially at first the capital investment will be greater for the nuclear power plant. The requirements for chemical processing and radioactive-waste disposal add to the uncertainties.

Very probably some new types of reactors will be tried for economical power generation. One particularly simple conception is the thermal, free-boiling reactor. Cooling would be effected by direct boiling of the water moderator, giving steam for a turbine-driven generator. A published engineering cost estimate on a reactor of this type designed to deliver 300,000 kw of electric power shows fuel cost less than for coal, a U^{235} fuel inventory valued at $5,000,000, and a total cost of 6.7 mills per kwh (about the same as for a coal plant). Another ingenious suggested reactor might use a homogeneous solution of U^{235} in molten bismuth as core. This fuel might be continuously processed by countercurrent molten-salt extraction to remove fission products. Without doubt other unconventional reactors will be invented.

The world's supply of nuclear fuel, like the supplies of other fuels, is limited. The total practicable resources of uranium have been estimated as 25×10^6 tons. If only the U^{235} is burned, the corresponding energy yield is about 12×10^{18} Btu. With breeding so that all the uranium plus the 1×10^6 tons of thorium could be burned, the yield would be almost 1800×10^{18} Btu. The world's reserves of fossil fuels, predominantly coal, are estimated as about 80×10^{18} Btu.

Hazards and Safeguards. Even though reactors may contain sufficient amounts of fissionable material for an explosive chain reaction, there is very little possibility that one of them should explode like an atomic bomb. The necessary conditions for such an explosion are very special indeed and are most unlikely to be achieved accidentally. The possibility always exists that a series of malfunctions of controls and interlocks may permit a nuclear reactor to go out of control and exceed its design power level. The probable consequences would be melting or vaporization of some core components, possible initiation of chemical reactions such as burning, and conceivably an explosion with enough force to break open the reactor, its shield, and possibly the containing building.

The real hazard in a reactor is its content of fission products. The amount of these products stored in a reactor is determined by its power level and by the time its fuel has been in place without reprocessing. For example, a reactor that has been operating steadily at 1000 kw for several months contains several million curies of fission products. If any accident, nuclear or otherwise, should open the reactor and melt or vaporize the fuel elements, a large fraction of these dangerously radioactive substances could be dispersed in the air, and a severe radiation hazard would be produced in the vicinity and probably for a distance of several miles downwind. It is for this reason that an A.E.C. committee on reactor safeguards has recommended that reactors ordinarily be surrounded by an area from which the public is excluded, the radius of this area in miles being about 0.01 times the square root of the power level in kilowatts. Precautions of this kind are particularly important for new and untested types of reactors.

Clearly all reactors are not equally safe, although of course each contains a number of emergency controls, safety interlocks, warning systems, etc. Those reactor types in which safety features are most inherent are generally thought to be the safest. The chief inherent safety feature is a sizable negative temperature coefficient, as in the simple water boiler. Although the expansion caused by increase in temperature always tends to reduce the reactivity, effects due to changes in absorption and fission cross sections with neutron temperature and with Doppler broadening of resonance peaks need to be taken into account before a conclusion about the temperature coefficient is reached. Another safety feature is present if any reasonable change in configuration can produce only reduction in k. Thus loss of D_2O from the Saclay reactor P-2, which very possibly could happen, would in itself stop the reaction. On the other hand, loss of H_2O coolant from some reactor cores must be expected to increase k. Some reactors contain voids that might conceivably be closed by gross mechanical accident or even by earthquake, with corresponding increase in k just at a time when control rods might be jammed. Large excess reactivity, especially in conjunction with sizable experimental holes in the core, would mark a reactor as slightly less safe than the average. Apart from high power, very high specific power can introduce a special hazard in that the fuel elements may become so radioactive that they will melt from their own heat even after shut-down if the reactor should lose its coolant. Dimensional changes in structural materials contribute to reactor hazards; for example, control rods might be made inoperative.

The best reactor safeguards are careful design, inherent safety features, sound operating procedure, interlocks and controls subject to frequent operational tests, and some caution with regard to untried materials. Actually the history of reactor behavior is good, there being no known instance of major hazard from malfunction; none has exploded or otherwise taken human life. This is certainly more than can be said for conventional steam plants and internal-combustion machines.

Chemical Processes. The construction and operation of nuclear reactors have posed many new chemical problems. Indeed, new reactor developments depend primarily upon new techniques in chemistry and metallurgy. As a random example, pure zirconium metal now appears to be a very promising structural material for thermal reactors because of its very low absorption cross section, and its exceptional corrosion resistance and strength at high temperatures. The low cross section, 0.18 barn, was not recognized until special samples free of the usual 2 per cent hafnium impurity (with a cross section of 115 barns) were prepared. Over a period of about 3 years a new technology of zirconium purification, reduction, and fabrication has emerged. Many other examples could be cited, but in this section we wish to consider only those chemical processes applied to fuel elements removed from reactors.

The nuclear fuel, whether ordinary uranium or U^{235} or Pu^{239}, cannot simply be left in the reactor until the fissionable material is consumed. Apart from the reduction in fuel mass, there are accumulated fission products which act as neutron-absorbing poisons, and usually even more decisive is the mechanical deterioration of the fuel slugs with reduction in stability and in heat transfer. A burn-up of about 1 per cent is a frequently quoted example. After this, the slugs must be removed from the reactor. If they are to be recovered they may be stored for a few months while the radioactivity declines, then dissolved, purified, and decontaminated of radioactive products, and converted again to metal and fabricated into useful shapes. Any secondary fuel produced by nuclear reaction, such as Pu^{239}, is also separated in the chemical process.

The requirements put upon the chemical and metallurgical processing are very severe. Losses of fissionable isotopes must be kept exceedingly low. For example, if the burn-up per pass is 1 per cent, and if the recovery process after each pass is 99.9 per cent efficient, before all the valuable fuel is consumed 10 per cent of it will have been lost. Moreover, the fission product radioactivity is so intense that the early process stages must be carried out entirely by remote control. In these circumstances, for a complex process of many steps an over-all yield of 99.9 per cent represents a minor miracle.

A typical processing cycle begins with the discharge of the "hot" slugs into a water channel about 20 ft deep, deep enough to absorb all harmful radiations. After a cooling period the slugs may be moved along to the processing area. The slugs and their jackets are dissolved (nitric acid would be suitable), but precautions must be taken with regard to the escape of gaseous and volatile fission products. Plutonium, uranium, and fission products may be separated by precipitation reactions in controlled oxidation states. The chemical properties summarized in chapter 11 show that dilute nitric acid should oxidize uranium to UO_2^{++} but would leave plutonium mostly as Pu(III) or Pu(IV). Plutonium in these oxidation states forms insoluble fluorides, and a precipitate of LaF_3, for example, would bring down the plutonium and some of the fission products. The precipitate can be dissolved, oxidized to PuO_2^{++}, and decontamination effected by a LaF_3 precipitate from this solution. A number of such cycles are required to produce adequately low fission product radioactivity in the plutonium fraction. This material can then be handled without shielding, except for protection from the exceedingly toxic plutonium itself. The uranium might be decontaminated and recovered by similar or by alternative cycles.

The first few reaction cycles are carried out in closed cells with concrete walls perhaps 6 ft thick. Stainless-steel vessels and piping are common, and filtration may use fritted stainless-steel filter disks. All operations are controlled remotely. The high radiation level itself affects processes and equipment. Continuous solvent extractions in place of precipitations are very attractive, but there is the possibility that radiation will decompose many organic solvents. Any defective equipment in the hot cells must be removed and replaced, entirely by remote control, since months of effort might be required to decontaminate a cell sufficiently to permit workers to enter. Considerable ingenuity has been devoted to special "disconnects" for fittings at each piece of process equipment and to mechanical devices to operate these from a distance with television viewing screens.

Another concern of process designers and operators is that at no time must a critical assembly of fissionable material be allowed to accumulate. A plant might be designed to process daily thousands of gallons of solutions containing several times the minimum critical mass. Unless this is done batchwise it is not easy to guarantee that no divergent chain reaction can ever occur. (In case of such an accident the attendant hazard would be serious but probably not widespread; certainly there would be no large atomic explosion.) The safeguards that have been considered for continuous operations include the use of neutron absorbers, unfavorable geometry such as tall narrow cylinders for all vessels, and of course careful material control in each stage.

Disposal of Radioactive Wastes. The radioactive products made in nuclear reactors and discharged from their separations plants are essentially different from the wastes in ordinary industrial pollution problems. The radioactivities are different substances not returned to natural ones by dilution, oxidation, precipitation, etc. In a sense the earth's crust will not again in our time be quite the same as before. If these products were mixed throughout all the volume of the oceans the resulting concentration of radioactivity would be small, a fraction of that normally present in sea water. Even so, this is not an altogether attractive prospect, with more and more reactors being built, and anyway the uniform mixing is easier said than done.

The major fission product wastes have so far simply been stored, usually in aqueous solution evaporated to minimum liquid volume. This procedure cannot be permanently satisfactory; the possibility of eventual corrosion or rupture of the tanks is a hazard to the surrounding areas and to ground waters. It is now believed that these radioactive materials can be incorporated in cement or adsorbed in clay and fired to give relatively stable bodies that can be buried in the ground in chosen, protected locations.

The methods finally selected for waste disposal need to be inexpensive. The cost simply of tank storage has been estimated as 44 cents per initial gallon, and more if cooling coils are required to remove the radioactive heat. These costs complicate the economics of nuclear-power production. Clearly chemical separations processes should give the radioactive wastes in the smallest volume of solution with the least bulk of added reagents. It is conceivable that some of the fission products may find economically sound useful applications; this can hardly eliminate disposal but may help pay for it.

B. MILITARY APPLICATIONS

Nuclear technology has evolved because of its military applications. The story of the atomic bomb is well known. Nuclear reactors will power submarines of extraordinary performance. Reactors may find military uses in supplying heat and electricity, and in powering aircraft. And of course the product radioisotopes are used widely in research laboratories of the Army, Navy, and Air forces as in university and industrial laboratories. But in this section we propose to discuss only direct applications of nuclear technology in the field of weapons.

Radiological Warfare. One of the simplest conceptions of a nuclear weapon, so far not put into practice, is the use of radioactive isotopes, possibly fission products, as a poisonous or harmful material to spread over enemy territory. (There is some evidence that this may have been at least vaguely an objective of the incompleted German reactor project during World War II.) One of the features claimed for radiological warfare (RW) is that by this means the use of a particular area might be denied to the enemy with fewer actual casualties than by conventional or atomic bombing.

It is not difficult to estimate approximately the amount of radioactive material required to make a given area very dangerous indeed because of the γ-ray dosage rate, with the assumption that the material is spread uniformly upon the surface of the ground. For a typical fission product mixture, with average γ energy of about 0.7 Mev, a contamination of 10^6 curies per square mile gives a dose rate of 4 r hr^{-1} a few feet above the ground. This level would be a deterrent to continuous occupation since about 100 to 200 hours' exposure would result in a lethal dose. Something like 100 megacuries per square mile would make the area almost impassable. If we take about 10 megacuries per square mile as an objective, we see that the entire fission product output of a 1,000,000-kw reactor for at least a month is needed to treat 100 square miles. The isolation of these products from the reactor fuel is no small matter, and the shielding required for safe handling before use prevents the weapon from being easily portable.

The actual dose received by persons exposed to RW agents will be somewhat different from that just calculated. There will be shielding effects from buildings, the distribution of the activity will not be uniform, and appreciable decontamination can result from rain and from deliberate clean-up operations. In the other direction, β irradiation of exposed skin can greatly exceed the γ-radiation effects, and any of the radioactivities taken into the body and retained there can be dangerous even in small amounts. For example, among the postulated 10 megacuries of fission products per square mile roughly 100,000 curies might be Sr^{89} and 2500 curies Sr^{90}. These isotopes, one with its short-lived daughter Y^{90} usually in equilibrium, are particularly dangerous bone-seeking radioactivities. The ingestion or inhalation of only a fraction of the few hundred millicuries that would be present in an area a few feet square very likely would produce serious or lethal consequences; however, these consequences would not be expected until months or years had passed, which would be a real military disadvantage. It is probably fair to conclude that RW, at least as conceived here, seems not to offer a very pleasant prospect either to user or to victim.

Explosive Nuclear Reaction. By this heading we refer to the somewhat misnamed atomic bomb. If a fission chain reaction is to proceed to the intensity of a major explosion, several necessary conditions are immediately apparent. The chain must operate on fast neutrons, otherwise the time τ between successive neutron generations (page 352) will be determined by the time required to slow neutrons to thermal energies, which is of the order of 10^{-3} sec, and the critical assembly will have moved apart in a small explosion before a really huge energy is generated.

A chain reaction based on fast neutrons requires no moderator, and the core is likely to be nearly pure fissionable material, U^{235} or Pu^{239}. (Actually U^{238} is fissionable by reaction with neutrons of energy greater than 1.1 Mev, and although the raw fission-neutron spectrum has as its average energy about 1.5 Mev the losses of effective neutrons by inelastic scattering and by radiative capture prevent a fast-neutron chain reaction in this material.) As in the case of the thermal-neutron chain reaction, there is a critical size or critical mass determined by the permissible surface losses of neutrons. In order of magnitude the critical mass must correspond to that of a sphere of radius R_c given by the mean free path of the neutron before reaction. In the notation of equation 3-2 the mean free path is $(n\sigma)^{-1}$, and $R_c \cong (n\sigma)^{-1} = 235(\rho \times 6 \times 10^{23}\sigma)^{-1}$, where ρ is the density in grams per cubic centimeter. The critical mass in grams is $M_c \cong 4\pi R_c{}^3\rho/3 = (4\pi/3\rho^2)[235/(6 \times 10^{23}\sigma)]^3$. Taking $\rho = 19$ g cm^{-3} and guessing $\sigma \cong 2.5 \times 10^{-24}$ cm^2 (the geometrical cross section), we have $R_c \cong 8$ cm and $M_c \cong 40$ kg. This is, of course, only a crude estimate.

If an object weighing 40 kg should be the site of a fission energy release of 8×10^{20} ergs (equivalent to 20,000 tons of TNT or 1 kg of U^{235}), and if all this energy were mechanical kinetic energy, the corresponding velocity would be about 2×10^8 cm sec^{-1}. Then the time required for its parts to separate by a few centimeters (and so end the reaction) would be of the order of magnitude of 10^{-8} sec. A fast-neutron generation can occur in this time. We may estimate τ crudely as the time for a 1-Mev neutron, velocity 1.4×10^9 cm sec^{-1}, to travel a mean free path, 8 cm, which gives $\tau \cong 6 \times 10^{-9}$ sec. For the neutron intensity and the energy release to become very large, the configuration of the fissionable material must be such that k is much greater than unity, say of the order of 2, and must remain so for a time t given by equation 12-1:

$$e^{(k-1)t/\tau} = \frac{N}{N_0} \cong 2.5 \times \frac{1000}{235} \times 6 \times 10^{23}.$$

This requires that the time $t \cong 60\tau \cong 4 \times 10^{-7}$ sec. Of course, as the nuclear explosion builds up, there is no possibility of providing a case strong enough to hold the critical assembly together. As assumed above, the only effective restraining force is that due to inertia. On this account the fissionable core may be enclosed in a layer of some dense material which adds to the inertia, and which also may reflect neutrons into the core; this special reflector is called the tamper.[1]

Bomb Assembly Problem. The requirement for a reasonably efficient fission bomb, that k be considerably greater than unity, is met if the core contains in good geometry considerably more than one critical mass. The assembly of the bomb, at the moment of detonation, may be effected by bringing together two near-critical pieces of fissionable material. However, unless this is done in a time shorter than about 4×10^{-7} sec, the build-up of fission rate during assembly could lead to only a small, premature explosion (a "fizzle"). If the parts are to move a distance of the order of 8 cm in 4×10^{-7} sec the required relative velocity is $\sim 2 \times 10^7$ cm sec^{-1}. This velocity is well above that even of artillery shells, which is $\sim 10^5$ cm sec^{-1}. Actually in one type of bomb a self-contained cannon shoots one part of the fissionable material into a mating part, the latter being surrounded by tamper. This is successful only if the assembly phase, duration $\sim 10^{-4}$ sec, is mostly completed before any stray neutron

[1] H. D. Smyth, *Atomic Energy for Military Purposes,* Princeton University Press, 1945.

happens to start the chain reaction. Important sources of stray neutrons are spontaneous fission (0.7 sec^{-1} per kg of U^{235}) and α, n reactions on impurity elements of sufficiently low Z to permit penetration of the Coulomb barrier. If the total number does not exceed about 1000 sec^{-1} the probability of a fizzle from this cause is small.

The bomb exploded at Hiroshima on August 6, 1945, is commonly reported to have been of this gun-assembled type, using U^{235} as fissionable material. One feature of this type is that it can be made with a surprisingly small external diameter. The United States atomic cannon shell, which is an atomic bomb, fits inside the 280-mm diameter cannon barrel.

It has been known for many years that detonations of ordinary high explosive in particular shapes can by focusing effects concentrate energy in a portion of the mass so that very high velocities result. Shaped-charge weapons eject material with velocities in excess of 10^6 cm sec^{-1}. Enough information has been made public to reveal that the implosion bomb uses this principle, in lenses of high explosive, to drive together very suddenly a mass of fissionable material. The Nagasaki bomb is reported to have been of this type.

Bomb Effects. The principal effects of the atomic bomb as a weapon are due to the shock wave (blast effect), to the thermal radiation (flash effect), to the nuclear radiations, and to residual radioactivity. The relative significance of these effects will depend upon the nature and power of the bomb, upon the nature of the target, and upon the position of the burst (whether in air, on the surface, under water, etc.). For a 20,000-ton-TNT-equivalent bomb exploded in air at the height chosen to inflict maximum damage, virtually complete destruction will extend over an area of radius 0.5 mile, and the radius of severe damage will be about 1 mile. At the same time the thermal radiation (ultraviolet, visible, and infrared) will heat the surface of objects at "ground zero" (directly below the bomb burst) to about 3000°C and will produce serious skin burns and set fires up to a radius of about 1 mile. (Perhaps 25 per cent of the fatal casualties at Hiroshima and Nagasaki were due to such skin burns.) However, it should be noted that this radiation does not penetrate through opaque materials and into shadows. (Smog may some day be a blessing.)

Of the nuclear radiations, only the γ rays and neutrons penetrate very far from the burst. The energy content of these radiations is of the order of 0.1 per cent of the total energy release (compared to about 30 per cent as thermal radiation). The nuclear radiations do only biological damage, but this will be severe within a radius of 0.5

mile. (From 5 to 15 per cent of the Hiroshima and Nagasaki fatalities have been attributed to this cause.) As for the residual radioactivity, this factor is negligible after an air burst of a 20-kiloton bomb. For surface or subsurface bursts or in the event of unfavorable meteorological conditions the resulting contamination could constitute a temporary hazard.

The damage radii due to the different effects vary in different ways with the magnitude of the bomb energy W (in kilotons of TNT equivalent). Approximate formulas for the two chief effects are:

$$\text{radius of severe blast} = (W/20)^{1/3} \text{ miles, and}$$

$$\text{radius of severe flash} \equiv D \cong (W/20)^{1/2} e^{-0.2(D-1)} \text{ miles.}$$

As an illustration, a 20-megaton-TNT-equivalent hydrogen bomb should produce severe blast over an area of 300 square miles and severe flash over the unprotected parts of an area of about 200 square miles. For nuclear radiation the absorption (exponential) factor is so great that lethal effects would not be expected beyond 1 or 2 miles in any case.

Hydrogen Bomb. Although both the United States and the Soviet Union have conducted tests of thermonuclear weapons, very little information about these tests has been officially released. The term thermonuclear means that the nuclear reactions occur in collisions between light-element nuclei because their thermal energies are great enough to permit penetration of the Coulomb barriers. Even with the nuclei of smallest atomic number the temperature required is of the order of 100,000,000°C. It is generally assumed that the bulk of the energy released is from the reactions $H^2 + H^2 = H^3 + H^1 + 4.0$ Mev and $H^2 + H^2 = He^3 + n + 3.3$ Mev. This would be a hydrogen or more precisely a deuterium bomb. The fuse for the reaction would be a powerful fission bomb, in which a temperature of the order of 50,000,000°C might be attained. In the presence of both deuterium and tritium this might set off the thermonuclear reaction $H^2 + H^3 = He^4 + n + 17.6$ Mev; this, in turn, might be used to set off the D,D reactions already written. Whether or not this assumed mechanism is the one actually used has not been confirmed.

A writer in *Time* magazine (April 12, 1954) described a device of this type in which the deuterium was said to be present as liquid hydrogen (presumably in a Dewar vessel) under refrigeration. This was called a "wet" hydrogen bomb, and it was said that the one exploded at Eniwetok on November 1, 1952, weighed altogether more than 65 tons. The writer in *Time* further stated that the March 1,

1954, explosion in the Pacific Proving Ground may have been a "dry" hydrogen bomb in which the main charge was not liquid deuterium but probably solid lithium deuteride made with the separated isotope Li^6. Whatever the true composition, it is likely that in thermonuclear weapons an energy release crudely equivalent to one Hiroshima atomic bomb results from each pound of charge that actually reacts.

Cobalt Bomb. Apart from its atomic-bomb fuse a thermonuclear bomb gives no fission products. However, it does produce a large amount of radioactivity by neutron reactions. Each pound of deuterium, reacting to produce an energy release equivalent to about 20,000 tons of TNT, can be expected to give $\sim$100 g of neutrons. In air most of these neutrons presumably produce radioactive carbon by $N^{14}(n, p)C^{14}$. Thus a 20-megaton hydrogen bomb produces $\sim$6 megacuries of C^{14}, which is quite harmless after dilution in a large volume of the atmosphere. However, if the hydrogen bomb should be made very much larger and if a neutron absorber which gives a shorter-half-life isotope were placed around it, the radioactivity so created could produce enormous damage. Cobalt has been suggested as the neutron absorber, the active product then being the 5.3-year Co^{60}. It may be seen that if 500 tons of deuterium react, surrounded by $\sim$100,000 tons of cobalt, the product would be about 7000 tons of Co^{60}, which is 7×10^{12} curies. If this were evenly distributed over the whole surface of the earth the world-wide dosage rate would be about 10 r per day. In this hypothetical case, and with no benefits from shielding or decontamination,[2] every person in the world should be dead within a few years. In any actual case the consequence of a 20,000-megaton-TNT-equivalent explosion of a "cobalt" bomb (or bombs) would surely be widespread death over much of our planet. The technological capacity for this destruction is practically within our present means.

EXERCISES

1. Assume that uranium metal is dispersed in heavy water at a concentration of 0.36 g per gram of D_2O. (*a*) What is the value of k_∞ for this mixture? (*b*) What is the radius of the sphere which is just critical?

Answers: (*a*) 1.3; (*b*) 85 cm.

2. The mixture in exercise 1 corresponds approximately to that in the Kjeller reactor. If that reactor is operated at 100 kw, what is the average thermal-neutron flux throughout the uranium?

Answer: 1.4×10^{11} cm^{-2} sec^{-1}.

[2] The oceans of the world could contain this activity probably without harm to marine life.

3. Suppose a submarine reactor contains 40 kg U^{235} and operates at 50,000 kw. How long can the submarine run before 3 per cent of the fuel is burned up?

4. Estimate the neutrino (or, rather, antineutrino) flux 50 ft from the reactor of exercise 4. *Answer:* $\sim 3 \times 10^{11}$ cm^{-2} sec^{-1}.

5. A water-cooled uranium-graphite reactor operates at a power level of 200,000 kw. The reactor core is a cube 18 ft on the side. The cooling water enters at about 20°C, flows through the reactor at the rate of 20,000 gal min^{-1}, and resides in the reactor core for an average of 2 sec. Estimate (*a*) the exit temperature of the water, (*b*) its radioactivity (in curies per liter) as it leaves the reactor, assuming the water to be pure, (*c*) the radioactivity of the water 1 hr after leaving the reactor if it contains 1.2 ppm phosphorus, 1.8 ppm sodium, and 0.9 ppm chlorine impurities.

6. Verify the statement on page 362 that Xe^{135} poisoning in a high-flux reactor such as the MTR reaches a maximum about 10 hr after shutdown.

7. After a reactor has operated for 1 yr at 500,000 kw, its fuel is processed and the fission product wastes are stored. Estimate the number of curies of fission product activity remaining 10 yr later.

REFERENCES

R. L. Murray, *Introduction to Nuclear Engineering,* New York, Prentice-Hall, Inc., 1954.

R. Stephenson, *Introduction to Nuclear Engineering,* New York, McGraw-Hill Book Co., 1954.

C. Goodman (Editor), *The Science and Engineering of Nuclear Power* (2 vols.), Cambridge, Mass., Addison-Wesley Press, 1947–1949.

F. J. Van Antwerpen (Editor), *Nuclear Engineering* (Proceedings of International Symposium held at Ann Arbor, Michigan, in June 1954), New York, *Am. Inst. Chem. Engrs.,* 1954.

I. Kaplan, *Nuclear Physics,* Cambridge, Mass., Addison-Wesley Publishing Co., 1955.

S. Glasstone and M. C. Edlund, *The Elements of Nuclear Reactor Theory,* New York, D. Van Nostrand, 1952.

H. S. Isbin, "Nuclear Reactor Catalog," *Nucleonics* **10,** No. 3, 10 (March 1952), and **11,** No. 6, 65 (June 1953).

"Research Reactors," *Nucleonics* **12,** No. 4, 7–16 (April 1954).

L. A. Ohlinger, "Engineering Aspects of Nuclear Reactors," *Nucleonics* **5,** No. 6, 38 (December 1949); **6,** No. 1, 10 (January 1950); **6,** No. 2, 54 (February 1950); **6,** No. 3, 46 (March 1950).

O. Dahl and G. Randers, "Heavy-Water Reactor at Kjeller, Norway," *Nucleonics* **9,** No. 5, 5 (November 1951).

L. Kowarski, "Development of the Second French Reactor," *Nucleonics* **12,** No. 8, 8 (August 1954).

F. W. Gilbert, "Canadian Facilities for Isotope Production and Bombardment," *Nucleonics* **10,** No. 1, 6 (January 1952).

J. R. Huffman, "The Materials Testing Reactor," *Nucleonics* **12,** No. 4, 20 (April 1954).

W. H. Zinn, "Basic Problems in Central-Station Nuclear Power," *Nucleonics* **10,** No. 9, 8 (September 1952).

"Liquid Metal Fuel Reactors," *Nucleonics* **12,** No. 7, 11–42 (July 1954).

S. Untermyer, "Boiling Reactors: Direct Steam Generation for Power," *Nucleonics* **12,** No. 7, 43 (July 1954).

"U. S. Power Reactor Program," *Nucleonics* **12,** No. 7, 48–51 (July 1954).

O. R. Frisch, "On the Feasibility of Coal-Driven Power Stations," *Bull. Atomic Scientists* **10,** 224 (June 1954).

H. Hurwitz, Jr., "Safeguard Considerations for Nuclear Power Plants," *Nucleonics* **12,** No. 3, 57 (March 1954).

R. B. Mesler and L. C. Widdoes, "Evaluating Reactor Hazards from Airborne Fission Products," *Nucleonics* **12,** No. 9, 39 (September 1954).

A. C. Herrington, R. G. Shaver, and C. W. Sorenson, "Permanent Disposal of Radioactive Wastes," *Nucleonics* **11,** No. 9, 34 (September 1953).

H. D. Smyth, *Atomic Energy for Military Purposes,* Princeton University Press, 1945.

L. N. Ridenour, "How Effective are Radioactive Poisons in Warfare?", *Bull. Atomic Scientists* **6,** 199 (July 1950).

The Effects of Atomic Weapons, Washington, D. C., Combat Forces Press, 1950 (available at $1.25 from Superintendent of Documents, Washington 25, D. C.).

L. N. Ridenour and H. A. Bethe, "The Hydrogen Bomb," *Scientific American* **182,** No. 3, 11 (March 1950), and No. 4, 18 (April 1950).

J. R. Arnold, "The Hydrogen-Cobalt Bomb," *Bull. Atomic Scientists* **6,** 290 (October 1950).

CHAPTER 13

SOME COSMIC PROBLEMS

A. ENERGY PRODUCTION IN STARS

The emission of radiation from stars at the observed rates and presumably over the last several billion years requires enormous sources of energy. Chemical reactions cannot possibly be of significance as stellar energy sources. Although the gravitational energy of contraction may in certain stars play an important role, it is now generally recognized that most stars derive the energy they radiate from exothermic nuclear reactions occurring in their interior. Before discussing the particular reactions believed to be of importance in some types of stars we state briefly what distinguishes the different types.

Characteristics of Stars. The observations made by astronomers show that stars differ widely in properties. Measured masses range over a factor of about a hundred. Surface temperatures, deduced from analyses of emission spectra, vary by a factor of about 25. The absolute luminosities, which depend only on surface temperature and area, range from about 10^{-4} to about 10^{4} times that of the sun. Even so, certain distinct classifications have been made. In the *main sequence stars,* and these include the sun, the luminosity is a definite function of the surface temperature; these are probably alike in structure but of various sizes. A class of stars too cool for their luminosity to fit into the main sequence are the *red giants.* The *white dwarfs* have small luminosities compared to main-sequence stars of the same surface temperature and therefore must be smaller in size. In addition there are *variable stars, super giants,* the rare *supernovae,* etc.

We may take the sun as representative of the main sequence stars. Its mass is 2.0×10^{33} g; its mean density 1.4 g cm^{-3}. The measured surface temperature is 6000°K; the estimated central temperature 15,000,000°K; and the rate of energy loss is 4.0×10^{33} erg sec^{-1}. The sun is believed to contain approximately 80 per cent hydrogen, 20 per cent helium, about 1 per cent carbon, nitrogen, and oxygen, and smaller amounts of all other elements. The extent to which its composition is kept uniform by mixing between the interior and the surface is an important uncertainty.

Carbon-Nitrogen Cycle. Without doubt nuclear reactions are the source of the sun's energy. At 15,000,000°K the average kinetic energy of thermal motion is of the order of $kT = 1.3$ kev. This is very much smaller than the height of Coulomb barriers between any nuclei; but very rare collisions of light nuclei with energies far above the average (in the "tail" of the Maxwellian distribution) may give very small reaction rates. H. Bethe in 1938 first proposed a sequence of reactions which is able to supply the sun's energy:

$$\begin{aligned} C^{12} + H^1 &\rightarrow N^{13} + \gamma, \\ N^{13} &\rightarrow C^{13} + e^+ + \nu \ (\beta \text{ decay}), \\ C^{13} + H^1 &\rightarrow N^{14} + \gamma, \\ N^{14} + H^1 &\rightarrow O^{15} + \gamma, \\ O^{15} &\rightarrow N^{15} + e^+ + \nu \ (\beta \text{ decay}), \\ N^{15} + H^1 &\rightarrow C^{12} + He^4. \end{aligned}$$

The net result of the cycle is the conversion of four protons into one helium nucleus, aside from the positrons (which are annihilated with two electrons) and the neutrinos. The carbon serves only as a catalyst, entering into the rate-determining step and being later regenerated. A recently published calculation of the rate of the over-all reaction, based upon extrapolations of the reaction cross sections into the "thermal" energy range, gives as the best approximation to the energy production:

$$700\rho[H][C][T/(15 \times 10^6)]^{20} \text{ erg g}^{-1} \text{ sec}^{-1},$$

where ρ is the density of the reacting matter in grams per cubic centimeter, [H] is the weight concentration of hydrogen, and [C] is the weight concentration of carbon and nitrogen. Because the rate of this reaction is extremely sensitive to temperature, the proposed cycle can be important only in the very hottest region of the sun's interior.

Proton-Proton Chain. E. Salpeter has directed attention to an alternate sequence of nuclear reactions which appears more probable as a result of new knowledge of β-decay selection rules. Among the available nuclei by far the lowest Coulomb barrier is for the reaction of two protons. But because He^2 cannot exist, the only possible reaction requires that a relatively slow β decay occur during the collision,

$$H^1 + H^1 \rightarrow H^2 + e^+ + \nu.$$

After this step relatively fast reactions complete a cycle which in effect transforms four protons into one helium nucleus:

$$H^2 + H^1 \rightarrow He^3 + \gamma,$$
$$He^3 + He^3 \rightarrow He^4 + 2H^1.$$

The energy production rate has been calculated to be

$$0.50\rho[\mathrm{H}]^2[T/(15 \times 10^6)]^4 \text{ erg g}^{-1} \text{ sec}^{-1}.$$

The best evidence available at present indicates that in the very center of the sun the carbon-nitrogen cycle is the faster reaction, and that in a larger interior region at slightly lower temperatures the proton-proton chain is more important because of its smaller temperature dependence. Those main sequence stars which are smaller and cooler than the sun are probably heated by the direct proton-proton reaction; in those larger than the sun the carbon-catalyzed reaction almost surely contributes most of the energy.

Other Stars. Main sequence stars much heavier than the sun must burn hydrogen at such a rate as to exhaust their supply in a time comparable to the age of the universe (as estimated in section D). These stars would then consist mostly of helium. Their fate is not known with certainty, but very likely they join the populations of stars outside the main sequence. Such a star would be expected to contract, gaining energy from the gravitational field only and actually increasing in interior temperature, until it either exploded from rotational momentum or reached a much higher temperature and density at which other nuclear reactions might supply energy. It has been suggested that at about $\rho = 2 \times 10^4$ g cm^{-3} and $T = 200{,}000{,}000$°K, the reaction $He^4 + He^4 = Be^8 + \gamma$ might maintain enough of the very unstable Be^8 in equilibrium to permit an appreciable rate for the reaction $Be^8 + He^4 \rightarrow C^{12} + \gamma$. At even higher temperatures further α, γ reactions could lead to even heavier elements.

Eventually all such fusion reactions must cease to be a source of energy, since beyond the region of iron the packing fraction curve turns upward and the reactions become endothermic. In that event gravitational contraction would presumably again set in, and, if the endothermic nuclear reactions should prevent the rise of temperature and increase in balancing radiation pressure, the gravitational collapse might be expected to produce a gigantic explosion. Perhaps supernovae are the result of such catastrophes.

B. COSMIC RAYS

Observed Effects. Not long after the discovery of radioactivity it was known that detection instruments such as ionization chambers showed the presence of radiations even when not deliberately exposed to radioactive sources. This background effect was attributed to traces of naturally occurring radioactive substances such as uranium and thorium and their decay products, and this assumption is of course partly correct. Shielding the chambers with thick lead absorbers reduced but never eliminated the effect. It was reasoned that if the radiations resulted from radioactive contamination of the ground, elevation of the ionization chambers to 1000 meters or more should greatly reduce the effect, because the ordinary β and γ rays would be strongly absorbed by the 100 g cm^{-2} or more of air. In the period 1910 to 1913 several daring experimenters carried instruments consisting of ionization chambers and electroscopes aloft in balloons to altitudes as great as 9000 meters; surprisingly enough the background discharge rate at that height was about twelve times as great as on the ground. The conclusion from this and other experiments was that a radiation of extraordinary penetrating power fell continuously upon the earth from somewhere beyond. Since about 1925 this radiation has been known as cosmic radiation.

The nature and source of the cosmic rays could be more directly investigated at altitudes of several hundred miles, outside the earth's atmosphere, but for obvious reasons almost all the measurements have been made at much lower altitudes. Two or more coincidence counters arranged in a line and triggered by the same ray have been used as a sort of telescope to determine the direction of the ray. Such telescopes show that at sea level the rays are essentially vertical; this is to be expected simply as a result of the greater atmospheric absorption in other directions. However, a slight east-west asymmetry is interpreted as resulting from deflection in the earth's magnetic field; this effect indicates that the primary rays (outside the atmosphere) are predominantly positively charged.

Another effect of the magnetic field of the earth is to separate the incident charged rays according to energy and direction. Those rays incident perpendicularly at the magnetic poles suffer no deflection, but only rays of at least several billion electron volts can reach the earth at the equator. Measurements made at sea level show that the intensity near the poles is 14 per cent greater than at the magnetic equator. At higher altitudes the differences are even greater. These data give information on the energy spectrum of the cosmic rays and on their energy loss in air. Energies of several billion electron volts are predominant, and the energy loss in the whole atmosphere is about 2.5 Bev per primary particle. The total energy flux of all the rays striking the earth's atmosphere is roughly equal to that of all the incident starlight, excepting of course sunlight.

This discussion has anticipated the fact that the cosmic rays observed at sea level—indeed, throughout most of the atmosphere—are not the primary particles but rather are almost entirely secondary radiations produced by interactions of the primaries with the top of the atmosphere. These interactions seem to be largely very-high-energy nuclear reactions resulting in the emission of many mesons (mostly π mesons) and nucleons, many of which undergo further nuclear reactions. Many μ mesons, produced in flight by π-meson decay, are found lower in the atmosphere, and they constitute most of the "hard component" of the cosmic radiation. With energies of many billions of electron volts these mesons may penetrate a meter of lead or more and are observed to appreciable depths below water or ground. They have been best studied in cloud chambers triggered by counter telescopes.

The "soft component," readily absorbed in a few inches of lead, consists largely of photons, electrons, and positrons. It accounts for about 10 per cent of the cosmic-ray ionization at sea level but increases rapidly with altitude, constituting about 75 per cent of all the rays at an altitude of 10,000 ft. Most of the photons and electrons occur in showers of many particles of common origin. Initially, high-energy photons and electrons presumably result from meson decay, and subsequently positron-electron pair creation by photons, and ionization and bremsstrahlung emission by electrons, tend to produce large cascades of these rays. These are easily observed in cloud chambers (figure 13-1) and by arrays of coincidence counters. Some showers of particles resulting from a single primary have been found to trip simultaneously several coincidence counters located as much as 300 meters apart in a horizontal plane. Such an extensive shower may contain more than 10^5 individual particles, with a total energy of 10^{15} or 10^{16} ev.

The whole study of the cosmic rays was begun as a result of measurements on radiation detector backgrounds, and the knowledge gained has recently been applied to the original problem. For

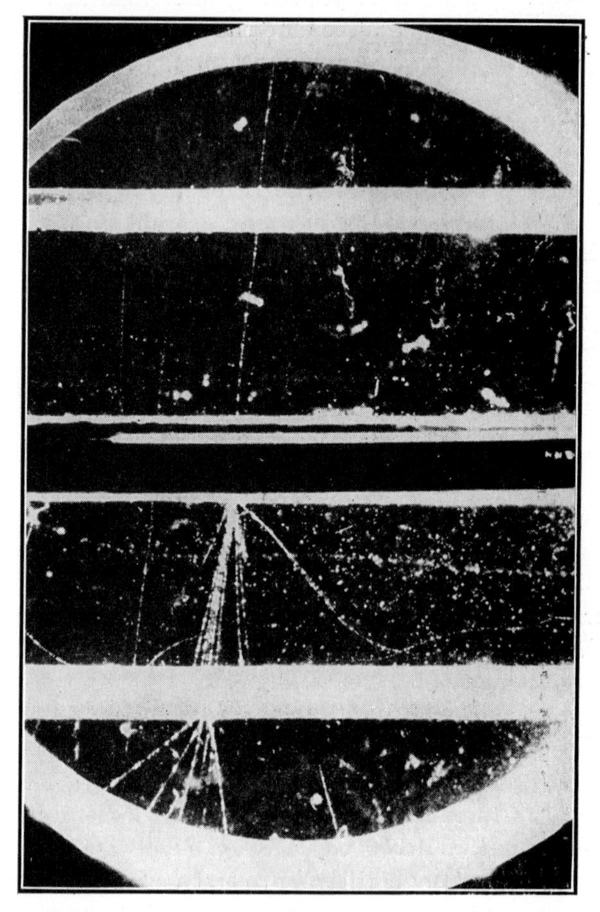

FIGURE 13-1. Cloud-chamber photograph of the development of a small electron shower. An electron entering the chamber at the top passes through a 1-cm lead plate and undergoes multiplication in the second (5-cm) lead plate. In the bottom lead plate (1-cm) some of the electrons are absorbed and others undergo further multiplication. (Courtesy R. P. Shutt.)

example, extraordinary reductions in Geiger counter background have been achieved by the use of electronic circuits which suppress all counts coincident with any count in near-by "shielding" counters. The array of shielding counters surrounds the working counter and is almost certain to give a response to any cosmic-ray mesons, showers, etc. A counter about 2 in. in diameter and 8 in. long, filled with 10 cm of argon and 0.5 cm. of ethylene, may have a natural background rate of about 500 counts per minute. An 8-in. thick iron shield reduces this to about 100 min^{-1}. (Iron is preferable to lead because it is less contaminated with natural radioactivities.) Only extremely great thicknesses of shield could remove much of this residual background. With a ring of about a dozen other Geiger counters placed around the first and operated as anticoincidence counters, the background can be reduced to 5 min^{-1}.

Primary Radiation. We have already suggested some of the evidence that the primary cosmic radiation arriving at the top of the earth's atmosphere consists predominantly of positively charged particles with energies in the billion-electron-volt range. Few if any electrons are included, and it is very unlikely that any appreciable fraction is positrons. The various positive mesons and the more unfamiliar positive particles (to be mentioned later) are too unstable to have arrived at the earth from any great distance; for example, the μ mesons with a half-life (at rest) of 1.5×10^{-6} sec can on the average travel only about 40 miles at 10 Bev. (Incidentally, a 1-Bev neutron could travel an average distance of about 400 million miles before decay.) The ionization and interactions of most of the primary particles are consistent with the view that they are protons with energies of 2 to 20 Bev. The energy spectrum extends much higher, to at least 100,000 Bev, but with greatly reduced intensity. More recent investigations reveal the presence of heavier nuclei: per 1000 protons there are about 80 helium nuclei, about 3 nuclei in the carbon-nitrogen-oxygen range, and 1 or 2 heavier nuclei. Their energy spectra, per nucleon, are about the same as the proton spectrum. As we shall see, the relative abundances of various nuclei in the primary radiation correspond roughly to the relative abundances of the elements in the universe.

Origin of the Cosmic Rays. The observation that cosmic-ray energies were of the order of 1 Bev, which is about the rest mass of a proton or neutron, led naturally to the hypothesis that the rays might result from the annihilation of nucleons somewhere in the universe. A different view, that the rays accompanied the creation of matter, has also been argued. The observation that essentially the primaries are nuclei of ordinary matter, including heavier nuclei, is hardly consistent with emission in elementary acts such as proton annihilation. It suggests very strongly that the primaries are ions which have somehow been accelerated by processes which are more ordinary in kind if not in scale.

In spite of the distortions caused by the earth's magnetic field, if the cosmic rays approached from some particular direction, for example from the sun, this should certainly have been revealed by the very careful measurements which have been made. What has been established is that any cosmic-ray intensity variations with either solar or sidereal time amount to less than 0.5 per cent. Thus if the cosmic rays observed on earth originate within our galaxy, then some kind of scattering process must confine and diffuse the rays until an essentially isotropic distribution results. Stray magnetic fields, very weak but of very large extent, as might be associated with moving clouds of partially ionized matter, may provide the wanted scattering mechanism.

It is certain that there is some connection between the sun and at least a part of the cosmic radiation. The continuous and systematic observations of cosmic-ray intensity that have been made in recent years at many stations around the world have shown large increases at times of unusual solar activity. For example, on November 19, 1949, recording meters at widely separated stations (Colorado, Greenland, England, New Zealand) produced sharp peaks beginning about one hour after the maximum of a solar flare. No increase was recorded at a station in Peru on the magnetic equator. The interpretation is that cosmic-ray primaries of only a few billion electron volts energy were emitted by the sun in connection with the solar flare. It is interesting that these sharp bursts of extra intensity, rare as they are, contribute perhaps 0.1 per cent of our total integrated cosmic-ray flux.

Perhaps the best of the current views of the origin of the cosmic rays is that they are emitted to some extent by our sun and to a much larger extent by others of the 10^{11} stars that make up our galaxy. Because magnetic fields, and especially varying magnetic fields, would seem to offer the most likely mechanism for ion acceleration, particular types of stars such as double stars, variable stars, and supernovae may be mostly responsible. Although the sun seems to emit only relatively low-energy cosmic rays, higher-energy ions may be emitted from larger, more active stars. The rays are confined mostly to the galactic region, about 1500 by 100,000 light years in extent, by random scattering from stray magnetic fields. The average density of matter in the galactic region, of the order of one atom per cubic centimeter, is low enough so that the mean free path before collision is millions of light years, and most cosmic rays reaching the earth have probably been traveling for several million years. It is possible that significant additional increase in energy occurs in this time as a result of the magnetic scattering processes.

New Unstable Particles. The cosmic radiation, including of course the secondary radiation, has been a happy hunting ground for those seeking to discover new "elementary" particles since 1932, when Anderson found the first positron tracks in his cloud chamber. Discovery of the mesons, that is of particles intermediate in mass between the electron and the proton, began in 1937 and continues today. By 1947 two mesons were known (μ and π); the number in 1954 is probably nearer ten and likely to become larger, or else the whole concept of elementary particles may be revised. The well-established mesons and other elementary particles are characterized in table 13-1.

TABLE 13-1

ELEMENTARY PARTICLES

Name	Symbol	Charge	Mass *	Spin	Statistics	Decay Process	Mean Lifetime (seconds)
Neutrino	ν	0	0	½	F	Stable	
Photon	γ	0	0	1	B	Stable	
Graviton		0	0	2	B	Stable	
Electron	e^-	-1	1	½	F	Stable	
Positron	e^+	$+1$	1	½	F	Stable	
Mu meson (muon)	μ^+	$+1$	210	½	F	$\mu^+ \rightarrow e^+ + 2\nu$	2.1×10^{-6}
	μ^-	-1	210	½	F	$\mu^- \rightarrow e^- + 2\nu$	2.1×10^{-6}
Pi meson (pion)	π^0	0	265	0	B	$\pi^0 \rightarrow 2\gamma$	$<10^{-14}$
	π^+	$+1$	276	0	B	$\pi^+ \rightarrow \mu^+ + \nu$	2.6×10^{-8}
	π^-	-1	276	0	B	$\pi^- \rightarrow \mu^- + \nu$	2.6×10^{-8}
Tau meson	τ^+	$+1$	966	0?	B	$\tau^+ \rightarrow 2\pi^+ + \pi^-$	2×10^{-10}
	τ^-	-1	966	0?	B	$\tau^- \rightarrow 2\pi^- + \pi^+$	2×10^{-10}
Theta meson	θ^0	0	975	0?	B	$\theta^0 \rightarrow \pi^+ + \pi^-$	1.5×10^{-10}
Proton	p	$+1$	1836	½	F	Stable	
Neutron	n	0	1838.5	½	F	$n \rightarrow p + e^- + \nu$	750
Lambda hyperon	Λ^0	0	2185	?	F	$\Lambda^0 \rightarrow p + \pi^-$	3×10^{-10}

* The unit is the mass of the electron.

Included is the best established of the hyperons, which is the name given to particles heavier than the neutron but lighter than the deuteron. Both groups, mesons and hyperons, were first discovered in cosmic-ray studies. The new high-energy accelerators produce many of these particles and often permit more convenient study of their properties. The graviton, although perhaps unfamiliar, is not a new particle but rather is a part of the formalism in which the gravitational field is treated similarly to the electromagnetic field (characteristic particle, the photon) and the nuclear force field (characteristic particle, the π meson).

The mass and the decay process of each of the various mesons and hyperons have been indicated by observations of tracks and decay events in cloud chambers or in nuclear emulsions. Correlations of measurable quantities, including track density, range, track curvature (in cloud chambers with magnetic fields), and angles between tracks at disintegration events, have given consistent mass values for the

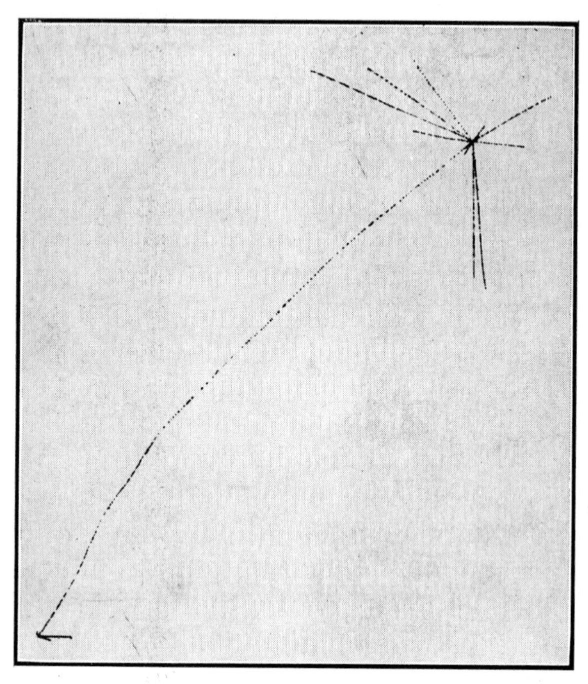

FIGURE 13-2. Double star produced in a photographic emulsion. The star in the upper right hand corner is produced by an incoming cosmic-ray particle (not identified in the picture). Among the eleven visible prongs emerging from this nuclear reaction is the long one towards the lower left corner which, by its grain density and scattering, has been identified as a π meson; since it causes another nuclear reaction (the smaller star at the lower left), it must be a π^-. (Courtesy J. Hornbostel and Brookhaven National Laboratory.)

better-known particles. The decay products also are revealed for those which decay within the chamber or emulsion, except that the participation of neutral particles can be inferred only from momentum or energy conservation. The lifetimes are obtained from the position of the decay event along the line of flight of the particle or from delayed-coincidence measurements with counters.

Apart from their decay processes, mesons may undergo reactions with nuclei. The π mesons, which are readily produced in high-energy nuclear collisions, readily react with nuclei (figure 13-2).

The primary reaction is essentially with a single nucleon, for example, $\pi^- + p \rightarrow n + \pi^0$, or with a pair of nucleons, for example, $\pi^- + p + n \rightarrow n + n$. Complex nuclear reactions result, with the emission of mesons, nucleons, deuterons, and other light nuclei. Before entering a nucleus, a slow negative meson may be captured into bound orbits about the nucleus. These orbits are quite analogous to the atomic electron orbits but of course are independent of them. Nuclear reaction then occurs usually by capture of the meson from its K-shell orbit. Characteristic "mesic X rays" due to meson transitions between orbits have been observed. The μ^- mesons also may enter bound orbits, but because of the much weaker interaction between μ mesons and nucleons, reaction is more probable than decay for only those atoms with $Z > 10$. The elementary reaction in this case is $\mu^- + p \rightarrow n + \nu$, and because the neutrino carries away most of the meson rest energy the residual nucleus is left with an excitation of only about 15 Mev. The positively charged mesons of course are not captured into bound orbits about nuclei, and because of the Coulomb barrier require high energies to react with nuclei.

Since the nuclear-emulsion and cloud-chamber techniques allow observation of individual events, a new particle or a new decay mode has often been claimed on the basis of very few events or even of a single photograph. On such evidence, gathered from careful studies of many thousands of plates, quite a number of "elementary" particles not included in table 13-1 have been described, both in cosmic-ray and high-energy accelerator studies. At least five additional kinds of mesons in the mass range 900 to 1200 electron masses, each possibly existing with either positive or negative charge, have been described; several of these may be τ mesons decaying by alternate modes, for example, to produce $2\pi^0 + \pi^+$ or even $\mu^+ + \nu$. Particles with masses intermediate between π mesons and protons and decaying into one charged π or μ meson and one or more neutral particles (π^0 or ν) have been given the generic name K mesons. Various kinds of K mesons have been produced in large numbers with accelerators operating in the billion-electron-volt energy range. The existence of charged hyperons seems well established. In particular, the following two decay modes have been reported: $\Lambda^+ \rightarrow n + \pi^+$, $Q = 135$ Mev, and $\Omega^- \rightarrow \Lambda^0 + \pi^-$, $Q = 65$ Mev.

It is expected that future investigations will bring some degree of order to the presently confusing array of elementary particles. That many of these particles are related is shown by their decay processes by which others are produced. One step toward unification of the many particles is the consideration of similar particles of different charge as manifestations of a single particle in different charge states. For example, the neutron and the proton may be represented as the two possible charge states of the nucleon. The number of possible charge states for a given particle is often described by the assignment to that particle of a new quantum number, the isotopic spin **T**, chosen so that $2\mathbf{T} + 1$ gives the number of charge states. For the nucleon, with the two values of charge 0 and +1, $\mathbf{T} = 1/2$. The π meson, existing as π^+, π^-, and π^0, is assigned $\mathbf{T} = 1$. The isotopic spin is recognized as an important quantum number in meson physics and is finding increasing favor as a useful quantum number in the classification of the energy states of light nuclei.

Radionuclides from Cosmic Rays. The impact of the primary and very-high-energy secondary cosmic rays, mostly near the top of the atmosphere, produces violent nuclear reactions in which many neutrons, protons, α particles, and other fragments are emitted. Nuclear emulsions exposed at high altitudes reveal many such spallation events; the charged fragments leave dense tracks emerging from the point of reaction, and the events are described as "stars." Among the fragments in significant yield are H^3, Be^7, and Be^{10} nuclei, and because these are radioactive they have been sought as natural products by radiochemical means. The estimated yield of Be^7, a 54-day electron-capture activity, is about 0.03 cm^{-2} sec^{-1}, and, since there is very little ordinary beryllium in the air to produce isotopic dilution, it may be found in the residue from the evaporation of rain water. According to J. Arnold its concentration in rain water is very roughly 4×10^{-20} atom per atom of hydrogen.

The nuclide H^3 is formed not only directly by the spallation reactions but also by the action of resulting fast neutrons on nitrogen, $N^{14}(n, H^3)C^{12}$. The total yield is estimated as about 0.4 cm^{-2} sec^{-1}, but because of dilution by ordinary hydrogen its detection is difficult without deliberate isotopic enrichment. Libby has found the tritium content of natural surface waters to be variable, but in the range 0.5 to 70 atoms per 10^{18} atoms of hydrogen.

Most of the neutrons produced by the cosmic rays are slowed to thermal energies and by n, p reaction with N^{14} produce C^{14}, the 5570-year β emitter. The production rate averaged over the whole atmosphere is approximately 2.2 cm^{-2} sec^{-1}. The lifetime is sufficiently long for the radioisotope to become thoroughly mixed with the carbon dioxide, dissolved bicarbonate, organic, and living carbon on the earth. The total amount of such carbon is about 8.2 g cm^{-2}, and the activity of this carbon is therefore $2.2/8.2 = 0.27$ disintegration $sec^{-1}\ g^{-1}$. This radioactivity is readily detected in counters provided that the ordinary high background is greatly reduced by shielding and by anticoincidence counters as mentioned on page 383.

C. GEO- AND COSMOCHRONOLOGY

Radiocarbon Dating. The discovery that all carbon in the world's living cycle is kept uniformly radioactive through the production of C^{14} by cosmic rays has led Libby and subsequently others to a rapidly expanding activity in the dating of carbon specimens by this means. Modern living carbon, for example in the wood of an elm tree in Chicago or in the oil of an Antarctic seal, contains enough C^{14} to undergo approximately 15 β disintegrations per minute per gram. (The activity of the carbon in the carbonate of modern sea shells is about 16 $min^{-1}\ g^{-1}$; the difference is attributed to a slight isotope-separation effect.) No doubt the C^{14} concentration in living carbon has been approximately the same for many thousands of years. Carbon from coal or petroleum is inactive because its age is very great compared to the 5570-year half-life of C^{14}. Carbon prepared from a cypress beam in the tomb of the Egyptian Pharaoh Sneferu (2625 B.C.) showed 8 disintegrations $min^{-1}\ g^{-1}$ corresponding to radioactive decay for almost one half-life. A very large number of samples, including wood, charcoal, peat, grain, shells, bone, cloth, beeswax, and corncobs, gathered from all over the world, have been dated by their radiocarbon content. Dates as old as 24,000 years have been established, and the method can certainly be extended back to 30,000 or 35,000 years ago.

One feature of recent results is that the wood produced today in American trees seems to have a 1 or 2 per cent lower specific activity than fresh wood had about a hundred years ago. This is presumably due to dilution of the normal carbon dioxide in the life cycle by inactive CO_2 from the combustion of coal and oil fuels.

Some other cosmic-ray-produced radionuclides may find applications in dating and similar studies. Libby finds that the isotopic abundance of H^3 in the surface water of many regions averages about (5 or 6) $\times 10^{-18}$ and on this basis has given approximate dates for vintage wines up to 25 years old.

Ages of Minerals. The very-long-lived natural radioactive substances, particularly U^{238}, U^{235}, Th^{232}, K^{40}, and Rb^{87}, can give information on the ages of the rocks which contain them. The several radiochemical methods that have been used for determinations of the time since the formation or solidification of particular minerals are discussed in the following paragraphs.

1. *Intensity of Coloration of Pleochroic Haloes.* Many types of radiation can produce coloration or discoloration in glass, quartz, mica, and a number of similar materials. Intense sources of α particles cause colorations in a short time, and even exceedingly small amounts of uranium or thorium are capable of producing visible effects within geological time intervals when present as minute inclusions in a mineral such as mica. The range of coloration from α particles is of the order of a few thousandths of a centimeter in mica, and the characteristic α-particle ranges for the various decay products cause the production of tiny concentric shells of varying coloration. Examined in thin sections under a microscope, these appear as circular areas known as pleochroic haloes; in polarized light the colors change with the plane of polarization. The many observed radii of the color bands have been fairly well correlated with the known α-particle ranges in mica of decay products of uranium or thorium, and in this way the nature of the inclusion is established. The amount of inclusion may be judged roughly from its size in the microscope field. Attempts have been made to evaluate the amount of radiation required for a particular degree of coloration and thus to establish a geologic time scale for these mica samples. Effects such as reversal of the intensity of coloration caused by overexposure (analogous to photographic solarization) must be taken into account, and no accurate results can be claimed.

2. *Ratio of Uranium to Helium Content.* Once an atom of U_I disintegrates, the chain of successive decays soon (say in less than about a million years) produces eight α particles. Because the ranges of these particles are very short in dense matter, most of the resulting helium atoms (the helium ions at rest are easily capable of acquiring two electrons by oxidizing almost any substance) may be trapped in the interior of the rock. In favorable cases, with very impervious fine-grained rocks and a low helium concentration (pressure) from small uranium contents, this helium has been retained throughout the geologic ages and now serves as an indicator of the fraction of uranium transformed since the formation of the ore. The thorium content of the rock also is a source of helium, and this must be taken into account. Very sensitive methods of assay for helium, uranium, and thorium are available and have permitted determinations on rocks with uranium and thorium contents below one part per million, and on metallic iron meteorites (where loss of helium in any process short of melting seems quite unlikely). The ages found, usually to be taken as lower limits, range up to something over 2000 million years.

For some meteorites larger values have been found; however, evidence has been presented which suggests that a considerable part of the helium in meteorites may have resulted from the action of cosmic radiation and that some meteorites may, therefore, be considerably younger than indicated.

3. *Ratio of Uranium or Thorium to* RaG *or* ThD *Content.* Lead (RaG and ThD) is a stable end product of the disintegration of uranium and thorium and, provided that there is no other source of lead in an ore, may be used as a quantitative indicator of disintegration. This lead method might be expected to be more reliable than the helium method since lead is not so likely to have been lost by slow diffusion; however, it is still quite possible that a lead-uranium or lead-thorium ratio has been changed by leaching or some other process. The distinction between these lead decay products (Pb^{206} from U_I and Pb^{208} from Th) and ordinary lead is made in a satisfactory way by mass spectrographic analysis; it is usually presumed that absence of Pb^{204} establishes the absence of ordinary lead. Age determinations from uranium-to-Pb^{206} and from thorium-to-Pb^{208} ratios do not always agree, but values ranging up to roughly 3000 million years are indicated.

4. *Ratio of Uranium Lead to Actinium Lead.* Probably the best method so far devised for very old rocks containing uranium involves determination of the ratio of Pb^{206} to Pb^{207}. This method should be free of many experimental errors and is less sensitive to chemical or mechanical loss of either uranium or lead than method 3. It is essential that the minerals not contain appreciable amounts of nonradiogenic lead; again absence of Pb^{204} is the criterion. The Pb^{206}/Pb^{207} ratio is an indicator of age because U^{238} and U^{235} decay at different rates. From mass spectrographic measurements of this ratio a convincing age scale of minerals more than 500 million years old can be established. Samples of two ores from a region in Canada known to be geologically very old (Huron Claim monazite and uraninite) have ages close to 2500 million years.

5. *Ratio of* RaD *to* RaG. This is a modification of method 3. Because RaD (Pb^{210}, 22-year half-life) is in equilibrium with U^{238} in old ores, radiochemical analysis for RaD plus mass spectrographic analysis for Pb^{206} give the information needed for age determination. The RaD analysis is made on the lead fraction by measurement of the RaF (Po^{210}) α particles as this nuclide comes to equilibrium with RaD.

6. *Ratio of* K^{40} *to Argon Content.* In this method the argon produced in the rock by decay of the natural radioactivity K^{40}, half-life 1.2×10^9 years, is measured. One difficulty is that K^{40} decays both

by electron capture to A^{40} and by β^- emission to Ca^{40}, and the fraction of decays that give A^{40} (about 0.10) is hard to determine with great precision. The method has been applied to a number of potassium-bearing minerals. A lepidolite about 2500 million years old has been dated in agreement with a Pb^{206}/Pb^{207} date.

7. *Ratio of* Rb^{87} *to* Sr^{87}. These species are best determined mass-spectrometrically, although any good analysis for total rubidium should be satisfactory. Ages by this method appear to be greater than those by the uranium and lead methods, reaching about 3500 million years. The half-life of 6.2×10^{10} years for Rb^{87} has been carefully determined from specific-activity measurements and should be reliable unless the decay scheme is complex and some radiations have not been observed.

8. *Ratio of Radiogenic Lead to* Pb^{204}. This method differs from the other lead-uranium methods in that it is applicable only to lead minerals which contain no uranium or no thorium. Because of the production of Pb^{206}, Pb^{207}, and Pb^{208} by the decay of uranium and thorium, the relative abundances of the lead isotopes throughout the world have changed continuously during geologic time. Lead ores deposited long ago contain a smaller proportion of radiogenic isotopes than does modern lead, and particularly the Pb^{206}/Pb^{204} and Pb^{208}/Pb^{204} ratios have been used to date galenas.

Age of the Earth. The terrestrial occurrence of the radioactive substances U^{238}, U^{235}, Th^{232}, and K^{40} gives some information about the time since the earth's genesis. Clearly conditions as we know them today cannot have existed for a time very long compared to their half-lives, 4.5×10^9 years, 7.1×10^8 years, 1.4×10^{10} years, and 1.2×10^9 years. If the earth's crust is an isolated system, it should be possible to reach some conclusions about its age by extensions of the methods described for dating minerals. The following relations may be derived between the lead isotope abundance ratios, at times 0 and t, and the modern ratio of uranium to lead, $(U/Pb)_t$:

$$\left(\frac{Pb^{206}}{Pb^{204}}\right)_t = \left(\frac{Pb^{206}}{Pb^{204}}\right)_0 + \frac{100}{1.48} \times \frac{139}{140}\left(\frac{U}{Pb}\right)_t (e^{\lambda_{238}t} - 1);$$

$$\left(\frac{Pb^{207}}{Pb^{204}}\right)_t = \left(\frac{Pb^{207}}{Pb^{204}}\right)_0 + \frac{100}{139 \times 1.48}\left(\frac{U}{Pb}\right)_t (e^{\lambda_{235}t} - 1).$$

The modern ratios $(Pb^{206}/Pb^{204})_t$ and $(Pb^{207}/Pb^{204})_t$ are measured on ordinary lead as 16.0 and 15.3. The primeval abundance ratios $(Pb^{206}/Pb^{204})_0$ and $(Pb^{207}/Pb^{204})_0$ are found from the lead in meteorites (where there is so little uranium that the radiogenic lead is negligible) as 9.4 and 10.3. Since the decay constants for the two uranium isotopes, λ_{238} and λ_{235}, are known, the two unknown quantities are t and $(U/Pb)_t$. Solution of the two equations gives $t = 5 \times 10^9$ years.

If the total uranium content of the earth were uniformly distributed through the whole volume, the concentrations of the radiogenic leads would be negligible, as in meteorites. Actually, the surface lead is appreciably enriched in Pb^{206} and Pb^{207} only because much of the earth's uranium is concentrated in the crust. It is possible that some correction should be made in the age calculation for the finite time required for the concentration process; however, even if the process has proceeded steadily up to the present time, the corrected age is only about 6×10^9 years. It is therefore quite probable that the earth as a planet was formed 5000 to 6000 million years ago.

Just what was its history between that date and the date of formation of the oldest surface rocks, roughly 2700 million years ago, is unknown. An earth originally at any reasonable temperature would have required a very short time to cool enough to form a solid crust unless it were continuously supplied with heat, presumably from radioactive decay processes. Today the very crust of the earth, of average depth about 25 miles, contains enough uranium, thorium, and potassium to supply more than half of the average heat loss of the earth, about 10^{-6} calorie cm^{-2} sec^{-1}, and this heat source would have been several times greater 5×10^9 years ago.

Very possibly the earth was formed at relatively low temperatures (as proposed by H. C. Urey) by gravitational accumulation of cosmic dust. At about the same time condensation of near-by dust eddies produced the other planets, the moon, and the sun. (In this formative phase the gaseous substances such as He, Ne, A, K, Xe, Hg, H_2O, CH_4, NH_3, etc., were mostly lost by the earth and the other inner planets.) The moon probably remains unchanged as a sample of the original cosmic accumulation. But the earth, because of internal radioactive heating, was melted and kept molten for almost 3000 million years. In this stage the metallic core was collected at the center, and the metallic oxides and silicates formed the surrounding mantle. As the radioactivities decayed away, especially U^{235} and K^{40}, the planet cooled, and at some moment roughly 2700 million years ago the first permanent solid crust appeared.

D. GENESIS OF THE ELEMENTS

Time of Formation. That the relative abundances of the isotopes of nearly all elements are essentially the same regardless of the source, that is, in various minerals, etc., has been well established by repeated mass spectrographic analyses. (Exceptions of course are the decay products of radioactive species as discussed in the preceding section.) This might be explained as a result of mixing processes that may have occurred in the early history of the earth. These comparisons have more recently been extended to include isotopic abundances in meteorites for a number of elements including carbon, gallium, copper, iron, and sulfur, and with the same result. For example, the S^{32}/S^{34} ratio in terrestrial sources ranges from 21.6 to 22.7, the variation being attributed to minor isotopic enrichments in geological and biological processes; the ratio in six different meteorites is uniquely 22.2. At the very least these findings strongly support the view that all the elements of the earth and of the solar system were formed by identical processes. Moreover, it has been carefully demonstrated that the ratio of U^{235} to U^{238} (1:139) and the isotopic abundance of K^{40} (0.012 per cent) are the same for uranium and potassium samples from various sources, including meteorites. This must mean that all these elements had their genesis at the same time; otherwise the processes of radioactive decay would have led to different isotope ratios for samples of different ages.

The date of genesis of our elements obviously must have been before the formation of the earth as a planet, thus at least 5×10^9 years ago. From the systematics of stable nuclei it seems quite unlikely that the original abundance of U^{235} exceeded that of U^{238}, and this limitation alone puts the time of genesis as no more than 6×10^9 years ago. A suggestion concerning the time that elapsed between the formation of the elements and the formation of the earth is provided by the β decay of ${}_{53}I^{129}$ to ${}_{54}Xe^{129}$. If I^{129}, half-life 1.7×10^7 years, had originally been about as abundant as I^{127}, then the earth must not have reached a form capable of retaining a gaseous atmosphere until at least 15 half-lives or 270 million years A.B. (After the Beginning), otherwise the abundance of Xe^{129} in the atmosphere today would be very much larger than it is. Actually the measured abundance of 26.4 per cent is unusually high for an odd-neutron isotope; some believe this is the residue of I^{129} decay and that the earth was formed just about 270,000,000 A.B.

On the basis of all available evidence a very attractive conclusion is that the elements of the earth, of the solar system, and probably of the known universe originated in one place approximately 6000 million years ago. An important part of the evidence is the observation of astronomers that all the galaxies are receding from each other at high velocities, velocities measured by the Doppler shift of all spectral lines toward the red (figure 13-3). The relative velocity between any pair of galaxies is found to be proportional to their distance apart. This is just the result that would be found if all the galaxies started from a common explosion and have been moving

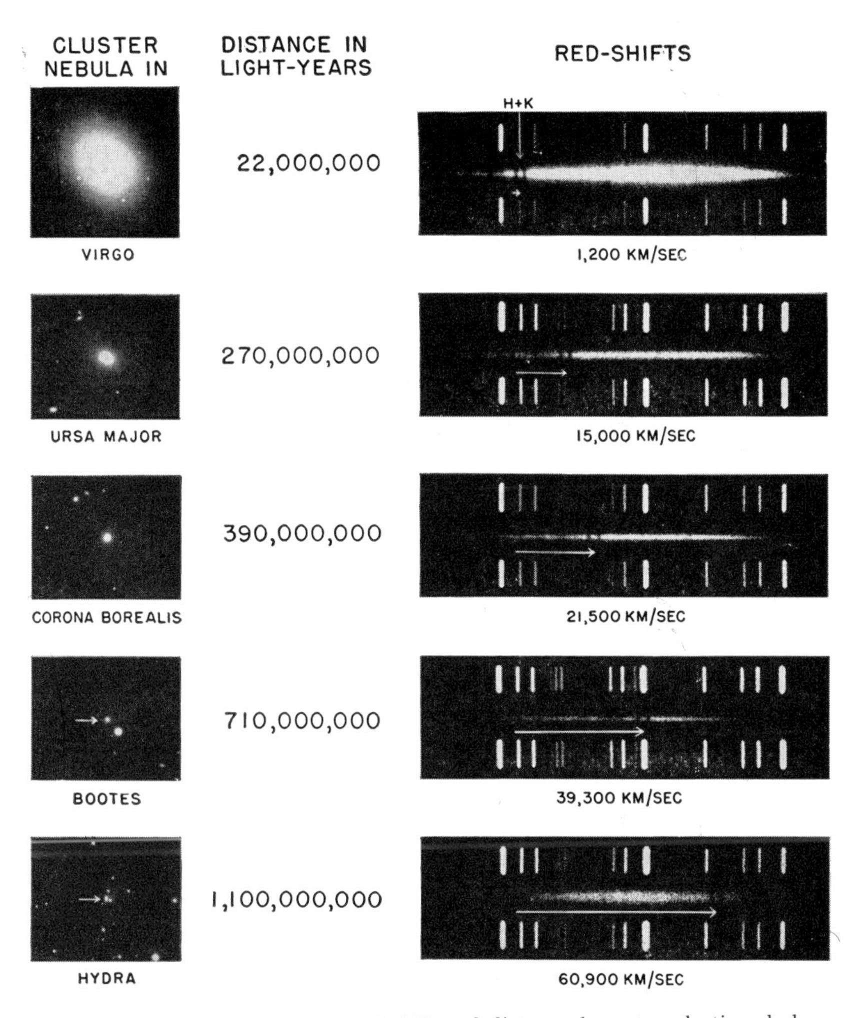

FIGURE 13-3. Relation between red shift and distance for extragalactic nebulae. At the left are direct photographs of the nebulae. The spectra at the right show the *H* and *K* lines of calcium. Helium spectra are shown for comparison, and the amount of the red shift is indicated for each spectrum by the length of an arrow. The velocities corresponding to the red shifts and the distances deduced from them are given. (Courtesy M. L. Humason, Mount Wilson and Palomar Observatories.)

apart at constant, particular velocities ever since. The velocities and separations observed today give the time since that fantastic explosion as roughly 6×10^9 years.

Cosmic Abundances of the Elements. Any hypothesis as to the mode of formation of the elements needs to be tested by comparison with the abundance distribution among the elements. Geologists and chemists have prepared tables of the abundances of elements in the earth's crust, based on averages of the analyses of igneous rocks. What is wanted is rather the average composition of the whole universe. The additional data that have been used to give rough estimates of such cosmic abundances are spectral analyses of the sun and stars, average densities of the planets, and especially classifications and analyses of meteorites. Figure 13-4 is a plot of typical results. Up to about $Z = 35$, the abundances decrease about exponentially with increasing Z; for $Z > 35$ they stay more nearly constant.

A more detailed test of any theory of element formation would be comparison with the abundance distribution of individual nuclides. It has been pointed out that the distribution of relative isotopic abundances for individual elements of even Z is generally different for the lighter and heavier groups. Among the lighter elements the tendency is for the lightest isotope to be an abundant one. The opposite is true for the heavier group; for each of the elements of even Z above $Z = 33$ the lightest isotope is rare, and the heaviest isotope is always abundant. This weighting of the heavy isotopes of the heavy elements would be explained if a high neutron density had shifted the peaks of the abundance distributions toward the heavier side of each stability parabola. Then subsequent β decays would have cut off the distributions at the heaviest β-stable isotopes, leaving these rather abundant. It seems necessary that all theories of the origin of the heavier elements provide either for formation in a region of high neutron content or for a subsequent high neutron flux. One hypothesis is that at least the heavier nuclides were formed by the break-up of large, relatively cold, polyneutron masses. In the next paragraphs we discuss very briefly two other theories as to the genesis of the elements.

Equilibrium Theory. It is quite possible that the matter of the universe has in the past gone through conditions of such high temperature that thermonuclear reactions were very rapid. If so, it would be expected that the various nuclear species would have achieved an equilibrium distribution according to the familiar principles of thermodynamics. Obviously free-energy data are lacking for such high temperatures and pressures, but the methods of statisti-

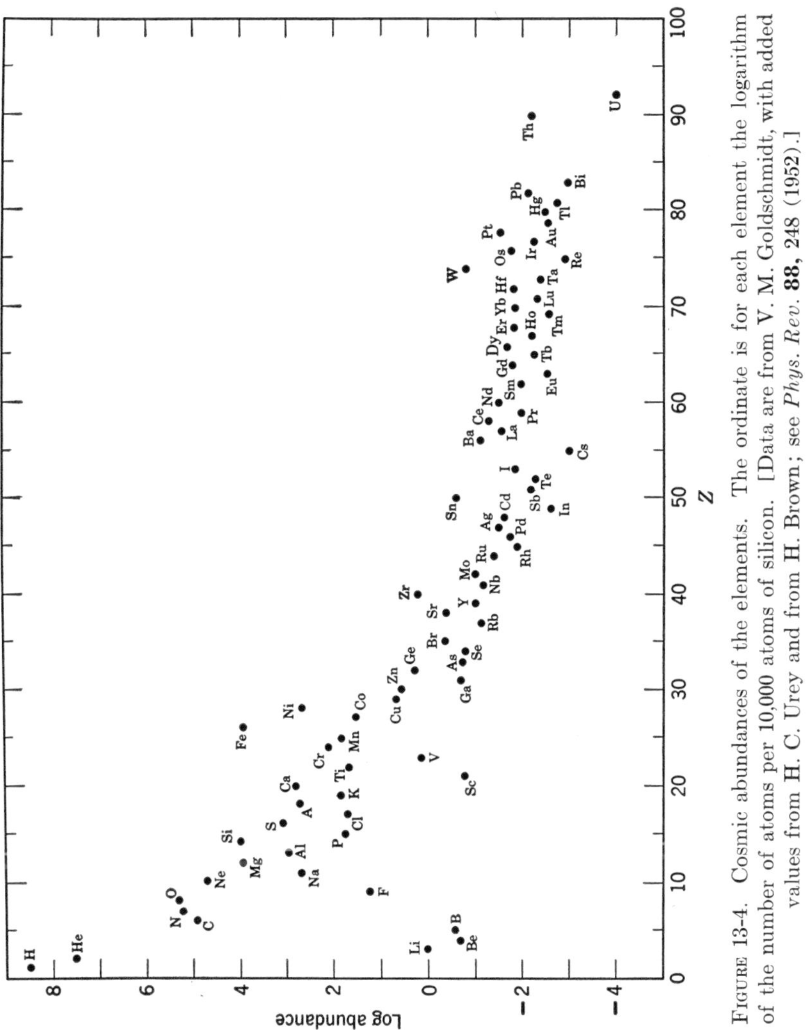

FIGURE 13-4. Cosmic abundances of the elements. The ordinate is for each element the logarithm of the number of atoms per 10,000 atoms of silicon. [Data are from V. M. Goldschmidt, with added values from H. C. Urey and from H. Brown; see *Phys. Rev.* **88**, 248 (1952).]

cal mechanics can give rough estimates of the equilibrium states. If a sudden expansion quenched the mixture, the high-temperature distribution might have been frozen and have persisted, except for radioactive decays, to the present time.

The dissociation of helium into hydrogen, He = 4H, is accompanied by a mass increase of 0.0287 atomic weight unit, or 26.7 Mev, approximately corresponding in the notation of chemical thermodynamics to $\Delta F^0 = +6.16 \times 10^{11}$ calories per mole of helium. The dissociation constant at room temperature is therefore $K = 10^{-464,000,000}$. It is possible to calculate under what conditions K for this reaction and for reactions between other light nuclei might be nearer unity and correspond to the light-element cosmic abundances. The best fit with these abundance data is obtained for a temperature of about 10^{10} °K and a pressure high enough to give a density of about 4×10^8 g cm^{-3}. However, no single temperature and density can give also the observed abundances of the very heavy elements and the distribution of relative isotopic abundances.

Formation from Neutrons. Some of the difficulties of equilibrium theories of element formation are avoided in another theory in which the elements are thought to have been formed in nonequilibrium processes during the very brief early stages of universe expansion. The primordial substance from which the elements were formed (sometimes called ylem) may have consisted of neutrons at a very high density and temperature, indeed, dissolved in the electromagnetic thermal radiation which was of even much higher density. As the minutes passed many neutrons decayed to protons and electrons, and from this process the high abundance of hydrogen may have arisen. As the temperature fell below about 10^9 °K, at an estimated age of 5 min, complex nuclei became thermodynamically stable, and reactions such as $H^1 + n \rightarrow H^2$ and $H^2 + n \rightarrow H^3$ began. Further thermonuclear reactions such as $H^3 + H^1 \rightarrow He^4$ and $H^2 + H^2 \rightarrow He^4$ could continue the building-up process.

At this point the theory begins to encounter its most serious difficulties. So far no mechanism for passing the gap at $A = 5$, for which there are no known nuclei, has been acceptable. A similar difficulty exists at $A = 8$. If nuclei of $A > 8$ can be formed, by these mechanisms or by entirely different ones, the neutron-capture process can account very well in a general way for the abundances of all elements beyond that mass. Because known fast-neutron capture cross sections increase exponentially with atomic weight up to about $A = 100$, the observed exponential decrease of abundances with increasing A in this region (figure 13-4) is consistent with the assumption that the abundances are determined by neutron-capture processes. Note that at these high temperatures neutrons do not become slowed to what would today be called thermal energies. Above $A = 100$, fast-neutron capture cross sections are essentially constant at $\sim$0.1 barn, and correspondingly the abundances of the heavier elements are essentially constant. More detailed features, such as the high abundances of magic-number nuclides, can also be correlated with neutron cross sections.

After about one hour very few free neutrons could remain, since their β-decay half-life is 13 min. By that time the whole structure of modern elementary abundances should have been fixed, except for subsequent adjustments by radioactive decays, a few of which continue to this day.

EXERCISES

1. Estimate the age of a rock which is found to contain 5×10^{-5} cc of helium at standard temperature and pressure and 3×10^{-7} g of uranium per gram. *Answer:* 1.2×10^9 years.

2. What is the kinetic energy of a μ meson resulting from the decay of a π meson at rest?

3. At approximately what stellar temperature would you expect the carbon cycle and the proton-proton cycle to proceed at equal rates, assuming the weight ratio of hydrogen to carbon to be 1000? *Answer:* 1.5×10^7 °K.

4. Calculate the age of a mineral which shows a Pb^{206}-to-Pb^{207} ratio of 14.0 and is essentially free of Pb^{204}. *Answer:* 1×10^9 years.

5. The radiation from the sun at normal incidence at the earth (93 million miles away) amounts to 0.135 joule cm^{-2} sec^{-1}. To produce this energy, at what rate is hydrogen being consumed in the sun, in grams per second? *Answer:* 5.9×10^{14}.

6. At sea level the cosmic radiation produces about 2 ion pairs per sec per cm^3 of air. At higher altitudes the intensity depends on the latitude, but for much of the United States it is about 10 ion pairs sec^{-1} cm^{-3} (of sea level air) at 10,000 ft and about 200 ion pairs sec^{-1} cm^{-3} (of sea level air) at 40,000 ft above sea level. Estimate the radiation dosage received per 24 hr in r units (probably we should say in rep units) from this source at (*a*) sea level, (*b*) 10,000 ft, (*c*) 40,000 ft.

7. If the sun's energy comes predominantly from the proton-proton chain, and if the neutrinos produced are absorbed only negligibly in the sun, what is the flux at the earth of neutrinos from this source? *Answer:* 6×10^{10} cm^{-2} sec^{-1}.

8. (*a*) Approximately what excitation energy is produced in the compound nucleus formed by the capture of a slow negative μ meson in lead? (*b*) By what energy is this reduced if the meson is initially in the *K* orbit of the lead atom? Consider the nucleus as a point charge.

9. Verify the statement on page 383 that a μ meson at 10 Bev can on the average travel only about 40 miles in a vacuum before it decays.

10. A proportional counter of about 6-liter volume, filled to 3 atmospheres with pure CO_2 and surrounded with heavy shielding and anticoincidence counters, is used for C^{14}-dating measurements. Three samples of CO_2 are

measured: sample A is "dead" CO_2 (age greater than 75,000 years) from coal, sample B is from contemporary wood, and sample C is of unknown age. The following counts are accumulated: 11,808 counts in 960 min for sample A, 21,749 counts in 180 min for sample B, and 20,583 counts in 480 min for sample C. Great care is taken to introduce the same weight of CO_2 into the counter at each filling. What is the age (and its standard deviation) of sample C? Take the half-life of C^{14} as 5568 ± 30 y.

REFERENCES

G. Gamow, *The Creation of the Universe,* New York, The Viking Press, 1952.

D. ter Haar, "Cosmogonical Problems and Stellar Energy," *Revs. Mod. Phys.* **22,** 119 (1950).

E. E. Salpeter, "Energy Production in Stars," *Ann. Rev. Nuclear Sci.,* Vol. II, p. 41, Stanford, Annual Reviews Inc., 1953.

"Nuclear Processes in the Stars" (International Astrophysical Colloquium), *Mém. Soc. Roy. Sci. Liége* **14,** 9–546 (1954).

L. Leprince-Ringuet, *Cosmic Rays,* New York, Prentice-Hall, 1950.

L. Biermann, "Origin and Propagation of Cosmic Rays," *Ann. Rev. Nuclear Sci.,* Vol. II, p. 335, Stanford, Annual Reviews Inc., 1953.

B. B. Rossi, *High Energy Particles,* New York, Prentice-Hall, 1952.

J. G. Wilson, *Progress in Cosmic Ray Physics* (2 vols.), Amsterdam, North Holland Publishing Company, 1952–1954.

B. B. Rossi, "Where Do Cosmic Rays Come From?", *Scientific American* **189,** No. 3, 64 (September 1953).

C. Dilworth, G. P. S. Occhialini, and L. Scarsi, "Heavy Mesons," *Ann. Rev. Nuclear Sci.,* Vol. IV, p. 271, Stanford, Annual Reviews Inc., 1954.

W. F. Libby, *Radiocarbon Dating,* University of Chicago Press, 1952.

E. C. Anderson, "The Production and Distribution of Natural Radiocarbon," *Ann. Rev. Nuclear Sci.,* Vol. II, p. 63, Stanford, Annual Reviews Inc., 1953.

W. F. Libby, "Tritium in Nature," *Scientific American* **190,** No. 4, 38 (April 1954).

T. P. Kohman and N. Saito, "Radioactivity in Geology and Cosmology," *Ann. Rev. Nuclear Sci.,* Vol. IV, p. 401, Stanford, Annual Reviews Inc., 1954.

K. Rankama and T. G. Sahama, *Geochemistry,* University of Chicago Press, 1950.

R. A. Alpher and R. C. Herman, "The Primeval Lead Isotopic Abundances and the Age of the Earth's Crust," *Phys. Rev.* **84,** 1111 (1951).

C. Patterson, H. Brown, G. Tilton, and M. Inghram, "Concentration of Uranium and Lead and the Isotopic Composition of Lead in Meteoritic Material," *Phys. Rev.* **92,** 1234 (1953).

H. C. Urey, "The Origin and Development of the Earth and Other Terrestrial Planets," *Geochim. et Cosmochim. Acta* **1,** 209 (1951).

R. A. Alpher and R. C. Herman, "The Origin and Abundance Distribution of the Elements," *Ann. Rev. Nuclear Sci.,* Vol. II, p. 1, Stanford, Annual Reviews Inc., 1953.

S. Katcoff, O. A. Schaeffer, and J. M. Hastings, "Half-Life of I^{129} and the Age of the Elements," *Phys. Rev.* **82,** 688 (1951).

H. C. Urey, "The Abundances of the Elements," *Phys. Rev.* **88,** 248 (1952) and **90,** 1131 (1953).

APPENDIX A

PHYSICAL CONSTANTS AND CONVERSION FACTORS *

Velocity of light	c	$= (2.99776 \pm 0.00004) \times 10^{10}$ cm sec^{-1}
Planck's constant	h	$= (6.624 \pm 0.002) \times 10^{-27}$ erg sec
Boltzmann constant	k	$= (1.38047 \pm 0.00026) \times 10^{-16}$ erg deg^{-1}
Electronic charge	e	$= (4.8025 \pm 0.0010) \times 10^{-10}$ absolute esu
		$= (1.60203 \pm 0.00034) \times 10^{-19}$ absolute coulomb
Electron mass	m	$= (9.1066 \pm 0.0032) \times 10^{-28}$ g
		$= (5.4862 \pm 0.0017) \times 10^{-4}$ physical atomic weight unit
Electron rest energy	mc^2	$= 0.5107$ Mev
Neutron mass	M_n	$= (1.67572 \pm 0.00031) \times 10^{-24}$ g
		$= 1.008982 \pm 0.000003$ physical atomic weight units
Hydrogen atom mass	M_{H}	$= (1.67432 \pm 0.00031) \times 10^{-24}$ g
		$= 1.008142 \pm 0.000003$ physical atomic weight units
Ratio of physical atomic weight to chemical atomic weight		1.000272 ± 0.000005
Avogadro number (chemical scale)	N	$= (6.0228 \pm 0.0011) \times 10^{23}$ mole^{-1}
Faraday constant (chemical scale)	F	$= 96{,}487 \pm 10$ absolute coulombs g-equiv.$^{-1}$
Energy equivalent of one mass unit (physical scale)		931.05 ± 0.15 Mev
Energy in ergs of one absolute-volt-electron		$(1.60203 \pm 0.00034) \times 10^{-12}$ erg
Energy in calories per mole for one absolute-volt-electron per molecule		$23{,}052 \pm 3$ cal$_{15}$ mole^{-1}
Photon wavelength at one electron volt		$(12{,}395 \pm 2) \times 10^{-8}$ cm
Bohr magneton	μ	$= \frac{h}{4\pi}\frac{e}{m} = (0.9273 \pm 0.0003) \times 10^{-20}$ erg gauss^{-1}
Number of seconds in one day		86,400
Number of seconds in one year		3.1558×10^7

* Mostly based on values given by R. T. Birge, *Revs. Mod. Phys.* **13,** 233 (1941).

APPENDIX B

RELATIVISTIC RELATIONS

Consider a particle of rest mass m_0 moving at a velocity v. If $\beta = v/c$, where c is the velocity of light, then the particle has

$$\text{mass} \equiv m = \frac{m_0}{\sqrt{1 - \beta^2}}, \tag{B-1}$$

$$\text{momentum} \equiv p = mv = \frac{m_0 v}{\sqrt{1 - \beta^2}} = \frac{m_0 \beta c}{\sqrt{1 - \beta^2}}, \tag{B-2}$$

$$\text{kinetic energy} \equiv T = m_0 c^2 \left(\frac{1}{\sqrt{1 - \beta^2}} - 1 \right) = mc^2 - m_0 c^2, \tag{B-3}$$

$$\text{total energy} \equiv E = mc^2 = \frac{m_0 c^2}{\sqrt{1 - \beta^2}}. \tag{B-4}$$

If a system A moves with a velocity $v(= \beta c)$ relative to another system B, a time interval Δt_A measured in system A will, in system B, appear as

$$\Delta t_B = \frac{\Delta t_A}{\sqrt{1 - \beta^2}}. \tag{B-5}$$

For a particle of zero rest mass (such as a photon or a neutrino), the following relations hold:

$$p = \frac{E}{c}, \tag{B-6}$$

$$E = h\nu, \tag{B-7}$$

where ν is the frequency and h is Planck's constant.

The following table lists, for a number of values of β, the corresponding kinetic energies of electrons, π mesons, and protons. For each value of β, the ratio of moving mass to rest mass is also given.

β	m/m_0	Kinetic Energy in Mev Electron	π Meson	Proton
0.10	1.005	0.00257	0.710	4.72
0.20	1.021	0.0107	2.96	19.7
0.30	1.048	0.0247	6.81	45.3
0.40	1.091	0.0465	12.8	85.5
0.50	1.155	0.0791	21.8	145
0.60	1.250	0.128	35.2	235
0.70	1.400	0.205	56.4	375
0.75	1.512	0.262	72.2	480
0.80	1.667	0.341	94.0	625
0.85	1.898	0.459	127	843
0.90	2.294	0.661	182	1.21×10^3
0.95	3.203	1.13	311	2.07×10^3
0.96	3.571	1.31	363	2.41×10^3
0.97	4.114	1.59	439	2.92×10^3
0.98	5.025	2.06	568	3.78×10^3
0.99	7.089	3.11	859	5.71×10^3
0.995	10.01	4.61	1.27×10^3	8.45×10^3
0.999	22.37	10.9	3.01×10^3	2.00×10^4
0.9999	70.71	35.6	9.83×10^3	6.54×10^4
0.99999	223.6	114	3.14×10^4	2.09×10^5

APPENDIX C

THERMAL NEUTRON CROSS SECTIONS

The data for this table are taken from the compilation by the AEC Neutron Cross Section Advisory Group in the U. S. Atomic Energy Commission Document AECU-2040 and its first three supplements (Nov. 20, 1952; June 15, 1953; and April 1, 1954).

Cross sections are given in barns for a neutron velocity of 2.20×10^5 cm sec^{-1} except in a few cases where the values given refer to a pile neutron spectrum; the latter values are shown in brackets. Absorption cross sections are shown in bold face. All other values are activation cross sections. Both activation and absorption cross sections for an isotope are given only when there is a substantial difference between the two values. Practically all the activation cross sections given are for n, γ reactions; cross sections for other reactions are labeled (n, p), (n, α), or (n, f). Where a cross section is given for a reaction leading to one of several isomers, the half-life of the product is listed in parentheses. An element cross section always refers to the natural isotopic mixture; an isotopic cross section is for the pure isotope.

The uncertainty in each last digit is ≤ 10.

H	**0.328**	O^{17}	$0.5(n,\alpha)$
H^2	5.7×10^{-4}	O^{18}	2.1×10^{-4}
He^3	$\mathbf{5.2 \times 10^{3}}(n,p)$	F^{19}	0.009
He^4	**0**	Ne	$\mathbf{<2.8}$
Li	**70**	Ne^{22}	0.04
Li^6	$\mathbf{930}(n,\alpha)$	Na^{23}	0.54
Li^7	0.033	Mg	**0.059**
Be^9	0.009	Mg^{24}	**0.033**
B	**750**	Mg^{25}	**0.27**
B^{10}	$\mathbf{3990}(n,\alpha)$	Mg^{26}	0.050
	$\mathbf{<0.2}(n,p)$	Al^{27}	0.21
B^{11}	<0.05	Si	**0.13**
C	**0.0045**	Si^{28}	**0.08**
C^{13}	0.0010	Si^{29}	**0.27**
C^{14}	$\mathbf{<2 \times 10^{2}}$	Si^{30}	0.110
N	**1.78**	P^{31}	0.23
N^{14}	$\mathbf{1.70}(n,p)$	S	**0.49**
	$\mathbf{0.10}(n,\gamma)$	S^{33}	$0.0023(n,p)$
N^{15}	2.4×10^{-5}	S^{34}	0.26
O	$\mathbf{<2 \times 10^{-4}}$	S^{36}	0.14

Cl	**31.6**
Cl^{35}	0.4×10^2
	0.17(*n*,*p*)
Cl^{37}	0.6
A	**0.62**
A^{36}	6
A^{38}	0.8
A^{40}	0.53
A^{41}	>0.06
K	**1.97**
K^{39}	**1.9**
K^{40}	$\mathbf{0.7 \times 10^2}$
K^{41}	**1.19**
Ca	**0.43**
Ca^{40}	**0.22**
Ca^{42}	**40**
Ca^{44}	0.6
Ca^{46}	0.25
Ca^{48}	1.1
Sc^{45}	10 (20s)
	12 (85d)
Ti	**5.6**
Ti^{46}	**0.6**
Ti^{47}	**1.6**
Ti^{48}	**8.0**
Ti^{49}	**1.8**
Ti^{50}	0.14
V	**5.1**
V^{50}	$\mathbf{3 \times 10^2}$
V^{51}	4.5
Cr	**2.9**
Cr^{50}	**16**
Cr^{52}	**0.73**
Cr^{53}	**18**
Cr^{54}	**<0.3**
Mn^{55}	13.4
Fe	**2.43**
	0.005(*n*,*α*)
Fe^{54}	**2.2**
	0.7
Fe^{56}	**2.6**
Fe^{57}	**2.4**
Fe^{58}	0.7
Co	17 (10.7m)
	20 (5.3y)
Co^{60m}	1.0×10^2
Co^{60}	6
Ni	**4.5**
Ni^{58}	**4.2**
Ni^{60}	**2.7**
Ni^{61}	**2**
Ni^{62}	**15**
Ni^{64}	2.6
Ni^{65}	6
Cu	**3.6**
Cu^{63}	**4.3**
Cu^{65}	**2.1**
Zn	**1.06**
Zn^{64}	0.5
Zn^{67}	$\mathbf{6 \times 10^{-6}}$(*n*,*α*)
Zn^{68}	0.10 (14h)
	1.0 (52m)
Zn^{70}	0.8×10^2
Ga	**2.7**
Ga^{69}	1.4, **2.0**
Ga^{71}	3.4, **4.9**
Ge	**2.4**
Ge^{70}	**3.3**
Ge^{72}	**0.94**
Ge^{73}	**14**
Ge^{74}	0.45, **0.60**
Ge^{76}	**0.35**
	0.03 (59s)
	0.20 (12h)
As^{75}	4.2
Se	**11.8**
Se^{74}	24, **48**
Se^{76}	**82**
	7 (18s)
Se^{77}	**40**
Se^{78}	**0.4**
Se^{80}	0.030 (59m)
	0.50 (17m)
Se^{82}	**2**
	0.05 (67s)
	0.004 (25m)
Br	**6.5**
Br^{79}	2.9 (4.4h)
	8.5 (18m)
Br^{81}	3.5
Kr	**28**
Kr^{78}	2.0
Kr^{80}	$\mathbf{0.9 \times 10^2}$
Kr^{82}	$\mathbf{0.5 \times 10^2}$
Kr^{83}	**205**
Kr^{84}	0.1 (4.4h)
	0.06 (10y)
Kr^{85}	**<15**
Kr^{86}	0.06
Kr^{87}	$<4.7 \times 10^2$
Rb	**0.70**
Rb^{85}	0.7 (19.5d)

Rb^{87}	0.12
Rb^{88}	$<2 \times 10^2$
Sr	**1.16**
Sr^{84}	1.0 (65d)
Sr^{86}	1.3 (2.7h)
Sr^{88}	0.005
Sr^{89}	$<1.1 \times 10^2$
Sr^{90}	1.0
Y^{89}	**1.4**
Zr	**0.178**
Zr^{90}	**0.1**
Zr^{91}	**1.5**
Zr^{92}	**0.3**
Zr^{94}	0.1
Zr^{96}	0.2
Nb^{93}	1.0 (6.6m)
	1.1
Nb^{94}	15 (35d)
Mo	**2.4**
Mo^{92}	<0.006
Mo^{95}	**13.4**
Mo^{96}	**1.2**
Mo^{97}	**2.1**
Mo^{98}	0.13
Mo^{100}	0.20
Ru	**2.5**
Ru^{96}	0.010
Ru^{102}	1.2
Ru^{104}	0.7
Rh^{103}	12 (4.3m)
	1.4×10^2 (44s)
Pd	**8**
Pd^{102}	5
Pd^{108}	11 (13.6h)
Pd^{110}	0.4 (22m)
Ag	**60**
Ag^{107}	44
Ag^{109}	2.8 (270d)
	1.1×10^2 (24s)
Cd	**2.4×10^3**
Cd^{106}	1.0
Cd^{110}	0.2 (49m)
Cd^{112}	0.020 (5y)
Cd^{113}	**1.95×10^4**
Cd^{114}	0.14 (43d)
	1.1 (2.3d)
Cd^{116}	1.4 (3.0h)
In	**190**
In^{113}	56 (50d)
	2.0 (72s)
In^{115}	1.5×10^2 (54m)
	52 (13s)
Sn	**0.65**
Sn^{112}	0.020 (30m)
	1.3 (112d)
Sn^{116}	0.006 (14d)
Sn^{118}	0.010 (245d)
Sn^{120}	0.001 (>400d)
	0.14 (27h)
Sn^{122}	0.16 (40m)
	0.0010 (136d)
Sn^{124}	0.004 (9.4d)
	0.2 (9.5m)
Sb	**5.5**
Sb^{121}	**5.7**
	7 (2.8d)
Sb^{123}	**3.9**
	0.03 (21m)
	0.03 (1.3m)
	2.5 (60d)
Te	**4.5**
Te^{120}	**0.7×10^2**
Te^{122}	**2.7**
	1.0 (100d)
Te^{123}	**3.9×10^2**
Te^{124}	**7**
	5 (58d)
Te^{125}	**1.5**
Te^{126}	0.07 (90d)
	0.8 (9.3h)
Te^{128}	0.015 (32d)
	0.13 (72m)
Te^{130}	<0.008 (30h)
	0.22 (25m)
I^{127}	6.3
I^{129}	11
I^{131}	6×10^2
Xe	**35**
Xe^{128}	**<5**
Xe^{129}	**0.5×10^2**
Xe^{130}	**<5**
Xe^{131}	**1.2×10^2**
Xe^{132}	0.2 (5.3d)
Xe^{134}	0.2 (9.1h)
Xe^{135}	**3.5×10^6**
Xe^{136}	0.15
Cs^{133}	0.016 (3h)
	26 (2.3y)
Cs^{135}	15
Cs^{137}	<2

Ba	**1.17**
Ba^{130}	0.030
Ba^{132}	6 (10y)
Ba^{134}	**2**
Ba^{135}	**5.6**
Ba^{136}	**0.4**
Ba^{137}	**4.9**
Ba^{138}	0.5
Ba^{139}	4
La	**8.9**
La^{139}	8.4
La^{140}	3
Ce	**0.70**
Ce^{136}	**0.3×10^2**
Ce^{138}	**9**
	<0.4 (140d)
Ce^{140}	0.3, **0.63**
Ce^{142}	1.0, **1.8**
Pr^{141}	**11.2**
Nd	**44**
Nd^{142}	**18**
Nd^{143}	**2.9×10^2**
Nd^{144}	**4.8**
Nd^{145}	**52**
Nd^{146}	1.8, **9.8**
Nd^{148}	3.7
Nd^{150}	**3**
Pm^{147}	0.6×10^2
Sm	**6.5×10^3**
Sm^{144}	<0.25
Sm^{149}	**[5×10^4]**
Sm^{151}	**[7×10^3]**
Sm^{152}	1.5×10^2
Sm^{154}	5.5
Eu	**4.5×10^3**
Eu^{151}	[1.4×10^3 (9.2h)]
	[9×10^3]
Eu^{152} (13y)	**[6×10^3]**
Eu^{153}	**[4.2×10^2]**
Eu^{154}	**[1.5×10^3]**
Eu^{155}	**[1.4×10^4]**
Gd	**4.4×10^4**
Gd^{152}	<125
Gd^{155}	**[7×10^4]**
Gd^{157}	**[1.6×10^5]**
Gd^{158}	4
Gd^{160}	1.5
Tb^{159}	**44**
Dy	**1.1×10^3**
Dy^{164}	[2.6×10^3 (1.3m)]
	[$<1 \times 10^3$ (2.4h)]
Dy^{165}	[5×10^3]
Ho^{165}	**64**
	0.6×10^2 (27h)
Er	**1.7×10^2**
Er^{170}	>7
Tm^{169}	**118**
Yb	**36**
Yb^{168}	[1.1×10^4]
Yb^{174}	0.6×10^2
Yb^{176}	5.5
Lu	**108**
Lu^{175}	0.4×10^2 (3.7h)
Lu^{176}	4.0×10^3 (6.8d)
Hf	**1.2×10^2**
Hf^{174}	**1.5×10^3**
Hf^{176}	**0.2×10^2**
Hf^{177}	3.8×10^2
Hf^{178}	**75**
Hf^{179}	**0.6×10^2**
Hf^{180}	10
Ta^{181}	0.030 (16m)
	21 (111d)
Ta^{182}	5.9×10^4
W	**19.2**
W^{180}	10
W^{182}	**19**
W^{183}	**11**
W^{184}	2.1 (73d)
	2.0
W^{186}	**34**
W^{187}	0.9×10^2
Re	**84**
Re^{185}	100
Re^{187}	**63**
	0.7×10^2 (17h)
Os	**14.7**
Os^{184}	$<2 \times 10^2$
Os^{190}	8 (16d)
Os^{192}	1.6
Os^{193}	0.6×10^2
Ir	**4.4×10^2**
Ir^{191}	2.6×10^2 (1.4m)
	7×10^2 (70d)
Ir^{193}	1.3×10^2 (19h)
Pt	**8.1**
Pt^{192}	0.9×10^2 (4.3d)

Pt^{196}	1.1 (18h)
Pt^{198}	3.9
Au^{197}	**98.0**
Au^{198}	3.5×10^4
Hg	$\mathbf{3.8 \times 10^2}$
Hg^{196}	$[\mathbf{3.1 \times 10^3}]$
Hg^{199}	$[\mathbf{2.5 \times 10^3}]$
Hg^{200}	$\mathbf{<60}$
Hg^{201}	$\mathbf{<60}$
Hg^{202}	3.0
Hg^{204}	0.43
Tl	**3.3**
Tl^{203}	**11.0,** 8
Tl^{205}	**0.77**
	0.10 (4.2m)
Pb	**0.17**
Pb^{204}	**0.8**
Pb^{206}	**0.026**
Pb^{207}	**0.69**
Pb^{208}	0.0006
Bi^{209}	**0.032**
	0.017 (5d)
Rn^{222}	0.72
Ra^{223}	$<1 \times 10^2(n,f)$
Ra^{226}	20
	$<1 \times 10^{-4}(n,f)$
Ra^{228}	36
	$<2(n,f)$
Ac^{227}	$\mathbf{5.5 \times 10^2}$
	$<2(n,f)$
Th^{227}	$1.5 \times 10^3(n,f)$
Th^{228}	$<0.3(n,f)$
Th^{229}	$45(n,f)$
Th^{230}	**27,** 35
	$<1 \times 10^{-3}(n,f)$
Th^{232}	**7.0,** 7.7
	$<2 \times 10^{-4}(n,f)$
Th^{233}	1.4×10^3
Th^{234}	1.8
	$<0.01(n,f)$
Pa^{230}	$1.5 \times 10^3(n,f)$
Pa^{231}	2.6×10^2
	$0.010(n,f)$
Pa^{232}	0.5×10^2
	$7.0 \times 10^2(n,f)$
Pa^{233}	0.4×10^2
	(1.2m + 6.7h)
	$<0.1(n,f)$
$Pa^{234}(UX_2)$	$<5 \times 10^2(n,f)$
$Pa^{234}(UZ)$	$<5 \times 10^3(n,f)$
U	**7.68**
	$4.18(n,f)$
U^{230}	$25(n,f)$
U^{231}	$2.5 \times 10^2(n,f)$
U^{232}	3×10^2
	$0.8 \times 10^2(n,f)$
U^{234}	72
	$<0.65(n,f)$
U^{235}	**687,** 107
	$580(n,f)$
U^{238}	**2.75,** 2.8
U^{239}	22
Np^{234}	$9 \times 10^2(n,f)$
Np^{236}	$10^5(n,f)$
Np^{237}	1.7×10^2
	$0.019(n,f)$
Np^{238}	$1.60 \times 10^3(n,f)$
Np^{239}	$3(n,f)$
Pu^{238}	4.3×10^2
	$18(n,f)$
Pu^{239}	$\mathbf{1.06 \times 10^3}$
	3.2×10^2
	$7.5 \times 10^2(n,f)$
Pu^{241}	4.0×10^2
	$1.08 \times 10^3(n,f)$
Pu^{242}	0.4×10^2
Am^{241}	7×10^2 (16h)
	$<0.5 \times 10^2$ (500y)
	$3.2(n,f)$
Am^{242m}	$2.0 \times 10^3(n,f)$
Am^{242}	$\mathbf{8.0 \times 10^3}$
	$3.5 \times 10^3(n,f)$
Am^{243}	0.5×10^2
	$<25(n,f)$
Cm^{240}	$2.0 \times 10^4(n,f)$
Cm^{242}	$<5(n,f)$

APPENDIX D

REACTION CROSS SECTIONS FOR 14-MEV NEUTRONS

The data for this table are taken from the compilation by the AEC Neutron Cross Section Advisory Group, U. S. Atomic Energy Commission Document AECU-2040 and its first three supplements.

Values are in barns. Where the listed cross section applies to formation of one of several isomers, the half-life is listed in parentheses.

Target	*n,p*	*n,α*	*n,2n*
Li^{6}	0.0067	0.026	
Be^{9}		0.010	
N^{14}			0.0057
O^{16}	0.05		
F^{19}	0.14		0.06
Na^{23}	0.03		
Mg^{24}	0.19		
Mg^{25}	0.04		
Al^{27}	0.070	0.11	
Si^{28}	0.22		
Si^{29}	0.10		
Si^{30}		0.08	
P^{31}	0.077	0.15	
S^{32}	0.37		
S^{34}	0.08	0.014	
Cl^{35}		0.14	0.004
Cl^{37}	0.033	0.19	
K^{39}			0.010
K^{41}	0.08	0.05	
Ti^{48}	0.09		
V^{51}	0.027	0.030	
Cr^{52}	0.08		
Mn^{55}		0.03	
Fe^{56}	0.11		
Co^{59}		0.052	
Ni^{58}			0.04
Ni^{61}	0.18		
Cu^{63}			0.50
Cu^{65}	0.019		1.00
Zn^{64}	0.39		0.22
Zn^{66}	0.10		
Ga^{69}	0.02	0.039	0.6
	(14h)		
Ga^{71}			0.70
Ge^{70}	0.13		0.7
Ge^{72}	0.06		
Ge^{73}	0.14		
Ge^{74}		0.015	
Ge^{76}			1.8
As^{75}	0.012	0.012	0.5
Se^{77}	0.04		
Se^{80}		0.04	
Se^{82}			1.5
			(57m)
Br^{79}			1.1
Br^{81}		0.10	0.8
			(4h)
Rb^{87}		0.04	
Sr^{88}	0.018	0.06	
		(4h)	
Y^{89}		0.07	
Zr^{90}	0.25	0.19	0.08
		(2.8h)	(4m)
Zr^{94}	0.011		
Mo^{92}			0.19
Mo^{97}	0.11		
Mo^{100}			4
Ru^{96}			0.48
Ru^{101}	0.002		
Rh^{103}		0.06	
Pd^{104}	0.13		
Pd^{105}	0.7		
Pd^{110}		0.014	2.0
Ag^{107}			0.55
Ag^{109}			0.8
Sb^{121}			0.8
			(15m)
Sb^{123}			1.2
Te^{128}			0.8
			(9h)
Te^{130}			0.6
I^{127}	0.2	0.018	1.1
	(9h)	(20m)	
Ba^{138}	0.006		
La^{139}	0.006		
Ce^{140}		0.012	
Pr^{141}			2.1
Sm^{152}		0.009	
Sm^{154}			0.22
Gd^{160}			1.5
Ta^{181}			0.9
Pt^{198}			3
Au^{197}			1.7
Tl^{205}	0.003		
Pb^{208}	0.001		
Bi^{209}		0.0012	

APPENDIX E

THICK-TARGET YIELDS FOR SOME NUCLEAR REACTIONS

The yields listed are those that would be obtained with thick targets of the pure target elements of natural isotopic composition, and in bombardments short compared to the product half-lives. The yields are given in microcuries per microampere hour ($\mu c/\mu ah$). Probably none of the numbers are reliable to better than ± 25 per cent. It may be noted that when data by different authors are given for the same reaction the yields of reference (a) appear to be systematically low by factors of between about 2 and 10.

Reaction	Bombarding Energy (Mev)	Yield ($\mu c/\mu ah$)	Reference
$Li^7(d,2n)Be^7$ / $Li^6(d,n)Be^7$	19	2	(a)
$B^{11}(d,n)C^{11}$	8	5×10^2	(a)
"	8	3.4×10^2	(b)
$C^{12}(d,n)N^{13}$	8	1×10^3	(a)
$O^{16}(\alpha,pn)F^{18}$	38	5×10^3	(a)
$O^{17}(d,n)F^{18}$ / $O^{18}(d,2n)F^{18}$	8	5.5	(b)
$Mg^{24}(d,\alpha)Na^{22}$	8	1.4	(b)
"	14	1.8	(c)
"	14	1.0	(a)
$Na^{23}(d,p)Na^{24}$	8	6×10^2	(b)
"	14	1.1×10^4	(c)
"	19	1.5×10^3	(a)
$Mg^{26}(d,\alpha)Na^{24}$	14	2.4×10^2	(c)
$Al^{27}(d,p\alpha)Na^{24}$	14	45	(c)
$Mg^{26}(d,p)Mg^{27}$	8	5×10^2	(a)
"	14	3×10^3	(a)
$Al^{27}(d,2p)Mg^{27}$	19	2.5×10^3	(a)
$Si^{30}(d,p)Si^{31}$	8	7.3×10^2	(b)
"	14	1.0×10^3	(c)
$P^{31}(d,p)P^{32}$	8	30	(a)
"	8	87	(b)
$P^{31}(d,p)P^{32}$	14	1.2×10^2	(a)
"	14	2.3×10^2	(c)
$Cl^{37}(d,\alpha)S^{35}$	19	8	(a)
$Cl^{37}(d,p)Cl^{38}$	8	10^3	(a)
"	14	4.1×10^4	(c)
$K^{41}(d,p)K^{42}$	8	1.3×10^2	(b)
"	14	0.5×10^2	(a)
"	14	2.2×10^2	(c)
"	19	1×10^2	(a)

Reaction	Bombarding Energy (Mev)	Yield ($\mu c/\mu ah$)	Reference
$Ca^{44}(d,\alpha)K^{42}$	19	3	(a)
$A^{40}(\alpha,pn)K^{42}$	38	2×10^3	(a)
$A^{40}(\alpha,p)K^{43}$	38	10^3	(a)
$Ca^{44}(d,p)Ca^{45}$	8	0.2	(b)
$Ti^{48}(d,\alpha)Sc^{46}$ (85d)	19	0.01	(a)
$Cr^{52}(d,2n)Mn^{52}$ (6d)	14	80	(c)
$Fe^{56}(d,\alpha)Mn^{54}$	8	0.3	(b)
"	14	1.0	(d)
$Mn^{55}(d,2n)Fe^{55}$	14	0.7	(d)
$Fe^{58}(d,p)Fe^{59}$	8	0.04	(b)
"	14	0.03	(a)
$Co^{59}(d,2p)Fe^{59}$	20	0.07	(e)
$Co^{59}(d,p)Co^{60}$ (5y)	14	1.1	(c)
$Fe^{54}(d,n)Co^{55}$	8	16	(b)
$Cu^{63}(d,p)Cu^{64}$	14	2.5×10^3	(c)
$Zn^{67}(d,2p)Cu^{67}$	19	10	(a)
$Cu^{63}(d,2n)Zn^{63}$	14	3.1×10^4	(c)
$Cu^{65}(d,2n)Zn^{65}$	14	3.4	(c)
$Ge^{74}(d,2n)As^{74}$	14	2	(a)
"	19	10	(a)
$As^{75}(d,p)As^{76}$	8	54	(b)
$As^{75}(d,2n)Se^{75}$	8	4	(b)
$Br^{81}(d,p)Br^{82}$	14	7.7×10^2	(c)
$Rb^{85}(d,p)Rb^{86}$ (19d)	8	1	(b)
$Sr^{88}(d,\alpha)Rb^{86}$ (19d)	14	1	(a)
$Sr^{88}(d,p)Sr^{89}$	8	2	(b)
"	14	10	(a)
"	14	35	(c)
$Sr^{88}(d,2n)Y^{88}$	14	38	(c)
$Y^{89}(d,2n)Zr^{89}$ (79h)	14	7	(a)
"	19	75	(a)
$Zr^{94}(d,p)Zr^{95}$	14	0.2	(a)
$Mo^{92}(d,\alpha)Nb^{90}$	14	2	(a)
$Mo^{97}(d,\alpha)Nb^{95}$ (35d)	14	0.05	(a)
$Zr^{96}(\alpha,n)Mo^{99}$	38	0.1	(a)
$Te^{130}(d,2n)I^{130}$	8	10	(b)
"	14	8.7×10^2	(c)
$Te^{130}(d,n)I^{131}$	8	0.6	(b)
"	8	1.0	(a)
"	14	20	(a)
"	14	87	(c)
$Au^{197}(d,2n)Hg^{197+197m_2}$	14	8×10^2	(d)
$Bi^{209}(d,n)Po^{210}$	14	2	(a)
$Pb^{208}(\alpha,2n)Po^{210}$	38	1	(a)

(a) W. M. Garrison and J. G. Hamilton, *Chemical Revs.* **49,** 237 (1951).
(b) A. F. Reid and A. S. Weil, U. S. Atomic Energy Commission Declassified Report AECD 2324.
(c) E. T. Clarke and J. W. Irvine, Jr., *Phys. Rev.* **70,** 893 (1946).
(d) J. W. Irvine, Jr., *Nucleonics* **3,** No. 2, 5 (August 1948).
(e) R. W. Dunn, *Nucleonics* **10,** No. 7, 8 (July 1952).

APPENDIX F

SOME MEASURED NUCLEAR SPINS

Nuclide	I	Nuclide	I	Nuclide	I	Nuclide	I
H^{1}	$\frac{1}{2}$	Ti^{47}	$\frac{5}{2}$	Ru^{101}	$\frac{5}{2}$	Eu^{151}	$\frac{5}{2}$
H^{2}	1	Ti^{49}	$\frac{7}{2}$	Rh^{103}	$\frac{1}{2}$	Eu^{153}	$\frac{5}{2}$
H^{3}	$\frac{1}{2}$	V^{50}	6	Pd^{105}	$\frac{5}{2}$	Tb^{159}	$\frac{3}{2}$
He^{3}	$\frac{1}{2}$	V^{51}	$\frac{7}{2}$	Ag^{107}	$\frac{1}{2}$	Ho^{165}	$\frac{7}{2}$
Li^{6}	1	Cr^{53}	$\frac{3}{2}$	Ag^{109}	$\frac{1}{2}$	Er^{167}	$\frac{7}{2}$
Li^{7}	$\frac{3}{2}$	Mn^{55}	$\frac{5}{2}$	Ag^{111}	$\frac{1}{2}$	Tm^{169}	$\frac{1}{2}$
Be^{9}	$\frac{3}{2}$	Co^{57}	$\frac{7}{2}$	Cd^{111}	$\frac{1}{2}$	Yb^{171}	$\frac{1}{2}$
B^{10}	3	Co^{59}	$\frac{7}{2}$	Cd^{113}	$\frac{1}{2}$	Yb^{173}	$\frac{5}{2}$
B^{11}	$\frac{3}{2}$	Cu^{63}	$\frac{3}{2}$	In^{113}	$\frac{9}{2}$	Lu^{175}	$\frac{7}{2}$
C^{12}	0	Cu^{64}	1	In^{115}	$\frac{9}{2}$	Lu^{176}	≥ 7
C^{13}	$\frac{1}{2}$	Cu^{65}	$\frac{3}{2}$	Sn^{115}	$\frac{1}{2}$	Ta^{181}	$\frac{7}{2}$
C^{14}	0	Zn^{67}	$\frac{5}{2}$	Sn^{117}	$\frac{1}{2}$	W^{183}	$\frac{1}{2}$
N^{14}	1	Ga^{69}	$\frac{3}{2}$	Sn^{119}	$\frac{1}{2}$	Re^{185}	$\frac{5}{2}$
N^{15}	$\frac{1}{2}$	Ga^{71}	$\frac{3}{2}$	Sb^{121}	$\frac{5}{2}$	Re^{187}	$\frac{5}{2}$
O^{16}	0	Ge^{73}	$\frac{9}{2}$	Sb^{123}	$\frac{7}{2}$	Os^{189}	$\frac{3}{2}$
O^{17}	$\frac{5}{2}$	As^{75}	$\frac{3}{2}$	Te^{123}	$\frac{1}{2}$	Ir^{191}	$\frac{3}{2}$
O^{18}	0	Se^{75}	$\frac{5}{2}$	Te^{125}	$\frac{1}{2}$	Ir^{193}	$\frac{3}{2}$
F^{19}	$\frac{1}{2}$	Se^{77}	$\frac{1}{2}$	I^{127}	$\frac{5}{2}$	Pt^{195}	$\frac{1}{2}$
Na^{22}	3	Se^{78}	0	I^{129}	$\frac{7}{2}$	Au^{197}	$\frac{3}{2}$
Na^{23}	$\frac{3}{2}$	Se^{79}	$\frac{7}{2}$	I^{131}	$\frac{7}{2}$	Hg^{199}	$\frac{1}{2}$
Na^{24}	4	Se^{80}	0	Xe^{129}	$\frac{1}{2}$	Hg^{201}	$\frac{3}{2}$
Al^{27}	$\frac{5}{2}$	Br^{79}	$\frac{3}{2}$	Xe^{131}	$\frac{3}{2}$	Tl^{203}	$\frac{1}{2}$
Si^{29}	$\frac{1}{2}$	Br^{81}	$\frac{3}{2}$	Cs^{133}	$\frac{7}{2}$	Tl^{205}	$\frac{1}{2}$
P^{31}	$\frac{1}{2}$	Kr^{83}	$\frac{9}{2}$	Cs^{134}	4	Pb^{207}	$\frac{1}{2}$
S^{33}	$\frac{3}{2}$	Rb^{85}	$\frac{5}{2}$	Cs^{134m}	8	Bi^{209}	$\frac{9}{2}$
S^{35}	$\frac{3}{2}$	Rb^{86}	2	Cs^{135}	$\frac{7}{2}$	Ac^{227}	$\frac{3}{2}$
Cl^{35}	$\frac{3}{2}$	Rb^{87}	$\frac{3}{2}$	Cs^{137}	$\frac{7}{2}$	Pa^{231}	$\frac{3}{2}$
Cl^{36}	2	Sr^{87}	$\frac{9}{2}$	Ba^{135}	$\frac{3}{2}$	U^{233}	$\frac{5}{2}$
Cl^{37}	$\frac{3}{2}$	Y^{89}	$\frac{1}{2}$	Ba^{137}	$\frac{3}{2}$	U^{235}	$\frac{5}{2}$
K^{39}	$\frac{3}{2}$	Zr^{91}	$\frac{5}{2}$	La^{139}	$\frac{7}{2}$	Np^{237}	$\frac{5}{2}$
K^{40}	4	Nb^{93}	$\frac{9}{2}$	Pr^{141}	$\frac{5}{2}$	Np^{239}	$\frac{1}{2}$
K^{41}	$\frac{3}{2}$	Mo^{95}	$\frac{5}{2}$	Nd^{143}	$\frac{7}{2}$	Pu^{239}	$\frac{1}{2}$
K^{42}	2	Mo^{97}	$\frac{5}{2}$	Nd^{145}	$\frac{7}{2}$	Pu^{241}	$\frac{5}{2}$
Ca^{43}	$\frac{7}{2}$	Tc^{99}	$\frac{9}{2}$	Sm^{147}	$\frac{7}{2}$	Am^{241}	$\frac{5}{2}$
Sc^{45}	$\frac{7}{2}$	Ru^{99}	$\frac{5}{2}$	Sm^{149}	$\frac{7}{2}$	Am^{243}	$\frac{5}{2}$

APPENDIX G

TABLE OF NUCLIDES

In this table are listed all the stable and radioactive nuclides whose existence has been fairly reliably established, together with the best available published information on some of their characteristics. The literature up to about January 1955 has been covered in the preparation of the table. The radioactive decay data are almost entirely based on the following compilations:

J. M. Hollander, I. Perlman, and G. T. Seaborg, "Table of Isotopes," *Revs. Mod. Phys.* **25,** 469 (1953).
K. Way, L. Fano, M. R. Scott, and K. Thew, *Nuclear Data,* U. S. National Bureau of Standards Circular No. 499 (1950), and Supplements 1, 2, and 3.
K. Way, C. L. McGinnis, M. Wood, K. Thew, A. L. Hankins, R. W. King, G. H. Fuller, "New Nuclear Data," *Nuclear Science Abstracts* **6,** No. 24B (1952); **7,** No. 24B (1953); **8,** No. 24B (1954).

Column 1 gives the chemical symbol and, as a superscript, the mass number of each nuclide. For the first listed isotope of each element the atomic number is shown as a subscript. Uncertainty in the mass assignment is indicated by a question mark in the superscript after the mass number(s) or, if the mass number is known to be one of several, by two or three mass values in the superscript. A question mark after the symbol *and* mass number indicates uncertainty in the chemical identification of the activity. An upper isomeric state of half-life greater than 1 millisecond is indicated by the symbol *m* following the mass number(s). Metastable states of shorter half-life are not listed as separate nuclides; if such an isomer is the decay product of another activity, this fact is shown under the parent nuclide by the letter *m* in parentheses following the symbol and energy of each delayed radiation in column 5. If at a given Z and A there are two or more excited isomeric states they are labeled m_1, m_2, etc., in order of increasing excitation energy. For the members of the natural radioactive families the common designations (such as ThB for Pb^{212}) are given in parentheses after the designation by element and mass number.

Column 2 lists per cent isotopic abundances for the naturally occurring nuclides. Column 3 gives isotopic masses, that is, atomic masses for the individual nuclides on the physical atomic weight scale. The uncertainty in the last digit of any mass value listed is less than 15. The mass and abundance data are largely taken from the compilation of K. T. Bainbridge in *Experimental Nuclear Physics*, Vol. I (E. Segrè, Editor), New York, John Wiley & Sons, 1953.

Half-lives are given in column 4. An attempt has been made to select a best value for each nuclide. The symbols used in this column are y = years, d = days, h = hours, m = minutes, s = seconds.

Column 5 lists information on modes of decay, radiations emitted and their energies, and the Q values. The symbols used are:

α	alpha decay,
β^-	negatron (negative beta) decay,
β^+	positron (positive beta) decay,
EC	electron capture,
IT	isomeric transition,
γ	gamma rays,
e^-	internal-conversion electrons,
n	neutrons,
Q	the Q value, that is, the total disintegration energy to the ground state of the product atom. Where different decay modes are possible, ambiguity is avoided by use of the following symbols:
Q_-	Q value for negatron decay,
Q_+	Q value for positron or electron-capture decay,
Q_α	Q value for α decay,
Q_{IT}	Q value for isomeric transition.

For a given nuclide, different decay modes or types of radiation are listed in order of decreasing abundance, when the relative abundances are known. Those modes known to occur in less than 10 per cent abundance are shown in parentheses. The numbers following the symbols are the measured energies of the radiations in millions of electron volts; in case of β^- and β^+ decays the energies listed are the maximum β-particle kinetic energies for each transition. The energies for each decay mode are given in order of decreasing abundance, and only those that occur in more than 10 per cent of the disintegrations are listed. In general no more than three or four energies are shown for a given type of radiation. When a greater variety of radiations (particularly γ rays) are known, only the most abundant ones are listed, with the energy range sometimes stated for the others. Sometimes only the notation "(others)" appears, indicating additional rays of the specified type, but each of abundance <10 per cent.

For gamma transitions the energy given is always the transition energy even if conversion electrons only are observed. The approximate magnitude of internal conversion coefficients is indicated by the order and manner in which the symbols γ and e^- are written:

$\gamma(e^-)$ means internal conversion coefficient $\alpha = e^-/\gamma < 0.1$,
γe^- means $0.1 < \alpha < 1$,
$e^-\gamma$ means $1 < \alpha < 10$,
$e^-(\gamma)$ means $\alpha > 10$.

For example, the notation IT $\gamma(e^-)$ 0.435 for Zn^{69m} indicates that the isomeric transition takes place largely by the emission of unconverted 0.435-Mev γ rays, the conversion coefficient being <0.1.

If one of the decay energies listed for a β^-, EC, or IT transition corresponds to the ground-state transition, it is followed by the symbol Q in parentheses. Otherwise the Q values, where known, are given separately. In case of several actual or possible decay modes for a given nuclide, ambiguity is avoided by use of the more specific symbols Q_+, Q_-, etc. Note that for positron transitions Q_+ equals the maximum positron energy (to the ground state) plus 1.02 Mev. Each value of Q_α includes the recoil energy of the atom as well as the kinetic energy of the α particles.

The letter (m) following a symbol or energy in column 5 indicates that the particular radiation is associated with the decay of a short-lived ($<10^{-3}$s) isomeric state in radioactive equilibrium with the parent activity.

If a nuclide decays to one of a pair of isomers but not to the other, this is indicated. For example, for Fe^{52} the notation "(to Mn^{52m})" indicates that the decay (by EC and β^+) goes to Mn^{52m}, but not to Mn^{52}.

Nuclide	Per Cent Abundance	Isotopic Mass	Half-life	Decay Modes, Radiations, and Energies
${}_0n^1$		1.008982	12.8m	β^- 0.782(Q)
${}_1H^1$	99.9849–99.9861	1.008142		
H^2	0.0139–0.0151	2.014735		
H^3		3.016997	12.46y	β^- 0.0176(Q)
${}_2He^3$	1.3×10^{-4} (atm) 1.7×10^{-5} (well)	3.016977		
He^4	99.9999	4.003873		
He^6		6.02047	0.82s	β^- 3.50(Q)
${}_3Li^6$	7.98	6.01702		
Li^7	92.02	7.01822		
Li^8		8.02502	0.83s	β^- 13; 2α; $Q = 16.0$
Li^9			0.168s	β^- ~8; n; 2α

Nuclide	Per Cent Abundance	Isotopic Mass	Half-life	Decay Modes, Radiations, and Energies
$_4Be^7$		7.01915	53.6d	EC; γ 0.479; $Q = 0.864$
Be^8		8.00785	10^{-16}s	2α 0.039; $Q = 0.078$
Be^9	100	9.01504		
Be^{10}		10.01671	2.5×10^6y	β^- 0.555(Q)
$_5B^8$			0.46s	β^+ 13.7; 2α
B^{10}	18.45–18.98	10.01611		
B^{11}	81.02–81.55	11.01279		
B^{12}		12.01816	0.027s	β^- 13.4(Q); (γ)
$_6C^{10}$		10.0206	19.1s	β^+ 2.1; γ 0.72; $Q = 3.9$
C^{11}		11.01492	20.4m	β^+ 0.99; $Q = 2.0$
C^{12}	98.892	12.00380		
C^{13}	1.108	13.00747		
C^{14}		14.007682	5570y	β^- 0.155(Q)
C^{15}			2.4s	β^- 8.8(Q); γ 5.5
$_7N^{12}$			0.0125s	β^+ 16.6; (3α)
N^{13}		13.009858	10.05m	β^+ 1.24; $Q = 2.26$
N^{14}	99.635	14.007515		
N^{15}	0.365	15.004863		
N^{16}		16.0107	7.38s	β^- 4.2, 10.3(Q); γ 6.13
N^{17}		17.0140	4.14s	β^- 3.7; n 0.9; $Q = 8.7$
$_8O^{14}$			72s	β^+ 1.83; γ 2.3; $Q = 5.1$
O^{15}		15.007768	118s	β^+ 1.683; $Q = 2.70$
O^{16}	99.758	16.000000		
O^{17}	0.0373	17.004533		
O^{18}	0.2039	18.00487		
O^{19}		19.0095	29.4s	β^- 2.9, 4.5; γ 0.20 (m), 1.37
$_9F^{17}$		17.007486	66s	β^+ 1.749; $Q = 2.77$
F^{18}		18.00667	112m	β^+ 0.649; $Q = 1.67$
F^{19}	100	19.004456		
F^{20}		20.00635	10.7s	β^- 5.41; γ 1.63; $Q = 7.04$
F^{21}			5s	
$_{10}Ne^{18}$			1.6s	β^+ 3.2
Ne^{19}		19.00792	18.2s	β^+ 2.18; $Q = 3.20$
Ne^{20}	90.92	19.99886		
Ne^{21}	0.257	21.00059		
Ne^{22}	8.82	21.99827		
Ne^{23}		23.00168	40.2s	β^- 4.21(Q); (γ)
$_{11}Na^{20}$			0.38s	β^+; α
Na^{21}			22.8s	β^+ 2.50
Na^{22}		22.00132	2.60y	β^+ 0.542; γ 1.277; (EC); $Q = 2.84$
Na^{23}	100	22.99714		
Na^{24}		23.99865	15.0h	β^- 1.390; γ 1.368, 2.754; $Q = 5.53$
Na^{25}		24.99779	58s	β^- 3.8(Q), 2.9; γ 0.97
$_{12}Mg^{23}$		23.0011	10.7s	β^+ 2.99
Mg^{24}	78.60	23.99270		
Mg^{25}	10.11	24.99382		
Mg^{26}	11.29	25.99087		
Mg^{27}		26.99295	9.45m	β^- 1.75, 1.59; γ 0.84, 1.02; $Q = 2.60$
Mg^{28}			21.2h	β^- 0.46; γ 0.032, 1.35, 0.40, 0.95
$_{13}Al^{24}$			2.10s	β^+; γ 1.38 to 7.1; (α)
Al^{25}			7.6s	β^+ 3.2

Nuclide	Per Cent Abundance	Isotopic Mass	Half-life	Decay Modes, Radiations, and Energies
Al^{26}			$\sim10^6$y	β^+ 1.16; EC; γ 1.83, 1.14
Al^{26m}		25.9962	6.6s	β^+ 3.2
Al^{27}	100	26.99014		
Al^{28}		27.99083	2.27m	β^- 2.865; γ 1.782; Q = 4.65
Al^{29}		28.9897	6.56m	β^- 2.5, 1.4; γ 1.28, 2.43; Q = 3.8
${}_{14}Si^{27}$		26.99525	4.9s	β^+ 3.48
Si^{28}	92.27	27.98584		
Si^{29}	4.68	28.98572		
Si^{30}	3.05	29.98331		
Si^{31}		30.98521	2.62h	β^- 1.47(Q); (γ)
Si^{32}			$\sim$700y	β^- $\sim$0.1
${}_{15}P^{28}$			0.28s	β^+ 10.6; γ 1.78 to 7.7
P^{29}			4.6s	β^+ 3.945; (γ)
P^{30}		29.98817	2.55m	β^+ 3.31; Q = 4.5
P^{31}	100	30.98362		
P^{32}		31.98409	14.30d	β^- 1.701(Q)
P^{33}			25.4d	β^- 0.27(Q)
P^{34}			12.4s	β^- 5.1, 3.2
${}_{16}S^{31}$		30.98886	2.40s	β^+ 3.85
S^{32}	95.1	31.98226		
S^{33}	0.74	32.98196		
S^{34}	4.2	33.97877		
S^{35}		34.98035	87.1d	β^- 0.167(Q)
S^{36}	0.016			
S^{37}			5.0m	β^- 1.6, 4.3(Q); γ 2.7
${}_{17}Cl^{32}$			0.31s	β^+ 9.4; γ 2.25, 4.33, 4.82
Cl^{33}			2.8s	β^+ 4.13; (γ)
Cl^{34}			1.58s	β^+ 4.45
Cl^{34m}			33.2m	β^+ 2.6, 1.3; IT γe^- 0.145(Q); γ 3.22, 2.10, 1.16; Q_+ = 5.6
Cl^{35}	75.4	34.98018		
Cl^{36}		35.97996	4.4×10^5y	β^- 0.714(Q)
Cl^{37}	24.6	36.97762		
Cl^{38}		37.98004	37.3m	β^- 4.81(Q), 1.11, 2.77; γ 2.15, 1.60
Cl^{38m}?			1.0s	γ 0.66
Cl^{39}			55.5m	β^- 1.65; γ 0.35, 1.35; Q = 3.3
${}_{18}A^{35}$			1.88s	β^+ 4.38; Q = 5.4
A^{36}	0.337	35.97893		
A^{37}		36.97850	35.0d	EC 0.82(Q)
A^{38}	0.063	37.97488		
A^{39}			$\sim$265y	β^- 0.565(Q)
A^{40}	99.600	39.97510		
A^{41}		40.97757	109m	β^- 1.245; γ 1.37(m); Q = 2.6
A^{42}			>3.5y	
${}_{19}K^{37}$			1.3s	β^+
K^{38}		37.9811	7.7m	β^+ 2.68; γ 2.16
K^{38}			0.95s	β^+ 4.57
K^{39}	93.08	38.97593		
K^{40}	0.0119	39.97658	1.2×10^9y	β^- 1.325(Q_-); EC; γ 1.46; Q_+ = 1.63
K^{41}	6.91	40.97484		
K^{42}		41.97588	12.51h	β^- 3.58(Q), 2.04; γ 1.51
K^{43}			22.4h	β^- 0.83, (others); γ 0.627, 0.369, (others)
K^{44}			22m	β^- 1.5, 4.9; γ 1.13, 2.07, 2.48
K^{45}?			34m	

Nuclide	Per Cent Abundance	Isotopic Mass	Half-life	Decay Modes, Radiations, and Energies
$_{20}Ca^{39}$		38.9835	1.00s	β^+ 6.7
Ca^{40}	96.97	39.97542		
Ca^{41}		40.9753	1.1×10^5y	EC
Ca^{42}	0.64	41.9720		
Ca^{43}	0.145	42.97237		
Ca^{44}	2.06	43.96920		
Ca^{45}			164d	β^- 0.254(Q)
Ca^{46}	0.0033			
Ca^{47}			4.8d	β^- 0.68, 2.06; γ 1.30, (others)
Ca^{48}	0.185	47.96763		
Ca^{49}			8.5m	β^- 2.7; γ
$_{21}Sc^{40}$			0.22s	β^+ 9.0; γ 3.75
Sc^{41}			0.873s	β^+ 4.94
Sc^{43}			3.84h	β^+ 1.18, 0.77; γ 0.375
Sc^{44}			3.92h	β^+ 1.463; γ 1.16; (EC); $Q = 3.64$
Sc^{44m}			2.44d	IT 0.27(Q)
Sc^{45}	100	44.97000		
Sc^{46}			85d	β^- 0.357; γ 0.885, 1.119; $Q = 2.36$
Sc^{46m}			19.5s	IT 0.142(Q)
Sc^{47}			3.43d	β^- 0.44, 0.62; γ 0.18
Sc^{48}		47.9683	44h	β^- 0.64; γ 1.32, 1.04, 0.98; $Q = 3.97$
Sc^{49}		48.9643	57m	β^- 2.0
$_{22}Ti^{43}$?			0.6s	
Ti^{44}			$\geq$23y	EC (to Sc^{44m}); γ 0.16
Ti^{45}			3.07h	β^+ 1.02; (EC); $Q = 2.04$
Ti^{46}	7.95			
Ti^{47}	7.75	46.9670		
Ti^{48}	73.45	47.9641		
Ti^{49}	5.51			
Ti^{50}	5.34			
Ti^{51}			5.80m	β^- 1.9, 2.2; γ 0.32
$_{23}V^{46}$			0.40s	β^+ ~6
V^{47}			32m	β^+ 1.9
V^{48}		47.9684	16.2d	β^+ 0.69; EC; γ 0.99, 1.32, 1.04; $Q = 4.02$
V^{49}			635d	EC; γ 0.119, 0.081
V^{50}	0.24	49.9622	$>10^{14}$y	$Q_- = 1.18$; $Q_+ = 2.39$
V^{51}	99.76	50.95953		
V^{52}		51.9611	3.76m	β^- 2.5; γ 1.4; $Q = 3.9$
V^{53}?			23h	β^- 0.6; γ
$_{24}Cr^{48}$			~23h	EC; γ 0.116, 0.305
Cr^{49}		48.9654	41.8m	β^+ 1.54, 1.39; γ 0.091, 0.063, 0.150
Cr^{50}	4.31	49.95999		
Cr^{51}			27.8d	EC; (γ)
Cr^{52}	83.76	51.95693		
Cr^{53}	9.55			
Cr^{54}	2.38			
Cr^{55}			3.52m	β^- 2.8
$_{25}Mn^{50}$?			0.28s	β^+ ~6.3
Mn^{51}			45m	β^+ 2.2
Mn^{52}		51.96202	6.0d	EC; β^+ 0.58; γ 0.73, 0.94, 1.46; $Q = 4.7$

Nuclide	Per Cent Abundance	Isotopic Mass	Half-life	Decay Modes, Radiations, and Energies
Mn^{52m}			21m	β^+ 2.66; γ 1.46; (IT); $Q_+ = 5.1$
Mn^{54}		53.9576	324d	EC; γ 0.84
Mn^{55}	100	54.95564		
Mn^{56}		55.95683	2.58h	β^- 2.81, 1.04, 0.65; γ 0.822, 1.81, 2.13; $Q = 3.63$
Mn^{57}			1.7m	β^- 2.6; γ 0.117, 0.134, (others)
$_{26}Fe^{52}$			8.3h	EC; β^+ 0.6 (to Mn^{52m})
Fe^{53}		52.9624	8.9m	β^+ 2.5; γ 0.370
Fe^{54}	5.84	53.9565		
Fe^{55}		54.95604	3.0y	EC 0.21(Q)
Fe^{56}	91.68	55.95286		
Fe^{57}	2.17	56.95365		
Fe^{58}	0.31			
Fe^{59}		58.9535	45.1d	β^- 0.46, 0.27; γ 1.10, 1.29
$_{27}Co^{54}$			0.18s	$\beta^+ \sim 7.4$
Co^{55}		54.95974	18.2h	β^+ 1.50, 1.03; EC; γ 0.935, 0.477, 1.41; $Q = 3.45$
Co^{56}		55.95781	80d	β^+ 1.50; EC; γ 0.835, others to 3.25; $Q = 4.6$
Co^{57}		56.9551	270d	EC; (β^+); γe^- 0.119, $e^-(\gamma)$ 0.014(m); $Q = 1.4$
Co^{58}			72d	EC; β^+ 0.47; γ 0.81; $Q = 2.3$
Co^{58m}			9.2h	IT $e^-(\gamma)$ 0.025(Q_{IT})
Co^{59}	100	58.95182		
Co^{60}		59.95250	5.2y	β^- 0.306; γ 1.173, 1.332; $Q = 2.81$
Co^{60m}			10.5m	IT $e^-(\gamma)$ 0.059(Q_{IT}); (β^-)
Co^{61}			99m	β^- 1.42(Q), 1.00; γ 0.5
Co^{62}			14m	β^- 2.8; γ 1.17, 1.0, 2.0, 1.7
$_{28}Ni^{56}$			6.4d	EC; γ 0.17, others to 1.75
Ni^{57}		56.9586	36h	EC; β^+ 0.84; γ 1.38, 1.91, 0.12; $Q = 3.24$
Ni^{58}	67.76	57 9536		
Ni^{59}		58.9530	$\sim 10^5$y	EC 1.07(Q)
Ni^{60}	26.16	59.94948		
Ni^{61}	1.25	60 94928		
Ni^{62}	3.66			
Ni^{63}		62.9487	85y	β^- 0.065(Q)
Ni^{64}	1.16	63.9473		
Ni^{65}		64.9498	2.56h	β^- 2.10(Q), 0.60, 1.01; γ 1.49, 1.12, 0.37
Ni^{66}			56h	β^-
$_{29}Cu^{58}$			3.04s	$\beta^+ > 7.5$
Cu^{58}			7.9m	β^+
Cu^{59}?			81s	β^+
Cu^{60}		59.9561	23.4m	β^+ 2.01, 2.96; γ 1.33, 1.76, 0.85; $Q = 6.19$
Cu^{61}		60.95168	3.33h	β^+ 1.205; EC; γ 0.655; $Q = 2.23$
Cu^{62}			9.8m	β^+ 2.92
Cu^{63}	69.1	62.9486		
Cu^{64}		63.9491	12.8h	EC; β^- 0.571(Q_-); β^+ 0.657; $Q_+ = 1.68$
Cu^{65}	30.9	64.9475		
Cu^{66}			5.1m	β^- 2.63(Q); (γ)
Cu^{67}			61h	β^- 0.39, 0.48, 0.58; γe^- 0.094, $\gamma(e^-)$ 0.18
Cu^{68}			32s	β^- 3; (γ)

Nuclide	Per Cent Abundance	Isotopic Mass	Half-life	Decay Modes, Radiations, and Energies
$_{30}Zn^{62}$			9.3h	EC; β^+ 0.66; γe^- 0.041
Zn^{63}		62.9522	38.3m	β^+ 2.36; (EC); (γ); $Q = 3.38$
Zn^{64}	48.89	63.9488		
Zn^{65}			245d	EC; γ 1.11; (β^+)
Zn^{66}	27.81			
Zn^{67}	4.11			
Zn^{68}	18.56			
Zn^{69}			52m	β^- 0.897(Q)
Zn^{69m}			13.8h	IT $\gamma(e^-)$ 0.435(Q_{IT})
Zn^{70}	0.62			
Zn^{71}			3h	β^- 1.5; γ 0.38, 0.49, 0.61; $Q_- = 3.0$
Zn^{71}			2.2m	β^- 2.4; γ 0.51
Zn^{72}			49h	β^- 0.3; γ
$_{31}Ga^{64}$			2.6m	β^+ ~5; γ 0.97, 2.2, 3.8; $Q = 7.2$
Ga^{65}			8.0m	β^+
Ga^{65}			15m	IT? $e^-\gamma$ 0.052, γ 0.092, 0.114; β^+ 2.2
Ga^{66}			9.4h	β^+ 4.14; EC; γ 1.04, 2.75, others 0.83 to 4.83; $Q = 5.16$
Ga^{67}			78h	EC; γe^- 0.092(m), others to 0.9
Ga^{68}			68m	β^+ 1.88; EC; γ 1.10; $Q = 2.90$
Ga^{69}	60.5			
Ga^{70}			21.4m	β^- 1.65; (γ)
Ga^{71}	39.5			
Ga^{72}			14.2h	β^- 0.6, 0.9, 1.5; γ 0.84, 2.508, 2.491, others; $Q = 4.0$
Ga^{73}			5.0h	β^- 1.4 (to Ge^{73m_2})
$_{32}Ge^{66}$			2.5h	β^+
Ge^{67}			20m	β^+ 3.4; γ 0.17
Ge^{68}			250d	EC
Ge^{69}			39.6h	EC; β^+ 1.22, 0.61; γ 1.12, others 0.09 to 1.61; $Q = 3.36$
Ge^{70}	20.55			
Ge^{71}			11.4d	EC 0.23(Q)
Ge^{72}	27.37			
Ge^{73}	7.61			
Ge^{73m_2}			0.33s	IT $e^-\gamma$ 0.054, $e^-(\gamma)$ 0.013(m_1); $Q_{IT} = 0.067$
Ge^{74}	36.74			
Ge^{75}			82m	β^- 1.14(Q), 0.88; γ 0.269, others 0.067 to 0.63
Ge^{75m}			48s	IT $e^-\gamma$ 0.139
Ge^{76}	7.67			
Ge^{77}			12h	β^- 2.20, 1.38, 0.71; γ 0.042 to 1.75
Ge^{77m}			52s	β^- 2.9 2.7; γ 0.215; IT γ 0.159
Ge^{78}			86m	β^- 0.9; γ
$_{33}As^{70}$			52m	β^+ 2.7; γ 2.0, 1.0
As^{71}			2.5d	EC; β^+ 0.81; γ 0 175, 0.023
As^{72}			26h	EC; β^+ 2.50, 3.34; γ 0.697 (m), others; $Q = 4.36$
As^{73}			76d	EC (to Ge^{73m_2})
As^{74}			17.5d	β^- 1.36(Q_-), 0.69; β^+ 0.82, 1.45; γ 0.596, 0.635; $Q_+ = 2.55$

Nuclide	Per Cent Abundance	Isotopic Mass	Half-life	Decay Modes, Radiations, and Energies
As^{75}	100			
As^{76}			26.5h	β^- 2.98(Q_-), 2.40, 1.76; γ 0.55, 1.20, 0.64; (β^+)
As^{77}			39h	β^- 0.700(Q); (γ)
As^{78}			90m	β^- 4.1(Q), 1.4; γ
As^{79}			9.0m	β^- 2.3 (to Se^{79m})
$_{34}Se^{70?}$			44m	β^+
Se^{72}			9.7d	EC
$Se^{73(m?)}$			7.1h	β^+ 1.32; EC; γe^- 0.067 (m); γ 0.36(m); $Q_+ = 2.77$
$Se^{73?}$			44m	β^+ 1.7
Se^{74}	0.87			
Se^{75}			127d	EC; γ 0.269, 0.138, others
Se^{76}	9.02			
Se^{77}	7.58			
Se^{77m}			17s	IT $e^-\gamma$ 0.162(Q_{IT})
Se^{78}	23.52			
Se^{79}			6.5×10^4y	β^- 0.16
Se^{79m}			3.9m	IT 0.096(Q_{IT})
Se^{80}	49.82			
Se^{81}			17m	β^- 1.38(Q)
Se^{81m}			57m	IT $e^-(\gamma)$ 0.103(Q)
Se^{82}	9.19			
Se^{83}			25m	β^- 1.5; γ 0.95, 0.18
Se^{83}			69s	β^- 3.4
Se^{84}			~2m	β^-
$_{35}Br^{74}$			36m	β^+; EC
Br^{75}			95m	β^+ 1.70, 0.8, 0.6, 0.3; EC; γ 0.6
Br^{76}			17h	β^+ 3.57, 0.6, 0.8, 1.1; γ 0.25 to 1.2; $Q = 4.6$
Br^{77}			57h	EC; (β^+); γ 0.023 to 1.00
Br^{78}			6.4m	β^+ 2.4; γ 0.108, 0.046
Br^{79}	50.52			
Br^{80}			18m	β^- 2.04(Q_-), 1.42; γ 0.62; (β^+; EC)
Br^{80m}			4.5h	IT $e^-(\gamma)$ 0.049, $e^-\gamma$ 0.037; $Q_{IT} = 0.086$
$Br^{80m?}$			5.0s	γ 0.21
Br^{81}	49.48			
Br^{82}			35.9h	β^- 0.465; γ 0.535 to 1.45
Br^{83}			2.3h	β^- 0.94; γ 0.051 (to Kr^{83m})
Br^{84}			30m	β^- 4.68, 1.72, 2.53; γ 0.89
Br^{85}			3.0m	β^- 2.5
Br^{87}			55.6s	β^- 2.6, 8.0; γ 5.4, others; (n)
Br^{88}			15.5s	β^-
$Br^{89?}$			4.5s	β^-; (n)
$_{36}Kr^{76}$			9.7h	β^+
Kr^{77}			1.1h	EC; β^+ 1.7; γ
Kr^{78}	0.354			
Kr^{79}			34.5h	EC; (β^+); γ 0.26, 0.044
$Kr^{79m?}$			55s	IT?; γ 0.127
Kr^{80}	2.27			
Kr^{81}			2.1×10^5y	EC
Kr^{81m}			13s	IT 0.19
Kr^{82}	11.56	81.9384		
Kr^{83}	11.55			
Kr^{83m}			114m	IT $e^-(\gamma)$ 0.032, $e^-(\gamma)$ 0.009; $Q_{IT} = 0.041$

Nuclide	Per Cent Abundance	Isotopic Mass	Half-life	Decay Modes, Radiations, and Energies
Kr^{84}	56.90	83.9385		
Kr^{85}			10.3y	β^- 0.666(Q); (γ)
Kr^{85m}			4.4h	β^- 0.855; γ 0.150; IT γe^- 0.305(Q_{IT}); $Q_- = 1.00$
Kr^{86}	17.37	85.9366		
Kr^{87}			78m	β^- 3.63(Q), 1.27; γ 0.41 1.89, 2.3
Kr^{88}			2.77h	β^- 0.52, 2.7; γe^- 0.028
Kr^{89}			3.2m	β^- 4.0
Kr^{90}			33s	β^- 3.2
Kr^{91}			9.8s	β^- ~3 6
Kr^{92}			3.0s	β^-
Kr^{93}			2.0s	β^-
Kr^{94}			1.4s	β^-
Kr^{95}			short	β^-
Kr^{97}			~1s	β^-
$_{37}Rb^{81}$			4.7h	EC; β^+ 0.99; γ 0.95
Rb^{82}			6.3h	EC; (β^+); γ 0.19 to 1.46
Rb^{82m}			76s	β^+ 4.2
Rb^{83}			83d	EC (to Kr^{83m}); γ 0.45, 0.15
Rb^{84}			34d	EC; (β^+; β^-); γ 0.89
Rb^{84m}			21m	IT γ 0.24, 0.46; (EC?)
Rb^{85}	72.15	84.9389		
Rb^{86}		85.9374	19d	β^- 1.82(Q_-), 0.72; γ 1.08
Rb^{86m}			1.02m	IT γ 0.56
Rb^{87}	27.85	86.9355	6 2 $\times 10^{10}$y	β^- 0.275(Q)
Rb^{88}		87.9393	17.7m	β^- 5.30(Q), 2.5; γ 1.86, 0.90, 2.8
Rb^{89}			15.4m	β^- 4.5; γ
Rb^{90}			2.7m	β^- 5.7; γ
Rb^{91}			1.67m	β^- 4.6; γ
Rb^{91}			14m	β^- 3.0; γ
$Rb^{92?}$			80s	β^-
$_{38}Sr^{81}$			29m	EC; β^+
Sr^{82}			26d	EC (to Rb^{82m}); γ 0.95, 0.4, 0.15
Sr^{83}			33h	EC; β^+ 1.15; γ 0.04 to 0.16
Sr^{84}	0.56			
Sr^{85}			65d	EC; γ 0.513(m)
Sr^{85m}			70m	IT $e^-(\gamma)$ 0.0075, γ 0.225; $Q_{IT} = 0.233$; EC; γ 0.150
Sr^{86}	9.86	85.9354		
Sr^{87}	7.02	86.9352		
Sr^{87m}			2.84h	IT γe^- 0.388(Q_{IT})
Sr^{88}	82.56	87.9336		
Sr^{89}		88.9310	54d	β^- 1.463(Q)
Sr^{90}			19.9y	β^- 0.61(Q)
Sr^{91}			9.7h	β^- 1.09, 1.36, 2.67(Q); γ 0.55 to 1.41
Sr^{92}			2.7h	β^-
Sr^{93}			7m	β^-
Sr^{94}			~2m	β^-
$_{39}Y^{82}$			70m	
Y^{83}			3.5h	
Y^{84}			3.7h	β^+ 2.0; EC; γ
Y^{85}			5h	
Y^{86}			14.6h	β^+ 1.80, 1.19; γ 1.4
Y^{87}			3.33d	EC (to Sr^{87m}); (β^+): γ 0.484

Nuclide	Per Cent Abundance	Isotopic Mass	Half-life	Decay Modes, Radiations, and Energies
Y^{87m}			14h	IT γe^- 0.381(Q)
Y^{88}		87.9376	104d	EC; (β^+); γ 0.908, 1.85; Q = 3.70
Y^{89}	100	88.9341		
Y^{89m}			14s	IT $\gamma(e^-)$ 0.915(Q_{IT})
Y^{90}			64h	β^- 2.18(Q)
Y^{91}			61d	β^- 1.537(Q); (γ)
Y^{91m}			50m	IT $\gamma(e^-)$ 0.551(Q_{IT})
Y^{92}			3.6h	β^- 3.60, 2.7, 1.3; γ
Y^{93}			10.0h	β^- 3.1; γ 0.7
Y^{94}			16.5m	β^- 5.4; γ 1.4
Y^{95}			10.5m	β^-
$_{40}Zr^{86}$			~17h	EC
Zr^{87}			94m	β^+ 2.10; EC; γ 0.65, 0.35
Zr^{88}			85d	EC; γ 0.406
Zr^{89}			79h	EC; β^+ 0.91 (to Y^{89m})
Zr^{89m}			4.4m	IT $\gamma(e^-)$ 0.587(Q_{IT}); (β^+)
Zr^{90}	51.46			
Zr^{90m}			0.83s	IT γ 2.30
Zr^{91}	11.23			
Zr^{92}	17 11			
Zr^{93}			9.5×10^5y	β^- 0.063(Q)
Zr^{94}	17.40			
Zr^{95}			65d	β^- 0.364, 0.396; γ 0.754, 0.722; Q = 1.12
Zr^{96}	2.80			
Zr^{97}			17.0h	β^- 1.91 (to Nb^{97m}); Q = 2.66
$_{41}Nb^{89}$			1.9h	β^+ 2.9 (to Zr^{89})
Nb^{89m}			0.8h	β^+ (to Zr^{89m})
Nb^{90}			14.7h	β^+ 1.2; γ 0.14, 1.14, 2.23(m)
Nb^{90m_1}			24s	
Nb^{90m_2}			0.01s	
Nb^{91}			long	EC
Nb^{91m}			62d	IT $e^-(\gamma)$ 0.105(Q_{IT})
Nb^{92}			10.1d	EC; γ 0.933
Nb^{92}			13h	EC; γ 2.35
Nb^{93}	100			
Nb^{93m}			3.65y	IT $e^-(\gamma)$ 0.0292(Q_{IT})
Nb^{94}			2.7×10^4y	β^- 0.50; γ 0.70, 0.87
Nb^{94m}			6.6m	IT $e^-\gamma$ 0.042(Q_{IT}); (β^-)
Nb^{95}			35d	β^- 0.165; γ 0.76
Nb^{95m}			3.7d	IT $e^-(\gamma)$ 0.232(Q_{IT})
Nb^{96}			23.3h	β^- 0.750; γ 0.770, others 0.216 to 1.19; Q = 3.16
Nb^{97}			72m	β^- 1.267; γ 0.665; Q = 1.93
Nb^{97m}			60s	IT $\gamma(e^-)$ 0.747(Q_{IT})
$Nb^{98?}$			30m	β^-
Nb^{99}			2.5m	β^- 3.2
$_{42}Mo^{90}$			5.7h	β^+ ~1.4; γ 0.1 to 1.1
Mo^{91}			15.5m	β^+ 3.3
Mo^{91m}			65s	β^+ 2.6; γ 0.3
Mo^{92}	15.86			
Mo^{93}			>2y	EC
Mo^{93m}			6.9h	IT γe^- 0.263, γ 0.685, 1.479; Q_{IT} = 2.43
Mo^{94}	9.12	93.9352		
Mo^{95}	15 70			
Mo^{96}	16.50	95.9356		

Nuclide	Per Cent Abundance	Isotopic Mass	Half-life	Decay Modes, Radiations, and Energies
Mo^{97}	9.45	96.9369		
Mo^{98}	23.75			
Mo^{99}			67h	β^- 1.23, 0.45; γ 0.04 to 0.78; $Q = 1.37$
Mo^{100}	9.62	99.9383		
Mo^{101}			14.6m	β^- 1.2, 2.2; γ 0.191, 0.960; $Q = 2.4$
Mo^{102}?			12m	β^-
Mo^{105}			~5m	β^-
$_{43}Tc^{92}$?			4.3m	β^+ 4.1; EC; γ 1.3
Tc^{93}			2.7h	EC; γ 1.35, 1.50, 2.0; β^+ 0.82, 0.64; $Q = 3.2$
Tc^{93m}			44m	IT γe^- 0.390; EC; γ 2.7
Tc^{94}			53m	β^+ 2.41; EC; γ 0.875, others to 3.27
Tc^{95}			20.0h	EC; γ 0.762, others
Tc^{95m}			60d	EC; γ 0.20 to 1.02; (IT; β^+); $Q_{IT} = 0.039$
Tc^{96}			4.2d	EC; γ 0.31 to 2.4
Tc^{96m}			52m	IT 0.034; (β^+)
Tc^{97}			$>10^4$y	EC
Tc^{97m}			90d	IT $e^-(\gamma)$ 0.096(Q_{IT})
Tc^{99}			2.12×10^5y	β^- 0.293(Q)
Tc^{99m}			6.04h	IT 0.0018; γ 0.1403; $Q_{IT} = 0.142$
Tc^{100}			15.7s	β^- 2.8; γ 0.55
Tc^{101}			14.3m	β^- 1.4; γ 0.30
Tc^{102}?			5s	β^-
Tc^{104}?			3.8m	β^-
Tc^{105}			short	β^-
$_{44}Ru^{94}$			~57m	EC
Ru^{95}			1.65h	EC; β^+ 1.1; γ 1.0, 0.5
Ru^{96}	5.50			
Ru^{97}			2.8d	EC; γ 0.217
Ru^{98}	1.91			
Ru^{99}	12.70			
Ru^{100}	12.69			
Ru^{101}	17.01			
Ru^{102}	31.52			
Ru^{103}			40d	β^- 0.22; γ 0.498 (to Rh^{103m}); $Q = 0.75$
Ru^{104}	18.67			
Ru^{105}			4.5h	β^- 1.150; γ 0.726 (to Rh^{105m}); $Q = 2.01$
Ru^{106}			1.0y	β^- 0.0392(Q)
Ru^{107}?			4m	β^- 4
$_{45}Rh^{97}$?			31m	β^+
Rh^{98}?			9m	β^+ 4.0
Rh^{99}?			4.5h	β^+ 0.74; γ 0.286
Rh^{100}			20h	EC; γ 0.30 to 2.38; (β^+); $Q = 3.64$
Rh^{101}			4.3d	EC; γ 0.144, 0.286
Rh^{102}			210d	β^- 1.15; β^+ 1.24, 0.76; EC?; γ 0.086 to 1.58
Rh^{103}	100			
Rh^{103m}			56m	IT $e^-(\gamma)$ 0.040(Q_{IT})
Rh^{104}			44s	β^- 2.6; γ 0.552
Rh^{104m}			4.4m	IT $e^-(\gamma)$ 0.052, γ 0.077
Rh^{105}			36.5h	β^- 0.570(Q); γ 0.32

Nuclide	Per Cent Abundance	Isotopic Mass	Half-life	Decay Modes, Radiations, and Energies
Rh^{105m}			45s	IT $e^-\gamma$ 0.130(Q_{IT})
Rh^{106}			30s	β^- 3.53(Q), others; γ 0.51 to 2.41
Rh^{107}?			26m	β^- 1.2
$_{46}Pd^{98}$?			15m	
Pd^{100}			4.0d	EC; γ 0.081, 1.8
Pd^{101}			8h	EC; β^+ 2.3
Pd^{102}	0.8			
Pd^{103}			17d	EC 0.53 (to Rh^{103m}); (γ)
Pd^{104}	9.3	103.9369		
Pd^{105}	22.6			
Pd^{105m}?			~23s	IT γe^- 0.23
Pd^{106}	27.2			
Pd^{107}			$\sim 7 \times 10^6$y	β^- 0.04
Pd^{108}	26.8	107.9369		
Pd^{109}			13.6h	β^- 0.961 (to Ag^{109m}); $Q = 1.05$
Pd^{109m}?			4.8m	IT γe^- 0.17
Pd^{110}	13.5	109.9410		
Pd^{111}			22m	β^- 2.13; γ 0.38 to 0.73
Pd^{111m}			5.5h	IT; β^-; γ 0.16, 1.77
Pd^{112}			21h	β^- 0.2
Pd^{113}			1.5m	
$_{47}Ag^{102}$?			16m	
Ag^{103}			1.1h	β^+ 1.3; EC; γ 0.55, 0.76
Ag^{104}			27m	β^+ 2.70; γ 0.555, others
Ag^{105}			40d	EC; γ 0.064 to 0.443
Ag^{106}			24.0m	β^+ 1.96, 1.45; γ 0.512; (β^-?)
Ag^{106}			8.6d	EC; γ 0.22 to 1.55
Ag^{107}	51.35			
Ag^{107m}			44s	IT $e^-(\gamma)$ 0.093(Q_{IT})
Ag^{108}			2.3m	β^- 1.77(Q_-); (EC; γ; β^+)
Ag^{109}	48.65			
Ag^{109m}			39s	IT $e^-(\gamma)$ 0.088(Q_{IT})
Ag^{110}		109.9422	24.2s	β^- 2.24, 2.82(Q); γ 0.66, 0.94, (others)
Ag^{110m}			270d	β^- 0.530, 0.080, 0.31; γ 0.116 to 1.51; (IT); $Q_- = 3.01$; $Q_{IT} = 0.116$
Ag^{111}			7.6d	β^- 1.04(Q); (γ)
Ag^{112}		111.9444	3.20h	β^- 3.5, 4.1(Q), 2.7; γ 0.62, 1.40
Ag^{113}		112.9443	5.3h	β^- 2.0(Q)
Ag^{114}			2m	β^-
Ag^{115}			21m	β^- ~3
$_{48}Cd^{104}$			59m	β^+ 0.93; γ 0.0666, 0.0835
Cd^{105}			55m	β^+ 0.80, 1.69; EC; γ 0.025 to 2.32
Cd^{106}	1.215			
Cd^{107}			6.7h	EC; (γ; β^+); (to Ag^{107m})
Cd^{108}	0.875			
Cd^{109}			470d	EC (to Ag^{109m}); $Q = 0.16$
Cd^{110}	12.39	109.9391		
Cd^{111}	12.75			
Cd^{111m_2}			48.6m	IT $e^-\gamma$ 0.150, γ (e^-) 0.246(m_1); $Q = 0.396$
Cd^{112}	24.07	111.9400		
Cd^{113}	12.26	112.9421		
Cd^{113m}			5.1y	β^- 0.57(Q_-)
Cd^{114}	28.86	113.9401		

Nuclide	Per Cent Abundance	Isotopic Mass	Half-life	Decay Modes, Radiations, and Energies
Cd^{115}		114.9436	53h	β^- 1.11, 0.58; γ 0.360, 0.500, 0.525; $Q_- = 1.45$
Cd^{115m}			43d	β^- 1.61(Q); γ 0.46 to 1.28
Cd^{116}	7.58	115.9421		
Cd^{117}			~50m	β^- 1.6, 3; γ
Cd^{117m}			3.0h	IT; γ 0.267 to 2.00
Cd^{118}			~30m	β^-
$_{49}In^{107}$			30m	β^+ ~2
In^{108}			50m	β^+ 2.31; (γ); $Q = 3.3$
In^{109}			4.3h	β^+ 0.75; EC; γ 0.058 to 0.43
In^{110}			66m	β^+ 2.25; EC; γ 0.654; $Q = 3.92$
In^{110m}			4.9h	EC; γ 0.12 to 0.94; (IT)
In^{111}			2.84d	EC; γ 0.171, 0.246(m_1)
In^{112}			14.5m	EC; β^- 0.66(Q_-); β^+ 1.52; $Q_+ = 2.54$
In^{112m}			20.7m	IT $e^-\gamma$ 0.155(Q_{IT})
In^{113}	4.23			
In^{113m}			104m	IT γe^- 0.392(Q_{IT})
In^{114}		113.9433	72s	β^- 1.98(Q_-); (EC; β^+; γ); $Q_+ = 2.1$
In^{114m}			49d	IT $e^-\gamma$ 0.190(Q_{IT})
In^{115}	95.77	114.9421	6×10^{14}y	β^- 0.6(Q)
In^{115m}			4.50h	IT γc^- 0.335(Q_{IT}); (β^-)
In^{116}		115.9440	13s	β^- 3.29(Q)
In^{116m}			54.0m	β^- 1.00, 0.87, 0.60; γ 0.137 to 2.09; $Q_- = 3.36$
In^{117}			70m	β^- 0.740; γ 0.565, 0.161
In^{117m}			2.1h	β^- 1.772, 1.616; IT $e^-\gamma$ 0.311, γ 0.16, 0.56, 0.72
In^{118}			4.5m	β^- 1.5; γ
In^{118}			$<$1m	β^- 4.0
In^{119}			17.5m	β^- 2.7
$_{50}Sn^{108}$			4.0h	EC
Sn^{109}			18m	EC; β^+; γ 0.678, 0.073
Sn^{111}			35m	EC; β^+ 1.51
Sn^{112}	0.95			
Sn^{113}			112d	EC (to In^{113m})
Sn^{114}	0.65	113.9411		
Sn^{115}	0.34	114.9415		
Sn^{116}	14.24	115.9381		
Sn^{117}	7.57	116.9417		
Sn^{117m}			14.0d	IT $e^-(\gamma)$ 0.159, $\gamma(e^-)$ 0.162; $Q_{IT} = 0.321$
Sn^{118}	24.01			
Sn^{119}	8.58			
Sn^{119m}			~250d	IT $e^-(\gamma)$ 0.065, $e^-\gamma$ 0.024; $Q_{IT} = 0.089$
Sn^{120}	32.97	119.9390		
Sn^{121}			27.5h	β^- 0.383(Q)
$Sn^{121m?}$			$>$400d	β^- 0.42
Sn^{122}	4.71	121.9426		
Sn^{123}			39.5m	β^- 1.26; γ 0.153; $Q = 1.41$
Sn^{123}			136d	β^- 1.42(Q)
Sn^{124}	5.98			
Sn^{125}			9.5m	β^- 2.04, 1.17, 0.5; γ 0.326, others; $Q = 2.4$
Sn^{125}			9.4d	β^- 2.37(Q); γ 1.90
Sn^{126}			~50m	β^-
Sn^{127}			1.5h	β^-

Nuclide	Per Cent Abundance	Isotopic Mass	Half-life	Decay Modes, Radiations, and Energies
$_{51}Sb^{116}$			15.5m	β^+ 2.40; γ 0.90, 1.30, 2.20
Sb^{116m}			60m	β^+ 1.45; γ 1.31, 0.95, 0.41
Sb^{117}			2.8h	EC; γ 0.156
Sb^{118}			3.5m	β^+ 3.1
Sb^{118}			5.1h	EC; γ 0.260, 1.5
Sb^{119}			39h	EC
Sb^{120}			16.5m	β^+ 1.70; EC; $Q = 2.7$
$Sb^{120?}$			6.0d	EC; γ ~1.1
Sb^{121}	57.25			
Sb^{122}			2.75d	β^- 1.40, 2.00, 0.72; γ 0.566, others 0.095 to 1.9
Sb^{122m}			3.5m	IT; $e^-(\gamma)$ 0.059, γ 0.074
Sb^{123}	42.75			
Sb^{124}			60d	β^- 0.61, 2.31, 0.23; γ 0.603, 1.71, 2.11; $Q = 2.9$
Sb^{124m_1}			1.3m	IT $e^-(\gamma)$ 0.012(Q_{IT}); β^- 3
Sb^{124m_2}			21m	IT $e^-(\gamma)$ 0.018(Q_{IT}); β^-
Sb^{125}			2.7y	β^- 0.30, 0.13, 0.62, 0.44; γ 0.035 to 0.64; $Q = 0.76$
Sb^{126}			9h	β^- ~1; γ 0.90, 0.4
$Sb^{\sim 126}$			28d	β^- 1.9
Sb^{127}			94h	β^- 1; γ 0.7
$Sb^?$			10m	β^-
Sb^{129}			4.2h	β^-
$Sb^{130?}$			40m	β^-
$Sb^{130?}$			12m	β^-
Sb^{131}			23m	β^-
Sb^{132}			2m	β^-
Sb^{133}			4.4m	β^-
$Sb^{134, 135}$			50s	β^-
$_{52}Te^{<118}$			2.5h	β^+
Te^{118}			6.0d	EC
Te^{119}			4.5d	EC; γ 0.2, 0.5, 1.6
Te^{120}	0.089			
Te^{121}			17d	EC; γ 0.575, 0.506
Te^{121m}			154d	IT $e^-(\gamma)$ 0.082, γ 0.213; $Q_{IT} = 0.295$
Te^{122}	2.46			
Te^{123}	0.87			
Te^{123m_2}			104d	IT $e^-(\gamma)$ 0.089, γe^- 0.159(m_1); $Q_{IT} = 0.248$
Te^{124}	4.61			
Te^{125}	6.99			
Te^{125m_2}			58d	IT $e^-(\gamma)$ 0.110, $e^-(\gamma)$ 0.035(m_1); $Q_{IT} = 0.145$
Te^{126}	18.71	125.9427		
Te^{127}			9.3h	β^- 0.7
Te^{127m}			115d	IT $e^-(\gamma)$ 0.089(Q_{IT})
Te^{128}	31 79	127.9471		
Te^{129}			72m	β^- 1.8; γ 0.3, 0.8
Te^{129m}			33.5d	IT $e^-(\gamma)$ 0.106(Q_{IT})
Te^{130}	34.49	129.9467		
Te^{131}			24.8m	β^- 2.0, 1.4; γ 0.16, 0.7
Te^{131m}			30h	IT $e^-\gamma$ 0.177(Q_{IT})
Te^{132}			78h	β^- 0.22; γ 0.23
Te^{133}			2m	β^- 1.3, 2.4; γ 0.6, 1.0
Te^{133m}			63m	IT 0.4
Te^{134}			44m	β^-
Te^{135}			<2m	β^-
$Te^?$			~1m	β^-

Nuclide	Per Cent Abundance	Isotopic Mass	Half-life	Decay Modes, Radiations, and Energies
$_{53}I^{119?}$			18m	
$I^{120?}$			30m	β^+ 4.0
I^{121}			1.5h	β^+ 1.2; γ 0.21
I^{122}			3.5m	β^+ 3.12
I^{123}			13.0h	EC; γ 0.160
I^{124}			4.5d	EC; β^+ 2.20, 1.50; γ 0.603, 0.73, 1.72, 1.95
I^{125}			60d	EC; $e^-(\gamma)$ 0.035(m_1); $Q = 0.13$
I^{126}			13.0d	EC; β^- 0.86, 1.26(Q_-); γ 0.67, 0.39, (others); (β^+); $Q_+ = 2.23$
I^{127}	100	126.946		
I^{128}			25.0m	β^- 2.02(Q_-); (EC; γ)
I^{129}			1.72×10^7y	β^- 0.150; $e^-(\gamma)$ 0.038; $Q = 0.19$
I^{130}			12.6h	β^- 0.60, 1.02; γ 0.53, 0.66, 0.74, 1.15, 0.41; $Q = 2.95$
I^{131}			8.06d	β^- 0.608, (others); γ 0.364, (others); $Q = 0.972$
I^{132}			2.33h	β^- 0.73 to 2.13; γ 0.67, 0.78, others 0.52 to 2.2
I^{133}			20.8h	β^- 1.3; γ 0.53
I^{134}			53m	β^- 1.5, 2.5; γ 0.86, 1.10, 1.78
I^{135}			6.7h	β^- 1.0, 0.5, 1.4; γ 1.8, 1.27
$I^{136?}$			86s	β^- 3.6, 5.0, 6.4(Q); γ 1.38, 2.8
I^{137}			22.0s	β^-; (n)
I^{138}			5.9s	β^-
I^{139}			2.7s	β^-
$_{54}Xe^{121}$			40m	β^+; γ 0.096
Xe^{122}			20h	EC; γ 0.182, 0.235
Xe^{123}			1.8h	β^+ 1.7; EC; γ 0.148
Xe^{124}	0.096			
Xe^{125}			18.0h	EC; γ 0.054, 0.187, (others)
Xe^{125m}			55s	IT; γ 0.075, 0.112; $Q_{IT} = 0.187$
Xe^{126}	0.090			
Xe^{127}			36.4d	EC; γ 0.057 to 0.365
Xe^{127m}			75s	IT $e^-\gamma$ 0.175, γ 0.125; $Q_{IT} = 0.30$
Xe^{128}	1.919			
Xe^{129}	26.44	128.9453		
Xe^{129m}			8.0d	IT $e^-(\gamma)$ 0.196, $e^-\gamma$ 0.040; $Q_{IT} = 0.236$
Xe^{130}	4.08			
Xe^{131}	21.18			
Xe^{131m_2}			12.0d	IT $e^-(\gamma)$ 0.164(Q_{IT})
Xe^{132}	26.89	131.9473		
Xe^{133}			5.27d	β^- 0.347; $e^-\gamma$ 0.081(m); $Q = 0.428$
Xe^{133m}			2.3d	IT $e^-\gamma$ 0.233(Q_{IT})
Xe^{134}	10.44			
Xe^{135}			9.13h	β^- 0.91; γ 0.250(m); $Q = 1.16$
Xe^{135m}			15.6m	IT γe^- 0.52(Q_{IT})
Xe^{136}	8.87			
Xe^{137}			3.9m	β^- 4
Xe^{138}			17m	β^-
Xe^{139}			41s	β^-
Xe^{140}			16s	β^-
Xe^{141}			1.7s	β^-
Xe^{143}			1.0s	β^-
Xe^{144}			~1s	β^-

Nuclide	Per Cent Abundance	Isotopic Mass	Half-life	Decay Modes, Radiations, and Energies
$_{55}Cs^{123}$			6m	β^+
Cs^{125}			45m	EC; β^+ 2.05; γ 0.112
Cs^{126}			1.6m	β^+ 3.8; γ 0.385
Cs^{127}			6.2h	EC; β^+ 1.063, 0.69; γ 0.406, 0.125
Cs^{128}			3.7m	β^+ 3.0, 2.5; EC; γ 0.440, 0.980, others; Q = 4.1
Cs^{129}			31h	EC; γ 0.385
Cs^{130}			30m	β^+ 1.97; EC; (β^-); Q_+ = 2.99; Q_- = 0.44
Cs^{131}			9.6d	EC 0.353(Q)
Cs^{132}			7.1d	EC; γ 0.67
Cs^{133}	100			
Cs^{134}			2.3y	β^- 0.65, 0.08; γ 0.20 to 1.37
Cs^{134m}			3.2h	IT $e^-\gamma$ 0.127, $e^-(\gamma)$ 0.010
Cs^{135}			3×10^6y	β^- 0.210
Cs^{136}			12.9d	β^- 0.34; γ 0.067 to 2.49
Cs^{137}			33y	β^- 0.52 (to Ba^{137m}); Q = 1.2
Cs^{138}			33m	β^- 3.40; γ 1.44, 0.98, 0.46; Q = 4.84
Cs^{139}			9.5m	β^-
Cs^{140}			66s	β^-
$Cs^{142?}$			~1m	β^-
$_{56}Ba^{124?}$			~12m	
Ba^{126}			96m	EC; γ 0.225, 0.70
Ba^{128}			2.4d	EC; γ 0.270
Ba^{129}			1.9h	β^+ 1.6
Ba^{130}	0.101			
Ba^{131}			12.0d	EC; γ 0.055 to 0.62
Ba^{132}	0.097			
Ba^{133}			9.5y	EC; γ 0.06 to 0.36
Ba^{133m}			39h	IT $e^-\gamma$ 0.276, $e^-(\gamma)$ 0.012; Q_{IT} = 0.288
Ba^{134}	2.42			
Ba^{135}	6.59			
Ba^{135m}			29h	IT $e^-\gamma$ 0.268(Q_{IT})
Ba^{136}	7.81			
Ba^{137}	11.32			
Ba^{137m}			2.60m	IT γe^- 0.662(Q_{IT})
Ba^{138}	71.66			
Ba^{139}			85m	β^- 2.23, 0.82, 2.38(Q); γe^- 0.163, γ 1.43
Ba^{140}			12.8d	β^- 1.022, 0.480; γ 0.030 to 0.54
Ba^{141}			18m	β^- 2.8; γ
Ba^{142}			6m	β^-
Ba^{143}			<0.5m	β^-
$_{57}La^{131}$			58m	β^+ 1.6
La^{132}			4.5h	β^+ 3.5; γ 1.0
La^{133}			4.0h	EC; (β^+); γ 0.8
La^{134}			6.5m	EC; β^+ 2.7
La^{135}			19h	EC; (γ)
La^{136}			9.5m	EC; β^+ 2.1
La^{137}			>400y	
La^{138}	0.089		~2×10^{11}y	EC; γ 1.39, 0.81, 0.54; (β^-)
La^{139}	99.911			
La^{140}			40.2h	β^- 1.34, others to 2.15; γ 0.09 to 1.60; Q = 3.86
La^{141}			3.7h	β^- 2.43(Q); (γ)
$La^{142?}$			74m	β^- >2.5; γ 0.63, 0.87
La^{143}			19m	β^-

Nuclide	Per Cent Abundance	Isotopic Mass	Half-life	Decay Modes, Radiations, and Energies
$_{58}Ce^{133}$			6.30h	EC; β^+ 1.3; γ 1.8
Ce^{134}			72h	EC
Ce^{135}			22h	EC; (β^+)
Ce^{136}	0.193			
Ce^{137}			36h	EC; γ 0.255
Ce^{138}	0.250			
Ce^{139}			140d	EC; $e^-\gamma$ 0.166
Ce^{140}	88.48			
Ce^{141}		140.9534	33d	β^- 0.442, 0.581(Q); γe^- 0.145
Ce^{142}	11.07			
Ce^{143}			33h	β^- 1.09, 1.39, 0.71; γ 0.290, others 0.13 to 0.72
Ce^{144}			282d	β^- 0.304(Q), 0.170; γ 0.034 to 0.134
$Ce^{145?}$			3.0m	β^- 2; γ
Ce^{146}			14m	β^- 0.7; γ 0.05 to 0.32
$_{59}Pr^{137}$			1.4h	β^+ 1.8
Pr^{138}			2.0h	EC; β^+ 1.4; γ 0.2, 1.3
Pr^{139}			4.2h	EC; (β^+; γ)
Pr^{140}			3.4m	β^+ 2.23; EC; Q = 3.25
Pr^{141}	100			
Pr^{142}			19.2h	β^- 2.15(Q); (γ)
Pr^{143}			13.7d	β^- 0.93(Q)
Pr^{144}			17.5m	β^- 2.98(Q); (γ)
$Pr^{145?}$			6.0h	β^- 1.7
Pr^{146}			24.6m	β^- 3.7, 2.2; γ 0.46, 1.49, 0.75; Q = 4.2
$_{60}Nd^{138?}$			22m	β^+ 2.4
Nd^{139}			5.50h	EC; β^+ 3.1; γ 1.3
Nd^{140}			3.3d	EC
Nd^{141}			2.42h	EC; (β^+; γ)
Nd^{142}	27.13			
Nd^{143}	12.20			
Nd^{144}	23.87	143.9561	$\sim 5 \times 10^{15}$y	α 1.9
Nd^{145}	8.30			
Nd^{146}	17.18			
Nd^{147}			11.3d	β^- 0.83, 0.38, 0.60; $e^-\gamma$ 0.092(m), γ 0.53, 0.32, (others); Q = 0.92
Nd^{148}	5.72			
Nd^{149}		148.9678	2.0h	β^- 1.5(Q), 1.1, 0.95; γ 0.030 to 0.65
Nd^{150}	5.60	149.9688		
Nd^{151}			15m	β^- 1.93; γ 0.085 to 1.14
$_{61}Pm^{141}$			20m	β^+ ~2.6
$Pm^{142?}$			260d	EC; γ 0.95
$Pm^{143?}$			320d	EC; γ 0.65, 0.44, 0.17
$Pm^{145?}$			16d	β^+ 0.45
Pm^{145}			~30y	EC
Pm^{146}			~2y	β^- 0.75
Pm^{147}			2.6y	β^- 0.225(Q)
Pm^{148}			42d	β^- 0.6; γ 0.9
Pm^{148}			5.3d	β^- 2.5; γ 0.8
Pm^{149}			54h	β^- 1.05; γ 0.285
Pm^{150}			2.7h	β^- 2.01, 3.00; γ 1.4, 0.3
Pm^{151}			27.5h	β^- 1.1; γ 0.065 to 0.72
$_{62}Sm^{144}$	3.16			
Sm^{145}			~410d	EC; $e^-\gamma$ 0.061
Sm^{146}			5×10^7y	α 2.55

Nuclide	Per Cent Abundance	Isotopic Mass	Half-life	Decay Modes, Radiations, and Energies
Sm^{147}	15.07		1.3×10^{11}y	α 2.15
Sm^{148}	11.27			
Sm^{149}	13.84			
Sm^{150}	7.47			
Sm^{151}			73y	β^- 0.076; γ 0.019; $Q = 0.095$
Sm^{152}	26.63			
Sm^{153}			47h	β^- 0.69, 0.62, 0.80; $e^-\gamma$ 0.069(m), 0.103(m), 0 548
Sm^{154}	22.53			
Sm^{155}			24m	β^- 1.8; γ 1.05, 0.25
Sm^{156}			~10h	β^- 0.9
$_{63}Eu^{144?}$			18m	β^+ 2.4
Eu^{145}			5d	EC; γ 0.2
$Eu^{146?}$			38h	EC; γ 0.4
Eu^{147}			24d	EC; γ 0.12, 0.21; (α)
Eu^{148}			54d	EC; γ 0.58
Eu^{149}			120d	γ 0.30, 0.57
Eu^{150}			14h	β^- 1.07
Eu^{151}	47.77			
Eu^{152}			13y	EC; β^- 0.70; γ 0.122(m), 0.244 to 1.09
Eu^{152}			9.2h	β^- 1.88; EC; γ 0.122, 0.344, others
Eu^{153}	52.23			
Eu^{154}			16y	β^- 1.45; EC; γ 1.116, 0.123, 1.415
Eu^{155}			1.7y	β^- 0.15, 0.24; γ 0.015 to 0.137
Eu^{156}			15.4d	β^- 0.5, 2.4; γ 2.0
$Eu^{157?}$			15.4h	β^- 1.0, 1.7; γ 0.6, 0.2
$Eu^{158?}$			60m	β^- 2.6; γ
$_{64}Gd^{148}$			>35y	α 3.16; EC?; $Q_\alpha = 3.25$
Gd^{149}			9d	EC; (α); $Q_\alpha = 3.1$
$Gd^{150?}$			long	α 2.7; $Q_\alpha = 2.8$
Gd^{151}			150d	EC; $e^-\gamma$ 0.265
Gd^{152}	0.20			
Gd^{153}			230d	EC; γe^- 0.104, 0.069, 0.097
Gd^{154}	2.15			
Gd^{155}	14.73			
Gd^{156}	20.47			
Gd^{157}	15.68			
Gd^{158}	24.87			
Gd^{159}			18.0h	β^- 0.9, 1.1; γ 0.058, 0.36
Gd^{160}	21.90			
Gd^{161}			3.73m	β^- 1.6; γ 0.102, 0.316, 0.360
$_{65}Tb^{149}$			4.1h	α 3.95; EC; $Q_\alpha = 4.06$
$Tb^{151?}$			19h	EC; α 3.44; $Q_\alpha = 3.53$
Tb^{153}			5.1d	EC; γ 1.2, 0.2
Tb^{154}			17.2h	EC; (β^+); γ 0.19 to 1.3
$Tb^{155?}$			190d	EC; γ 1.4
Tb^{156}			5.0h	EC; β^+ 1.3
$Tb^{156?}$			~17h	β^- 2.34
$Tb^{157?}$			4.7d	EC; γ 1.4
Tb^{159}	100			
Tb^{160}			73d	β^- 0.86, 0.52; γ 0.093 to 1.27, $e^-\gamma$ 0.086(m)
Tb^{161}			6.75d	β^- 0.5; γ 0.049
$_{66}Dy^{149-153?}$			7m	α 4.21
$Dy^{149-153?}$			19m	α 4.06

Nuclide	Per Cent Abundance	Isotopic Mass	Half-life	Decay Modes, Radiations, and Energies
$Dy^{149-153?}$			2.3h	α 3.61
Dy^{156}	0.0524			
Dy^{157}			8.2h	EC; γ 0.325
Dy^{158}	0.0902			
Dy^{159}			134d	EC
Dy^{160}	2.294			
Dy^{161}	18.88			
Dy^{162}	25.53			
Dy^{163}	24.97			
Dy^{164}	28.18			
Dy^{165}			2.32h	β^- 1.25(Q), 0.88, ~0.3; γ 0.094 to 1.0
Dy^{165m}			1.2m	IT $e^-\gamma$ 0.106(Q_{IT}); (β^-; γ)
Dy^{166}			3.4d	β^- 0.2
$_{67}$Ho?			4m	α 4.2
Ho^{160}			22m	EC; γ 1.2; (β^+)
Ho^{161}			2.5h	EC; γ 0.090, 0.17
Ho^{162}			5.0h	EC; γ 0.19, 0.71, 0.95
Ho^{163}?			5.2d	EC; γ 0.5, 1.4
Ho^{164}			37m	β^- 0.90, 0.99; γ 0.037, 0.046, 0.073, 0.090
Ho^{165}	100			
Ho^{166}			27.3h	β^- 1.76, 1.84(Q); $e^-\gamma$ 0.080(m), (γ)
Ho^{166m}			>30y	β^- 0.18, 0.28, 1.1; γ 0.080 to 0.845
$_{68}Er^{160}$			30h	
Er^{161}			3.6h	EC; γ 0.065 to 1.12
Er^{162}	0.136			
Er^{163}			75m	EC; γ 0.43, 1.10
Er^{163}?			2.7d	β^+?
Er^{164}	1.56			
Er^{165}			10.0h	EC; γ 0.2, 1.1
Er^{166}	33.41			
Er^{167}	22.94			
Er^{168}	27.07			
Er^{169}			9.4d	β^- 0.33
Er^{170}	14.88			
Er^{171}			7.5h	β^- 1.05, 0.67; $e^-\gamma$ 0.113(m), γ 0.176 to 0.42
$_{69}Tm^{165}$			25h	EC; γ 0.20 to 1.38
Tm^{166}			7.7h	EC; γ 1.7; (β^+)
Tm^{167}			9.6d	EC; γ 0.22, 0.95
Tm^{168}			85d	EC; γ 0.21, 0.85; (β^-)
Tm^{169}	100			
Tm^{170}			129d	β^- 0.968(Q), 0.88; $e^-\gamma$ 0.084(m)
Tm^{171}			680d	β^- 0.10
Tm^{172}?			2–3d	β^-
$_{70}Yb^{166}$			58h	EC
Yb^{167}			18m	EC; γ 0.118
Yb^{168}	0.140			
Yb^{169}			32d	EC; γ 0.023 to 0.308
Yb^{170}	3.03			
Yb^{171}	14.31			
Yb^{172}	21.82			
Yb^{173}	16.13			
Yb^{174}	31.84			

Nuclide	Per Cent Abundance	Isotopic Mass	Half-life	Decay Modes, Radiations, and Energies
Yb^{175}			4.2d	β^- 0.50, 0.1; γ 0.138 to 0.40
Yb^{176}	12.73			
Yb^{177}			1.8h	β^- 1.3; γ 0.150(m)
$_{71}Lu^{170}$			1.7d	EC; γ 2.5
Lu^{171}			8.5d	EC; γ 1.2
$Lu^{171?}$			~2y	EC; γ 1
Lu^{172}			6.7d	EC; γ 1.2
Lu^{172}			4.0h	β^+ 1.2; EC?
Lu^{173}			~500d	EC; γ 0.2, 0.8
Lu^{174}			165d	EC; β^- 0.6; γ 1
Lu^{175}	97.40			
Lu^{176}	2.60		4.6×10^{10}y	β^- 0.4; γ 0.31, 0.20; $e^-(\gamma)$ 0.089(m); Q_- = 1.0
Lu^{176m}			3.7h	β^- 1.1, 1.2(Q); $e^-(\gamma)$ 0.089(m)
Lu^{177}			6.8d	β^- 0.50(Q), 0.17, 0.37; γ 0.112, 0.206
$Lu^{178,\,179?}$			22m	
$_{72}Hf^{170?}$			112m	β^+ 2.4
Hf^{171}			16h	EC; γ 0.63, 1.02
Hf^{172}			~5y	EC; γ 0.3, 0.8
Hf^{173}			23.6h	EC; γ 0.121, 0.30
Hf^{174}	0.199			
Hf^{175}			70d	EC; γ 0.089 to 1.5
Hf^{176}	5.23	175.9923		
Hf^{177}	18.55			
Hf^{178}	27.23	177.9938		
Hf^{179}	13.73			
Hf^{179m}			19s	IT $e^-(\gamma)$ 0.160, γ 0.22; Q_{IT} = 0.38
Hf^{180}	35.07	180.004		
Hf^{180m}			5.5h	IT $e^-\gamma$ 0.058, γ 0.093 to 0.444
Hf^{181}			46d	β^- 0.408; $e^-\gamma$ 0.132(m_2), γ 0.345(m_1), 0.480(m_1), $e^-\gamma$ 0.135; Q_- = 1.02
$_{73}Ta^{176}$			8.0h	EC; γ 0.1 to 2
Ta^{177}			53h	EC; γ 0.1, 1.4
Ta^{178}			2.1h	EC; γ 1.4; (β^+)
Ta^{178}			9.3m	EC; γ 1.5; (β^+)
$Ta^{179?}$			~600d	EC; γ 0.1, 0.7
Ta^{180}	0.0123			
Ta^{180m}			8.15h	EC; $e^-\gamma$ 0.093(m); β^- 0.71, 0.61, $e^-\gamma$ 0.102
Ta^{181}	99.99			
Ta^{182}			111d	β^- 0.510; γ 0.0334 to 1.454, 0.100(m), 1.22(m)
Ta^{182m}			16.5m	IT $e^-\gamma$ 0.180; (β^-)
Ta^{183}			5.2d	β^- 0.56; γ 0.0465, 0.108, 0.0526, 0.246, others to 0.406
Ta^{184}			9.3h	β^- 1.4; γ 0.41, 0.86, 1.10
Ta^{185}			48m	β^- 1.6, 0.15
$_{74}W^{176}$			80m	EC; γ 1.3; (β^+)
W^{177}			2.2h	EC; γ 0.5, 1.2, 0.13
$W^{178?}$	$\sim 2.5 \times 10^{-7}$		$\sim 6 \times 10^8$y	α 3.2
W^{178}			21.5d	EC; (γ)
$W^{179?}$			30m	EC
W^{180}	0.135			
W^{180m}			0.0055s	γ 0.35, 0.22
W^{181}			140d	EC; γ 0.136, 0.152

Nuclide	Per Cent Abundance	Isotopic Mass	Half-life	Decay Modes, Radiations, and Energies
W^{182}	26.4	182.004		
W^{183}	14.4	183.0032		
W^{183m}			5.5s	IT $e^-\gamma$ 0.08, γ 0.12, 0.17
W^{184}	30.6	184.006		
W^{185}			73d	β^- 0.428
W^{185m}			1.85m	IT 0.075
W^{186}	28.4			
W^{187}			23.9h	β^- 0.62, 1.33(Q); γ 0.072(m), 0.134(m), others 0.48 to 0.78
W^{188}			65d	β^-
$_{75}Re^{182}$			13h	EC; γ 0.11 to 0.35
$Re^{182?}$			64h	EC; γ 0.11 to 0.35
Re^{183}			155d	EC; γ 0.081, 0.25
Re^{184}			50d	EC; γ 0.16 to 0.89
Re^{184}			2.2d	EC or IT; γ 0.043, 0.16
Re^{185}	37.07			
Re^{186}			3.87d	β^- 1.07(Q_-), 0.93; γe^- 0.137(m), (others); (EC)
Re^{187}	62.93		$\sim 5 \times 10^{10}$y	β^- <0.008
Re^{188}			17h	β^- 2.07; γ 0.153(m), (others)
Re^{188m}			19m	IT $e^-\gamma$ 0.064, γ 0.105
$Re^{189?}$			150d	β^- 0.2; γ 1.0
$Re^{189?}$			9.8m	β^- 1.8
$_{76}Os^{182}$			24h	EC
Os^{183}			12.0h	EC; γ 0.15, 0.4, 1.6
Os^{184}	0.018			
Os^{185}			97d	EC 1.0(Q); γ 0.163 to 0.88
Os^{186}	1.59			
Os^{187}	1.64			
$Os^{187m?}$			35h	
Os^{188}	13.3			
Os^{189}	16.1			
Os^{190}	26.4			
$Os^{190m?}$			9.5m	
Os^{191}			15d	β^- 0.143; $e^-\gamma$ 0.042, γe^- 0.129; Q = 0.314
Os^{191m}			14h	IT $e^-(\gamma)$ 0.074
Os^{192}	41.0			
Os^{193}			31h	β^- 1.10(Q); (γ)
Os^{194}			2y	β^-
$_{77}Ir^{187}$			11.8h	EC; γ 1.3; (β^+)
Ir^{188}			42h	EC; γ 1.8, 0.156; (β^+)
Ir^{189}			11d	
Ir^{190}			12.6d	EC; γ 0.2, 0.6
$Ir^{190?}$			3.2h	β^+ 1.7; γ 0.2, 0.8
Ir^{191}	38.5			
Ir^{191m}			6.9s	IT $e^-\gamma$ 0.125
Ir^{192}			74.4d	β^- 0.66, others; EC; γ 0.316, 0.296, 0.308, 0.468, (others); Q_- = 1.49
Ir^{192m}			1.4m	IT $e^-(\gamma)$ 0.056(Q_{IT}); (β^-)
Ir^{193}	61.5			
Ir^{194}		194.0264	19h	β^- 2.24, 1.90, 0.98, γ 0.33, (others 0.29 to 2.05)
Ir^{195}			2.3h	β^- 1.2, 2.1(Q); γ 0.42, 0.66, 0.88, >1
$Ir^{196?}$			9.7d	β^- 0.08; γ 0.58, 0.76, $\sim$1
$Ir^{197?}$			7m	β^- 1.6, 0.6; γ 1.8
$Ir^{198?}$			50s	β^- 3.6; γ 0.78

Nuclide	Per Cent Abundance	Isotopic Mass	Half-life	Decay Modes, Radiations, and Energies
$_{78}Pt^{187}$			2.5h	
Pt^{188}			10.5d	EC; γ 0.180, 0.114, 0.043, 0.053
Pt^{189}			10.5h	
Pt^{190}	0.012		$\sim 10^{12}$y	α 3.3
Pt^{191}			3.0d	EC; γ 0.042 to 0.62
Pt^{192}	0.78			
Pt^{193m}			4.5d	IT $e^-\gamma$ 0.135
Pt^{194}	32.8	194.0240		
Pt^{195}	33.7	195.0264		
Pt^{195m}			3.5d	IT $e^-(\gamma)$ 0.130, 0.031, 0.099
Pt^{196}	25.4			
Pt^{197}			18h	β^- 0.670; γ 0.077; $Q = 0.75$
Pt^{197m}			78m	IT $e^-(\gamma)$ 0.337
Pt^{198}	7.23			
Pt^{199}			31m	β^- 1.8
$_{79}Au^{183-187}$			4.3m	EC; β^+; (α); $Q_\alpha = 5.18$
Au^{187}			$\sim$15m	
Au^{189}			42m	
$Au^{191?}$			18h	EC; γ 0.053 to 0.405
Au^{191}			3.0h	γ 0.048, 0.091, 0.130, 0.159
Au^{192}			4.8h	EC; β^+ 1.9; γ 0.137 to 1.158
$Au^{191-193?}$			2.0s	
Au^{193}			17h	EC; γ 0.100 to 0.186
Au^{193m}			<1h	IT $e^-\gamma$ 0.032, γ 0.258, (others)
Au^{194}			39h	EC; γ 0.29 to 2.1; (β^+)
Au^{195}			180d	EC; γ 0.031, 0.099, 0.145
Au^{195m}			30s	IT $e^-(\gamma)$ 0.057, γ 0.262; $Q_{IT} = 0.32$
Au^{196}			5.6d	EC; γ 0.33, 0.36; (β^-)
Au^{196}			14h	
Au^{197}	100			
Au^{197m}			7.4s	IT $e^-\gamma$ 0.130, γe^- 0.279; $Q_{IT} = 0.41$
Au^{198}			2.69d	β^- 0.963, (others); γ 0.4118, (others); $Q_- = 1.375$
Au^{199}			3.15d	β^- 0.30, 0.25; γ 0.159, $e^-\gamma$ 0.050(m_1), γe^- 0.209(m_1); $Q = 0.46$
Au^{200}			48m	β^- 2.2; γ 0.39, 1.13
Au^{201}			26m	β^- 1.5; (γ)
$Au^{202?}$			$\sim$25s	
Au^{203}			55s	β^- 1.9; γ 0.69
$_{80}Hg^{189}$			25m	$e^-\gamma$ 0.0286
$Hg^{190?}$			90m	
$Hg^{\leq 191}$			$\sim$3h	$e^-\gamma$ 0.088
$Hg^{191?}$			12.4h	EC
Hg^{191}			57m	EC; γ 0.253, 0.274
$Hg^{<195?}$			0.7m	α 5.60
Hg^{192}			5.7h	EC; β^+ 1.18; γ 0.031 to 1.4
Hg^{193}			4h	EC (to Au^{193}); $e^-\gamma$ 0.038, γ 0.186
Hg^{193m}			12h	EC (to Au^{193m}); IT $e^-(\gamma)$ 0.101, $e^-\gamma$ 0.039; $Q_{IT} = 0.140$
$Hg^{194m?}$			0.40s	IT $e^-\gamma$ 0.048, 0.134
Hg^{195}			9.5h	EC (to Au^{195}); γ 0.061, 0.179, 0.600, 0.779
Hg^{195m}			40h	EC (to Au^{195m}); IT $e^-(\gamma)$ 0.123, 0.037, γ 0.56; $Q_{IT} = 0.160$

Nuclide	Per Cent Abundance	Isotopic Mass	Half-life	Decay Modes, Radiations, and Energies
Hg^{196}	0.146			
Hg^{197}			65h	EC; $e^-\gamma$ 0.077, 0.191
Hg^{197m_2}			23h	IT $e^-(\gamma)$ 0.165, $e^-\gamma$ 0.133(m_1); (EC to Au^{197m}); Q_{IT} = 0.298
Hg^{198}	10.02			
Hg^{199}	16.84			
Hg^{199m_2}			44m	IT $e^-(\gamma)$ 0.368, γe^- 0.159(m_1); Q_{IT} = 0.527
Hg^{200}	23.13			
Hg^{201}	13.22			
Hg^{202}	29.80			
Hg^{203}		203.0355	48d	β^- 0.208; γe^- 0.279; Q = 0.487
Hg^{204}	6.85			
Hg^{205}		205.0398	5.5m	β^- 1.8
$_{81}Tl^{197m}$			0.54s	IT $e^-\gamma$ 0.384
Tl^{198}			5.3h	EC; γ 0.195 to 0.675
Tl^{198m}			1.8h	IT $e^-\gamma$ 0.261, γ 0.282, $e^-(\gamma)$ 0.048
Tl^{199}			7.4h	EC (to Hg^{199}); γ 0.050 to 0.491
Tl^{200}			27h	EC; γ 0.116 to 1.36
Tl^{201}			3.0d	EC; $e^-\gamma$ 0.030, 0.032, γ 0.135, 0.168
Tl^{202}			12d	EC; γ 0.439
Tl^{203}	29.50	203.0350		
Tl^{204}		204.0370	4.0y	β^- 0.765(Q_-); (EC; Q_+ = 0.4)
Tl^{205}	70.50	205.0379		
Tl^{206}		206.0402	4.19m	β^- 1.51(Q)
$Tl^{207}_{(AcC'')}$		207.0419	4.79m	β^- 1.44(Q); (γ)
$Tl^{208}_{(ThC'')}$		208.0468	3.1m	β^- 1.79, 1.28, 1.5; γ 2.61, 0.58(m), 0.51, 0.86; Q = 4.99
Tl^{209}		209.0505	2.2m	β^- 1.99; γ 0.12, 0.45, 1.56; Q = 4.1
$Tl^{210}_{(RaC'')}$		210.0554	1.32m	β^- 1.8
$_{82}Pb^{198}$			25m	EC
Pb^{199}			1.3h	EC
Pb^{200}			18h	EC; γ 0.139, 0.320
Pb^{201}			8.4h	EC; γ 0.325, 0.583
$Pb^{201m?}$			50s	IT; γ 0.67, 0.25, 0.42
Pb^{202}			$\sim 3 \times 10^5$y	
Pb^{202m}			3.5h	IT, γe^- 0.78, 0.12, γ 0.42, 0.96, 0.66; Q_{IT} = 2.16
$Pb^{202m?}$			5.6s	IT, γ 0.89
Pb^{203}		203.0366	52h	EC $\sim$1.5(Q); γ 0.28, (others)
Pb^{204}	1.48	204.0361		
Pb^{204m_2}			68m	IT γe^- 0.911, γ 0.374(m_1), 0.89(m_1); Q_{IT} = 2.17
Pb^{206}	23.6	206.0386		
Pb^{207}	22.6	207.0403		
Pb^{207m}			0.84s	IT γ 1.06, 0.55; Q_{IT} = 1.6
Pb^{208}	52.3	208.0414		
Pb^{209}		209.0462	3.2h	β^- 0.63(Q)
$Pb^{210}_{(RaD)}$		210.0496	22y	β^- 0.023 (to RaE); $e^-(\gamma)$ 0.0465; Q = 0.069
$Pb^{211}_{(AcB)}$		211.0545	36.1m	β^- 1.39(Q), 0.5; γ 0.065 to 0.83
$Pb^{212}_{(ThB)}$		212.0579	10.6h	β^- 0.355, 0.589(Q); γ 0.2386, (others)
$Pb^{214}_{(RaB)}$		214.0663	26.8m	β^- 0.59, 0.65; γ 0.053 to 0.351

Nuclide	Per Cent Abundance	Isotopic Mass	Half-life	Decay Modes, Radiations, and Energies
$_{83}Bi^{<198}$			1.7m	α 6.2
Bi^{198}			7m	EC; (α)
Bi^{199}			25m	EC; (α)
Bi^{200}			35m	EC
Bi^{201}			62m	EC; (α)
Bi^{201}			2h	EC
Bi^{202}			95m	EC
Bi^{203}			12h	EC; (α)
Bi^{204}			12h	EC; γ 0.217, 0.374(m_1)
Bi^{205}			14.5d	EC; γ 0.284 to 1.86
Bi^{206}			6.4d	EC; γ 0.107 to 1.72
Bi^{207}			~50y	EC (to Pb^{207m} and Pb^{207}); γ 0.55, 1.78; Q = 2.40
Bi^{209}	100	209.0455	~2 × 10^{17}y?	α? 3
$Bi^{210}_{(RaE)}$		210.0495	5.00d	β^- 1.17(Q_-); (α); Q_α = 5.06
Bi^{210}			2.6 × 10^6y	α 4.94; Q_α = 5.03; (β^-); Q_- = 1.14
$Bi^{211}_{(AcC)}$		211.0530	2.16m	α 6.618, 6.272; Q_α = 6.746; γ 0.353; (β^-)
$Bi^{212}_{(ThC)}$		212.0573	60.5m	β^- 2.250(Q_-); α 6.051, 6.090; γ 0.040 to 2.20; Q_α = 6.205
Bi^{213}		213.0608	47m	β^- 1.39, 0.96; γ 0.43, 0.120; Q_- = 1.51; (α); Q_α = 5.97
$Bi^{214}_{(RaC)}$		214.0653	19.7m	β^- 1.65, 3.17(Q_-); γ 0.45 to 2.42; (α); Q_α = 5.610
Bi^{215}		215.0686	8m	β^-
$_{84}Po^{200}$			11m	EC; α 5.84
Po^{201}			18m	EC; α 5.70
Po^{202}			56m	EC; α 5.59
Po^{203}			47m	EC
Po^{204}			3.8h	EC; (α)
Po^{205}			1.5h	EC; (α)
Po^{206}			9d	EC; γ 0.8; (α); Q_α = 5.321
Po^{207}			5.7h	EC; γ 1.3; (α)
Po^{208}		208.0456	2.93y	α 5.108; Q_α = 5.208
Po^{209}		209.0475	~10^2y	α 4.877; (EC; γ); Q_α = 4.972
Po^{210}		210.0483	138.4d	α 5.298; Q_α = 5.401; (γ)
$Po^{211}_{(AcC')}$		211.0523	0.52s	α 7.434; Q_α = 7.58; (γ)
Po^{211m}			25s	α 7.14 (to Pb^{207m})
$Po^{212}_{(ThC')}$		212.0549	3.0 × 10^{-7}s	α 8.776, (others to 10.53); Q_α = 8.946
Po^{213}		213.0592	4.2 × 10^{-6}s	α 8.336; Q_α = 8.496
$Po^{214}_{(RaC')}$		214.0618	1.64 × 10^{-4}s	α 7.680; Q_α = 7.826
$Po^{215}_{(AcA)}$		215.0664	1.83 × 10^{-3}s	α 7.365; Q_α = 7.505; (β^-)
$Po^{216}_{(ThA)}$		216.0692	0.158s	α 6.774; Q_α = 6.902
$Po^{217?}$			short	α 6.5
$Po^{218}_{(RaA)}$		218.0768	3.05m	α 5.998; Q_α = 6.110; (β^-)
$_{85}At^{<202}$			43s	α 6.50; EC
$At^{<203}$			1.7m	α 6.35; EC
$At^{203?}$			7m	α 6.10; EC
At^{204}			25m	EC
At^{205}			25m	α 5.90; EC
At^{206}			2.6h	EC
At^{207}			2.0h	EC; α 5.75
At^{208}			6.3h	EC
At^{208}			1.7h	EC; (α)
At^{209}			5.5h	EC; γ 0.084 to 0.78; (α)

Nuclide	Per Cent Abundance	Isotopic Mass	Half-life	Decay Modes, Radiations, and Energies
At^{210}			8.3h	EC; γ 1.18, 0.25, 1.48, 0.047(m), others; (α)
At^{211}			7.23h	EC 0.9(Q_+); α 5.862; (γ); Q_α = 5.975
At^{212}?			0.25s	
At^{213}?				α 9.2
At^{214}		214.0630	~2 × 10^{-6}s	α 8.78; Q_α = 8.95
At^{215}		215.0656	~10^{-4}s	α 8.00; Q_α = 8.15
At^{216}		216.0697	~3 × 10^{-4}s	α 7.79; Q_α = 7.94
At^{217}		217.0722	0.018s	α 7.02; Q_α = 7.15
At^{218}		218.0764	~2s	α 6.63; Q_α = 6.75; (β^-)
At^{219}		219.0793	0.9m	α 6.27; Q_α = 6.39; (β^-)
$_{86}Rn^{206}$?			6.5m	α 6.25
Rn^{207}?			11m	EC; α 6.09
Rn^{208}			23m	EC; α 6.138
Rn^{209}			30m	EC; α 6.04
Rn^{210}			2.7h	α 6.036; Q_α = 6.153; (EC)
Rn^{211}			16h	EC; γ 0.07 to 0.60; α 5.778, 5.847
Rn^{212}		212.0562	23m	α 6.262; Q_α = 6.382
Rn^{215}		215.0656	~10^{-6}s	α 8.6
Rn^{216}		216.0675	~10^{-4}s	α 8.01; Q_α = 8.16
Rn^{217}		217.0716	~10^{-3}s	α 7.74; Q_α = 7.89
Rn^{218}		218.0735	0.019s	α 7.12; Q_α = 7.25
$Rn^{219}_{(An)}$		219 0778	3.92s	α 6.824, 6.559, 6.434; γ 0.067 to 0.59; Q_α = 6.951
$Rn^{220}_{(Tn)}$		220.0799	54.5s	α 6.280; Q_α = 6.396
Rn^{221}			25m	β^-; α
$Rn^{222}_{(Rn)}$		222.0866	3.825d	α 5.484; Q_α = 5.585
$_{87}Fr^{212}$			19.3m	EC; α 6.387, 6.409, 6.339
Fr^{217}?				α 8.3
Fr^{218}		218.0754	5 × 10^{-3}s	α 7.85; Q_α = 8.00
Fr^{219}		219.0775	0.02s	α 7.30; Q_α = 7.44
Fr^{220}		220.0809	27.5s	α 6.69; Q_α = 6.81
Fr^{221}		221.0830	4.8m	α 6.30, 6.05; γ 0.220; Q_α = 6.42
Fr^{222}			14.8m	β^-; (α)
$Fr^{223}_{(AcK)}$		223.0892	21m	β^- 1.15(Q_-); γ 0.049, 0.080; (α)
$_{88}Ra^{213}$			2.7m	α 6.90
Ra^{219}		219.0782	~10^{-3}s	α 8.0; Q_α = 8.1
Ra^{220}		220.0795	0.03s	α 7.43; Q_α = 7.57
Ra^{221}		221.0828	30s	α 6.71; Q_α = 6.83
Ra^{222}		222.0845	38s	α 6.51; Q_α = 6.63
$Ra^{223}_{(AcX)}$		223.0879	11.68d	α 5.704, 5.596, (others); γ 0.026 to 0.44; Q_α = 5.855
$Ra^{224}_{(ThX)}$		224.0900	3.64d	α 5.681; (γ); Q_α = 5.784
Ra^{225}		225.0934	14.8d	β^- 0.31; γe^- 0.040
Ra^{226}		226.0957	1622y	α 4.777; (γ); Q_α = 4.863
Ra^{227}		227.0998	41.2m	β^- 1.31(Q_-); (γ)
$Ra^{228}_{(MsTh_1)}$		228.1021	6.7y	β^- 0.012
Ra^{230}?			1h	β^- 1.2
$_{89}Ac^{221}$?				α 7.6
Ac^{222}		222.0869	5.5s	α 6.96; Q_α = 7.09
Ac^{223}		223.0886	2.2m	α 6.64; Q_α = 6.76
Ac^{224}		224.0915	2.9h	EC; α 6.17; Q_α = 6.28
Ac^{225}		225.0932	10.0d	α 5.80; Q_α = 5.90
Ac^{226}		226.0965	29h	β^- 1.17(Q_-)
Ac^{227}		227.0984	22.0y	β^- 0.04; (α; γ)

Nuclide	Per Cent Abundance	Isotopic Mass	Half-life	Decay Modes, Radiations, and Energies
$Ac^{228}_{(MsTh_2)}$		228.1021	6 13h	β^- 1.11, 0.45, 2.18(Q_-); γ 0.057(m), others to 1.64
Ac^{229}			66m	β^-
$_{90}Th^{223}$		223.0904	~0.1s	α 7.55; Q_α = 7.69
Th^{224}		224.0912	~1s	α 7.13; Q_α = 7.26
Th^{225}		225.0938	8.0m	α 6.57; EC; Q_α = 6.69
Th^{226}		226.0952	30.9m	α 6.30, 6.18; Q_α = 6.41
$Th^{227}_{(RdAc)}$		227.0984	18.17d	α 5.651 to 6.030; γ 0.030 to 0.28; Q_α = 6.138
$Th^{228}_{(RdTh)}$		228.0998	1.90y	α 5.421, 5.338; $e^-(\gamma)$ 0.084, (γ); Q_α = 5.518
Th^{229}		229.1028	7340y	α 4.85, 4.94, 5.02; Q_α = 5.11
$Th^{230}_{(Io)}$		230.1047	8.0×10^4y	α 4.685, 4.619; $e^-(\gamma)$ 0.068, (γ); Q_α = 4.768
$Th^{231}_{(UY)}$		231.1082	25.6h	β^- 0.302, 0.094, 0.216; γ 0.022 to 0.230; Q_- = 0.324
Th^{232}	100	232.1103	1.4×10^{10}y	α 4.00, 3.95; $e^-(\gamma)$ 0.055; Q_α = 4.07
Th^{233}		233.1138	23.3m	β^- 1.23(Q_-); (γ)
$Th^{234}_{(UX_1)}$		234.1165	24.1d	β^- 0.193(Q_-), 0.103; γ 0.029 to 0.100
$_{91}Pa^{225}$?			2.0s	α
Pa^{226}		226.0982	1.8m	α 6.81; Q_α = 6.93
Pa^{227}		227.0995	38.3m	α 6.46; EC; Q_α = 6.58
Pa^{228}		228.1020	22h	EC; α 6.09, 5.85; Q_α = 6.20
Pa^{229}		229.1033	1.5d	EC; (α)
Pa^{230}		230.1060	17.7d	EC; (β^-; β^+); γ 0.049 to 0.46
Pa^{231}		231.1078	3.43×10^4y	α 5.001, 4.938, 5.018, 4.724; γ 0.027 to 0.383; Q_α = 5.131
Pa^{232}		232.1108	1.32d	β^- 0.30; γ 0.047 to 1.15; Q_- = 1.24
Pa^{233}		233.1125	27.4d	β^- 0.25, 0.14; γ 0.015 to 0.416; Q_- = 0.57
$Pa^{234}_{(UZ)}$		234.1159	6.7h	β^- 0.16, 0.55, 0.33, 1.15; γ 0.064 to 0.92; Q_- = 2.08
$Pa^{234m}_{(UX_2)}$			1.18m	β^- 2.31(Q_-); (IT; γ)
Pa^{235}		235.1185	24m	β^- 1.4
Pa^{237}			10m	β^-
$_{92}U^{227}$		227.1017	1.3m	α 6.8; Q_α = 7.14
U^{228}		228.1023	9.3m	α 6.67; EC; Q_α = 6.79
U^{229}		229.1047	58m	EC; α 6.42; Q_α = 6.53
U^{230}		230.1055	20.8d	α 5.85, 5.78; γ; Q_α = 5.95
U^{231}		231.1082	4.3d	EC; γ 0.051, 0.064, 0.076; (α)
U^{232}		232.1095	74y	α 5.31, 5.25; $e^-\gamma$ 0.060; Q_α = 5.40
U^{233}		233.1119	1.62×10^5y	α 4.823, 4.779; $e^-\gamma$ 0.043; Q_α = 4.91
$U^{234}_{(U_{II})}$	0.0058	234.1138	2.48×10^5y	α 4.763, 4.707; $e^-\gamma$ 0.055; Q_α = 4.85
$U^{235}_{(AcU)}$	0.715	235.1170	7.13×10^8y	α 4.40, 4.58; γ 0.184, 0.094, 0.143; Q_α = 4.66
U^{236}		236.1191	2.39×10^7y	α 4.499; γ 0.05; Q_α = 4.58
U^{237}		237.1223	6.75d	β^- 0.25, 0.08; γ 0.059, 0.207, others 0.027 to 0.43; Q_- = 0.51
$U^{238}_{(U_I)}$	99.28	238.1249	4.49×10^9y	α 4.18; γ 0.05; Q_α = 4.25
U^{239}		239.1287	23.5m	β^- 1.21; γ 0.074; Q_- = 1.28
U^{240}			14.1h	β^- 0.36(Q)

Nuclide	Per Cent Abundance	Isotopic Mass	Half-life	Decay Modes, Radiations, and Energies
$_{93}Np^{231}$		231.1103	50m	α 6.28
$Np^{232?}$			13m	EC; γ
Np^{233}		233.1132	35m	EC; (α)
Np^{234}			4.40d	EC; γ 0.177, 0.442, 0.80, 1.42
Np^{235}		235.1172	410d	EC 0.17(Q_+); (α)
Np^{236}		236.1202	22h	EC; β^- 0.51, 0.36; $e^-\gamma$ 0.150
Np^{237}		237.1216	2.20×10^6y	α 4.77; $\gamma(e^-)$ 0.087(m)
Np^{238}		238.1251	2.10d	β^- 1.26, 0.26; $e^-\gamma$ 0.044, γ 0.102, others to 1.03
Np^{239}		239.1273	2.33d	β^- 0.33, 0.44, others; γ 0.013 to 0.33; $Q_- = 0.715$
Np^{240}		240.1300	7.3m	β^- 2.16, 1.59, 1.26; γ 0.56, 0.90, 1.40
Np^{241}		241.1325	60m	β^- 0.89; γ 0.15, 0.20, 0.26, 0.58
$_{94}Pu^{232}$		232.1134	36m	EC; α 6.58
Pu^{234}		234.1162	9.0h	EC; (α); $Q_\alpha = 6.30$
Pu^{235}		235.1184	26m	EC; (α)
Pu^{236}		236.1196	2.7y	α 5.75; $e^-\gamma$ 0.045; $Q_\alpha = 5.85$
Pu^{237}			~40d	EC
Pu^{238}		238.1237	89.6y	α 5.495, 5.452; $e^-(\gamma)$ 0.044; $Q_\alpha = 5.589$
Pu^{239}		239.1265	24,360y	α 5.150, 5.137, 5.100; γ 0.053, (others); $Q_\alpha = 5.238$
Pu^{240}		240.1286	6580y	α 5.162, 5.118; $e^-(\gamma)$ 0.050; $Q_\alpha = 5.250$
Pu^{241}		241.1315	13.0y	β^- 0.0205(Q_-); (α; γ)
Pu^{242}		242.1341	$\sim 5 \times 10^5$y	α 4.88; $Q_\alpha = 4.96$
Pu^{243}		243.1374	4.98h	β^- 0.57, 0.47, 0.37; γ 0.085, $e^-(\gamma)$ 0.1
Pu^{244}			8×10^7y	α
$_{95}Am^{237}$			1.3h	EC; (α)
Am^{238}			2.1h	EC; $e^-\gamma$
Am^{239}		239.1274	12h	EC; (α)
Am^{240}			2.1d	EC
Am^{241}		241.1315	470y	α 5.476, 5.433, (others); γe^- 0.060(m), 0.017, 0.013; $Q_\alpha = 5.628$
Am^{242}		242.1349	~100y	β^- 0.593; EC; γ 0.038, 0.053; (α)
Am^{242m}			16.0h	β^- 0.628; EC; IT γe^- 0.035(Q_{IT}), γ 0.038, 0.053
Am^{243}		243.1369	8.8×10^3y	α 5.267, 5.225; γ 0.075; $Q_\alpha = 5.430$
Am^{244}			26m	β^- 1.5
$_{96}Cm^{238}$		238.1271	2.5h	EC; α 6.50; $Q_\alpha = 6.61$
$Cm^{239?}$			~3h	EC
Cm^{240}		240.1304	26.8d	α 6.25; $Q_\alpha = 6.37$
Cm^{241}			35d	EC; (α)
Cm^{242}		242.1342	162d	α 6.110, 6.066; γ 0.044; $Q_\alpha = 6.213$
Cm^{243}		243.1369	~100y	α 5.777, 5.732; γ 0.226, 0.278; $Q_\alpha = 6.15$
Cm^{244}		244.1388	18y	α 5.798, 5.755; $Q_\alpha = 5.895$
Cm^{245}			1.2×10^4y	α 5.36
Cm^{246}			4×10^3y	α
Cm^{247}			>60d	
$_{97}Bk^{243}$		243.1386	4.6h	EC; (α)
Bk^{244}			~5h	EC

Nuclide	Per Cent Abundance	Isotopic Mass	Half-life	Decay Modes, Radiations, and Energies
Bk^{245}		245.1423	4.95d	(α)
Bk^{246}		246.1455	1.8d	EC; γ 0.82
Bk^{249}			290d	β^- 0.10; (α)
Bk^{250}			3.13h	β^- 0.9, 1.9; γ 0.9
$_{98}Cf^{244}$		244.1421	25m	α 7.15; EC?
Cf^{246}		246.1454	35.7h	α 6.75; $Q_\alpha = 6.86$
Cf^{247}			2.5h	EC
Cf^{248}			250d	α 6.26
Cf^{249}			~400y	α 5.82
Cf^{250}			~10y	α 6.03, 5.99
Cf^{251}			~700y	α
Cf^{252}			2.1y	α 6.12, 6.08
Cf^{253}			19d	β^-
99^{246}			"minutes"	EC
$99^{247?}$			7.3m	α 7.35; EC?
99^{253}			19d	α 6.62
99^{254m}			37h	β^- 1.1
$99^{255?}$			~30d	
$100^{250?}$			~30m	α 7.7
100^{254}			3.3h	α 7.20; $e^-(\gamma)$ 0.042
$100^{255?}$			~15h	α 7.1

Note added in September 1956:

Since the first printing of this book the following new transuranium nuclides have been reported. Also the names einsteinium (symbol E), fermium (symbol Fm), and mendelevium (symbol Mv) have been suggested for elements 99, 100, and 101.

Nuclide	Half-life	Decay Modes, Radiations, and Energies
$_{94}Pu^{245}$	11h	β^-
Pu^{246}	11d	β^- 0.15; γ
$_{95}Am^{245}$	2.0h	β^- 0.90; γ 0.036, 0.12, 0.26
Am^{246}	25m	β^- 1.22; γ 1.07, 0.80, 0.10, 0.02; $Q_- = 2.4$
$_{96}Cm^{248}$	4×10^5y	α 5.05
$_{97}Bk^{247}$	7000y	α 5.50, 5.67, 5.30; γ 0.085, 0.26, 0.42
Bk^{248}	~18h	β^- 0.67; EC
$_{98}Cf^{245}$	44m	EC; α 7.11
Cf^{254}	~70d	spontaneous fission
$_{99}E^{251}$	1.5d	EC; α 6.48
E^{252}	~150d	α 6.64
E^{254}	~1y	α 6.44
$_{100}Fm^{252}$	30h	α 7.1
Fm^{253}	3d	EC
Fm^{256}	3.1h	spontaneous fission
$_{101}Mv^{256}$	1h	EC

NAME INDEX

Page numbers in *italics* refer to the chapter bibliographies.

SUBJECT INDEX